type cosmic

digital type collection

serif

institute of typography
engineering research

evergreen

Bitstream Inc.	Athenaeum House 215 First street Cambridge, MA02142 USA ☎617-497-6222 ☎617-868-4732
Linotype AG	Margenthaler Alle 55-75 D6236 Eschborn bei Frankfurt Germany ☎0-61-96-403-581 ☎0-61-96-403-792
Linotype Limited	Brentside Executive Centre Great West Road, Brentford Middlesex TW8 9HD UK ☎01-847-9100 ☎01-847-4800
Adobe Systems Inc.	1585 Charleston Road Mountain View, CA94039-7900 USA ☎415-961-4400 ☎415-960-0886
Emigre Graphics	48 Shattuck Square, #175 Berkeley, CA94704-1140 USA ☎415-845-9021 ☎415-644-0820

Special Thanks to

Emigre Graphics
Rudy Vanderlans
Zuzana Licko

Bitstream Inc.
Robert Friedman
Mattew Carter
Cherie Cone
C. Rey Boelig

Adobe Systems Inc.
Leslie Bixel
Paul Anderson
Masumi Abe

Mitsubishi Corporation
Takahisa Nakagawa

Linotype AG
Günter Zorn
Jürgen Krufczyk

Morisawa & Company Ltd.
Akihiko Morisawa

Linotype Limited
Richard Sage

Transform Corporation
Hiroko Sakomura

This book was printed on 100% chlorine-free bleached paper according to the TCF standard.

EVERGREEN is a label of Benedikt Taschen Verlag GmbH.

© 1991 by Robundo Publishing Inc., Tokyo, Japan
© for this edition: 1994 by Benedikt Taschen Verlag GmbH, Hohenzollernring 53, D-50672 Cologne

Printed in the Czech Republic

ISBN 3-8228-9238-6

Introduction

The advent of the information age and DTP are something we take for granted now. Most western industrial nations (and the USA in particular) now have first-rate, user-friendly desktop publishing systems. Over 2000 European typefaces have been developed and marketed as outline fonts worldwide. But many users so far have been unable to use DTP as much as they would like because vital font specifications are missing. This book aims to be a bible for digital fonts in the Roman alphabet.

The far-reaching changes which DTP brought about in word processing, design, typesetting and print are comparable with the revolution when Gutenberg invented moveable type. Tailor-made, labour-saving systems are now within everyone's reach, heralding the dawn of a new golden age of print.

The only problem is, many people have little idea of the different typefaces available. The main offenders here are the typesetting companies, who are mostly afraid of losing out to 'homeworkers'. For years now, they have been successfully making us believe that choosing and combining typefaces is something only trained craftspeople with years of experience can do. The result? Type as design gives way to the purely commercial considerations of type as a consumer product.

In this book, we will be showing you modern typefaces and fonts with the help of the companies which supply them. We will try to see typefaces as total creative designs and how to use them to best effect [is this what author means?]. But as a user, you need to develop your own design ideas about using typefaces to give a balanced overall effect. As well as a certain creative flair, experience day in day out is vital.

„Type Cosmic" would not have been possible without the help and assistance of many different companies and individuals. In particular, I would like to thank Adobe Systems Inc. and Linotype Inc. The two companies work together on developing and marketing typefaces. Many of the typefaces credited to Linotype in this book are also available from Adobe Systems.

Vorwort

Es ist schon lange her, seit das Aufkommen des Informationszeitalters und des DTP-Zeitalters für große Aufregung gesorgt haben. Mittlerweile gibt es in den meisten westlichen Industrieländern – allen voran die USA – praxisnahe und hervorragende Desktop-Publishing-Systeme. Weltweit wurden bereits mehr als 2000 europäische Schriftarten als Outline-Zeichensätze entwickelt und verkauft. Allerdings konnten viele Nutzer DTP-Verfahren bislang nicht im gewünschten Umfang einsetzen, da es an den dafür dringend erforderlichen Schriftmusterheften fehlte. Das vorliegende Buch will hierbei ein Hilfsmittel sein, ein Musterheft für digitalisierte Schriften des lateinischen Alphabets.

Die grundlegenden Wandlungen, die in den Bereichen Textverarbeitung, Design, Satz und Druck durch die Möglichkeiten des DTP eingeleitet werden, sind durchaus vergleichbar mit der „Revolution", die seinerzeit durch Gutenbergs Erfindung des Buchdrucks ausgelöst wurde. Differenzierte und arbeitserleichternde Systeme gelangen in die Hände des einzelnen und verkünden den Beginn einer neuen Blütezeit der Druckkultur.

Leider gibt es bezüglich der Kenntnisse über die verschiedenen Schrifttypen bei vielen Menschen ein ausgeprägtes Wissensvakuum. Hierzu trägt vor allem die Geschäftspolitik der meisten Satzunternehmen bei, die die „Heimwerker"-Konkurrenz fürchten und erfolgreich propagieren, Schrifttypen könnten nur von jahrelang ausgebildeten Fachkräften richtig ausgewählt und kombiniert werden. Zudem ist der Konkurrenzkampf immens, und jede Firma wird darauf bedacht sein, den anderen so wenig anwendbares Material in die Hände zu geben wie eben möglich. Folge: Das gestalterische Phänomen Schrift wird von einer häufig rein wirtschaftlichen Betrachtungsweise des Konsumguts Schrift überlagert.

Im vorliegenden Buch wurden die Schrifttypen und Zeichensätze jüngerer Zeit mit Hilfe der jeweiligen Anbieterfirmen zusammengestellt. Es wird versucht, die Schrifttypen als Ganzes der bildnerischen Gestaltung zu erfassen und ihrem Ideal anzunähern. Jeder Anwender muß allerdings einen gestalterischen Blick entwickeln, mit er bei der Verwendung der Zeichensätze ein ästhetisches Gleichgewicht herstellt. Dafür ist neben einer gewissen Begabung die tägliche praktische Anwendung unabdingbar.

Das Buch „Type Cosmic" wäre nicht ohne die Hilfe und Unterstützung vieler Firmen und Einzelpersonen zustandegekommen. Mein besonderer Dank gilt den Unternehmen Adobe System Inc. und Linotype Inc. Beide Firmen arbeiten bei Schriftentwicklung und Vertrieb zusammen. Ein großer Teil der Schriften, die in diesem Buch Linotype zugeschrieben wird, wird auch von Adobe System vertrieben.

Préambule

L'apparition de l'ère informatique et de l'ère de la publication assistée par ordinateur suscite le plus vif intérêt depuis longtemps déjà. On trouve désormais dans la plupart des pays industriels occidentaux, en tout premier lieu aux Etats-Unis, des systèmes de PAO conviviaux et tout à fait étonnants. Dans le monde entier, plus de 2000 polices européennes, sous forme de jeux de caractères tracés sont développées et en vente. En effet, de nombreux utilisateurs ne pouvaient pas tirer tout le parti qu'ils attendaient de la PAO dans la mesure où il n'existait pas de cahier des charges en la matière. C'est la raison pour laquelle nous présentons ce livre qui doit contribuer à la création d'un cahier des charges pour les polices numérisées de l'alphabet latin.

Les bouleversements intervenus dans le traitement de texte, la stylique, la composition et l'impression grâce aux développements de la PAO sont tout à fait comparables à ce qu'il y a lieu d'appeler la „révolution" du temps de Gutenberg avec son invention de l'imprimerie. Des systèmes personnalisés et conviviaux sont maintenant à la portée de l'individu et annoncent l'aube d'un nouvel épanouissement de la culture imprimée.

Malheureusement, les connaissances portant sur les différentes polices sont bien minces chez la plupart des gens. La raison vient tout d'abord de la politique commerciale de la plupart des fabricants de polices de caractères qui craignent la concurrence des travailleurs à domicile et dont le nombre croît sans cesse, tandis que les polices ne pouvaient être sélectionnées et combinées judicieusement que par des techniciens bénéficiant d'une longue expérience. En outre, la lutte parmi les concurrents est acharnée et chaque société entend ne pas mettre entre les mains du concurrent un outil risquant de causer sa propre perte. Résultat : le phénomène créatif qu'est l'écriture devient un bien de consommation perçu purement d'un point de vue économique.

Ce livre a pour but de présenter les polices et les jeux de caractères les plus récents, avec l'aide des fabricants. Le but recherché consiste à aborder les polices de caractères comme un phénomène culturel et à se rapprocher de son idéal. En effet, l'utilisateur doit développer son esprit créatif pour parvenir à un équilibre dans l'application des jeux de caractères. C'est pourquoi le talent ne saurait se passer d'une pratique quotidienne.

Le livre „Type Cosmic" n'aurait pas vu le jour sans l'assistance et le soutien de nombreuses sociétés et personnes individuelles. J'adresse en particulier tous mes remerciements aux sociétés Adobe Systems, Inc. et Linotype, Inc. Ces deux sociétés ont collaboré au développement et à la commercialisation des polices. Une grande partie des polices attribuées dans ce livre à Linotype sont également commercialisées par Adobe System.

Aldine 401 Bold
② Like **Bembo Bold**
③ Bitstream

④ # ABCDEFGHIJK
LMNOPQRSTU
VWXYZ
abcdefghijklmnopq
rstuvwxyz
1234567890&$¢£¥
fiflæœÆŒÅßÇÌÎÏïã
§†----—/()''""";,.,!¿?¿

10/11
⑤ In our house we had a cat with the grandiose name of Gonnosuke. Usually with cats and dogs we k
now who the mother is but not the father. A cat with a large belly wondered into the house of my y
ounger sister and her husband and gave birth to five kittens. While the mother was a pure white th
oroughbred Chinchila, the kittens were black and white tabbies of mixed breed. One of these cam
e to our house about two weeks after its birth and was given the name Gonnosuke. At that time we
already had one female Shiba dog and one female brown tabby cat in our house comprising only 1

16/17
⑥ In our house we had a cat with the grandiose name of Gonno
suke. Usually with cats and dogs we know who the mother is
but not the father. A cat with a large belly wondered into the
house of my younger sister and her husband and gave birth to

24/25
⑦ In our house we had a cat with the grand
iose name of Gonnosuke. Usually with ca
ts and dogs we know who the mother is b

⑧
80

Type Cosmic comes in two volumes, each of which can be used independently. Each volume is in three parts. The one-line samples on the contents page[s? The Contents could be one or more pages] will help you find the typeface you want. The index is useful if you only know the name of a typeface and would like to see what it looks like. The typeface library contains the typeface itself and helps y u use it in text, design and layout. Of course, you can also use it as a catalogue when offering typefaces to your clients.

Type Cosmic besteht aus zwei Bänden, die jedoch unabhängig voneinander genutzt werden können. Jeder Band ist in drei Teile gegliedert: Das Eine-Zeile-Muster im Inhaltsverzeichnis hilft bei der Auswahl der Schriften. Der Index ist nützlich, sofern nur der Schriftname bekannt ist und der Nutzer das zugehörige Schriftbild sehen möchte. Die Schriftsatz-Bibliothek erfaßt das Schriftbild und unterstützt die praktische Umsetzung in Text, Design und Layout. Natürlich kann das Buch auch als Katalog beim Schrifterwerb benutzt werden.

Type Cosmic se compose de deux volumes, que l'on peut utiliser indépendamment l'un de l'autre. Chaque volume se présente en trois parties : l'exemple d'une ligne dans la table des matières aide à la sélection des polices. L'index joue un rôle lorsque l'on ne connaît que le nom de la police et que l'utilisateur souhaite voir l'aspect de la police en question. La bibliothèque de polices contient des exemples clairs de texte, de stylique et de composition. Bien entendu, le livre peut également servir de catalogue d'achat.

How to use this book

Typeface library
① Typeface name (supplier), number and style name
② Original typeface name
Please note that, as well as using its own name, Bitstream adds 'like...' and the original name
③ Supplier
④ Standard font
⑤-⑦ Examples (standard word and letter spacing)
Print typefaces (10, 16, 24 point)
Screen fonts (12-60 pt)
Please note: The number after the point size indicates line spacing (based on standard line)
For instance: 10/11 means 10 pt type on 11 pt line spacing
⑧ No. of pages

Benutzerhinweise

Zeichensatz-Bibliothek
① Schriftname laut Anbieter sowie Nummer und Stilbezeichnung
② Originalname der Schrift
Hinweis: Bitstream gibt neben der eigenen Bezeichnung den Originalnamen mit „like" an
③ Schriftanbieter
④ Normaler Zeichensatz
⑤-⑦ Beispiele (normaler Wort- und Buchstabenabstand)
Druckerschrift (10, 16, 24 pt.)
Bildschirmschrift (12-60 pt.)
Hinweis: Die Zahl, die von der Angabe der Schriftgröße mit einem Schrägstrich abgetrennt ist, gibt den Zeilenabstand an (jeweils ausgehend von der Zeilengrundlinie)
Beispiel: 10/11 bedeutet Schriftgröße 10 pt., Zeilenabstand 11 pt.
⑧ Seitenzahl

Conseils pour l'utilisateur

Bibliothèque de polices
① Nom de la police selon le fabricant, avec numéro et désignation
② Nom d'origine de la police
Exemple : Bistream est défini par sa propre désignation et son nom d'origine avec „like"
③ Fabricant de la police
④ Jeu de caractères normal
⑤-⑦ Exemples (espacement normal entre les mots et entre les lettres)
Impression (10, 16, 24 pt.)
Ecran (12-60 pt.)
Exemple : Le chiffre séparé du corps par une barre oblique indique l'interlignage (toujours par rapport à la ligne de base)
Soit : 10/11 indique un corps de 10 points et un inter-lignage de 11 points.
⑧ Numéro de page

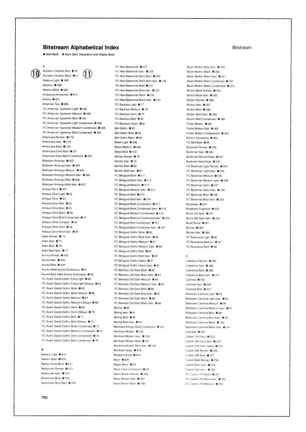

One-line samples

⑨ upper- and lower-case letters and numbers next to one another on a line (11 pt). Each line starts with the lower-case letters, so you can compare one typeface with another. The number at the end of each line is the page number where you'll find the complete typeface.

Eine-Zeile-Muster

⑨ Klein- und Großbuchstaben sowie Zahlen stehen in einer Zeile nebeneinander; Schriftgröße 11 pt. Jede Zeile beginnt mit den Kleinbuchstaben, so daß die Schriften miteinander verglichen werden können. Die Zahl hinter jeder Zeile gibt die Seite an, auf der das jeweilige Schriftmuster zu finden ist.

Exemples d'une ligne

⑨ lettres minuscules, majuscules et chiffres se trouvent sur une même ligne; corps 11 points. Chaque ligne commence par des minuscules, de sorte que l'on peut comparer les polices. Le chiffre à la fin de chaque ligne indique la page à laquelle se trouve la police complète.

Index page

⑩ Lists typeface suppliers in alphabetical order. Each typeface is shown by its original name. Where there is more than one typeface with the same name, light faces are shown first.
⑪ The numbers after the typeface name show where to find the appropriate type sample.

Index-Seite

⑩ Die Schriftenanbieter sind in alphabetischer Reihenfolge aufgelistet. Jede Schrift wird mit Originalnamen bezeichnet. Folgen Schriften gleichen Namens hintereinander, wird der dünne Schnitt zuerst genannt.
⑪ Die Ziffern nach dem Schriftnamen zeigen, auf welcher Seite der Schrift-Bibliothek das zugehörige Schriftmuster zu finden ist.

Page d'index

⑩ Les fabricants de police sont classés par ordre alphabétique. Chaque police est identifiée par son nom d'origine. Au cas où plusieurs polices du même nom se succèdent, la plus fine est présentée en premier.
⑪ Les chiffres suivant le nom de la police renvoient au page à laquelle se trouve l'exemple d'application.

Digital typefaces: a beginner's guide

Since ancient history, people have carved letters in stone or painted them on wood, parchment and paper. In the Middle Ages, Johannes Gutenberg invented moving lead type, and books became available to all. Once the type was cast, there was no limit on how many copies of a book could be printed.

Five hundred years later, we have reached the age of electronic word processing. Printing itself has not changed very much; but what do the 'letters' in electronic typesetting look like? Before, you could actually handle letters and plates and get an idea of how the final printed page would look. But digitalized typefaces are held in a computer's memory or on disk, so it's hard to see what they really look like. Perhaps that's the main reason why so many designers, editors and users are at a bit of a loss when it comes to digital typefaces. The typeface and setting examples in this book are designed to help fill that gap. Because, even with computer typesetting, you still have to know what typefaces look like before you can use them properly.

Einführung in digitalisierte Schriften

Seit uralten Zeiten hat der Mensch Sätze, die aus tausenden von Zeichen bestehen, in Stein gemeißelt oder später mit Pinseln auf Holz, Pergament und Papier geschrieben. Im Mittelalter schließlich erfand Johannes Gutenberg Bleilettern und ermöglichte damit den Buchdruck auf breiter Front. Das Original konnte nun – einmal gesetzt – beliebig vervielfältigt werden.

Fünf Jahrhunderte später befinden wir uns im Zeitalter der elektronischen Textverarbeitung. Am Wesen des Druckvorgangs hat sich wenig geändert. Wie aber sieht die „Form" mit den „Originalbuchstaben" in der elektronischen Setzerei aus? Früher konnte man die Lettern und Druckplatten in die Hand nehmen und sich ein Bild von der Schrift machen. Die digitalisierten Schriften aber sind im Computerspeicher oder auf Disketten aufbewahrt, so daß ihre reale Gestalt nicht erfaßt werden kann. Dies mag der Hauptgrund sein, warum viele Designer, Redakteure und Anwender den digitalisierten Schriften gegenüber eine gewisse Ratlosigkeit an den Tag legen. Hier will das vorliegende Buch mit seinen Schrift- und Satzmustern helfen. Denn: Die Kenntnis des Schriftbildes ist auch in der elektronischen Setzerei Grundvoraussetzung für die Beherrschung des Handwerks.

Introduction aux polices numérisées

Depuis des temps immémoriaux, l'homme grave dans la pierre des phrases composées de milliers de caractères, plus tard avec des pinceaux sur le bois, puis le parchemin et enfin le papier. C'est alors qu'au Moyenâge Johannes Gutenberg inventa des lettres de plomb et permit ainsi l'impression de livres sur front large. Il suffit de composer l'original une fois pour toute et de le reproduire à l'infini.

Cinq siècles plus tard, nous nous trouvons à l'ère du traitement de texte électronique. le processus d'impression proprement dit n'a pas beaucoup changé. Mais à quoi ressemblent les lettres dans la composition électronique ? Auparavant, on pouvait tenir les lettres et les plaques dans les mains et s'imaginer ce que donnerait l'impression. Maintenant, les polices numérisées sont stockées en mémoire dans l'ordinateur ou sur disquettes, de sorte qu'il est difficile de s'imaginer à quoi elles ressemblent vraiment. C'est probablement la raison pour laquelle de nombreux concepteurs, rédacteurs et utilisateurs des polices numérisées se sentent quelque peu perdus. C'est justement à cet état de fait que ce livre entend remédier en proposant des échantillons de police et de composition. En effet, la connaissance de l'image d'impression est la condition sine qua non de la maîtrise de l'outil, même avec la PAO.

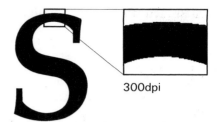

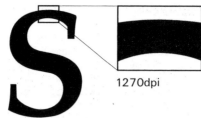

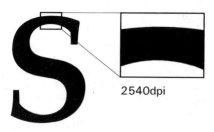

Fig. 1: Resolution and jagged edges
(Palatino 220 pt)
1a: 300 dpi LaserWriter II NTX
1b: 1270 dpi Linotron 300R
(medium resolution)
1c: 2540 dpi Linotron 300R (high resolution).

Abbildung 1: Auflösungsgrad und Zacken
(Palatino 220 pt.)
1a: 300 dpi LaserWriter II NTX
1b: 1270 dpi Linotron 300R
(mittlerer Auflösungsgrad)
1c: 2540 dpi Linotron 300R
(hoher Auflösungsgrad)

Illustration 1: Définition et dents
(Palatino 220 points)
1a : 300 dpi, LaserWriter II NTX
1b : 1270 dpi Linotron 300R
(définition moyenne)
1c : 2540 dpi Linotron 300R
(haute définition)

More precision

Many suppliers' advertisements run something like this: „Outline fonts take the jagged edges out of print". But printouts from low-resolution printers are often very poor quality - you can see the dots with the naked eye (Fig. 41a). Resolution is governed by the number of dots in a 1-inch line and is expressed in dots per inch (dpi). In other words, no matter how fine the resolution is, it still comes down to clusters of tiny dots.

If a printer's resolution is coarser than that of the human eye, outline typefaces are almost bound to appear as dots. To what extent the outline fonts typical of digital typefaces resemble analog photosetting typefaces depends on the printer. As Fig. 41c shows, jagged edges disappear at resolutions over 2000 dpi.

With bitmapped fonts, typefaces are made up of clusters of dots. Dark (print) areas have a value of 1 and light (backgroud) areas 0. A format developed some years ago shows typefaces not as dots, but as lines. The only trouble is, the higher your printer's resolution, the more data is involved and the more memory it takes up.

A solution was soon found to this problem. This involved taking a number of points on the outline of the typeface and linking their coordinates to give the shape of the typeface ('vector fonts'). The only problem is, vectors are always straight lines. The only way of getting a curve is to use a lot of short vectors one after the other. Which again increases the number of data points and the amount of data involved. To enable us to show curves without using too many dots, we now use a formula which gives the curve by a process of approximation.

Verbesserte Genauigkeit

Zahlreiche Anbieter werben mit dem Versprechen: „Durch Outline-Zeichensätze verschwinden die Zacken von den Schriften". Ein Ausdruck, geliefert von einem Drucker mit niedriger Auflösung, bietet jedoch oft nur unbefriedigende Ergebnisse – mit bloßem Auge sind die Punkte genau zu erkennen (Abbildung 41a). Der Auflösungsgrad wird durch die Anzahl von Punkten auf einer Linie von 1 Zoll bestimmt und in der Einheit dpi (dot per inch) ausgedrückt. Das bedeutet: Wie hoch der Auflösungsgrad auch immer sein mag, stets handelt es sich um eine Ansammlung sehr kleiner Punkte.

Solange der Auflösungsgrad des Druckers den Auflösungsgrad des menschlichen Auges nicht übersteigt, läßt sich kaum vermeiden, daß Outline-Zeichensätze als Dot-Zeichensätze gesehen werden. Inwieweit sich die für digitalisierte Schriften charakteristischen Outline-Zeichensätze den Analog-Zeichensätzen des Fotosatzes annähern, hängt vom Drucker ab. Wie Abbildung 41c zeigt, sind die Zacken bei einem Auflösungsgrad von über 2000 dpi nicht mehr zu erkennen.

Bei Bitmap-Zeichensätzen setzen sich die Schriften aus einer Ansammlung von Punkten zusammen. Die ausgefüllte Fläche wird mit 1 und die Grundfläche mit 0 in Daten beschrieben. Ein vor einigen Jahren entwickeltes Format stellte die Schriften nicht mehr als Punkte, sondern als Linien dar. Problem: Je höher der Auflösungsgrad des Druckers, desto größer die Datenmenge und desto mehr belegter Speicherplatz.

Bald fand man eine Lösung für dieses Problem. Auf den Konturlinien der Schrift wurden einige Punkte bestimmt und ihre Koordinaten miteinander verbunden, so daß eine Form der Schrift entstand (sog. Vektor-Zeichensätze). Allerdings sind Vektoren gerade, d.h. zur Darstellung von Kurven müssen viele kurze Vektoren aneinandergereiht werden. In der Folge nehmen die Anzahl der Datenpunkte und die Datenmenge zu. Zur Kurvendarstellung mit wenigen Punkten ist daher heute ein Format in Gebrauch, das mit zahlreichen Funktionsgleichungen die Kurven ermittelt.

Une précision accrue

De nombreux fabricants proposent le slogan : „Les jeux de caractères tracés font disparaître les dents des polices". Mais une sortie papier obtenue sur une imprimante de faible définition donne souvent des résultats peu satisfaisants - on voit bien les points à l'oeil nu (illustration 41a). La définition s'exprime en nombre de points sur une ligne d'un pouce et en unités dpi (points au pouce). Ainsi, une définition élevée correspond à l'accumulation d'une multitude de très petits points.

Tant que la définition de l'imprimante ne dépasse pas la définition de l'oeil humain, il est pratiquement inévitable que les jeux de caractères tracés fassent penser aux imprimantes matricielles par points. Le degré selon lequel les jeux de caractères tracés caractéristiques des polices numérisées se rapprochent des polices analogiques de la photocomposition dépend de l'imprimante. Comme le montre l'illustration 41c, les dents n'apparaissent plus lorsque la définition dépasse 2000 dpi.

Avec les polices bitmap, les polices se composent d'une accumulation de points. La surface remplie est décrite par des chiffres 1 et les surface de base par des 0 dans les données. Un format développé il y a quelques années ne présentait plus les polices comme des points mais comme des lignes. Mais un problème se pose : plus la définition de l'imprimante est élevée, plus la quantité de données et donc l'occupation en mémoire grandissent.

On ne tarda pas à trouver une solution. Quelques points étaient définis sur le contour et leurs coordonnées étaient alors reliées pour produire une forme d'écriture (que l'on appela jeu de caractères vectoriels). Il s'agit bien de vecteurs, c'est-à-dire que de nombreux petits vecteurs doivent être reliés pour représenter des courbes. Mais le nombre des points de données et la quantité des données augmentent. On utilise donc aujourd'hui un format permettant de tracer des courbes avec de nombreuses équations de fonction et un petit nombre de points.

Font

A font is a collection of upper- and lower-case letters of the alphabet and numbers, accents and symbols, all produced to a common design. Any typefaces which are merely light or bold or wider/narrower versions of the basic design are called the 'type family'.

A font has 256 boxes for holding the various characters (Fig. 2). Each box is numbered from 00 to FF in the hexadecimal system. Not all the 256 boxes have characters in them, as there are fonts which do not have lower-case letters or symbols, for example. With Proteus from Letraset, boxes underlined in gray are blank. Sometimes these boxes are used for characters which are not part of the standard character set (e.g. fi, ff).

The proper name for these numbers is 'ASCII code' (American Standard Code Information Interchange). This code is converted to the eight-bit (8 bits = 1 byte) format data of the binary system. For alphabet-based languages, the 256 codes are enough. Languages with tens of thousands of characters, such as Chinese, need a hexadecimal system with four-digit codes. These use the JIS (Japan Industrial Standard) code. Calling up the ASCII table as in Fig. 2 on screen requires special typeface software (Fontographer or FontStudio). You can see the keyboard layout for each font by opening the keyboard direct from the desktop menu.

Zeichensatz

Der Zeichensatz ist eine Sammlung von Groß- und Kleinbuchstaben des Alphabets sowie von Zahlen, Akzenten und Symbolen, die alle einem einheitlichen Gestaltungskonzept unterworfen sind. Daher werden alle Schriften, die sich nur durch Schnitt und Schriftbreite unterscheiden als „Familie" bezeichnet.

Ein Zeichensatz zur Aufbewahrung der Zeichen besitzt 256 Kästen (Abbildung 2). Jeder Kasten ist mit einer Nummer von 00 bis FF im Hexadezimalsystem gekennzeichnet. Nicht alle 256 Kästen sind mit Zeichen gefüllt, da es Zeichensätze gibt, die beispielsweise keine Kleinbuchstaben oder keine Symbole besitzen. Im Fall von „Proteus" von Letraset sind die grau unterlegten Kästen leer. Mitunter werden in solchen Kästen Lettern aufbewahrt, die nicht zu den Standardzeichen gehören.

Die genaue Bezeichnung für die Nummer lautet „ASCII-Code" (American Standard Code Information Interchange). Dieser Code wird in die achtstellige (8 bits = 1 byte) Information des Binärsystems umgesetzt. Bei Sprachen auf der Grundlage des Alphabets reichen die 256 Code-Nummern aus. Bei Sprachen mit einigen zehntausend Schriftzeichen – wie z.B. Chinesisch – wird ein Hexadezimalsystem mit vierstelligen Codes erforderlich. Diese werden durch den JIS-Code (Japan Industrial Standard) ausgedrückt. Um die ASCII-Tabelle wie in Abbildung 2 auf dem Bildschirm erscheinen zu lassen, ist eine spezielle Schriftsatz-Software erforderlich (Fontographer oder FontStudio). Einen Überblick über die Tastenbelegung bei den unterschiedlichen Schriften erhält man durch Öffnen der Tastatur direkt vom Schreibtischmenü aus.

Jeu de caractères

Le jeu de caractères est un ensemble de majuscules et de minuscules de l'alphabet ainsi que de chiffres, d'accents et de symboles, soumis à un concept bien défini. C'est la raison pour laquelle toutes les polices seulement distinctes par le corps et l'épaisseur sont désignées sous le nom de „famille".

Une police possède 256 cases pour ses différents caractères (illustration 2). Chaque case est désignée par un numéro de 00 à FF en système hexadécimal. Certaines des 256 cases restent vides dans la mesure où des minuscules ou des symboles peuvent être absents de certaines polices. Dans le cas de „Proteus" de Letraset, les cases grises restent vides. Ces cases sont réservées à des lettres ne faisant pas partie des caractères standard.

La désignation précise du numéro est en „code ASCII" (Code standard américain pour l'échange d'information). Ce code est converti en données à huit bits (8 bits = 1 octet) du système binaire. Pour les langues à base alphabétique, le code à 256 numéros suffit. Mais pour les langues comprenant plusieurs dizaines de milliers de caractères, comme le chinois par exemple, on utilise un système hexadécimal à quatre chiffres, que l'on exprime par le code JIS (norme industrielle japonaise).

Un logiciel spécial (Fontographer ou FontStudio) est nécessaire pour afficher à l'écran le tableau ASCII, voir illustration 2. Pour découvrir les touches des différentes polices, il suffit d'afficher le clavier à partir du menu de bureau.

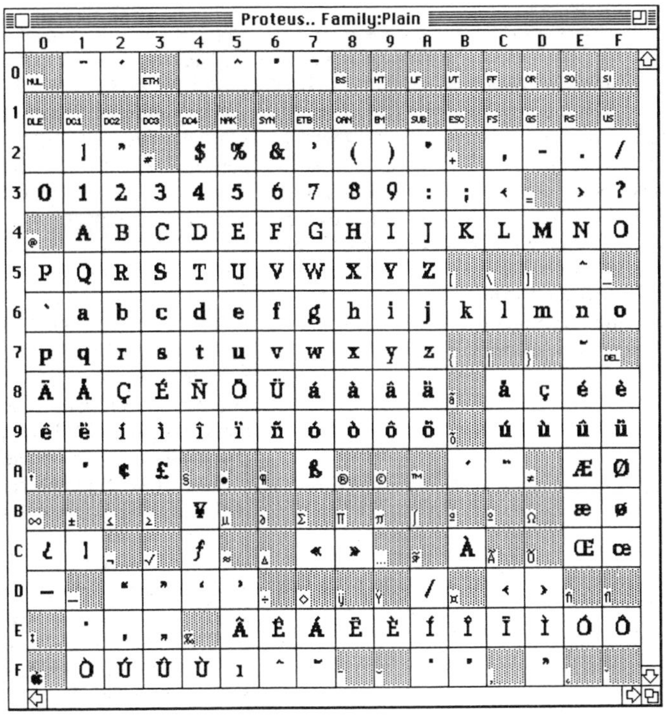

Fig. 2:
ASCII table

Abbildung 2:
ASCII-Tabelle

Illustration 2:
tableau ASCII

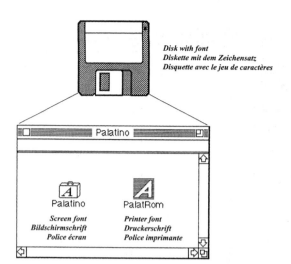

Disk with font
Diskette mit dem Zeichensatz
Disquette avec le jeu de caractères

Fig.3: Two typefaces included on the typeface disk

Abbildung 3: Zwei Schriftarten, die in der Schriftendiskette enthalten sind

Illustration 3 : Deux polices contenus sur la disquette

Palatino

Palatino	PalatRom
Screen font	*Printer font*
Bildschirmschrift	*Druckerschrift*
Police écran	*Police imprimante*

The Macintosh font

Macintosh was the first to make fonts for screens and printers in 72 dpi graphics data. On screen and paper, dots were reproduced on a 1:1 ratio, on the principle of What You See Is What You Get (WYSIWYG). Before long, technology put printer resolution on a par with photosetting, while screen resolution stopped at 150 dpi. So Macintosh created two kinds of fonts: bitmap fonts for screen displays and outline fonts for printers. These are called screen or printer fonts respectively.

If you buy a typeface for the Macintosh on disk, when you open it, you will see two symbols (Fig. 3). The suitcase symbol on the left is for screen fonts, the square on the right for printer fonts. To use both typefaces all the time, you need to install special software in both your computer and printer.

A file may contain a number of fonts, and symbols can change, so we recommend that you read your supplier's user manual very carefully and make sure you know where the font you want is. Be careful when changing names yourself! This is where things can go wrong. If a font is not divided into screen and printer characters and is only included in one form, you will need special graphics software to use it.

Der Macintosh-Zeichensatz

Als erste Firma entwickelte Macintosh für den Bildschirm und für den Drucker Zeichensätze, die aus 72 dpi-Grafikdaten bestanden. Auf dem Bildschirm wurden ebenso wie im Ausdruck die Punkte 1:1 wiedergegeben – getreu dem Motto „What You See Is What You Get (WYSIWYG)". Innerhalb kurzer Zeit erreichte der Auflösungsgrad des Druckers dank technischer Weiterentwicklungen das Niveau des Fotosatzes, während die Auflösung des Bildschirms bei 150 dpi stehenblieb. In der Folge schuf Macintosh zwei Arten von Zeichensätzen: Bitmap-Zeichensätze für die Bildschirmdarstellung und Outline-Zeichensätze für den Drucker. Je nach Verwendungsart werden sie als Bildschirmschrift oder Druckerschrift bezeichnet.

Wer Schriften für den Macintosh auf Diskette erwirbt und diese öffnet, sieht zwei Symbole (Abbildung 3). Das Koffersymbol links steht für Bildschirmschrift, das quadratische Symbol rechts für Druckerschrift. Um beide Schriften ständig benutzen zu können, müssen sie mit spezieller Software sowohl im System des Computers als auch im Drucker installiert werden.

Da mehrere Zeichensätze in einem Ordner enthalten sein oder sich die Symbole ändern können, sollte man das Benutzerhandbuch des jeweiligen Anbieters genau lesen und sich vergewissern, wo sich der gewünschte Zeichensatz befindet. Die Bezeichnung unter dem Symbol ist eine Art Namensschild des Zeichensatzes. Vorsicht bei eigenmächtigen Änderungen der Bezeichnung! Es kann zu Fehlfunktionen kommen. Sollte der Zeichensatz nicht in Bildschirm- und Druckerschrift unterteilt und lediglich in einer Form enthalten sein, kann er nur mit einem speziellen Grafikprogramm verwendet werden.

Le jeu de caractères Macintosh

Macintosh fut la première société à développer pour l'écran et pour l'imprimante des jeux de caractères composés de données graphiques de 72 dpi. On voyait ainsi apparaître à l'écran la copie conforme de ce que serait l'impression, à la même échelle, selon la formule „What You See Is What You Get (WYSIGYG) - tel écran, tel écrit". La définition de l'imprimante ne tarda pas à rattraper le niveau de la photocomposition grâce à des développements techniques sophistiqués tandis que la définition de l'écran en restait à 150 dpi. C'est alors que Macintosh créa deux types de jeux de caractères : des jeux de caractères bitmap pour la représentation écran et des jeux de caractères tracés pour l'imprimante. Selon le type d'application, ils sont désignés sous les noms de police écran ou de police imprimante.

L'acquéreur de polices Macintosh sur disquette verra deux symboles (illustration 3). Le symbole „valise", à gauche, correspond à police écran, le symbole carré, à droite) police imprimante. Les deux polices doivent être installées dans le système de l'ordinateur tout comme dans l'imprimante, grâce à un logiciel spécial, pour qu'elles soient utilisables en permanence.

Comme plusieurs jeux de caractères sont contenus dans un dossier ou bien dans la mesure où les symboles peuvent varier, il convient de lire attentivement le manuel du fabricant et de s'assurer de l'endroit dans lequel se trouve le jeu de caractères voulu. La désignation du symbole fait penser à une plaque signalétique pour le jeu de caractères. Nous déconseillons vivement de modifier la désignation de sa propre initiative! Cela risque de causer de graves problèmes. Si un jeu de caractères n'est pas disponible en format écran et en format imprimante, mais sous une seule forme, il faut recourir à un programme graphique particulier.

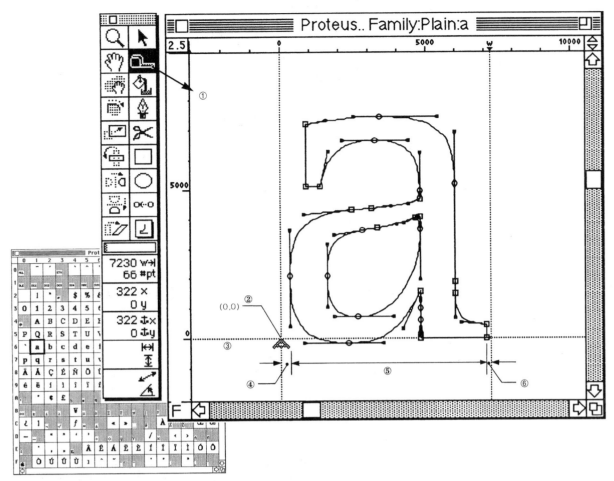

Fig. 4: Outline typescript processing window (FontStudio by Letraset)

① *Centimetre scale*
② *Origin of letter*
③ *Baseline*
④ *Front porch width*
⑤ *Typeface width*
⑥ *Back porch width*

Abbildung 4: Fenster zur Bearbeitung der Outline-Schrift (FontStudio) von Letraset

① *Zentimetermaß*
② *Ursprung des Buchstabens*
③ *Grundlinie*
④ *Vorbreite*
⑤ *Schriftbreite*
⑥ *Nachbreite*

Illustration 4: Fenêtre de traitement de script de caractères tracés (FontStudio) de Letraset

① *Centimètre*
② *Origine de la lettre*
③ *Ligne de base*
④ *Largeur avant*
⑤ *Largeur d'écriture*
⑥ *Largeur après*

Outline font 1

Fig. 4 shows the design for the installed typeface by the FontStudio software, which generates and handles outline fonts. At a glance you can see the outlines for the coordinate origin (0,0), baseline and the lines showing the width.
□ and ○ on the contour lines are corner or curve points for showing the contours. Where the ends of straight lines intersect dots, these are called Bezier checkpoints. Curves are then generated using the functional equations for the coordinates of the Bezier points and the points on the contours. Front and back porch width can be determined using the centimetre scale.

Outline-Zeichensätze 1

Abbildung 4 zeigt den Entwurf der installierten Schrift durch das Programm FontStudio, das Outline-Zeichensätze erzeugt und bearbeitet. Auf den ersten Blick sind die Hilfslinien für den Koordinaten-Nullpunkt (0,0), die Grundlinie und die Linien, die die Schriftbreite anzeigen, zu erkennen.
□ und ○ auf den Konturlinien sind Eck-bzw. Kurvenpunkte zur Darstellung der Konturen. Die Endpunkte der Geraden, die die Punkte durchstoßen, heißen Bezier-Kontrollpunkte. Die Kurven werden nun durch die Funktionsgleichungen der Koordinaten der Bezier-Punkte und den Punkten, die sich auf der Kontur befinden, errechnet. Vor- und Nachbreite lassen sich mit Hilfe des Zentimetermaßes bestimmen.

Jeux de caractères tracés 1

L'illustration 4 montre l'esquisse de la police installée par le programme FontStudio qui génère et traite les jeux de caractères tracés. Il suffit d'un coup d'oeil pour reconnaître les lignes d'aide pour l'origine des coordonnées (0, 0), la ligne de base et les lignes affichant la largeur d'écriture.
□ et ○ sont des points angulaires ou de courbe pour la représentation des contours. Lorsqu'une droite coupe un point, l'intersection se nomme point de contrôle. Les courbes se calculent maintenant à l'aide des équations des coordonnées des points Bezier et des points situés sur le contour. La largeur avant et la largeur après se calculent au centimètre.

11

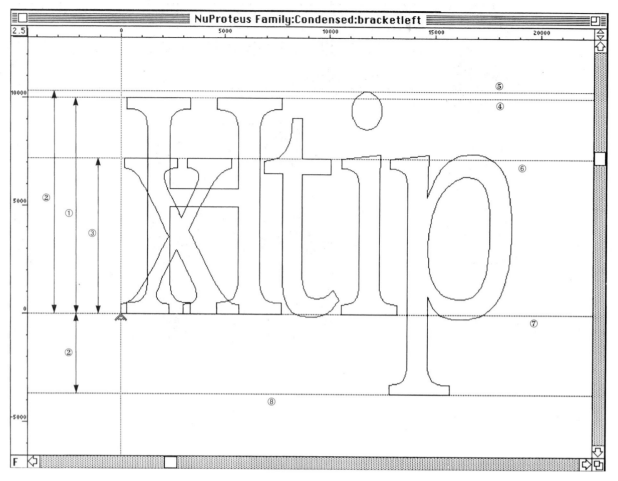

Fig. 5: The outlines needed to define characters (we have superimposed a number of different typefaces to show you what we mean)

① *Body height*
② *Ascenders, descenders*
③ *x height*
④ *Capital line*
⑤ *Ascender line*
⑥ *x line*
⑦ *Baseline*
⑧ *Descender line*

Abbildung 5: Zur Bearbeitung von Zeichen notwendige Hilfslinien (zur Verdeutlichung liegen mehrere Schriften übereinander)

① *Versalhöhe*
② *Oberlänge, Unterlänge*
③ *x-Höhe*
④ *Versallinie*
⑤ *Oberlänge-Linie*
⑥ *x-Linie*
⑦ *Grundlinie*
⑧ *Unterlänge-Linie*

Illustration 5: Lignes d'aide nécessaires au traitement de caractères (plusieurs polices sont présentées l'une au-dessus de l'autre)

① *Hauteur du corps*
② *Lettre longue, lettre à queue*
③ *Hauteur x*
④ *Ligne majuscule*
⑤ *Ligne de lettre longue*
⑥ *Ligne X*
⑦ *Ligne de base*
⑧ *Ligne de lettre à queue*

Outline font II

Fig. 5 shows the window with the outlines which are used as the basis when designing fonts. Deciding where to put the outlines is one of the main tasks when designing a new font, as it will have an effect on what the characters look like. In the past, many people thought (wrongly) that digital typefaces weren't very precise. This was because the means of reproducing them weren't good enough at the time. But FontStudio and other outline software provide a resolution of 15,000 x 15,000 pixels; and you can work in units of a hundredth of a millimetre! This means that today's outline fonts have a form and precision which matches that of analogue photosetting typefaces.

Outline-Zeichensätze II

Abbildung 5 zeigt das Fenster mit den Hilfslinien, die Grundlage beim Entwurf von Zeichensätzen sind. Bei der Neugestaltung von Zeichensätzen ist die Bestimmung der Hilfslinien einer der entscheidenden Arbeitsvorgänge, da er das Erscheinungsbild des Zeichens beeinflußt. In der Vergangenheit ist häufig der falsche Eindruck entstanden, digitalisierte Schriften besäßen nur eine geringe Präzision. Grund für dieses Vorurteil waren die unzureichenden Darstellungsmöglichkeiten. Das Programm „FontStudio" und die übrige Outline-Software bieten jedoch eine Auflösung von 15 000 x 15 000 Pixel. Zudem kann man mit Einheiten von einem Hundertstel Millimeter Größe arbeiten. Dadurch entsprechen heute Gestaltung und Präzision von Outline-Zeichensätzen denen von Analog-Zeichensätzen des Fotosatzes.

Jeux de caractères tracés II

L'illustration 5 montre la fenêtre contenant les lignes d'aide, condition sine qua non pour l'esquisse de jeux de caractères. La définition des lignes d'aide constitue une phase décisive pour le remodelage des jeux de caractères dans la mesure où cela influence l'aspect du caractère. On a souvent eu par le passé la fausse impression que les polices numérisées étaient d'une précision médiocre. Ce préjugé se fondait sur les possibilités de représentation tout à fait insuffisantes. Le programme „FontStudio" et l'autre logiciel Outline permettent cependant une définition de 15.000 x 15.000 pixels. En outre, on peut également travailler avec les centièmes de millimètre. De nos jours, l'aspect et la précision des jeux de caractères tracés sont comparables à ceux des jeux de caractères analogiques de la photocomposition.

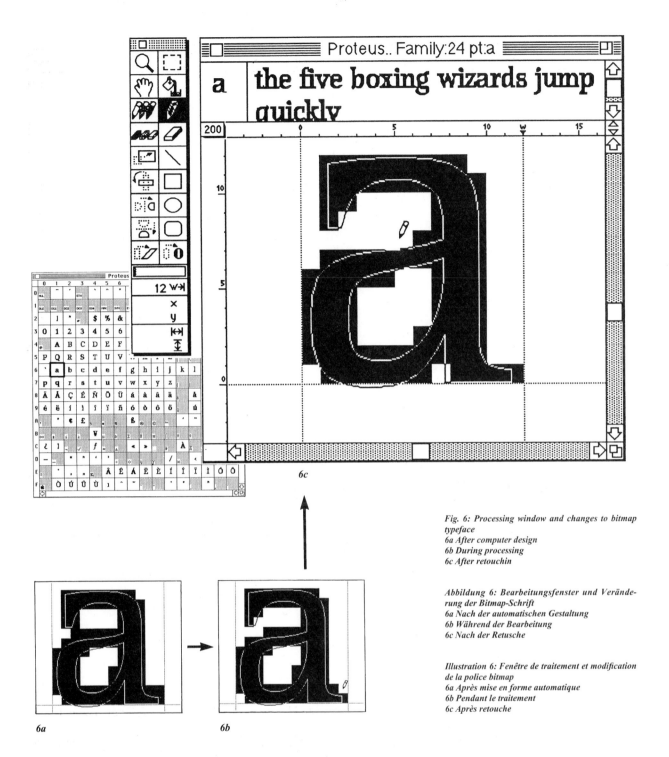

6c

Fig. 6: Processing window and changes to bitmap
typeface
6a After computer design
6b During processing
6c After retouchin

Abbildung 6: Bearbeitungsfenster und Veränderung der Bitmap-Schrift
6a Nach der automatischen Gestaltung
6b Während der Bearbeitung
6c Nach der Retusche

Illustration 6: Fenêtre de traitement et modification
de la police bitmap
6a Après mise en forme automatique
6b Pendant le traitement
6c Après retouche

6a   *6b*

Bitmap font I

Bitmap fonts for screen displays are not
designed from scratch each time. They
are created by automatically converting
the outline font for the printer. They are
then polished (retouched).

Fig. 6a shows what a computer-designed
letter looks like in the unpolished state.
The letter is then retouched bit by bit and
moulded to the contours (Figs. 6b and
6c).

Bitmap-Zeichensätze I

Die Bitmap-Zeichensätze für die Bild-
schirmdarstellung werden nicht von
Grund auf neugestaltet. Sie entstehen
durch automatische Umrechnung des
Outline-Zeichensatzes für den Drucker.
Anschließend erfolgt die Überarbeitung
(Retusche).
Abbildung 6a zeigt das ungeschliffene
Aussehen eines Bitmap-Buchstabens
nach der automatischen Gestaltung.
Anschließend wird der Buchstabe bit für
bit retuschiert und entsprechend den
Konturen angepaßt (Abbildungen 6b und
6c).

Jeux de caractères bitmap

Les jeux de caractères bitmap pour la
représentation écran ne sont pas recom-
posés en partant de zéro. Ils sont le fruit
du recalcul automatique du jeu de caractères tracés pour l'imprimante. Les retou-
ches viennent ensuite.
L'illustration 6a montre l'aspect brut
d'une lettre bitmap après mise en forme
automatique. Ensuite, la lettre est
retouchée un bit après l'autre et adaptée
aux contours (illustrations 6b et 6c).

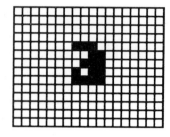

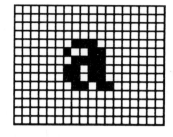

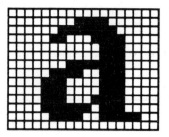

10 pt (real font)
10 pt (Realfont)
10 points (police réelle)

12 pt (real font)
12 pt (Realfont)
12 points (police réelle)

24 pt (real font)
24 pt (Realfont)
24 points (police réelle)

Fig. 7: Bitmap of screen fonts

Abbildung 7: Bitmap der Bildschirmschriften

Illustration 7: Bitmap des polices écran

Bitmap font II

If you buy a typeface and open the screen fonts that come with it, you'll find the typeface comes in anything from two to five sizes. Linotype's Palatino, for instance, comes in 10, 12, 14, 18 and 24 points. Interestingly enough, the bitmaps for the different sizes are different shapes. The reason for this is that the size of the pixels on screen does not change in proportion to the size of the type. The character is therefore forced to adjust to suit the pixel grid and change its original outline form accordingly.

The screen font which is preset as bitmap in certain sizes is called a real font. If you select a typeface size which is not one of the real fonts, the Macintosh uses an algorithm to enlarge or reduce the real font bitmaps accordingly. The choice of real fonts in 10, 12, 14 and 18 pt sizes ensures there are a lot of common denominators which can be multiplied by one another.

Now, you might think there's no point in having a real font in 24 pt – don't you just double the 12 pt? But it helps to have real fonts in as many sizes as possible, because the smaller the screen fonts get, the more they differ from the original outline forms. Which goes against the idea of 'What you see is what you get'. Comparing Fig. 7 centre (12 pt) and right (24 pt) shows that the 24 pt typeface isn't just twice the size of the 12 pt size, but has more detailed bitmaps.

Bitmap-Zeichensätze II

Wer nach dem Erwerb einer Schrift die mitgelieferten Bildschirmschriften öffnet, findet den Zeichensatz in zwei bis fünf Größen - Palatino von Linotype wird z.B. in 10, 12, 14, 18 und 24 pt. angeboten. Interessanterweise zeigen die Bitmaps der verschiedenen Größen unterschiedliche Formen. Grund: Die Größe der Bildschirm-Pixel verändert sich nicht proportional mit der Schriftgröße. Notgedrungen wird daher das Zeichen dem Pixel-Raster angepaßt und entsprechend der ursprünglichen Outline-Form verändert.

Die Bildschirmschrift, die von vornherein in bestimmten Größen als Bitmap installiert ist, heißt Realfont. Wird nun eine Schriftgröße ausgewählt, die nicht zu den Realfonts gehört, wird sie beim Macintosh-System den Bitmaps der Realfonts entsprechend algorithmisch vergrößert bzw. verkleinert erzeugt. Die Wahl von Realfonts in den Größen 10, 12, 14, 18 pt. garantiert, daß es viele gemeinsame Teiler gibt, die miteinander multipliziert werden können.

Nun könnte man denken, es sei nicht notwendig einen Realfont von 24 pt. zu haben, da diese Größe lediglich eine Verdoppelung von 12 pt. ist. Es ist jedoch unverzichtbar, Realfonts in möglichst großen Größen zu haben, denn je kleiner die Bildschirmschriften werden, desto mehr entfernen sie sich von den ursprünglichen Outline-Formen. Folge: Das Gebot „What you see is what you get" wird verletzt. Der Vergleich von Abbildung 7 Mitte (12 pt.) und rechts (24 pt.) verdeutlicht, daß der Buchstabe in 24 pt. keineswegs nur eine einfache Vergrößerung der 12-pt.-Version ist, sondern feinere Bitmaps besitzt.

Police bitmap II

Celui qui ouvre les polices écran après avoir acheté une police trouve le jeu de caractères en deux à cinq formats - le Palatino de Linotype est par exemple disponible en 10, 12, 14, 18 et 24 points. Il est intéressant de constater que les images bitmap des différents formats présentent des formes diverses. La raison est que la taille des pixels de l'écran ne change pas en proportion de la taille des polices. De ce fait, le caractère est modulé en fonction de la trame des pixels, ce qui modifie la forme d'origine du contour.

La police écran installée au préalable en mode bitmap dans des corps bien définis, s'appelle police réelle. Si l'on sélectionne maintenant un autre corps, différent des polices réelles, il sera agrandi ou réduit selon l'algorithme du système Macintosh en fonction du bitmat des polices réelles. La sélection de polices réelles en formats 10, 12, 14, 18 points garantit la présence de nombreux communs diviseurs que l'on peut multiplier entre eux.

On pourrait maintenant penser qu'une police réelle de 24 points est inutile dans la mesure où ce corps ne correspond qu'au double de 12 points. Il est cependant inévitable de disposer de polices réelles dans les corps les plus grands possibles dans la mesure où plus les polices écrans sont petites, plus elles s'éloignent des formes de contours d'origine. Conséquence : la formule WYSIWYG „What You See Is What You Get" n'est plus respectée. La comparaison de l'illustration 7 centre (12 points) et droite (24 points) signifie que la lettre en 24 points n'est pas simplement le double de la version de 12 points, mais qu'elle possède un bitmap plus fin.

14

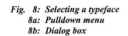

Fig. 8: *Selecting a typeface*
　　8a: *Pulldown menu*
　　8b: *Dialog box*

Abbildung 8: *Methoden der Schriftart-Einstellung*
　　8a: *Pulldown-Menü*
　　8b: *Dialogbox*

Illustration 8: *Méthodes de sélection de police*
　　8a: *Menu déroulant*
　　8b: *Boîte de dialogue*

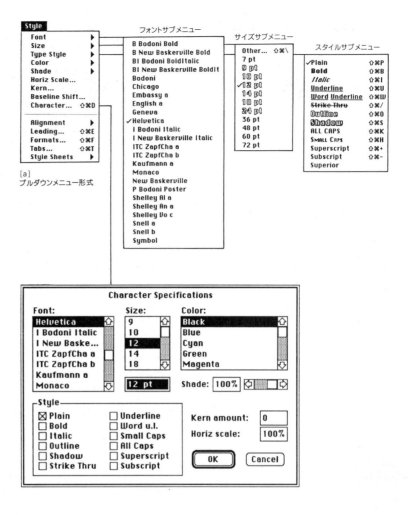

Fig. 9: *List of typefaces,*
　　　　Suitcase II software

Abbildung 9: *Schriftübersicht im Programm*
　　　　Suitcase II

Illustration 9: *Vue générale dans le*
　　　　programme Suitcase II

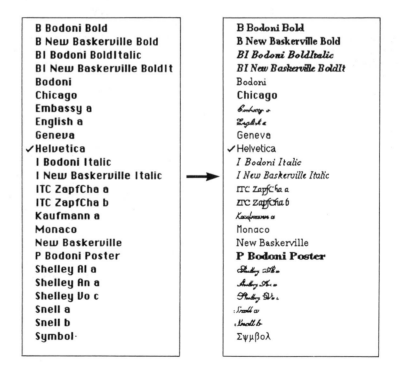

15

Choosing a typeface: attitudes

Of course, the Macintosh applications software has a special menu for selecting typefaces. We will run through the procedure to follow using QuarkXPress as an example: if you're using another software package, consult the manual supplied.

There are four stages in selecting a typeface: 1. Marking out area. 2. Selecting the typeface. 3. Selecting the size. 4. Selecting the style. Always make sure you take the first step first - otherwise, the software has no idea what block of the text you want to use.

Steps 2-4 don't necessarily have to be carried out in that order. You could skip step 2, for instance, and the software would then use the default font or typeface you were last using.

It's best to select the size before the style (bold, italic etc.) The best sizes to select are whole multiples of a real font.

The mouse has an important role to play here. If you move it about on the table, and you will see a dot or arrow make the same movements on the screen. This dot or arrow is called the cursor. In word processing, it looks like a | or a I. You move the cursor to the front of the word you want and click the mouse button. Then you drag the mouse until the cursor reaches the last letter of the word. Now release the mouse button: the highlighted word is now underlined in black, with the letters in white (on a monochrome monitor, of course).

You can run through the steps below either by using pulldown menus or by using dialog boxes you can open with the mouse. Fig. 8 shows a typical dialog box.

Zeichensatz-Auswahl: Einstellungen

Selbstverständlich verfügt das Anwendungsprogramm von Macintosh über ein spezielles Menü für die Schrifteinstellung. Am Beispiel des Programms QuarkXPress sollen im folgenden die nötigen Arbeitsschritte verdeutlicht werden. Bei einer anderen Software ist entsprechend dem jeweiligen Handbuch vorzugehen.

Die Einstellung der Schrift erfolgt in vier Schritten: 1. Markieren des Bereichs. 2. Auswählen der Schrift. 3. Einstellen der Größe. 4. Einstellen des Stils. Dabei ist stets darauf zu achten, den ersten Schritt auch tatsächlich zuerst zu vollziehen. Andernfalls kann das Programm nicht erkennen, welcher Textbereich bearbeitet werden soll.

Die Schritte 2 bis 4 müssen nicht zwingend nacheinander durchgeführt werden. Wird z.B. der 2. Schritt übersprungen, verwendet das Programm die Grundschrift (Defaultfont) oder die Schriftart, mit der unmittelbar zuvor gearbeitet wurde.

Die Größe sollte möglichst vor dem Stil (kursiv, fett etc.) bestimmt werden. Am besten wählt man sich für eine Größe, die sich durch Multiplikation eines Realfonts ergibt.

Bei der Einstellung hat die Maus eine wichtige Funktion. Wird sie auf dem Tisch hin- und herbewegt, sieht man auf dem Bildschirm einen Punkt oder Pfeil, der die entsprechenden Bewegungen nachvollzieht. Dieser Punkt oder Pfeil wird Cursor genannt. Bei der Textbearbeitung hat er die Form | oder I. Der Cursor wird vor das zu aktivierende Wort bewegt und anschließend die Maustaste gedrückt. Die gedrückte Maus wird nun so weit bewegt, bis der Cursor den letzten Buchstaben des Wortes erreicht hat. Dann die Maustaste loslassen: Das aktivierte Wort ist jetzt schwarz unterlegt, die Schriften erscheinen weiß (beim Schwarzweißmonitor).

Die folgenden Schritte können entweder mit Pulldown-Menüs nacheinander vollzogen werden oder mit Hilfe von Dialogboxen, die sich mit der Maus öffnen lassen. Abbildung 8 zeigt ein Beispiel für eine solche Dialogbox.

Sélection du jeu de caractères : Réglages

Bien évidemment, le programme d'application Macintosh dispose d'un menu spécial pour la sélection des polices. L'exemple du programme QuarkXPress décrit les phases nécessaires. Il faudra toujours s'appuyer sur le manuel accompagnant le logiciel.

La sélection de la police s'effectue en quatre temps : 1. Marquage de la zone. 2. Sélection de la police. 3. Sélection du format. 4. Sélection du style. Pour ce faire, il ne faut jamais oublier de marquer la zone sinon le programme ne sait pas ce qu'il doit traiter.

Les phases 2 à 4 doivent se dérouler dans cet ordre. Si, par exemple, on saute la seconde phase, le programme applique la police par défaut ou bien la dernière police utilisée.

Le format doit être défini avant le style (italique, gras, etc.), autant que faire se peut. Le mieux est de choisir un format résultant de la multiplication d'une police réelle.

La souris joue un rôle important dans la sélection. Lorsque l'on déplace la souris, on voit un point ou une flèche à l'écran traduisant les mouvements de la souris. Ce point ou cette flèche s'appelle curseur. Pour le traitement de texte, il prend la forme d'une barre verticale ou d'un I. Il faut amener le curseur devant le mot à activer, puis appuyer sur la touche souris. Déplacer alors la souris en maintenant le bouton enfoncé, jusqu'à ce que le curseur ait atteint la dernière lettre du mot. Puis relâcher la souris : le mot activé apparaît en vidéo inversée (noir pour le fond, blanc pour les lettres, dans le cas d'un moniteur monochrome).

Les phases suivantes peuvent s'effectuer à l'aide de menus déroulants ou de boîtes de dialogue que l'on ouvre avec la souris. L'illustration XX montre un exemple de boîte de dialogue de ce type.

Selecting the font: typeface name and size

The typeface menu only shows the faces the system can handle. In other words: there may well be other typefaces installed on your hard disk, but the system doesn't recognize them. To save typefaces into the system or access them from the system, you need software such as Font/DA Mover, Suitcase II or Master Juggler.

The pulldown menu shows typefaces in alphabetical order. If you've got Suitcase II installed in your system, you press the option key (just before you go from the main menu to the sub-menu) to see the typeface list in the typeface concerned (Fig. 9). Now use the mouse to move the cursor (arrow) to the typeface you want. Once the name is underlined, release the mouse button. You have now selected your typeface. The text you highlighted before now appears in the typeface you want. As soon as you flag an area of text, the 'Typeface' sub-menu identifies the typeface with an apostrophe (in front of the typeface used).

You select the size by opening the sub-menu after 'Typeface'. The procedure is then the same as above. The outline numbers show the real font sizes. If the size you want is not on the menu, select 'Other' and enter the details of what you want via the keyboard. Most typesetting software gives you a wide range of type sizes: QuarkXPress, for instance, lets you choose any size from 2 to 500 point.

Zeichensatz-Auswahl: Schriftname und -größe

Im Schrift-Menü erscheinen nur solche Schriften, die das jeweilige System verarbeiten kann. Das heißt: Auf der Festplatte können durchaus noch weitere Schriften installiert sein, die jedoch vom System nicht erkannt werden. Um Schriften ins System zu speichern oder vom System aus zugänglich zu machen, bieten sich Programme wie Font/DA Mover, Suitcase II oder Master Juggler an.

Das Pulldown-Menü listet die Schriften in alphabetischer Reihenfolge auf. Sofern Suitcase II im System installiert ist, wird durch Drücken der Wahltaste - unmittelbar bevor man vom Hauptmenü ins Untermenü geht - die Schriftenübersicht im Stil der jeweiligen Schrift gezeigt (Abbildung 9). Nun wird der Cursor (Pfeil) mittels der Maus auf die gewünschte Schrift bewegt. Sobald der Name unterlegt ist, läßt man die Maustaste los. Damit ist die Auswahl der Schrift beendet. Die vorher markierte Textstelle erscheint nun in der gewünschten Schrift. Sobald eine Textstelle markiert ist, identifiziert das Untermenü Schrift die Schriftart mit einem Häkchen (es steht vor der benutzen Schrift).

Die Größe wird durch Öffnen des nach Schrift folgenden Untermenüs vorgenommen. Die Arbeitsläufe entsprechen den oben geschilderten. Die konturiert dargestellten Zahlen geben die Größen der Realfonts an. Sofern eine Größe gewünscht wird, die nicht im Menü enthalten ist, wählt man „other" und bestimmt sie durch Eingabe über die Tastatur. Die Schriftgrößen-Auswahl ist bei Satz-Software im allgemeinen sehr groß, z.B. ist bei QuarkXPress die Wahl von Größen zwischen 2 pt. und 500 pt. möglich.

Sélection de jeu de caractères : nom et corps de police

Le menu des polices ne comporte que les polices que le système peut traiter. Cela signifie que l'on peut installer sur le disque dur des polices que le système ne reconnaît pas. Des programmes comme Font/DA Mover, Suitcase II ou Master Juggler permettent de mémoriser des polices dans le système ou de les rendre accessibles au système.

Le menu déroulant dresse la liste des polices par ordre alphabétique. Si le programme SuitCase II est installé dans le système, il suffit d'appuyer sur la touche de sélection, juste avant de quitter le menu principal pour passer au sous-menu, pour visualiser la police dans son propre style (illustration 9). Déplacer alors le curseur (flèche) avec la souris pour l'amener sur la police désirée. Dès que le nom apparaît en vidéo inversée, relâcher la souris. La police est alors sélectionnée. La portion de texte marquée au préalable apparaît alors dans la police désirée. Dès qu'une portion de texte est marquée, le sous-menu des polices identifie la police par un petit crochet (devant la police utilisée).

Pour sélectionner un format, il faut ouvrir le sous-menu suivant la police. Le déroulement des opérations correspond à la description ci-dessus. Les chiffres représentés en contour indiquent le format des polices réelles. Si l'on souhaite un format non contenu dans le menu, choisir „other" et entrer la dimension au clavier. La sélection des tailles de caractères est généralement très vaste au niveau du logiciel, par exemple avec QuarkXPress, on a le choix entre 2 et 500 points.

| Univers 53

SWISS 742
Extended

Zurich e : Plain | Univers 55

SWISS 742

Zurich a : Plain | *Univers 56*

SWISS 742
Italic

Zurich a : Italic | Univers 45

SWISS 742
light

Zurich b : Plain | *Univers 46*

SWISS 742
light italic

Zurich b : Italic |

How fonts work

The styles in the pulldown menu are in three groups: the first is 'standard, bold, italic', the second 'underlined, outline, shadow', the third 'shade, horizontal scale'. Each group has different features, which we will now look at in more detail.

Style group 1

When working, always bear in mind that 'standard' is a default font in photosetting. If you don't choose a specific style, all typefaces will appear in 'standard' form. 'Bold' and 'italic' thicken and slant the typeface respectively. As a user, you will need to know whether the system generates 'bold' or 'italic' faces automatically or whether they are included in the font. You can usually find this out from the supplier's catalogue or type sample books. If you can't find the style you want in the type family concerned, this means there isn't a screen or a printer font. You can save yourself problems here by giving the typeface name and using style commands to change it. Given the enormous range of typefaces available (semi-bold, light, black, condensed, expanded, etc.), this is about the most user-friendly method.

Wirkung der Zeichensätze

Die im Pulldown-Menü erscheinenden Stile sind in drei Gruppen unterteilt: Die erste Stilgruppe ist „standard, fett, kursiv"; die zweite „unterstrichen, konturiert, schattiert"; die dritte „Tonwert (shade)", „Schriftbreite (horizontal scale)". Jede Stilgruppe weist unterschiedliche Merkmale auf, die im folgenden näher erläutert werden.

Stilgruppe 1

Bei allen Arbeiten sollte berücksichtigt werden, daß „Standard" eine Grundschrift beim Fotosatz ist. Erfolgt kein Befehl für einen bestimmten Stil, erscheint jede Schriftart in „standard". In „fett" oder „kursiv" wird dann die „standard"-Schrift verdickt bzw. schräggestellt. Für den Anwender ist es wichtig zu wissen, ob die Stile „fett" und „kursiv" durch automatische Errechnung des Systems erzeugt werden oder ob sie im Zeichensatz enthalten sind. Diese Angabe ist im allgemeinen dem Katalog der Anbieter oder Schriftmusterbüchern zu entnehmen. Sind in der betreffenden Schriftfamilie die gewünschten Stile nicht zu finden, gibt es davon weder eine Bildschirm- noch eine Druckerschrift. Hier kann man sich helfen, indem man den Schriftnamen festlegt und durch Stilbefehle die Schrift verändert. Diese Methode ist in Anbetracht der vielfältigen Schriftvariationen, die angeboten werden – z.B. halbfett, leicht (light), schwarz (black), schmal (condensed), breit (expanded) -, am anwenderfreundlichsten.

Fonctionnement des polices

Les styles apparaissant dans le menu déroulant se répartissent en trois groupes : le premier est „standard, gras, italique"; le second „souligné, contour, ombre"; le troisième „nuance", „largeur d'écriture". Chaque groupe de style présente des caractéristiques différentes que nous allons examiner plus en détail.

Groupe de styles 1

Il existe un jeu de caractères de base pour la photocomposition. En l'absence de définition d'un style particulier, les polices apparaissent en mode „standard". En mode „gras" ou „italique", les lettres „standard" sont épaissies ou penchée, selon le cas. L'utilisateur doit donc savoir si les styles „gras" et „italique" sont créés par calcul automatique dans le système ou bien s'ils sont déjà compris dans le jeu de caractères. Cette information se trouve généralement dans le catalogue du fabricant ou dans les brochures présentant des échantillons. Si les styles recherchés ne figurent pas dans la famille concernée, c'est qu'il n'existe ni de jeu écran ni de jeu imprimante. Pour sortir de cette impasse, il suffit de définir le nom de la police et de modifier le style des caractères à l'aide de commandes. Cette méthode est la plus conviviale compte tenu des nombreuses variantes proposées, par exemple demi-gras, fin, noir, condensé, étendu.

| **Univers 63**

SWISS 742
Bold Extended

Zurich e : Bold | **Univers 65**

SWISS 742
Bold

Zurich a : Bold | ***Univers 66***

SWISS 742
Bold Italic

Zurich a : Bold+Italic |

Fig. 10: Relationship between screen and printer fonts (Bitstream SWISS 742: Univers).

Abbildung 10: Beziehung zwischen Bildschirm- und Druckerschriften (Bitstream SWISS 742: Univers).

Illustration 10: Relation entre les polices écran et les polices imprimante (Bitstream SWISS 742: Univers).

Style group 2

While the indications 'bold' and 'italic' depend on the font and the system concerned, the 'underlined', 'outline' and 'shadow' options are generated by the software.

Most suppliers' fonts do not include font data with such styles; rather, they are achieved by converting the original font data in the software.

The versions in style group 2 are already available as bitmap fonts, so most software has these styles. Most typesetting software, such as QuarkXPress, also offers other styles, such as 'underline word', 'strikeout' and 'small capitals'. You can have any combination of styles you want.

Stilgruppe 2

Während die Bestimmungen „fett" und „kursiv" vom Zeichensatz und vom System abhängig sind, werden die Stile „unterstrichen", „konturiert" und „schattiert" durch Programmoperationen erstellt.

Die Zeichensätze der meisten Anbieter enthalten keine Schriftdaten mit solchen Stilen. Sie werden vielmehr durch Umrechnung der ursprünglichen Schriftdaten im Programm gestaltet.

Da die Variationen der Stilgruppe 2 bereits als Bitmap-Zeichensätze vorlagen, verfügen die meisten Programme über diese Stile. Die meisten Satzprogramme, so auch QuarkXPress, bieten noch weitere Stilvarianten - z.B. „Wort unterstrichen", „durchgestrichen" und „Kapitälchen". Alle Variationen lassen sich miteinander kombinieren.

Groupe de styles 2

Tandis que les définitions „gras" et „italique" dépendent du jeu de caractères et du système, les styles „souligné", „contour" et „ombré" sont liés à des opérations effectuées avec le programme.

Les jeux de caractères de la plupart des fabricants ne contiennent aucune donnée pour ces différents styles. Il faut donc recalculer les données d'origine dans le programme. Comme les variantes du groupe de styles 2 se présentent déjà comme des jeux de caractères bitmap, la plupart des programmes disposent de ces styles. La majeure partie des programmes, même QuarkXPress, offrent un nombre de variantes de styles plus impressionnant encore, par exemple „soulignement mot à mot", „barrés" et „petites majuscules". Toutes les variantes peuvent se combiner entre elles.

Style group 3

As well as the style submenu, the typesetting software has a submenu you can use to create your own style effects, irrespective of the system. The 'font width' and 'shading' versions are exam-

Stilgruppe 3

Im Satz-Programm gibt es neben dem Stil-Untermenü ein Untermenü für eigenständige Stil-Effekte, die vom System unabhängig sind. Die in den Abbildungen gezeigten Varianten „Schriftbreite" und „Tonwert" sind Beispiele, die im Layout eingesetzt werden, um optische Effekte zu erzielen. Die Varianten wer-

Groupe de styles 3

Le programme contient outre le sous-menu styles un autre sous-menu pour les effets de styles qui ne dépendent pas du système. Les variantes représentées sur les illustrations „largeur d'écriture" et „nuance" sont des exemples pouvant intervenir dans la composition pour produire des effets visuels. Les variantes sont calculées et réalisées grâce à des données d'écriture résidentes.

Comme nous l'avons vu, tous les styles à l'exception de „standard" sont générés automatiquement par le programme ou par le système, sous réserve que la police

① **Style Variation**
② **Style** Variation
③ ~~**Style Variation**~~
④ outline Style Variation
⑤ **Style Variation**
⑥ Style Variation
⑦ Style Variation

Fig. 11: Style effects
Abbildung 11: Stil-Effekte
Illustration 11: Effets de style

50% Style Variation
75% **Style Variation**
100% **Style Variation**
125% **Style Variation**
150% **Style Variati**

Fig. 12: Font width
Abbildung 12: Schriftbreite
Illustration 12: Largeur d'écriture

50% Style Variation
80% **Style Variation**

Fig. 13: Shading
Abbildung 13: Tonwert
Illustration 13: Ombres

ples which can be used in a layout for visual effect. They are calculated and designed from installed font data.

As we have seen, all styles except 'standard' are generated automatically by the system or the software where there are no fonts in the desired style. The only problem with this automatic method is, it tends to make things look worse rather than better. For the sake of clear typography, it is also best to avoid making any more changes to styles which themselves are altered, such as sloping an italic font, extending a condensed font etc.

Explication to Fig. 11:

① *underline*
② *underline word*
③ *strikeout*
④ *outline*
⑤ *shadow*
⑥ *outline + shadow*
⑦ *small capitals*

den mittels installierten Schriftdaten errechnet und gestaltet.

Wie wir gesehen haben, werden alle Stile außer „standard" entweder vom System oder vom Programm automatisch erzeugt, sofern es keine im gewünschten Stil gestalteten Schriften gibt. Problem dieser „Automatik": Die ursprüngliche Form der Schrift wird eher verunstaltet als verschönert. Im Sinne einer klaren Typographie sollte zudem darauf verzichtet werden, dem veränderten Stil eine zusätzliche Veränderung der gleichen Art hinzuzufügen – z.B. kursive Schrift schrägstellen, schmale Schrift verlängern o.ä.

Erklärung zu Abbildung 11:

① *unterstrichen*
② *Wort unterstrichen*
③ *durchgestrichen*
④ *konturiert*
⑤ *schattiert*
⑥ *konturiert + schattiert*
⑦ *Kapitälchen*

n'existe pas déjà dans le style voulu. Mais cet „automatisme" pose un problème: la forme d'origine de la police est soit malmenée soit embellie. Pour que la typographie reste claire, il faut se refuser à ajouter au nouveau style une nouvelle modification du même ordre, par exemple pencher une écriture cursive, prolonger une écriture déjà fine, etc.

Explication d'illustration 11:

① *Soulignement*
② *Soulignement mot à mot*
③ *Barré*
④ *Contour*
⑤ *Ombré*
⑥ *Contour + ombré*
⑦ *Petites majuscules*

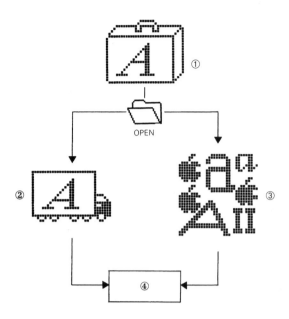

Installing fonts: screen fonts

There are two ways of using screen font data in the system or software: you can either load the font data into the system computer, or you can put the font file outside the system with the suitcase symbol and access it from there.

Method #1 uses Font DA/Mover, method #2 Suitcase II. The trouble with method #1 is it takes up a lot of memory: the more fonts you have on disk, the fuller the system file. If you hold the data outside the system, on the other hand, you only have to open the font file and then load one font. The advantage of this is that you don't overload the system unnecessarily, and there is no limit to the number of fonts you can use.

Fig. 14: Installing screen fonts
① *Screen font file*
② *Font/DA Mover*
③ *Suitcase II*
④ *System*

Illustration 14: Installation de la police écran
① *Fichier de polices écran*
② *Font/DA Mover*
③ *Suitcase II*
④ *Système*

Abbildung 14: Installation der Bildschirmschrift
① *Bildschirmschrift-Datei*
② *Font/DA Mover*
③ *Suitcase II*
④ *System*

Installing fonts: printer fonts

For installing Adobe and Linotype fonts, we usually use Font Downloader (FDL), while we use LaserWriter Font Utility (LFU) for fonts such as Bitstream and Emigré. The Fontographer font design software also uses LFU.

To load fonts, you save them either to the printer RAM or a printer hard disk which can be inside or outside the unit. But beware: if you load the fonts into RAM and then switch the printer off, you lose all the font data. When loading, FDL and LFU ask whether fonts are to be loaded to the printer RAM or onto diskette. With FDL, loading onto diskette is more efficient and makes accessing fonts in the applications software faster.

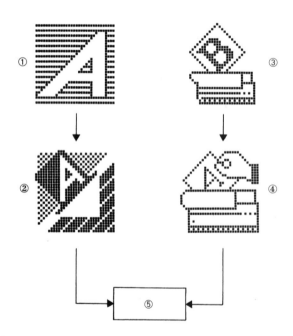

Fig. 15: Installing printer fonts
① *Printer font file*
   (Adobe, Linotype)
② *Font Downloader*
③ *Printer font file*
   (Bitstream etc.)
④ *LaserWriter Font Utility*
⑤ *Printer*

Illustration 15: Installation de la police imprimante
① *Fichier de polices imprimantes*
   (Adobe, Linotype)
② *Font Downloader*
③ *Fichier de police imprimante*
   (Bitstream, par exemple)
④ *LaserWriter Font Utility*
⑤ *Imprimante*

Abbildung 15: Installation der Druckerschrift
① *Druckerschrift-Datei*
   (Adobe, Linotype)
② *Font Downloader*
③ *Druckerschrift-Datei*
   (Bitstream u.a.)
④ *LaserWriter Font Utility*
⑤ *Drucker*

Installation der Zeichensätze: Bildschirmschriften

Es gibt zwei Methoden, um die Daten der Bildschirmschriften mit dem System oder dem Programm zu benutzen: Entweder werden die Schriften-Daten in den Systemordner geladen oder die Schrift-Datei mit dem Koffersymbol wird außerhalb des Systems plaziert und zugänglich gemacht.

Bei der ersten Methode benutzt man Font DA/Mover, bei der zweiten Suitcase II. Problematisch bei der ersten Methode ist der benötigte Speicherplatz, denn: Je mehr Schriften geladen werden, desto voller wird die Systemdatei. Bei der Plazierung der Daten außerhalb des Systems wird hingegen nur eine Schrift von der zuvor geöffneten Schrift-Datei geladen. Vorteile: Das System wird nicht unnötig belastet, und die Zahl der Schriften, mit denen der Nutzer arbeitet, unterliegt keinen Beschränkungen.

Installation der Zeichensätze: Druckerschriften

Für die Installation der Zeichensätze von Adobe und Linotype wird im allgemeinen Font Downloader (FDL) angewendet, während man für Schrift-Sätze wie Bitstream und Emigre LaserWriter Font Utility (LFU) verwendet. Auch das Programm Fontographer zum Entwerfen von Schriften arbeitet mit LFU.

Für das Laden der Schriften werden diese entweder in den Drucker-RAM oder auf eine Druckerfestplatte, die sich inner- oder außerhalb des Geräts befinden kann, gespeichert. Achtung: Alle Schriftdaten werden gelöscht, wenn die Schriften in RAM geladen und der Drucker dann ausgeschaltet wird. Beim Ladevorgang fragen FDL und LFU, ob die Schriften in den Drucker-RAM oder auf Diskette geladen werden. Bei FDL ist das Laden auf Diskette leistungsfähiger und die Zugriffsgeschwindigkeit zu den Schriften im Anwendungsprogramm schneller.

Installation des jeux de caractères : polices écran

Deux méthodes sont possibles pour utiliser les données des polices écran avec le système ou bien avec le programme : charger les données dans le dossier système ou placer le fichier avec le symbole valise en dehors du système, en le rendant accessible.

La première méthode fait appel à Font DA/Mover, la seconde à Suitcase II. Le volume de mémoire nécessaire pour la première méthode constitue un problème dans la mesure où le fichier système s'engorge au fur et à mesure que l'on accumule les polices. Par contre, en plaçant les données en dehors du système, une seule police est chargée à partir du fichier ouvert au préalable. Les avantages sont évidents : le système n'est pas surchargé inutilement et le nombre de polices à la disposition des utilisateurs est illimité.

Installation des jeux de caractères : polices imprimante

On emploie généralement Font Downloader (FDL) pour installer les jeux de caractères Adobe et Linotype, tandis que Font Utility (LU) sert plutôt pour des jeux comme Bitstream et Emigre Laser-Writer. Par ailleurs, le programme Fontographer pour la conception de polices fonctionne avec LFU.

Les polices sont chargées dans la RAM de l'imprimante ou bien sur un disque dur, qui peut se trouver à l'intérieur comme à l'extérieur de l'ordinateur. Attention : toutes les données d'écriture sont effacées lorsque l'on éteint l'imprimante après avoir chargé les polices dans la RAM. Pendant le processus de chargement, FDL et LFU demandent si les polices sont chargées dans la RAM de l'imprimante ou sur disquette. Avec FDL, un chargement sur disquette est plus performant et la vitesse d'accès aux polices dans le programme d'utilisation plus rapide.

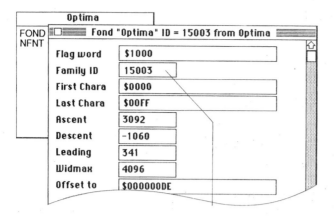

Font ID: This combines the different styles in a 'family'

Schrift-ID: Hier werden die Stilvariationen zu einer „Familie" zusammengefaßt

Identification de police : récapitulatif des variantes de styles dans une „famille"

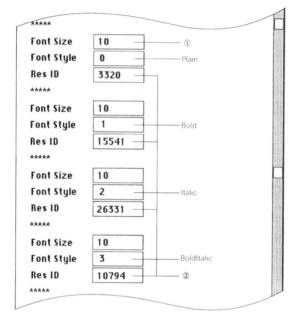

Fig. 16: Typical FOND (FONT family Descriptor) - Resources
① Real font size
② Real font ID (equals NFNT ID)

Abbildung 16: Beispiel der FOND (FONT Family Descriptor)-Ressourcen
① Größe der Realfonts
② Realfont-ID (entsprechen NFNT-ID)

Illustration 16: Exemple des ressources FOND (descripteur de famille de police)
① Taille des polices réelles
② ID de police réelle (correspondant à l'ID NFNT)

ID nos.

As a general rule, always use Suitcase II rather than Font/DA Mover if possible. Why? Because Font/DA Mover changes the so-called 'font resources'. With Macintosh, fonts and software have additional names you could call 'personal data'. These give characteristics and relations with other files. Individual description contents are given an ID no. These are also called resources.

Fig. 16 shows the FOND-ID number of the screen font 'Optima': 15003. Real font IDs are then listed by font size and style. The opened FOND resource shows that the real font ID nos. are the same as the NFNT ID nos. NFNT resources contain the ID number and real fonts in bitmap form.

If you use Font/DA Mover to load fonts, screen fonts will sometimes appear with the same FOND and NFNT number. If the two numbers are the same, the software changes one of them to avoid confusion. This is logical, but may set off a chain reaction, i.e. if you load another font at a later date and the numbers clash again. The software will then change one of the numbers... and so on. If you try and print a document produced under this system on a system which is still using the old numbers, the printout may not be what you expect.

Suitcase II operates in a different way, without changing the ID nos. It suppresses one of the fonts, depending on which has priority. The advantage of this is it keeps the original font file ID nos. the same.

Über die ID-Nummer

Allgemein gilt: Wo immer möglich, sollte Suitcase II dem Programm Font/DA Mover vorgezogen werden. Grund: Font/DA Mover verändert die sog. Schrift-Ressourcen. Bei Macintosh enthalten die Zeichensätze und Programme zusätzliche Beschreibungen, die man als „Personalangaben" bezeichnen könnte. Hierin sind Eigenschaften und Zusammenhänge mit anderen Dateien exakt beschrieben. Dem einzelnen Inhalt der Beschreibung ist eine ID-Nummer zugeteilt. Diese Nummern bezeichnet man auch als Ressourcen.

Abbildung 16 zeigt die FOND-ID-Nummer der Bildschirmschrift „Optima": 15003. Darunter sind ID-Nummern der Realfonts nach Schriftgröße und Stil aufgelistet. Auf der abgebildeten geöffneten FOND-Ressource ist zu erkennen, daß die ID-Nummern der Realfonts mit der NFNT-ID-Nummer identisch ist. Die NFNT-Ressourcen beinhalten ID-Nummer und Realfonts in Bitmap.

Will man mit Font/DA Mover Schriften laden, erscheinen gelegentlich Bildschirmschriften mit gleicher FOND- und NFNT-Nummer. Treffen zwei identische ID-Nummern aufeinander ändert das Programm eine der beiden Nummern, damit es nicht zu Überschneidungen kommt. Dies ist zwar logisch, kann jedoch eine Kettenreaktion in Gang setzen, nämlich dann, wenn die geänderte Nummer mit einer weiteren, zu einem späteren Zeitpunkt geladenen Schrift übereinstimmt. Wieder vergibt das Programm eine neue Nummer etc... Wird nun ein mit diesem System angefertigtes Dokument mit einem System ausgedruckt, das noch die ursprünglichen Nummern besitzt, enthält der Ausdruck nicht die gewünschten Schriften.

Suitcase II arbeitet hier anders, denn es ändert die ID-Nummern nicht. Je nach Vorrang wird der Gebrauch der einen Schrift untersagt. Vorteil: Die Original-ID-Nummern der Schriften-Dateien bleiben erhalten.

Numéro d'identification

La règle d'or est la suivante : lorsque cela est possible, accorder la préférence à Suitcase II sur le programme Font/DA Mover, pour la bonne raison que Font/DA Mover modifie les „ressources". Avec Macintosh, les jeux de caractères et les programmes s'accompagnent de descriptions que l'on peut qualifier d'"informations privées". Il s'agit de propriétés et des relations avec les autres fichiers. Un numéro d'identification est attribué aux différents articles de la description. Ces numéros s'appellent des ressources.

L'illustration 16 présente le numéro d'identification FOND de la police écran „Optima" : 15003. On trouve ensuite le numéro d'identification des polices réelles classées par taille et par style. La représentation de la ressource FOND ouverte montre que les numéros d'identification des polices réelles sont les mêmes que les numéros d'identification NFNT. Les ressources NFNT contiennent les numéros d'identification et les polices réelles bitmap.

Lorsque l'on charge des polices avec Font/DA Mover, il arrive que les polices écran apparaissent avec le même numéro FOND et NFNT. En cas de conflit entre deux numéros d'identiques, le programme change un des deux numéros pour supprimer toute interférence. Ceci a beau être logique, on risque cependant d'assister à une réaction en chaîne si le second numéro est le même que le troisième et ainsi de suite, le programme changeant tous les numéros et si l'on imprime un document réalisé avec ce système et possédant encore l'ancien numéro, la sortie papier ne présentera pas les polices voulues.

Suitcase II fonctionne de manière différente dans la mesure où il ne change pas les numéros d'identification. Selon les priorités, telle ou telle police sera écartée. Avantage : les numéros d'identification d'origine des fichiers de polices sont conservés.

As an introduction to Macintosh fonts, this is very short, but I hope it has given you an idea of what digital fonts are about. I've tried to keep explanations short and snappy rather than the long-winded versions you find in computer manuals. If you think you now know enough about computer typefaces and design, perhaps you're ready for the next step. With your own applications software, you'll find it much easier to use fonts or design your own. This is what Susanna Ricco and Rudy Vadallance of Emigré have done, for instance. Some of their typefaces are now on sale, and are included in this book. The technical conditions are ideal: printer resolution is improving all the time, and fonts are being created to match. Without exaggerating, we can say that we are on the threshold of a new era of word processing; it may have already begun, as the example of Emigré shows.

M. Iiyama

Zwar war die Vorstellung der Macintosh-Zeichensätze nur kurz, doch ich hoffe, Sie haben sich ein Bild der digitalisierten Schrift machen können. Ich habe versucht, die oft umständlichen Erklärungen in Computerbüchern, knapp und prägnant zusammenzufassen. Wenn Sie meinen, nun ausreichend über Wesen und Gestalt von elektronischen Schriften informiert zu sein, sollten Sie den nächsten Schritt wagen: Mit Ihrem Anwendungsprogramm wird es viel leichter sein, mit den Schriften zu arbeiten oder eigene Zeichensätze zu entwerfen. Dies haben beispielsweise Susanna Ricco und Rudy Vadallance von Emigre getan. Einige ihrer Zeichensätze, die sie inzwischen erfolgreich verkauft haben, sind in diesem Buch enthalten. Die technischen Voraussetzungen sind bestens - Drucker werden mit immer besserer Auflösung angeboten, die entsprechenden Schriften sind im Entstehen begriffen. Ohne Übertreibung läßt sich sagen, daß wir einem neuen Zeitalter der Textver- und -bearbeitung entgegensehen. Vielleicht aber hat dieses neue Zeitalter bereits begonnen, wie das Beispiel Emigre zeigt.

M. Iiyama

Il est vrai que la présentation des jeux de caractères Macintosh était brève mais j'espère cependant que vous comprenez mieux les polices numérisées. Je me suis efforcé de résumer succinctement les explications souvent ténébreuses des manuels informatiques. Si vous souhaitez maintenant des informations détaillées sur la nature et l'aspect des polices électroniques, vous devez passer à la phase suivante : grâce à votre programme d'utilisation, il vous sera beaucoup plus facile de travailler avec les polices ou de développer vos propres jeux de caractères. C'est ce que Susanna Ricco et Rudy Vadallance de la société Emigre ont fait, par exemple. Ce livre contient un certain nombre des jeux de caractères qu'ils commercialisent déjà avec succès. Les conditions techniques requises sont idéales; les imprimantes sont proposées avec une définition sans cesse améliorée, les polices correspondantes sont en plein essor. Sans exagérer, nous pouvons dire que nous entrons dans une nouvelle ère du traitement de texte. Cette ère a peut-être déjà commencé, comme le montre l'exemple d'Emigre.

M. Iiyama

Literature
James Craig, Basic Typography – A Design Manual, 1989
Peter Karow, Digital Formats for Typefaces, 1989
Arthur Naimann, The Macintosh Bible, 1990

Software
Fontographer (English, Version 3.1, January 1991), Altsys. Co.
FontStudio (English, Version 1.0, January 1991) Letraset

Literatur
James Craig: Basic Typography – A Design Manual, 1989
Peter Karow: Digital Formats for Typefaces, 1989
Arthur Naimann: The Macintosh Bible, 1990.

Software
Fontographer (engl., Version 3.1, Januar 1991), Altsys, Co. FontStudio (engl., Version 1.0, Januar 1991), Letraset

Bibliographie
James Craig: Basic Typography – A Design Manual, 1989
Peter Karow: Digital Formats for Typefaces, 1989
Arthur Naimann: The Macintosh Bible, 1990.

Logiciel
Fontographer (anglais, version 3.1, janvier 1991), Altsys, Co.
FontStudio (anglais, version 1.0, janvier 1991), Letraset

Translation by Andrew Fenner in association with First Edition Translations, Cambridge, UK.

Übersetzung von Hiroko Hashimoto in Zusammenarbeit mit Jordan/Lenz, TARGET DATA, Dortmund

Traduction de Patrick Cochet-Balmet en association avec First Edition Translations Ltd, Cambridge, Grande-Bretagne

Century Oldstyle — Century Old Style, Revival 707

5pt	ABCDEFGHIJKLMNOPQRSTUVWXYZABCDEFGHIJKLMNOPQ	abcdefghijklmnopqrstuvwxyzabcdefghijklmnopqrstuvwxyzabcde	12345678901234567890123456789012345678901234
6pt	ABCDEFGHIJKLMNOPQRSTUVWXYZABCDEFGHIJ	abcdefghijklmnopqrstuvwxyzabcdefghijklmnopqrstuv	12345678901234567890123456789012345
7pt	ABCDEFGHIJKLMNOPQRSTUVWXYZABCDE	abcdefghijklmnopqrstuvwxyzabcdefghijklmno	12345678901234567890123456789012345678
8pt	ABCDEFGHIJKLMNOPQRSTUVWXYZA	abcdefghijklmnopqrstuvwxyzabcdefghijl	12345678901234567890123456789012345
9pt	ABCDEFGHIJKLMNOPQRSTUVWX	abcdefghijklmnopqrstuvwxyzabcdel	12345678901234567890123456789
10pt	ABCDEFGHIJKLMNOPQRSTUV	abcdefghijklmnopqrstuvwxyzabc	12345678901234567890123456
11pt	ABCDEFGHIJKLMNOPQRST	abcdefghijklmnopqrstuvwxyz	12345678901234567890123456
12pt	ABCDEFGHIJKLMNOPQR	abcdefghijklmnopqrstuvwx	12345678901234567890123
13pt	ABCDEFGHIJKLMNOPQ	abcdefghijklmnopqrstuvv	12345678901234567890
14pt	ABCDEFGHIJKLMNOI	abcdefghijklmnopqrstu	12345678901234567890
15pt	ABCDEFGHIJKLMNC	abcdefghijklmnopqrst	12345678901234567895
16pt	ABCDEFGHIJKLMN	abcdefghijklmnopqr	12345678901234567
18pt	ABCDEFGHIJKLN	abcdefghijklmnop	12345678901234560
20pt	ABCDEFGHIJKI	abcdefghijklmnc	12345678901234
24pt	ABCDEFGHI	abcdefghijklm	123456789012
28pt	ABCDEFGI	abcdefghijk	1234567890
32pt	ABCDEFC	abcdefghij	123456789
36pt	ABCDEF	abcdefgh	12345678
40pt	ABCDEI	abcdefgl	1234567
45pt	ABCDE	abcdefg	123456'
50pt	ABCD	abcdef	123456
60pt	ABCI	abcde	12345
70pt	ABC	abcd	1234

25

Bodoni Roman — Bodoni, Modern 421

5pt	ABCDEFGHIJKLMNOPQRSTUVWXYZABCDEFGHIJKLMNOP	abcdefghijklmnopqrstuvwxyzabcdefghijklmnopqrstuvwxyzabcdefgl	1234567890123456789012345678901234567890123456789012345
6pt	ABCDEFGHIJKLMNOPQRSTUVWXYZABCDEFGHI	abcdefghijklmnopqrstuvwxyzabcdefghijklmnopqrstuvw	123456789012345678901234567890123456789012345
7pt	ABCDEFGHIJKLMNOPQRSTUVWXYZABCI	abcdefghijklmnopqrstuvwxyzabcdefghijklmnop	12345678901234567890123456789012345678
8pt	ABCDEFGHIJKLMNOPQRSTUVWXYZ	abcdefghijklmnopqrstuvwxyzabcdefghijkl	1234567890123456789012345678901234
9pt	ABCDEFGHIJKLMNOPQRSTUVW	abcdefghijklmnopqrstuvwxyzabcdefg	1234567890123456789012345678901
10pt	ABCDEFGHIJKLMNOPQRSTU	abcdefghijklmnopqrstuvwxyzabco	123456789012345678901234567
11pt	ABCDEFGHIJKLMNOPQRS'	abcdefghijklmnopqrstuvwxyza	12345678901234567890123456
12pt	ABCDEFGHIJKLMNOPQI	abcdefghijklmnopqrstuvwxy	1234567890123456789012
13pt	ABCDEFGHIJKLMNOP(	abcdefghijklmnopqrstuvw	12345678901234567890123
14pt	ABCDEFGHIJKLMNO	abcdefghijklmnopqrstuv	12345678901234567890
15pt	ABCDEFGHIJKLMN(	abcdefghijklmnopqrsti	123456789012345678
16pt	ABCDEFGHIJKLMI	abcdefghijklmnopqrs	123456789012345678
18pt	ABCDEFGHIJKLI	abcdefghijklmnop(	12345678901234(
20pt	ABCDEFGHIJK	abcdefghijklmno	1234567890123
24pt	ABCDEFGHI	abcdefghijklm	12345678901:
28pt	ABCDEFGI	abcdefghijk]	1234567890
32pt	ABCDEF(	abcdefghij	123456789
36pt	ABCDEF	abcdefghi	12345678
40pt	ABCDE]	abcdefgl	1234567
45pt	ABCDF	abcdefg	123456'
50pt	ABCD	abcdef	123456
60pt	ABCI	abcde	12345
70pt	ABC	abcd	1234

5pt	ABCDEFGHIJKLMNOPQRSTUVWXYZABCDEFGHIJKLMNOP(	abcdefghijklmnopqrstuvwxyzabcdefghijklmnopqrstuvwxyzabcdefghijklmnopqr	1234567890123456789012345678901234567890123456789012345678901234567890123456789012345678901234(
6pt	ABCDEFGHIJKLMNOPQRSTUVWXYZABCDEFGHIJ	abcdefghijklmnopqrstuvwxyzabcdefghijklmnopqrstuvwxyzabcdef	123456789012345678901234567890123456789012345(
7pt	ABCDEFGHIJKLMNOPQRSTUVWXYZABCD	abcdefghijklmnopqrstuvwxyzabcdefghijklmnopqrstuvwx	1234567890123456789012345678901234567890123456789
8pt	ABCDEFGHIJKLMNOPQRSTUVWXYZ/	abcdefghijklmnopqrstuvwxyzabcdefghijklmnopqr	1234567890123456789012345678901234
9pt	ABCDEFGHIJKLMNOPQRSTUVW:	abcdefghijklmnopqrstuvwxyzabcdefghijklm	1234567890123456789012345678901234567890
10pt	ABCDEFGHIJKLMNOPQRSTU	abcdefghijklmnopqrstuvwxyzabcdefghij	12345678901234567890123456
11pt	ABCDEFGHIJKLMNOPQRS1	abcdefghijklmnopqrstuvwxyzabcdef	12345678901234567890123456789012345
12pt	ABCDEFGHIJKLMNOPQR	abcdefghijklmnopqrstuvwxyzabc	12345678901234567890123
13pt	ABCDEFGHIJKLMNOP(	abcdefghijklmnopqrstuvwxyza	12345678901234567890
14pt	ABCDEFGHIJKLMNOI	abcdefghijklmnopqrstuvwxy	1234567890123456789(
15pt	ABCDEFGHIJKLMN(	abcdefghijklmnopqrstuvw:	12345678901234567 8
16pt	ABCDEFGHIJKLMN	abcdefghijklmnopqrstuv	12345678901234567
18pt	ABCDEFGHIJKLN	abcdefghijklmnopqrst	1234567890123456
20pt	ABCDEFGHIJKI	abcdefghijklmnopq	12345678901234
24pt	ABCDEFGHI	abcdefghijklmnc	12345678901
28pt	ABCDEFGH	abcdefghijklm	1234567890
32pt	ABCDEFG	abcdefghijkl	123456789
36pt	ABCDEF	abcdefghijk	12345678
40pt	ABCDEI	abcdefghij	1234567
45pt	ABCDI	abcdefgh	123456
50pt	ABCD	abcdefg	12345
60pt	ABCI	abcdef	12345
70pt	ABC	abcde	1234

27

5pt	ABCDEFGHIJKLMNOPQRSTUVWXYZABCDEFGHIJKLMNOP(	abcdefghijklmnopqrstuvwxyzabcdefghijklmnopqrstuvwxyzabcdefg	1234567890123456789012345678901234567890123
6pt	ABCDEFGHIJKLMNOPQRSTUVWXYZABCDEFGHI.	abcdefghijklmnopqrstuvwxyzabcdefghijklmnopqrstuvw	1234567890123456789012345678901234567890123-
7pt	ABCDEFGHIJKLMNOPQRSTUVWXYZABCD	abcdefghijklmnopqrstuvwxyzabcdefghijklmnop	12345678901234567890123456789012345678
8pt	ABCDEFGHIJKLMNOPQRSTUVWXYZ.	abcdefghijklmnopqrstuvwxyzabcdefghijkl	1234567890123456789012345678901234
9pt	ABCDEFGHIJKLMNOPQRSTUVW:	abcdefghijklmnopqrstuvwxyzabcdefg	12345678901234567890123456789(
10pt	ABCDEFGHIJKLMNOPQRSTU\	abcdefghijklmnopqrstuvwxyzabc	12345678901234567890123456
11pt	ABCDEFGHIJKLMNOPQRS1	abcdefghijklmnopqrstuvwxyz	123456789012345678901234:
12pt	ABCDEFGHIJKLMNOPQR	abcdefghijklmnopqrstuvwx	12345678901234567890123
13pt	ABCDEFGHIJKLMNOP(	abcdefghijklmnopqrstuvw	12345678901234567890]
14pt	ABCDEFGHIJKLMNOl	abcdefghijklmnopqrstu	123456789012345678
15pt	ABCDEFGHIJKLMN(	abcdefghijklmnopqrst	12345678901234567
16pt	ABCDEFGHIJKLMↃ	abcdefghijklmnopqr:	1234567890123456'
18pt	ABCDEFGHIJKLↃ	abcdefghijklmnop	12345678901234!
20pt	ABCDEFGHIJK	abcdefghijklmnc	1234567890123⊿
24pt	ABCDEFGHI	abcdefghijkln	123456789011
28pt	ABCDEFGI	abcdefghijk	123456789(
32pt	ABCDEFↃ	abcdefghij	123456789
36pt	ABCDEF	abcdefgh	1234567⅞
40pt	ABCDEⅠ	abcdefgl	1234567
45pt	ABCDⅠ	abcdef₷	123456
50pt	ABCD	abcdef	123456
60pt	ABCⅠ	abcdε	1234⅖
70pt	ABC	abcd	1234

Helvetica Regular — Swiss 721

5pt	ABCDEFGHIJKLMNOPQRSTUVWXYZABCDEFGHIJKLMNOF	abcdefghijklmnopqrstuvwxyzabcdefghijklmnopqrstuvwxyzabcdefg	123456789012345678901234567890123456789012
6pt	ABCDEFGHIJKLMNOPQRSTUVWXYZABCDEFGH	abcdefghijklmnopqrstuvwxyzabcdefghijklmnopqrstuvw)	12345678901234567890123456789012345678901234
7pt	ABCDEFGHIJKLMNOPQRSTUVWXYZABCI	abcdefghijklmnopqrstuvwxyzabcdefghijklmnopc	1234567890123456789012345678901234567£
8pt	ABCDEFGHIJKLMNOPQRSTUVWXYZ	abcdefghijklmnopqrstuvwxyzabcdefghijkli	123456789012345678901234567890123
9pt	ABCDEFGHIJKLMNOPQRSTUVW	abcdefghijklmnopqrstuvwxyzabcdefg	1234567890123456789012345678901
10pt	ABCDEFGHIJKLMNOPQRSTU	abcdefghijklmnopqrstuvwxyzabc(	12345678901234567890123456;
11pt	ABCDEFGHIJKLMNOPQRS	abcdefghijklmnopqrstuvwxyza	12345678901234567890123
12pt	ABCDEFGHIJKLMNOPQI	abcdefghijklmnopqrstuvwxy	123456789012345678901
13pt	ABCDEFGHIJKLMNOP(	abcdefghijklmnopqrstuvw	1234567890123456789
14pt	ABCDEFGHIJKLMNOF	abcdefghijklmnopqrstuv	123456789012345678
15pt	ABCDEFGHIJKLMN(	abcdefghijklmnopqrstı	12345678901234567£
16pt	ABCDEFGHIJKLMI	abcdefghijklmnopqrs	123456789012345 7
18pt	ABCDEFGHIJKLI	abcdefghijklmnopc	123456789012345
20pt	ABCDEFGHIJK	abcdefghijklmno	12345678901234
24pt	ABCDEFGHI	abcdefghijklm	123456789011
28pt	ABCDEFGI	abcdefghijkl	1234567890(
32pt	ABCDEF(	abcdefghij	123456789
36pt	ABCDEF	abcdefgh	1234567£
40pt	ABCDE	abcdefg|	1234567
45pt	ABCDE	abcdefç	123456
50pt	ABCD	abcdef	12345(
60pt	ABCI	abcde	12345
70pt	ABC	abcd	1234

5pt	ABCDEFGHIJKLMNOPQRSTUVWXYZABCDEFGHIJKLMNOP	abcdefghijklmnopqrstuvwxyzabcdefghijklmnopqrstuvwxyzabcdef	12345678901234567890123456789012345678901234567890123
6pt	ABCDEFGHIJKLMNOPQRSTUVWXYZABCDEFGHI	abcdefghijklmnopqrstuvwxyzabcdefghijklmnopqrstuvv	1234567890123456789012345678901234567890123
7pt	ABCDEFGHIJKLMNOPQRSTUVWXYZABCI	abcdefghijklmnopqrstuvwxyzabcdefghijklmnop	12345678901234567890123456789012345678
8pt	ABCDEFGHIJKLMNOPQRSTUVWXYZ	abcdefghijklmnopqrstuvwxyzabcdefghijk	12345678901234567890123456789012
9pt	ABCDEFGHIJKLMNOPQRSTUVW	abcdefghijklmnopqrstuvwxyzabcdef	1234567890123456789012345678
10pt	ABCDEFGHIJKLMNOPQRSTU	abcdefghijklmnopqrstuvwxyzabc	12345678901234567890123456
11pt	ABCDEFGHIJKLMNOPQRS	abcdefghijklmnopqrstuvwxyz	1234567890123456789012340
12pt	ABCDEFGHIJKLMNOPQF	abcdefghijklmnopqrstuvwx	12345678901234567890120
13pt	ABCDEFGHIJKLMNOP(	abcdefghijklmnopqrstuvv	12345678901234567890
14pt	ABCDEFGHIJKLMNOI	abcdefghijklmnopqrstuv	12345678901234567890
15pt	ABCDEFGHIJKLMN(	abcdefghijklmnopqrst	12345678901234567
16pt	ABCDEFGHIJKLMN	abcdefghijklmnopqrs	12345678901234567
18pt	ABCDEFGHIJKLI	abcdefghijklmnop	123456789012345
20pt	ABCDEFGHIJKI	abcdefghijklmno	123456789012340
24pt	ABCDEFGHI	abcdefghijklm	12345678901
28pt	ABCDEFGI	abcdefghijk	12345678900
32pt	ABCDEFC	abcdefghij	123456789
36pt	ABCDEF	abcdefgh	12345678
40pt	ABCDEI	abcdefg	1234567
45pt	ABCDE	abcdefg	123456
50pt	ABCD	abcdef	123456
60pt	ABCI	abcde	12345
70pt	ABC	abcd	1234

5pt	ABCDEFGHIJKLMNOPQRSTUVWXYZABCDEFGHIJKLMNOF	abcdefghijklmnopqrstuvwxyzabcdefghijklmnopqrstuvwxyzabcdefg	1234567890123456789012345678901234567890123456789012
6pt	ABCDEFGHIJKLMNOPQRSTUVWXYZABCDEFGHI	abcdefghijklmnopqrstuvwxyzabcdefghijklmnopqrstuvw	1234567890123456789012345678901234567890123
7pt	ABCDEFGHIJKLMNOPQRSTUVWXYZABCI	abcdefghijklmnopqrstuvwxyzabcdefghijklmnop	1234567890123456789012345678901234567
8pt	ABCDEFGHIJKLMNOPQRSTUVWXYZ	abcdefghijklmnopqrstuvwxyzabcdefghijk	1234567890123456789012345678901234567890123
9pt	ABCDEFGHIJKLMNOPQRSTUVW	abcdefghijklmnopqrstuvwxyzabcdefg	12345678901234567890123456789
10pt	ABCDEFGHIJKLMNOPQRSTU	abcdefghijklmnopqrstuvwxyzabc	123456789012345678901234567
11pt	ABCDEFGHIJKLMNOPQRS	abcdefghijklmnopqrstuvwxyzc	12345678901234567890123
12pt	ABCDEFGHIJKLMNOPQI	abcdefghijklmnopqrstuvwxy	123456789012345678901234
13pt	ABCDEFGHIJKLMNOP(	abcdefghijklmnopqrstuvv	1234567890123456789012
14pt	ABCDEFGHIJKLMNO	abcdefghijklmnopqrstu	12345678901234567890
15pt	ABCDEFGHIJKLMN(	abcdefghijklmnopqrst	123456789012345678
16pt	ABCDEFGHIJKLMN	abcdefghijklmnopqr:	1234567890123456;
18pt	ABCDEFGHIJKL/	abcdefghijklmnop	12345678901234
20pt	ABCDEFGHIJK	abcdefghijklmnc	123456789012:
24pt	ABCDEFGHI	abcdefghijkln	12345678901
28pt	ABCDEFGI	abcdefghijk	123456789(
32pt	ABCDEFC	abcdefghij	12345678!
36pt	ABCDEF	abcdefgh	1234567{
40pt	ABCDEI	abcdefg	1234567
45pt	ABCDI	abcdef¡	123456
50pt	ABCD	abcdef	12345(
60pt	ABCI	abcde	12345
70pt	ABC	abcd	1234

Optima Roman — Zapf Humanist 601

5pt	ABCDEFGHIJKLMNOPQRSTUVWXYZABCDEFGHIJKLMNOPQR!	abcdefghijklmnopqrstuvwxyzabcdefghijklmnopqrstuvwxyzabcdef;	1234567890123456789012345678901234567890123
6pt	ABCDEFGHIJKLMNOPQRSTUVWXYZABCDEFGHIJKL	abcdefghijklmnopqrstuvwxyzabcdefghijklmnopqrstuv	12345678901234567890123456789012345678901234.
7pt	ABCDEFGHIJKLMNOPQRSTUVWXYZABCDEF	abcdefghijklmnopqrstuvwxyzabcdefghijklmnop	1234567890123456789012345678901234567
8pt	ABCDEFGHIJKLMNOPQRSTUVWXYZAE	abcdefghijklmnopqrstuvwxyzabcdefghijk	123456789012345678901234567890123
9pt	ABCDEFGHIJKLMNOPQRSTUVWX'	abcdefghijklmnopqrstuvwxyzabcdef;	12345678901234567890123456789(
10pt	ABCDEFGHIJKLMNOPQRSTUV\	abcdefghijklmnopqrstuvwxyzabc	1234567890123456789012345?
11pt	ABCDEFGHIJKLMNOPQRSTl	abcdefghijklmnopqrstuvwxyza	12345678901234567890123.
12pt	ABCDEFGHIJKLMNOPQRS	abcdefghijklmnopqrstuvwx'	12345678901234567890123.
13pt	ABCDEFGHIJKLMNOPQ	abcdefghijklmnopqrstuvv	12345678901234567890?
14pt	ABCDEFGHIJKLMNOP(	abcdefghijklmnopqrstu\	1234567890123456789
15pt	ABCDEFGHIJKLMNO	abcdefghijklmnopqrst	1234567890123456?8
16pt	ABCDEFGHIJKLMN(	abcdefghijklmnopqr;	123456789012345?7
18pt	ABCDEFGHIJKLM	abcdefghijklmnop(	123456789012345
20pt	ABCDEFGHIJKL/	abcdefghijklmnc	123456789012З∢
24pt	ABCDEFGHIJ	abcdefghijklm	12345678901.
28pt	ABCDEFGH	abcdefghijk	123456789(
32pt	ABCDEFG	abcdefghij	123456789
36pt	ABCDEF(	abcdefgh	1234567ε
40pt	ABCDEF	abcdefgl	1234567
45pt	ABCDE	abcdef{	123456
50pt	ABCDI	abcdef	123456
60pt	ABCE	abcde	12345
70pt	ABC	abcd	1234

Serif

Old Face

Transitional

Modern Face

Slab Serif

One-Line

Bitstream Fonts   34

Linotype Fonts   60

Page

Dutch 823 — Aster Roman
abcdefghijklmnopqrstuvwxyzABCDEFGHIJKLMNOPQRSTUVWXYZ1234567890&   74

Dutch 823 Italic — Aster Italic
abcdefghijklmnopqrstuvwxyzABCDEFGHIJKLMNOPQRSTUVWXYZ1234567890&   75

Dutch 823 Bold — Aster Bold
abcdefghijklmnopqrstuvwxyzABCDEFGHIJKLMNOPQRSTUVWXY1234567890&   76

Dutch 823 Bold Italic — Aster Bold Italic
abcdefghijklmnopqrstuvwxyzABCDEFGHIJKLMNOPQRSTUVWXY1234567890&   77

Aldine 401 — Bembo Roman
abcdefghijklmnopqrstuvwxyzABCDEFGHIJKLMNOPQRSTUVWXYZ1234567890&   78

Aldine 401 Italic — Bembo Italic
abcdefghijklmnopqrstuvwxyzABCDEFGHIJKLMNOPQRSTUVWXYZ1234567890&   79

Aldine 401 Bold — Bembo Bold
abcdefghijklmnopqrstuvwxyzABCDEFGHIJKLMNOPQRSTUVWXYZ1234567890&   80

Aldine 401 Bold Italic — Bembo Bold Italic
abcdefghijklmnopqrstuvwxyzABCDEFGHIJKLMNOPQRSTUVWXYZ1234567890&   81

ITC Berkeley Old Style Book, Venetian 519 — ITC Berkeley Old Style Book
abcdefghijklmnopqrstuvwxyzABCDEFGHIJKLMNOPQRSTUVWXYZ1234567890&   82

ITC Berkeley Old Style Book Italic, Venetian 519 — ITC Berkeley Old Style Book Italic
abcdefghijklmnopqrstuvwxyzABCDEFGHIJKLMNOPQRSTUVWXYZ1234567890&   83

ITC Berkeley Old Style Medium, Venetian 519 — ITC Berkeley Old Style Medium
abcdefghijklmnopqrstuvwxyzABCDEFGHIJKLMNOPQRSTUVWXYZ1234567890&   84

ITC Berkeley Old Style Medium Italic, Venetian 519 — ITC Berkeley Old Style Medium Italic
abcdefghijklmnopqrstuvwxyzABCDEFGHIJKLMNOPQRSTUVWXYZ1234567890&   85

ITC Berkeley Old Style Bold, Venetian 519 — ITC Berkeley Old Style Bold
abcdefghijklmnopqrstuvwxyzABCDEFGHIJKLMNOPQRSTUVWXYZ1234567890&   86

ITC Berkeley Old Style Bold Italic, Venetian 519 — ITC Berkeley Old Style Bold Italic
abcdefghijklmnopqrstuvwxyzABCDEFGHIJKLMNOPQRSTUVWXYZ1234567890&   87

ITC Berkeley Old Style Black/Head, Venetian 519 — ITC Berkeley Old Style Black
abcdefghijklmnopqrstuvwxyzABCDEFGHIJKLMNOPQRSTUVWXYZ1234567890&   88

ITC Berkeley Old Style Black Italic/Head, Venetian 519 — ITC Berkeley Old Style Black Italic
abcdefghijklmnopqrstuvwxyzABCDEFGHIJKLMNOPQRSTUVWXYZ1234567890&   89

Revival 565 — Berling
abcdefghijklmnopqrstuvwxyzABCDEFGHIJKLMNOPQRSTUVWXYZ1234567890&   90

Revival 565 Italic — Berling Italic
abcdefghijklmnopqrstuvwxyzABCDEFGHIJKLMNOPQRSTUVWXYZ1234567890&   91

Revival 565 Bold — Berling Bold
abcdefghijklmnopqrstuvwxyzABCDEFGHIJKLMNOPQRSTUVWXYZ1234567890&   92

Revival 565 Bold Italic — Berlig Bold Italic
abcdefghijklmnopqrstuvwxyzABCDEFGHIJKLMNOPQRSTUVWXYZ1234567890& 93

Bitstream Carmina Light, Calligraphic 811 — Bitstream Carmina Light
abcdefghijklmnopqrstuvwxyzABCDEFGHIJKLMNOPQRSTUVWXYZ1234567890& 94

Bitstream Carmina Light Italic, Calligraphic 811 — Bitstream Carmina Light Italic
abcdefghijklmnopqrstuvwxyzABCDEFGHIJKLMNOPQRSTUVWXYZ1234567890& 95

Bitstream Carmina Medium, Calligraphic 811 — Bitstream Carmina Medium
abcdefghijklmnopqrstuvwxyzABCDEFGHIJKLMNOPQRSTUVWXYZ1234567890& 96

Bitstream Carmina Medium Italic, Calligraphic 811 — Bitstream Carmina Medium Italic
abcdefghijklmnopqrstuvwxyzABCDEFGHIJKLMNOPQRSTUVWXYZ1234567890& 97

Bitstream Carmina Bold, Calligraphic 811 — Bitstream Carmina Bold
abcdefghijklmnopqrstuvwxyzABCDEFGHIJKLMNOPQRSTUVWX1234567890& 98

Bitstream Carmina Bold Italic, Calligraphic 811 — Bitstream Carmina Bold Italic
abcdefghijklmnopqrstuvwxyzABCDEFGHIJKLMNOPQRSTUVWXY1234567890& 99

Bitstream Carmina Black, Calligraphic 811 — Bitstream Carmina Black
abcdefghijklmnopqrstuvwxyzABCDEFGHIJKLMNOPQRSTU1234567890& 100

Bitstream Carmina Black Italic, Calligraphic 811 — Bitstream Carmina Black Italic
abcdefghijklmnopqrstuvwxyzABCDEFGHIJKLMNOPQRSTU1234567890& 101

Caxton Light, Calligraphic 816 — Caxton Light
abcdefghijklmnopqrstuvwxyzABCDEFGHIJKLMNOPQRSTUVWXYZ1234567890& 102

Caxton Light Italic, Calligraphic 816 — Caxton Light Italic
abcdefghijklmnopqrstuvwxyzABCDEFGHIJKLMNOPQRSTUVWXYZ1234567890& 103

Caxton Book, Calligraphic 816 — Caxton Book
abcdefghijklmnopqrstuvwxyzABCDEFGHIJKLMNOPQRSTUVWXYZ1234567890& 104

Caxton Book Italic, Calligraphic 816 — Caxton Book Italic
abcdefghijklmnopqrstuvwxyzABCDEFGHIJKLMNOPQRSTUVWXYZ1234567890& 105

Caxton Bold, Calligraphic 816 — Caxton Bold
abcdefghijklmnopqrstuvwxyzABCDEFGHIJKLMNOPQRSTUVWXYZ1234567890& 106

Caxton Bold Italic, Calligraphic 816 — Caxton Bold Italic
abcdefghijklmnopqrstuvwxyzABCDEFGHIJKLMNOPQRSTUVWXYZ1234567890& 107

Cloister Open Face/Head, Venetian 215 — Cloister Open Face
abcdefghijklmnopqrstuvwxyzABCDEFGHIJKLMNOPQRSTUVWXYZ1234567890& 108

Calligraphic 810 — Diotima
abcdefghijklmnopqrstuvwxyzABCDEFGHIJKLMNOPQRSTUVWX1234567890& 109

Calligraphic 810 Italic — Diotima Italic
abcdefghijklmnopqrstuvwxyzABCDEFGHIJKLMNOPQRSTUVWXYZ1234567890& 110

ITC Galliard, Aldine 701 — ITC Galliard Roman
abcdefghijklmnopqrstuvwxyzABCDEFGHIJKLMNOPQRSTUVWXYZ1234567890& 111

ITC Galliard Italic, Aldine 701 — ITC Galliard Italic
abcdefghijklmnopqrstuvwxyzABCDEFGHIJKLMNOPQRSTUVWXYZ1234567890& 112

ITC Galliard Bold, Aldine 701 — ITC Galliard Bold
abcdefghijklmnopqrstuvwxyzABCDEFGHIJKLMNOPQRSTUVWX1234567890& 113

ITC Galliard Bold Italic, Aldine 701 — ITC Galliard Bold Italic
abcdefghijklmnopqrstuvwxyzABCDEFGHIJKLMNOPQRSTUVWXYZ1234567890& 114

ITC Galliard Black, Aldine 701 — ITC Galliard Black
abcdefghijklmnopqrstuvwxyzABCDEFGHIJKLMNOPQRSTUV1234567890& 115

ITC Galliard Black Italic, Aldine 701 — ITC Galliard Black Italic
abcdefghijklmnopqrstuvwxyzABCDEFGHIJKLMNOPQRSTUVWXY1234567890& 116

ITC Galliard Ultra/Head, Aldine 701 — ITC Galliard Ultra
abcdefghijklmnopqrstuvwxyzABCDEFGHIJKLMNOPQRST1234567890& 117

ITC Galliard Ultra Italic/Head, Aldine 701 — ITC Galliard Ultra Italic
abcdefghijklmnopqrstuvwxyzABCDEFGHIJKLMNOPQRSTUV1234567890& 118

Original Garamond, Aldine 430 — Stempel Garamond
abcdefghijklmnopqrstuvwxyzABCDEFGHIJKLMNOPQRSTUVWXYZ1234567890& 119

Original Garamond Italic, Aldine 430 — Stempel Garamond Italic
abcdefghijklmnopqrstuvwxyzABCDEFGHIJKLMNOPQRSTUVWXYZ1234567890& 120

Original Garamond Bold, Aldine 430 — Stempel Garamond Bold
abcdefghijklmnopqrstuvwxyzABCDEFGHIJKLMNOPQRSTUVWXYZ1234567890& 121

Original Garamond Bold Italic, Aldine 430 — Stempel Garamond Bold Italic
abcdefghijklmnopqrstuvwxyzABCDEFGHIJKLMNOPQRSTUVWXYZ1234567890& 122

American Garamond, Aldine 511 — Garamond No.3 Roman
abcdefghijklmnopqrstuvwxyzABCDEFGHIJKLMNOPQRSTUVWXYZ1234567890& 123

American Garamond Italic, Aldine 511 — Garamond No.3 Italic
abcdefghijklmnopqrstuvwxyzABCDEFGHIJKLMNOPQRSTUVWXYZ1234567890& 124

American Garamond Bold, Aldine 511 — Garamond No.3 Bold
abcdefghijklmnopqrstuvwxyzABCDEFGHIJKLMNOPQRSTUVWXYZ1234567890& 125

American Garamond Bold Italic, Aldine 511 — Garamond No.3 Bold Italic
abcdefghijklmnopqrstuvwxyzABCDEFGHIJKLMNOPQRSTUVWXYZ1234567890& 126

Italian Garamond, Aldine 525 — Simoncini Garamond
abcdefghijklmnopqrstuvwxyzABCDEFGHIJKLMNOPQRSTUVWXYZ1234567890& 127

Italian Garamond Italic, Aldine 525 — Simoncini Garamond Italic
abcdefghijklmnopqrstuvwxyzABCDEFGHIJKLMNOPQRSTUVWXYZ1234567890& 128

Italian Garamond Bold, Aldine 525 — Simoncini Garamond Bold
abcdefghijklmnopqrstuvwxyzABCDEFGHIJKLMNOPQRSTUVWXYZ1234567890& 129

ITC Garamond Light, Aldine 851 — ITC Garamond Light Roman
abcdefghijklmnopqrstuvwxyzABCDEFGHIJKLMNOPQRSTUVWXYZ1234567890& 130

ITC Garamond Light Italic, Aldine 851 — ITC Garamond Light Italic

abcdefghijklmnopqrstuvwxyzABCDEFGHIJKLMNOPQRSTUVWXYZ1234567890&

131

ITC Garamond Book, Aldine 851 — ITC Garamond Book

abcdefghijklmnopqrstuvwxyzABCDEFGHIJKLMNOPQRSTUVWXYZ1234567890&

132

ITC Garamond Book Italic, Aldine 851 — ITC Garamond Book Italic

abcdefghijklmnopqrstuvwxyzABCDEFGHIJKLMNOPQRSTUVWXYZ1234567890&

133

ITC Garamond Bold, Aldine 851 — ITC Garamond Bold

abcdefghijklmnopqrstuvwxyzABCDEFGHIJKLMNOPQRSTUVWXYZ1234567890&

134

ITC Garamond Bold Italic, Aldine 851 — ITC Garamond Bold Italic

abcdefghijklmnopqrstuvwxyzABCDEFGHIJKLMNOPQRSTUVWXYZ1234567890&

135

ITC Garamond Ultra/Head, Aldine 851 — ITC Garamond Ultra

abcdefghijklmnopqrstuvwxyzABCDEFGHIJKLMNOPQRSTUVW1234567890&

136

ITC Garamond Ultra Italic/Head, Aldine 851 — ITC Garamond Ultra Italic

abcdefghijklmnopqrstuvwxyzABCDEFGHIJKLMNOPQRSTUVWX1234567890&

137

ITC Garamond Light Condensed, Aldine 851 — ITC Garamond Light Condensed

abcdefghijklmnopqrstuvwxyzABCDEFGHIJKLMNOPQRSTUVWXYZ1234567890&

138

ITC Garamond Light Condensed Italic, Aldine 851 — ITC Garamond Light Condensed Italic

abcdefghijklmnopqrstuvwxyzABCDEFGHIJKLMNOPQRSTUVWXYZ1234567890&

139

ITC Garamond Book Condensed, Aldine 851 — ITC Garamond Book Condensed

abcdefghijklmnopqrstuvwxyzABCDEFGHIJKLMNOPQRSTUVWXYZ1234567890&

140

ITC Garamond Book Condensed Italic, Aldine 851 — ITC Garamond Book Condensed Italic

abcdefghijklmnopqrstuvwxyzABCDEFGHIJKLMNOPQRSTUVWXYZ1234567890&

141

ITC Garamond Bold Condensed, Aldine 851 — ITC Garamond Bold Condensed

abcdefghijklmnopqrstuvwxyzABCDEFGHIJKLMNOPQRSTUVWXYZ1234567890&

142

ITC Garamond Bold Condensed Italic, Aldine 851 — ITC Garamond Bold Condensed Italic

abcdefghijklmnopqrstuvwxyzABCDEFGHIJKLMNOPQRSTUVWXYZ1234567890&

143

ITC Garamond Ultra Condensed/Head, Aldine 851 — ITC Garamond Ultra Condensed

abcdefghijklmnopqrstuvwxyzABCDEFGHIJKLMNOPQRSTUVWXYZ1234567890&

144

ITC Garamond Ultra Condensed Italic/Head, Aldine 851 — ITC Garamond Ultra Condensed Italic

abcdefghijklmnopqrstuvwxyzABCDEFGHIJKLMNOPQRSTUVWXYZ1234567890&

145

Goudy Old Style, Venetian 521 — Goudy Old Style

abcdefghijklmnopqrstuvwxyzABCDEFGHIJKLMNOPQRSTUVWXYZ1234567890&

146

Goudy Old Style Italic, Venetian 521 — Goudy Old Style Italic

abcdefghijklmnopqrstuvwxyzABCDEFGHIJKLMNOPQRSTUVWXYZ1234567890&

147

Goudy Bold, Venetian 521 — Goudy Bold

abcdefghijklmnopqrstuvwxyzABCDEFGHIJKLMNOPQRSTUVWXYZ1234567890&

148

Goudy Bold Italic, Venetian 521 — Goudy Bold Italic

abcdefghijklmnopqrstuvwxyzABCDEFGHIJKLMNOPQRSTUVWXYZ1234567890&

149

Goudy Extra Bold, Venetian 521 — Goudy Extra Bold
abcdefghijklmnopqrstuvwxyzABCDEFGHIJKLMNOPQRSTUVWXYZ1234567890& 150

Goudy Catalogue, Venetian 522 — Goudy Catalogue
abcdefghijklmnopqrstuvwxyzABCDEFGHIJKLMNOPQRSTUVWXYZ1234567890& 151

Goudy Handtooled, Venetian 523 — Goudy Handtooled
abcdefghijklmnopqrstuvwxyzABCDEFGHIJKLMNOPQRSTUVWXYZ1234567890& 152

Goudy Heavyface, Freeform 744 — Goudy Heavyface
abcdefghijklmnopqrstuvwxyzABCDEFGHIJKLMNOPQRSTUV1234567890& 153

Goudy Heavyface Condensed, Freeform 744 — Goudy Heavyface Condensed
abcdefghijklmnopqrstuvwxyzABCDEFGHIJKLMNOPQRSTUVWXYZ1234567890& 154

Elegant Garamond, Aldine 424 — Granjon Roman
abcdefghijklmnopqrstuvwxyzABCDEFGHIJKLMNOPQRSTUVWXYZ1234567890& 155

Elegant Garamond Italic, Aldine 424 — Granjon Italic
abcdefghijklmnopqrstuvwxyzABCDEFGHIJKLMNOPQRSTUVWXYZ1234567890& 156

Elegant Garamond Bold, Aldine 424 — Granjon Bold
abcdefghijklmnopqrstuvwxyzABCDEFGHIJKLMNOPQRSTUVWXYZ1234567890& 157

Imperial/Newstext, Dutch 812 — Imperial Roman
abcdefghijklmnopqrstuvwxyzABCDEFGHIJKLMNOPQRSTUVWX1234567890& 158

Imperial Italic/Newstext, Dutch 812 — Imperial Italic
abcdefghijklmnopqrstuvwxyzABCDEFGHIJKLMNOPQRSTUVWXY1234567890& 159

Imperial Bold/Newstext, Dutch 812 — Imperial Bold
abcdefghijklmnopqrstuvwxyzABCDEFGHIJKLMNOPQRSTUVW1234567890& 160

Dutch 766 — Imprint Roman
abcdefghijklmnopqrstuvwxyzABCDEFGHIJKLMNOPQRSTUVWXYZ1234567890& 161

Dutch 766 Italic — Imprint Italic
abcdefghijklmnopqrstuvwxyzABCDEFGHIJKLMNOPQRSTUVWXYZ1234567890& 162

Dutch 766 Bold — Imprint Bold
abcdefghijklmnopqrstuvwxyzABCDEFGHIJKLMNOPQRSTUVWXYZ1234567890& 163

ITC Leawood Book, Calligraphic 826 — ITC Leawood Book
abcdefghijklmnopqrstuvwxyzABCDEFGHIJKLMNOPQRSTUVWXYZ1234567890& 164

ITC Leawood Book Italic, Calligraphic 826 — ITC Leawood Book Italic
abcdefghijklmnopqrstuvwxyzABCDEFGHIJKLMNOPQRSTUVWXYZ1234567890& 165

ITC Leawood Medium, Calligraphic 826 — ITC Leawood Medium
abcdefghijklmnopqrstuvwxyzABCDEFGHIJKLMNOPQRSTUVWXYZ1234567890& 166

ITC Leawood Medium Italic, Calligraphic 826 — ITC Leawood Medium Italic
abcdefghijklmnopqrstuvwxyzABCDEFGHIJKLMNOPQRSTUVWXYZ1234567890& 167

ITC Leawood Bold, Calligraphic 826 — ITC Leawood Bold
abcdefghijklmnopqrstuvwxyzABCDEFGHIJKLMNOPQRSTUVWXY1234567890& 168

ITC Leawood Bold Italic, Calligraphic 826 — ITC Leawood Bold Italic

abcdefghijklmnopqrstuvwxyzABCDEFGHIJKLMNOPQRSTUVWXYZ1234567890& 169

ITC Leawood Black/Head, Calligraphic 826 — ITC Leawood Black

abcdefghijklmnopqrstuvwxyzABCDEFGHIJKLMNOPQRSTUVW1234567890& 170

ITC Leawood Black Italic/Head, Calligraphic 826 — ITC Leawood Black Italic

abcdefghijklmnopqrstuvwxyzABCDEFGHIJKLMNOPQRSTUVWX1234567890& 171

Matt Antique, Calligraphic 555 — Matt Antique (Garth)

abcdefghijklmnopqrstuvwxyzABCDEFGHIJKLMNOPQRSTUVWXYZ1234567890& 172

Matt Antique Italic, Calligraphic 555 — Matt Antique Italic

abcdefghijklmnopqrstuvwxyzABCDEFGHIJKLMNOPQRSTUVWXYZ1234567890& 173

Matt Antique Bold, Calligraphic 555 — Matt Antique Bold

abcdefghijklmnopqrstuvwxyzABCDEFGHIJKLMNOPQRSTUVWXYZ1234567890& 174

ITC Novarese Book, Latin 671 — ITC Novarese Book

abcdefghijklmnopqrstuvwxyzABCDEFGHIJKLMNOPQRSTUVWXYZ1234567890& 175

ITC Novarese Book Italic, Latin 671 — ITC Novarese Book Italic

abcdefghijklmnopqrstuvwxyzABCDEFGHIJKLMNOPQRSTUVWXYZ1234567890& 176

ITC Novarese Medium, Latin 671 — ITC Novarese Medium

abcdefghijklmnopqrstuvwxyzABCDEFGHIJKLMNOPQRSTUVWXYZ1234567890& 177

ITC Novarese Medium Italic, Latin 671 — ITC Novarese Medium Italic

abcdefghijklmnopqrstuvwxyzABCDEFGHIJKLMNOPQRSTUVWXYZ1234567890& 178

ITC Novarese Bold, Latin 671 — ITC Novarese Bold

abcdefghijklmnopqrstuvwxyzABCDEFGHIJKLMNOPQRSTUVWXYZ1234567890& 179

ITC Novarese Bold Italic, Latin 671 — ITC Novarese Bold Italic

abcdefghijklmnopqrstuvwxyzABCDEFGHIJKLMNOPQRSTUVWXYZ1234567890& 180

ITC Novarese Ultra/Head, Latin 671 — ITC Novarese Ultra

abcdefghijklmnopqrstuvwxyzABCDEFGHIJKLMNOPQRSTUVWX1234567890& 181

Zapf Calligraphic 801 — Palatino Roman

abcdefghijklmnopqrstuvwxyzABCDEFGHIJKLMNOPQRSTUVWXYZ1234567890& 182

Zapf Calligraphic 801 Italic — Palatino Italic

abcdefghijklmnopqrstuvwxyzABCDEFGHIJKLMNOPQRSTUVWXYZ1234567890& 183

Zapf Calligraphic 801 Bold — Palatino Bold

abcdefghijklmnopqrstuvwxyzABCDEFGHIJKLMNOPQRSTUVWXYZ1234567890& 184

Zapf Calligraphic 801 Bold Italic — Palatino Bold Italic

abcdefghijklmnopqrstuvwxyzABCDEFGHIJKLMNOPQRSTUVWXYZ1234567890& 185

Aldine 721 Light — Plantin Light

abcdefghijklmnopqrstuvwxyzABCDEFGHIJKLMNOPQRSTUVWXYZ1234567890& 186

Aldine 721 Light Italic — Plantin Light Italic

abcdefghijklmnopqrstuvwxyzABCDEFGHIJKLMNOPQRSTUVWXYZ1234567890& 187

Aldine 721 — Plantin Roman
abcdefghijklmnopqrstuvwxyzABCDEFGHIJKLMNOPQRSTUVWXYZ1234567890& 188

Aldine 721 Italic — Plantin Italic
abcdefghijklmnopqrstuvwxyzABCDEFGHIJKLMNOPQRSTUVWXYZ1234567890& 189

Aldine 721 Bold — Plantin Bold
abcdefghijklmnopqrstuvwxyzABCDEFGHIJKLMNOPQRSTUVWXYZ1234567890& 190

Aldine 721 Bold Italic — Plantin Bold Italic
abcdefghijklmnopqrstuvwxyzABCDEFGHIJKLMNOPQRSTUVWXYZ1234567890& 191

Aldine 721 Bold Condensed — Plantin Bold Condensed
abcdefghijklmnopqrstuvwxyzABCDEFGHIJKLMNOPQRSTUVWXYZ1234567890& 192

Classical Garamond, Aldine 421 — Sabon Roman
abcdefghijklmnopqrstuvwxyzABCDEFGHIJKLMNOPQRSTUVWXYZ1234567890& 193

Classical Garamond Italic, Aldine 421 — Sabon Italic
abcdefghijklmnopqrstuvwxyzABCDEFGHIJKLMNOPQRSTUVWXYZ1234567890& 194

Classical Garamond Bold, Aldine 421 — Sabon Bold
abcdefghijklmnopqrstuvwxyzABCDEFGHIJKLMNOPQRSTUVWXYZ1234567890& 195

Classical Garamond Bold Italic, Aldine 421 — Sabon Bold Italic
abcdefghijklmnopqrstuvwxyzABCDEFGHIJKLMNOPQRSTUVWXYZ1234567890& 196

Schneidler Light, Kuenstler 460 — Schneidler Light
abcdefghijklmnopqrstuvwxyzABCDEFGHIJKLMNOPQRSTUVWXYZ1234567890& 197

Schneidler Light Italic, Kuenstler 460 — Schneidler Light Italic
abcdefghijklmnopqrstuvwxyzABCDEFGHIJKLMNOPQRSTUVWXYZ1234567890& 198

Schneidler, Kuenstler 460 — Schneidler
abcdefghijklmnopqrstuvwxyzABCDEFGHIJKLMNOPQRSTUVWXYZ1234567890& 199

Schneidler Italic, Kuenstler 460 — Schneidler Italic
abcdefghijklmnopqrstuvwxyzABCDEFGHIJKLMNOPQRSTUVWXYZ1234567890& 200

Schneidler Medium, Kuenstler 460 — Schneidler Medium
abcdefghijklmnopqrstuvwxyzABCDEFGHIJKLMNOPQRSTUVWXYZ1234567890& 201

Schneidler Medium Italic, Kuenstler 460 — Schneidler Medium Italic
abcdefghijklmnopqrstuvwxyzABCDEFGHIJKLMNOPQRSTUVWXYZ1234567890& 202

Schneidler Bold, Kuenstler 460 — Schneidler Bold
abcdefghijklmnopqrstuvwxyzABCDEFGHIJKLMNOPQRSTUVWX1234567890& 203

Schneidler Bold Italic, Kuenstler 460 — Schneidler Bold Italic
abcdefghijklmnopqrstuvwxyzABCDEFGHIJKLMNOPQRSTUVWXYZ1234567890& 204

Schneidler Black, Kuenstler 460 — Schneidler Black
abcdefghijklmnopqrstuvwxyzABCDEFGHIJKLMNOPQRSTUV1234567890& 205

Schneidler Black Italic, Kuenstler 460 — Schneidler Black Italic
abcdefghijklmnopqrstuvwxyzABCDEFGHIJKLMNOPQRSTUVWX1234567890& 206

ITC Tom's Roman, Revival 758 — ITC Tom's Roman
abcdefghijklmnopqrstuvwxyzABCDEFGHIJKLMNOPQRSTUVWXYZ1234567890& 207

Kuenstler 480 — Trump Mediaeval
abcdefghijklmnopqrstuvwxyzABCDEFGHIJKLMNOPQRSTUVWXYZ1234567890& 208

Kuenstler 480 Italic — Trump Mediaeval Italic
abcdefghijklmnopqrstuvwxyzABCDEFGHIJKLMNOPQRSTUVWXYZ1234567890& 209

Kuenstler 480 Bold — Trump Mediaeval Bold
abcdefghijklmnopqrstuvwxyzABCDEFGHIJKLMNOPQRSTUVWXYZ1234567890& 210

Kuenstler 480 Bold Italic — Trump Mediaeval Bold Italic
abcdefghijklmnopqrstuvwxyzABCDEFGHIJKLMNOPQRSTUVWXYZ1234567890& 211

Kuenstler 480 Black — Trump Mediaeval Black
abcdefghijklmnopqrstuvwxyzABCDEFGHIJKLMNOPQRSTUV1234567890& 212

Windsor Light, Revival 801 — Windsor Light
abcdefghijklmnopqrstuvwxyzABCDEFGHIJKLMNOPQRSTUVWXYZ1234567890& 213

Windsor, Revival 801 — Windsor Roman
abcdefghijklmnopqrstuvwxyzABCDEFGHIJKLMNOPQRSTUV1234567890& 214

Windsor Light Condensed/Head, Revival 801 — Windsor Light Condensed
abcdefghijklmnopqrstuvwxyzABCDEFGHIJKLMNOPQRSTUVWXYZ1234567890& 215

Windsor Elongated/Head, Revival 801 — Windsor Elongated
abcdefghijklmnopqrstuvwxyzABCDEFGHIJKLMNOPQRSTUVWXYZ1234567890& 216

Windsor Outline/Head, Revival 801 — Windsor Outline
abcdefghijklmnopqrstuvwxyzABCDEFGHIJKLMNOPQRSTUV1234567890& 217

Americana, Flareserif 721 — Americana Roman
abcdefghijklmnopqrstuvwxyzABCDEFGHIJKLMNOPQRSTUVW1234567890& 218

Americana Italic, Flareserif 721 — Americana Italic
abcdefghijklmnopqrstuvwxyzABCDEFGHIJKLMNOPQRSTUVWX1234567890& 219

Americana Bold, Flareserif 721 — Americana Bold
abcdefghijklmnopqrstuvwxyzABCDEFGHIJKLMNOPQRSTUV1234567890& 220

Americana Extra Bold Flareserif 721 — Americana Extra Bold
abcdefghijklmnopqrstuvwxyzABCDEFGHIJKLMNOPQRSTUVW1234567890& 221

Americana Extra Bold Condensed, Flareserif 721 — Americana Extra Bold Condensed
abcdefghijklmnopqrstuvwxyzABCDEFGHIJKLMNOPQRSTUVWXYZ1234567890& 222

Baskerville, Transitional 401 — Baskerville Roman
abcdefghijklmnopqrstuvwxyzABCDEFGHIJKLMNOPQRSTUVWXYZ1234567890& 223

Baskerville Italic, Transitional 401 — Baskerville Italic
abcdefghijklmnopqrstuvwxyzABCDEFGHIJKLMNOPQRSTUVWXYZ1234567890& 224

Baskerville Bold, Transitional 401 — Baskerville Bold
abcdefghijklmnopqrstuvwxyzABCDEFGHIJKLMNOPQRSTUVWXYZ1234567890& 225

Baskerville Bold Italic, Transitional 401 — Baskerville Bold Italic
abcdefghijklmnopqrstuvwxyzABCDEFGHIJKLMNOPQRSTUVWXYZ1234567890& 226

ITC New Baskerville, Transitional 402 — ITC New Baskerville
abcdefghijklmnopqrstuvwxyzABCDEFGHIJKLMNOPQRSTUVWXYZ1234567890& 227

ITC New Baskerville Italic, Transitional 402 — ITC New Baskerville Italic
abcdefghijklmnopqrstuvwxyzABCDEFGHIJKLMNOPQRSTUVWXYZ1234567890& 228

ITC New Baskerville Semi Bold, Transitional 402 — ITC New Baskerville Semi Bold
abcdefghijklmnopqrstuvwxyzABCDEFGHIJKLMNOPQRSTUVWXYZ1234567890& 229

ITC New Baskerville Semi Bold Italic, Transitional 402 — ITC New Baskerville Semi Bold Italic
abcdefghijklmnopqrstuvwxyzABCDEFGHIJKLMNOPQRSTUVWXYZ1234567890& 230

ITC New Baskerville Bold, Transitional 402 — ITC New Baskerville Bold
abcdefghijklmnopqrstuvwxyzABCDEFGHIJKLMNOPQRSTUVWXYZ1234567890& 231

ITC New Baskerville Bold Italic, Transitional 402 — ITC New Baskerville Bold Italic
abcdefghijklmnopqrstuvwxyzABCDEFGHIJKLMNOPQRSTUVWXYZ1234567890& 232

ITC New Baskerville Black, Transitional 402 — ITC New Baskerville Black
abcdefghijklmnopqrstuvwxyzABCDEFGHIJKLMNOPQRSTUVWXY1234567890& 233

ITC New Baskerville Black Italic, Transitional 402 — ITC New Baskerville Black Italic
abcdefghijklmnopqrstuvwxyzABCDEFGHIJKLMNOPQRSTUVWXYZ1234567890& 234

Bernhard Modern, Engravers' Oldstyle 126 — Bernhard Modern
abcdefghijklmnopqrstuvwxyzABCDEFGHIJKLMNOPQRSTUVWXYZ1234567890& 235

Bernhard Modern Italic, Engravers' Oldstyle 126 — Bernhard Modern Italic
abcdefghijklmnopqrstuvwxyzABCDEFGHIJKLMNOPQRSTUVWXYZ1234567890& 236

Bernhard Modern Bold, Engravers' Oldstyle 126 — Bernhard Modern Bold
abcdefghijklmnopqrstuvwxyzABCDEFGHIJKLMNOPQRSTUVWXYZ1234567890& 237

Bernhard Modern Bold Italic, Engravers' Oldstyle 126 — Bernhard Modern Bold Italic
abcdefghijklmnopqrstuvwxyzABCDEFGHIJKLMNOPQRSTUVWXYZ1234567890& 238

Bookman, Revival 710 — Bookman Roman
abcdefghijklmnopqrstuvwxyzABCDEFGHIJKLMNOPQRSTUVWXYZ1234567890& 239

Bookman Italic, Revival 710 — Bookman Italic
abcdefghijklmnopqrstuvwxyzABCDEFGHIJKLMNOPQRSTUVWXYZ1234567890& 240

Bookman/Head, Revival 710 — Bookman Roman/Head
abcdefghijklmnopqrstuvwxyzABCDEFGHIJKLMNOPQRSTUVWXY1234567890& 241

Bookman Italic/Head, Revival 710 — Bookman Italic/Head
abcdefghijklmnopqrstuvwxyzABCDEFGHIJKLMNOPQRSTUVWX1234567890& 242

ITC Bookman Light, Revival 711 — ITC Bookman Light Roman
abcdefghijklmnopqrstuvwxyzABCDEFGHIJKLMNOPQRSTUVWXYZ1234567890& 243

ITC Bookman Light Italic, Revival 711 — ITC Bookman Light Italic
abcdefghijklmnopqrstuvwxyzABCDEFGHIJKLMNOPQRSTUVWXY1234567890& 244

ITC Bookman Medium, Revival 711 — ITC Bookman Medium

abcdefghijklmnopqrstuvwxyzABCDEFGHIJKLMNOPQRSTUVWX1234567890& 245

ITC Bookman Medium Italic, Revival 711 — ITC Bookman Medium Italic

abcdefghijklmnopqrstuvwxyzABCDEFGHIJKLMNOPQRSTUVWX1234567890& 246

ITC Bookman Demi, Revival 711 — ITC Bookman Demi

abcdefghijklmnopqrstuvwxyzABCDEFGHIJKLMNOPQRSTUVW1234567890& 247

ITC Bookman Demi Italic, Revival 711 — ITC Bookman Demi Italic

abcdefghijklmnopqrstuvwxyzABCDEFGHIJKLMNOPQRSTUV1234567890& 248

ITC Bookman Bold/Head, Revival 711 — ITC Bookman Bold

abcdefghijklmnopqrstuvwxyzABCDEFGHIJKLMNOPQRST1234567890& 249

ITC Bookman Bold Italic/Head, Revival 711 — ITC Bookman Bold Italic

abcdefghijklmnopqrstuvwxyzABCDEFGHIJKLMNOPQRS1234567890& 250

Bruce Old Style, Revival 704 — Bruce Old Style

abcdefghijklmnopqrstuvwxyzABCDEFGHIJKLMNOPQRSTUVWXYZ1234567890& 251

Bruce Old Style Italic, Revival 704 — Bruce Old Style Italic

abcdefghijklmnopqrstuvwxyzABCDEFGHIJKLMNOPQRSTUVWXYZ1234567890& 252

Caslon Old Face, Dutch 761 — Caslon Old Face

abcdefghijklmnopqrstuvwxyzABCDEFGHIJKLMNOPQRSTUVWXYZ1234567890& 253

Caslon Old Face Italic, Dutch 761 — Caslon Old Face Italic

abcdefghijklmnopqrstuvwxyzABCDEFGHIJKLMNOPQRSTUVWXYZ1234567890& 254

Caslon Old Face Heavy, Dutch 761 — Caslon Old Face Heavy

abcdefghijklmnopqrstuvwxyzABCDEFGHIJKLMNOPQRSTUVWXYZ1234567890& 255

Caslon 540, Dutch 771 — Caslon 540 Roman

abcdefghijklmnopqrstuvwxyzABCDEFGHIJKLMNOPQRSTUVWXYZ1234567890& 256

Caslon 540 Italic, Dutch 771 — Caslon 540 Italic

abcdefghijklmnopqrstuvwxyzABCDEFGHIJKLMNOPQRSTUVWXYZ1234567890& 257

Caslon Bold, Dutch 776 — Caslon Bold Roman

abcdefghijklmnopqrstuvwxyzABCDEFGHIJKLMNOPQRSTUVWX1234567890& 258

Caslon Bold Italic, Dutch 776 — Caslon Bold Italic

abcdefghijklmnopqrstuvwxyzABCDEFGHIJKLMNOPQRSTUVWXYZ1234567890& 259

Caslon Openface, Engravers' Oldstyle 124 — Caslon Openface

abcdefghijklmnopqrstuvwxyzABCDEFGHIJKLMNOPQRSTUVWXYZ1234567890& 260

ITC Caslon 224 Book, Dutch 785 — ITC Caslon 224 Book

abcdefghijklmnopqrstuvwxyzABCDEFGHIJKLMNOPQRSTUVWXYZ1234567890& 261

ITC Caslon 224 Book Italic, Dutch 785 — ITC Caslon 224 Book Italic

abcdefghijklmnopqrstuvwxyzABCDEFGHIJKLMNOPQRSTUVWXYZ1234567890& 262

ITC Caslon 224 Medium, Dutch 785 — ITC Caslon 224 Medium

abcdefghijklmnopqrstuvwxyzABCDEFGHIJKLMNOPQRSTUVWXYZ1234567890& 263

ITC Caslon 224 Medium Italic, Dutch 785 — ITC Caslon 224 Medium Italic

abcdefghijklmnopqrstuvwxyzABCDEFGHIJKLMNOPQRSTUVWXYZ1234567890&

264

ITC Caslon 224 Bold, Dutch 785 — ITC Caslon 224 Bold

abcdefghijklmnopqrstuvwxyzABCDEFGHIJKLMNOPQRSTUVWXYZ1234567890&

265

ITC Caslon 224 Bold Italic, Dutch 785 — ITC Caslon 224 Bold Italic

abcdefghijklmnopqrstuvwxyzABCDEFGHIJKLMNOPQRSTUVWXYZ1234567890&

266

ITC Caslon 224 Black/Head, Dutch 785 — ITC Caslon 224 Black

abcdefghijklmnopqrstuvwxyzABCDEFGHIJKLMNOPQRSTUVWX1234567890&

267

ITC Caslon 224 Black Italic/Head, Dutch 785 — ITC Caslon 224 Black Italic

abcdefghijklmnopqrstuvwxyzABCDEFGHIJKLMNOPQRSTUVWX1234567890&

268

Century Oldstyle, Revival 707 — Century Oldstyle Roman

abcdefghijklmnopqrstuvwxyzABCDEFGHIJKLMNOPQRSTUVWXYZ1234567890&

269

Century Oldstyle Italic, Revival 707 — Century Oldstyle Italic

abcdefghijklmnopqrstuvwxyzABCDEFGHIJKLMNOPQRSTUVWXYZ1234567890&

270

Century Oldstyle Bold, Revival 707 — Century Oldstyle Bold

abcdefghijklmnopqrstuvwxyzABCDEFGHIJKLMNOPQRSTUVWXYZ1234567890&

271

Bitstream Charter, Transitional 801 — Bitstream Charter

abcdefghijklmnopqrstuvwxyzABCDEFGHIJKLMNOPQRSTUVWXYZ1234567890&

272

Bitstream Charter Italic, Transitional 801 — Bitstream Charter Italic

abcdefghijklmnopqrstuvwxyzABCDEFGHIJKLMNOPQRSTUVWXYZ1234567890&

273

Bitstream Charter Bold, Transitional 801 — Bitstream Charter Bold

abcdefghijklmnopqrstuvwxyzABCDEFGHIJKLMNOPQRSTUVWXYZ1234567890&

274

Bitstream Charter Bold Italic, Transitional 801 — Bitstream Charter Bold Italic

abcdefghijklmnopqrstuvwxyzABCDEFGHIJKLMNOPQRSTUVWXYZ1234567890&

275

Bitstream Charter Black, Transitional 801 — Bitstream Charter Black

abcdefghijklmnopqrstuvwxyzABCDEFGHIJKLMNOPQRSTUV1234567890&

276

Bitstream Charter Black Italic, Transitional 801 — Bitstream Charter Black Italic

abcdefghijklmnopqrstuvwxyzABCDEFGHIJKLMNOPQRSTUVW1234567890&

277

ITC Clearface Regular, Revival 814 — ITC Clearface Regular

abcdefghijklmnopqrstuvwxyzABCDEFGHIJKLMNOPQRSTUVWXYZ1234567890&

278

ITC Clearface Regular Italic, Revival 814 — ITC Clearface Regular Italic

abcdefghijklmnopqrstuvwxyzABCDEFGHIJKLMNOPQRSTUVWXYZ1234567890&

279

ITC Clearface Bold, Revival 814 — ITC Clearface Bold

abcdefghijklmnopqrstuvwxyzABCDEFGHIJKLMNOPQRSTUVWXYZ1234567890&

280

ITC Clearface Bold Italic, Revival 814 — ITC Clearface Bold Italic

abcdefghijklmnopqrstuvwxyzABCDEFGHIJKLMNOPQRSTUVWXYZ1234567890&

281

ITC Clearface Heavy, Revival 814 — ITC Clearface Heavy

abcdefghijklmnopqrstuvwxyzABCDEFGHIJKLMNOPQRSTUVWXYZ1234567890&

282

ITC Clearface Heavy Italic, Revival 814 — ITC Clearface Heavy Italic
abcdefghijklmnopqrstuvwxyzABCDEFGHIJKLMNOPQRSTUVWXYZ1234567890& 283

ITC Clearface Black/Head, Revival 814 — ITC Clearface Black
abcdefghijklmnopqrstuvwxyzABCDEFGHIJKLMNOPQRSTUVWXYZ1234567890& 284

ITC Clearface Black Italic/Head, Revival 814 — ITC Clearface Black Italic
abcdefghijklmnopqrstuvwxyzABCDEFGHIJKLMNOPQRSTUVWXYZ1234567890& 285

ITC Clearface Contour/Head, Revival 814 — ITC Clearface Contour
abcdefghijklmnopqrstuvwxyzABCDEFGHIJKLMNOPQRSTUVWXYZ1234567890& 286

Dutch 809 — Concorde
abcdefghijklmnopqrstuvwxyzABCDEFGHIJKLMNOPQRSTUVWXYZ1234567890& 287

Dutch 809 Italic — Concorde Italic
abcdefghijklmnopqrstuvwxyzABCDEFGHIJKLMNOPQRSTUVWXYZ1234567890& 288

Dutch 809 Bold — Concorde Bold
abcdefghijklmnopqrstuvwxyzABCDEFGHIJKLMNOPQRSTUVWXYZ1234567890& 289

ITC Cushing Book, Revival 721 — ITC Cushing Book
abcdefghijklmnopqrstuvwxyzABCDEFGHIJKLMNOPQRSTUVWXYZ1234567890& 290

ITC Cushing Book Italic, Revival 721 — ITC Cushing Book Italic
abcdefghijklmnopqrstuvwxyzABCDEFGHIJKLMNOPQRSTUVWXYZ1234567890& 291

ITC Cushing Medium, Revival 721 — ITC Cushing Medium
abcdefghijklmnopqrstuvwxyzABCDEFGHIJKLMNOPQRSTUVWXYZ1234567890& 292

ITC Cushing Medium Italic, Revival 721 — ITC Cushing Medium Italic
abcdefghijklmnopqrstuvwxyzABCDEFGHIJKLMNOPQRSTUVWXYZ1234567890& 293

ITC Cushing Bold, Revival 721 — ITC Cushing Bold
abcdefghijklmnopqrstuvwxyzABCDEFGHIJKLMNOPQRSTUVWXYZ1234567890& 294

ITC Cushing Bold Italic, Revival 721 — ITC Cushing Bold Italic
abcdefghijklmnopqrstuvwxyzABCDEFGHIJKLMNOPQRSTUVWXYZ1234567890& 295

ITC Cushing Heavy, Revival 721 — ITC Cushing Heavy
abcdefghijklmnopqrstuvwxyzABCDEFGHIJKLMNOPQRSTUVWXYZ1234567890& 296

ITC Cushing Heavy Italic, Revival 721 — ITC Cushing Heavy Italic
abcdefghijklmnopqrstuvwxyzABCDEFGHIJKLMNOPQRSTUVWXYZ1234567890& 297

Transitional 521 — Electra
abcdefghijklmnopqrstuvwxyzABCDEFGHIJKLMNOPQRSTUVWXYZ1234567890& 298

Transitional 521 Cursive — Electra Cursive
abcdefghijklmnopqrstuvwxyzABCDEFGHIJKLMNOPQRSTUVWXYZ1234567890& 299

Transitional 521 Bold — Electra Bold
abcdefghijklmnopqrstuvwxyzABCDEFGHIJKLMNOPQRSTUVWXYZ1234567890& 300

ITC Grouch/Head, Dutch 791 — ITC Grouch
abcdefghijklmnopqrstuvwxyzABCDEFGHIJKLMNOPQRSTUVWXY1234567890& 301

Kis Roman, Dutch 721 — Janson Roman
abcdefghijklmnopqrstuvwxyzABCDEFGHIJKLMNOPQRSTUVWXYZ1234567890& 302

Kis Italic, Dutch 721 — Janson Italic
abcdefghijklmnopqrstuvwxyzABCDEFGHIJKLMNOPQRSTUVWXYZ1234567890& 303

Life, Dutch 806 — Life
abcdefghijklmnopqrstuvwxyzABCDEFGHIJKLMNOPQRSTUVWXYZ1234567890& 304

Life Italic, Dutch 806 — Life Italic
abcdefghijklmnopqrstuvwxyzABCDEFGHIJKLMNOPQRSTUVWXYZ1234567890& 305

Life Bold, Dutch 806 — Life Bold
abcdefghijklmnopqrstuvwxyzABCDEFGHIJKLMNOPQRSTUVWXYZ1234567890& 306

Life Bold Italic, Dutch 806 — Life Bold Italic
abcdefghijklmnopqrstuvwxyzABCDEFGHIJKLMNOPQRSTUVWXYZ1234567890& 307

Latin 725 — Meridien Roman
abcdefghijklmnopqrstuvwxyzABCDEFGHIJKLMNOPQRSTUVWXYZ1234567890& 308

Latin 725 Italic — Meridien Italic
abcdefghijklmnopqrstuvwxyzABCDEFGHIJKLMNOPQRSTUVWXYZ1234567890& 309

Latin 725 Medium — Meridien Medium
abcdefghijklmnopqrstuvwxyzABCDEFGHIJKLMNOPQRSTUVWXYZ1234567890& 310

Latin 725 Medium Italic — Meridien Medium Italic
abcdefghijklmnopqrstuvwxyzABCDEFGHIJKLMNOPQRSTUVWXYZ1234567890& 311

Latin 725 Bold — Meridien Bold
abcdefghijklmnopqrstuvwxyzABCDEFGHIJKLMNOPQRSTUVWXY1234567890& 312

Latin 725 Bold Italic — Meridien Bold Italic
abcdefghijklmnopqrstuvwxyzABCDEFGHIJKLMNOPQRSTUVWXYZ1234567890& 313

Lapidary 333 — Perpetua Roman
abcdefghijklmnopqrstuvwxyzABCDEFGHIJKLMNOPQRSTUVWXYZ1234567890& 314

Lapidary 333 Italic — Perpetua Italic
abcdefghijklmnopqrstuvwxyzABCDEFGHIJKLMNOPQRSTUVWXYZ1234567890& 315

Lapidary 333 Bold — Perpetua Bold
abcdefghijklmnopqrstuvwxyzABCDEFGHIJKLMNOPQRSTUVWXYZ1234567890& 316

Lapidary 333 Bold Itatlic — Perpetua Bold Italic
abcdefghijklmnopqrstuvwxyzABCDEFGHIJKLMNOPQRSTUVWXYZ1234567890& 317

Lapidary 333 Black/Head — Perpetua Black
abcdefghijklmnopqrstuvwxyzABCDEFGHIJKLMNOPQRSTUVWXYZ1234567890& 318

Romana, Revival 750 — Romana Normal
abcdefghijklmnopqrstuvwxyzABCDEFGHIJKLMNOPQRSTUVWXYZ1234567890& 319

Romana Bold, Revival 750 — Romana Bold
abcdefghijklmnopqrstuvwxyzABCDEFGHIJKLMNOPQRSTUVWXYZ1234567890& 320

ITC Tiffany Light, Revival 831 — ITC Tiffany Light

abcdefghijklmnopqrstuvwxyzABCDEFGHIJKLMNOPQRSTUVWXY1234567890& 321

ITC Tiffany Light Italic, Revival 831 — ITC Tiffany Light Italic

abcdefghijklmnopqrstuvwxyzABCDEFGHIJKLMNOPQRSTUVWXYZ1234567890& 322

ITC Tiffany Medium, Revival 831 — ITC Tiffany Medium

abcdefghijklmnopqrstuvwxyzABCDEFGHIJKLMNOPQRSTUVWX1234567890& 323

ITC Tiffany Medium Italic, Revival 831 — ITC Tiffany Medium Italic

abcdefghijklmnopqrstuvwxyzABCDEFGHIJKLMNOPQRSTUVWXY1234567890& 324

ITC Tiffany Demi, Revival 831 — ITC Tiffany Demi

abcdefghijklmnopqrstuvwxyzABCDEFGHIJKLMNOPQRSTUVW1234567890& 325

ITC Tiffany Demi Italic, Revival 831 — ITC Tiffany Demi Italic

abcdefghijklmnopqrstuvwxyzABCDEFGHIJKLMNOPQRSTUVWX1234567890& 326

ITC Tiffany Heavy/Head, Revival 831 — ITC Tiffany Heavy

abcdefghijklmnopqrstuvwxyzABCDEFGHIJKLMNOPQ1234567890& 327

ITC Tiffany Heavy/Head Italic, Revival 831 — ITC Tiffany Heavy Italic

abcdefghijklmnopqrstuvwxyzABCDEFGHIJKLMNOP1234567890& 328

Dutch 801 Roman/Head — Times Roman (18pt)

abcdefghijklmnopqrstuvwxyzABCDEFGHIJKLMNOPQRSTUVWXYZ1234567890& 329

Dutch 801 Italic/Head — Times Italic (18pt)

abcdefghijklmnopqrstuvwxyzABCDEFGHIJKLMNOPQRSTUVWXYZ1234567890& 330

Dutch 801 Roman — Times Roman

abcdefghijklmnopqrstuvwxyzABCDEFGHIJKLMNOPQRSTUVWXYZ1234567890& 331

Dutch 801 Italic — Times Italic

abcdefghijklmnopqrstuvwxyzABCDEFGHIJKLMNOPQRSTUVWXYZ1234567890& 332

Dutch 801 Semi-Bold — Times Semi-Bold

abcdefghijklmnopqrstuvwxyzABCDEFGHIJKLMNOPQRSTUVWXYZ1234567890& 333

Dutch 801 Semi-Bold Italic — Times Semi-Bold Italic

abcdefghijklmnopqrstuvwxyzABCDEFGHIJKLMNOPQRSTUVWXYZ1234567890& 334

Dutch 801 Bold — Times Bold

abcdefghijklmnopqrstuvwxyzABCDEFGHIJKLMNOPQRSTUVWXYZ1234567890& 335

Dutch 801 Bold Italic — Times Bold Italic

abcdefghijklmnopqrstuvwxyzABCDEFGHIJKLMNOPQRSTUVWXYZ1234567890& 336

Dutch 801 Extra Bold — Times Extra Bold

abcdefghijklmnopqrstuvwxyzABCDEFGHIJKLMNOPQRSTUVWXYZ1234567890& 337

ITC Zapf International Light, Elliptical 717 — ITC Zapf International Light

abcdefghijklmnopqrstuvwxyzABCDEFGHIJKLMNOPQRSTUVWXYZ1234567890& 338

ITC Zapf International Light Italic, Elliptical 717 — ITC Zapf International Light Italic

abcdefghijklmnopqrstuvwxyzABCDEFGHIJKLMNOPQRSTUVWXYZ1234567890& 339

ITC Zapf International Medium, Elliptical 717 — ITC Zapf International Medium

abcdefghijklmnopqrstuvwxyzABCDEFGHIJKLMNOPQRSTUVWXYZ1234567890& 340

ITC Zapf International Medium Italic, Elliptical 717 — ITC Zapf International Medium Italic

abcdefghijklmnopqrstuvwxyzABCDEFGHIJKLMNOPQRSTUVWXYZ1234567890& 341

ITC Zapf International Demi, Elliptical 717 — ITC Zapf International Demi

abcdefghijklmnopqrstuvwxyzABCDEFGHIJKLMNOPQRSTUVWXYZ1234567890& 342

ITC Zapf International Demi Italic, Elliptical 717 — ITC Zapf International Demi Italic

abcdefghijklmnopqrstuvwxyzABCDEFGHIJKLMNOPQRSTUVWXYZ1234567890& 343

ITC Zapf International Heavy/Head, Elliptical 717 — ITC Zapf International Heavy

abcdefghijklmnopqrstuvwxyzABCDEFGHIJKLMNOPQRSTUV1234567890& 344

ITC Zapf International Heavy Italic/Head, Elliptical 717 — ITC Zapf International Heavy Italic

abcdefghijklmnopqrstuvwxyzABCDEFGHIJKLMNOPQRSTUVW1234567890& 345

Bauer Bodoni, Modern 405 — Bauer Bodoni Roman

abcdefghijklmnopqrstuvwxyzABCDEFGHIJKLMNOPQRSTUVWXYZ1234567890& 346

Bauer Bodoni Italic, Modern 405 — Bauer Bodoni Italic

abcdefghijklmnopqrstuvwxyzABCDEFGHIJKLMNOPQRSTUVWXYZ1234567890& 347

Bauer Bodoni Bold, Modern 405 — Bauer Bodoni Bold

abcdefghijklmnopqrstuvwxyzABCDEFGHIJKLMNOPQRSTUVWXYZ1234567890& 348

Bauer Bodoni Bold Italic, Modern 405 — Bauer Bodoni Bold Italic

abcdefghijklmnopqrstuvwxyzABCDEFGHIJKLMNOPQRSTUVWXYZ1234567890& 349

Bauer Bodoni Black, Modern 405 — Bauer Bodoni Black

abcdefghijklmnopqrstuvwxyzABCDEFGHIJKLMNOPQRSTUVWXYZ1234567890& 350

Bauer Bodoni Black Italic, Modern 405 — Bauer Bodoni Black Italic

abcdefghijklmnopqrstuvwxyzABCDEFGHIJKLMNOPQRSTUVWXYZ1234567890& 351

Bauer Bodoni Bold Condensed, Modern 405 — Bauer Bodoni Bold Condensed

abcdefghijklmnopqrstuvwxyzABCDEFGHIJKLMNOPQRSTUVWXYZ1234567890& 352

Bauer Bodoni Black Condensed, Modern 405 — Bauer Bodoni Black Condensed

abcdefghijklmnopqrstuvwxyzABCDEFGHIJKLMNOPQRSTUVWXYZ1234567890& 353

Bodoni Book, Modern 421 — Bodoni Book Roman

abcdefghijklmnopqrstuvwxyzABCDEFGHIJKLMNOPQRSTUVWXYZ1234567890& 354

Bodoni Book Italic, Modern 421 — Bodoni Book Italic

abcdefghijklmnopqrstuvwxyzABCDEFGHIJKLMNOPQRSTUVWXYZ1234567890& 355

Bodoni, Modern 421 — Bodoni Roman

abcdefghijklmnopqrstuvwxyzABCDEFGHIJKLMNOPQRSTUVWXYZ1234567890& 356

Bodoni Italic, Modern 421 — Bodoni Italic

abcdefghijklmnopqrstuvwxyzABCDEFGHIJKLMNOPQRSTUVWXYZ1234567890& 357

Bodoni Bold, Modern 421 — Bodoni Bold

abcdefghijklmnopqrstuvwxyzABCDEFGHIJKLMNOPQRSTUVWXYZ1234567890& 358

Bodoni Bold Italic, Modern 421 — Bodoni Bold Italic

abcdefghijklmnopqrstuvwxyzABCDEFGHIJKLMNOPQRSTUVWXYZ1234567890& 359

Bodoni Bold Condensed/Head, Modern 421 — Bodoni Bold Condensed

abcdefghijklmnopqrstuvwxyzABCDEFGHIJKLMNOPQRSTUVWXYZ1234567890& 360

Poster Bodoni/Head, Modern 721 — Poster Bodoni

abcdefghijklmnopqrstuvwxyzABCDEFGHIJKLMNOPQRS1234567890& 361

Poster Bodoni Italic/Head, Modern 721 — Poster Bodoni Italic

abcdefghijklmnopqrstuvwxyzABCDEFGHIJKLMNOPQRS1234567890& 362

Onyx/Head, Modern 741 — Poster Bodoni Compressed

abcdefghijklmnopqrstuvwxyzABCDEFGHIJKLMNOPQRSTUVWXYZ1234567890& 363

Modern 735 — Bodoni Campanile

abcdefghijklmnopqrstuvwxyzABCDEFGHIJKLMNOPQRSTUVWXYZ1234567890& 364

Transitional 411 — Bulmer

abcdefghijklmnopqrstuvwxyzABCDEFGHIJKLMNOPQRSTUVWXYZ1234567890& 365

Transitional 411 Italic — Bulmer Italic

abcdefghijklmnopqrstuvwxyzABCDEFGHIJKLMNOPQRSTUVWXYZ1234567890& 366

Transitional 511 — Caledonia Roman

abcdefghijklmnopqrstuvwxyzABCDEFGHIJKLMNOPQRSTUVWXYZ1234567890& 367

Transitional 511 Italic — Caledonia Italic

abcdefghijklmnopqrstuvwxyzABCDEFGHIJKLMNOPQRSTUVWXYZ1234567890& 368

Transitional 511 Bold — Caledonia Bold

abcdefghijklmnopqrstuvwxyzABCDEFGHIJKLMNOPQRSTUVWXYZ1234567890& 369

Transitional 511 Bold Italic — Caledonia Bold Italic

abcdefghijklmnopqrstuvwxyzABCDEFGHIJKLMNOPQRSTUVWXYZ1234567890& 370

Century Expanded, Century 701 — Century Expanded Roman

abcdefghijklmnopqrstuvwxyzABCDEFGHIJKLMNOPQRSTUVWXYZ1234567890& 371

Century Expanded Italic, Century 701 — Century Expanded Italic

abcdefghijklmnopqrstuvwxyzABCDEFGHIJKLMNOPQRSTUVWXYZ1234567890& 372

Century Bold, Century 701 — Century Bold

abcdefghijklmnopqrstuvwxyzABCDEFGHIJKLMNOPQRSTUVWXYZ1234567890& 373

Century Bold Italic, Century 701 — Century Bold Italic

abcdefghijklmnopqrstuvwxyzABCDEFGHIJKLMNOPQRSTUVWXYZ1234567890& 374

Century Schoolbook, Century 702 — Century Schoolbook Roman

abcdefghijklmnopqrstuvwxyzABCDEFGHIJKLMNOPQRSTUVWXYZ1234567890& 375

Century Schoolbook Italic, Century 702 — Century Schoolbook Italic

abcdefghijklmnopqrstuvwxyzABCDEFGHIJKLMNOPQRSTUVWXYZ1234567890& 376

Century Schoolbook Bold, Century 702 — Century Schoolbook Bold

abcdefghijklmnopqrstuvwxyzABCDEFGHIJKLMNOPQRSTUV1234567890& 377

Century Schoolbook Bold Italic, Century 702 — Century Schoolbook Bold Italic
abcdefghijklmnopqrstuvwxyzABCDEFGHIJKLMNOPQRSTUV1234567890& 378

Century Schoolbook Bold Condensed, Century 702 — Century Schoolbook Bold Condensed
abcdefghijklmnopqrstuvwxyzABCDEFGHIJKLMNOPQRSTUVWXYZ1234567890& 379

Century Schoolbook/Text, Monospace 722 — Century Schoolbook Monospace
abcdefghijklmnopqrstuvwxyzABCDEFGHIJKLMNOPQRSTUVWXYZ1234567890& 380

ITC Century Light, Century 711 — ITC Century Light Roman
abcdefghijklmnopqrstuvwxyzABCDEFGHIJKLMNOPQRSTUVWXYZ1234567890& 381

ITC Century Light Italic, Century 711 — ITC Century Light Italic
abcdefghijklmnopqrstuvwxyzABCDEFGHIJKLMNOPQRSTUVWXYZ1234567890& 382

ITC Century Book, Century 711 — ITC Century Book
abcdefghijklmnopqrstuvwxyzABCDEFGHIJKLMNOPQRSTUVWXYZ1234567890& 383

ITC Century Book Italic, Century 711 — ITC Century Book Italic
abcdefghijklmnopqrstuvwxyzABCDEFGHIJKLMNOPQRSTUVWXYZ1234567890& 384

ITC Century Bold, Century 711 — ITC Century Bold
abcdefghijklmnopqrstuvwxyzABCDEFGHIJKLMNOPQRSTUVWXY1234567890& 385

ITC Century Bold Italic, Century 711 — ITC Century Bold Italic
abcdefghijklmnopqrstuvwxyzABCDEFGHIJKLMNOPQRSTUVWX1234567890& 386

ITC Century Ultra/Head, Century 711 — ITC Century Ultra
abcdefghijklmnopqrstuvwxyzABCDEFGHIJKLMNOPQR1234567890& 387

ITC Century Ultra Italic/Head, Century 711 — ITC Century Ultra Italic
abcdefghijklmnopqrstuvwxyzABCDEFGHIJKLMNOP1234567890& 388

ITC Century Light Condensed, Century 711 — ITC Century Light Condensed
abcdefghijklmnopqrstuvwxyzABCDEFGHIJKLMNOPQRSTUVWXYZ1234567890& 389

ITC Century Light Condensed Italic, Century 711 — ITC Century Light Condensed Italic
abcdefghijklmnopqrstuvwxyzABCDEFGHIJKLMNOPQRSTUVWXYZ1234567890& 390

ITC Century Book Condensed, Century 711 — ITC Century Book Condensed
abcdefghijklmnopqrstuvwxyzABCDEFGHIJKLMNOPQRSTUVWXYZ1234567890& 391

ITC Century Book Condensed Italic, Century 711 — ITC Century Book Condensed Italic
abcdefghijklmnopqrstuvwxyzABCDEFGHIJKLMNOPQRSTUVWXYZ1234567890& 392

ITC Century Bold Condensed, Century 711 — ITC Century Bold Condensed
abcdefghijklmnopqrstuvwxyzABCDEFGHIJKLMNOPQRSTUVWXYZ1234567890& 393

ITC Century Bold Condensed Italic, Century 711 — ITC Century Bold Condensed Italic
abcdefghijklmnopqrstuvwxyzABCDEFGHIJKLMNOPQRSTUVWXYZ1234567890& 394

ITC Century Ultra Condensed/Head, Century 711 — ITC Century Ultra Condensed
abcdefghijklmnopqrstuvwxyzABCDEFGHIJKLMNOPQRSTUVWXYZ1234567890& 395

ITC Century Ultra Condensed Italic/Head, Century 711 — ITC Century Ultra Condensed Italic
abcdefghijklmnopqrstuvwxyzABCDEFGHIJKLMNOPQRSTUVWXYZ1234567890& 396

De Vinne/Text, Industrial 731 — De Vinne/Text
abcdefghijklmnopqrstuvwxyzABCDEFGHIJKLMNOPQRSTUVWXYZ1234567890&

397

De Vinne Italic/Text, Industrial 731 — De Vinne Italic/Text
abcdefghijklmnopqrstuvwxyzABCDEFGHIJKLMNOPQRSTUVWXYZ1234567890&

398

De Vinne/Text 8-pt. Master, Industrial 731 — De Vinne/Text 8-pt.
abcdefghijklmnopqrstuvwxyzABCDEFGHIJKLMNOPQRSTUVWXYZ1234567890&

399

De Vinne Italic/Text 8-pt. Master, Industrial 731 — De Vinne Italic/Text 8-pt.
abcdefghijklmnopqrstuvwxyzABCDEFGHIJKLMNOPQRSTUVWXYZ1234567890&

400

Transitional 551 Medium — Fairfield
abcdefghijklmnopqrstuvwxyzABCDEFGHIJKLMNOPQRSTUVWXYZ1234567890&

401

Transitional 551 Medium Italic — Fairfield Italic
abcdefghijklmnopqrstuvwxyzABCDEFGHIJKLMNOPQRSTUVWXYZ1234567890&

402

ITC Fenice Light, Industrial 817 — ITC Fenice Light
abcdefghijklmnopqrstuvwxyzABCDEFGHIJKLMNOPQRSTUVWXYZ1234567890&

403

ITC Fenice Light Italic, Industrial 817 — ITC Fenice Light Italic
abcdefghijklmnopqrstuvwxyzABCDEFGHIJKLMNOPQRSTUVWXYZ1234567890&

404

ITC Fenice Regular, Industrial 817 — ITC Fenice Regular
abcdefghijklmnopqrstuvwxyzABCDEFGHIJKLMNOPQRSTUVWXYZ1234567890&

405

ITC Fenice Regular Italic, Industrial 817 — ITC Fenice Regular Italic
abcdefghijklmnopqrstuvwxyzABCDEFGHIJKLMNOPQRSTUVWXYZ1234567890&

406

ITC Fenice Bold, Industrial 817 — ITC Fenice Bold
abcdefghijklmnopqrstuvwxyzABCDEFGHIJKLMNOPQRSTUVWXYZ1234567890&

407

ITC Fenice Bold Italic, Industrial 817 — ITC Fenice Bold Italic
abcdefghijklmnopqrstuvwxyzABCDEFGHIJKLMNOPQRSTUVWXYZ1234567890&

408

ITC Fenice Ultra/Head, Industrial 817 — ITC Fenice Ultra/Head
abcdefghijklmnopqrstuvwxyzABCDEFGHIJKLMNOPQRSTUV1234567890&

409

ITC Fenice Ultra Italic/Head, Industrial 817 — ITC Fenice Ultra Italic/Head
abcdefghijklmnopqrstuvwxyzABCDEFGHIJKLMNOPQRSTUV1234567890&

410

Latin Extra Condensed/Head, Latin 711 — Latin Extra Condensed/Head
ABCDEFGHIJKLMNOPQRSTUVWXYZ1234567890&

411

Century 725 — Madison
abcdefghijklmnopqrstuvwxyzABCDEFGHIJKLMNOPQRSTUVWXYZ1234567890&

412

Century 725 Italic — Madison Italic
abcdefghijklmnopqrstuvwxyzABCDEFGHIJKLMNOPQRSTUVWXYZ1234567890&

413

Century 725 Bold — Madison Bold
abcdefghijklmnopqrstuvwxyzABCDEFGHIJKLMNOPQRSTUVWXYZ1234567890&

414

Century 725 Black — Madison Black
abcdefghijklmnopqrstuvwxyzABCDEFGHIJKLMNOPQ1234567890&

415

Century 725 Condensed — Madison Condensed
abcdefghijklmnopqrstuvwxyzABCDEFGHIJKLMNOPQRSTUVWXYZ1234567890&

416

Century 725 Bold Condensed — Madison Bold Condensed
abcdefghijklmnopqrstuvwxyzABCDEFGHIJKLMNOPQRSTUVWXYZ1234567890&

417

Normande, Modern 710 — Normande
abcdefghijklmnopqrstuvwxyzABCDEFGHIJKLMNOP1234567890&

418

Normande Italic, Modern 710 — Normande Italic
abcdefghijklmnopqrstuvwxyzABCDEFGHIJKLMNOPQ1234567890&

419

Century 751 — Primer
abcdefghijklmnopqrstuvwxyzABCDEFGHIJKLMNOPQRSTUVWXYZ1234567890&

420

Century 751 Italic — Primer Italic
abcdefghijklmnopqrstuvwxyzABCDEFGHIJKLMNOPQRSTUVWXYZ1234567890&

421

Modern 880/Newstext — Telegraph (Linotype Modern)
abcdefghijklmnopqrstuvwxyzABCDEFGHIJKLMNOPQRSTUVWXYZ1234567890&

422

Modern 880 Italic/Newstext — Telegraph Italic (Linotype Modern)
abcdefghijklmnopqrstuvwxyzABCDEFGHIJKLMNOPQRSTUVWXYZ1234567890&

423

Modern 880 Bold/Newstext — Telegraph Bold (Linotype Modern)
abcdefghijklmnopqrstuvwxyzABCDEFGHIJKLMNOPQRSTUVWXYZ1234567890&

424

Industrial 736 — Torino
abcdefghijklmnopqrstuvwxyzABCDEFGHIJKLMNOPQRSTUVWXYZ1234567890&

425

Industrial 736 Italic — Torino Italic
abcdefghijklmnopqrstuvwxyzABCDEFGHIJKLMNOPQRSTUVWXYZ1234567890&

426

ITC Zapf Book Light, Elliptical 716 — ITC Zapf Book Light
abcdefghijklmnopqrstuvwxyzABCDEFGHIJKLMNOPQRSTUVWXYZ1234567890&

427

ITC Zapf Book Light Italic, Elliptical 716 — ITC Zapf Book Light Italic
abcdefghijklmnopqrstuvwxyzABCDEFGHIJKLMNOPQRSTUVWXYZ1234567890&

428

ITC Zapf Book Medium, Elliptical 716 — ITC Zapf Book Medium
abcdefghijklmnopqrstuvwxyzABCDEFGHIJKLMNOPQRSTUVWXYZ1234567890&

429

ITC Zapf Book Medium Italic, Elliptical 716 — ITC Zapf Book Medium Italic
abcdefghijklmnopqrstuvwxyzABCDEFGHIJKLMNOPQRSTUVWXYZ1234567890&

430

ITC Zapf Book Demi, Elliptical 716 — ITC Zapf Book Demi
abcdefghijklmnopqrstuvwxyzABCDEFGHIJKLMNOPQRSTUVWXYZ1234567890&

431

ITC Zapf Book Demi Italic, Elliptical 716 — ITC Zapf Book Demi Italic
abcdefghijklmnopqrstuvwxyzABCDEFGHIJKLMNOPQRSTUVWXYZ1234567890&

432

ITC Zapf Book Heavy/Head, Elliptical 716 — ITC Zapf Book Heavy
abcdefghijklmnopqrstuvwxyzABCDEFGHIJKLMNOPQRSTUVWXY1234567890&

433

ITC Zapf Book Heavy Italic/Head, Elliptical 716 — ITC Zapf Book Heavy Italic
abcdefghijklmnopqrstuvwxyzABCDEFGHIJKLMNOPQRSTUVWXYZ1234567890&

434

ITC American Typewriter Light, Typewriter 911 — ITC American Typewriter Light

abcdefghijklmnopqrstuvwxyzABCDEFGHIJKLMNOPQRSTUVWXYZ1234567890&   435

ITC American Typewriter Medium, Typewriter 911 — ITC American Typewriter Medium

abcdefghijklmnopqrstuvwxyzABCDEFGHIJKLMNOPQRSTUVWX1234567890&   436

ITC American Typewriter Bold, Typewriter 911 — ITC American Typewriter Bold

abcdefghijklmnopqrstuvwxyzABCDEFGHIJKLMNOPQRST1234567890&   437

ITC American Typewriter Light Condensed, Typewriter 911 — ITC American Typewriter Light Condensed

abcdefghijklmnopqrstuvwxyzABCDEFGHIJKLMNOPQRSTUVWXYZ1234567890&   438

ITC American Typewriter Medium Condensed, Typewriter 911— ITC American Typewriter Medium Condensed

abcdefghijklmnopqrstuvwxyzABCDEFGHIJKLMNOPQRSTUVWXYZ1234567890&   439

ITC American Typewriter Bold Condensed, Typewriter 911 — ITC American Typewriter Bold Condensed

abcdefghijklmnopqrstuvwxyzABCDEFGHIJKLMNOPQRSTUVWXYZ1234567890&   440

Egyptian 710 — Antique No.3

abcdefghijklmnopqrstuvwxyzABCDEFGHIJKLMNOPQRSTUVWXYZ1234567890&   441

News 706/Newstext — Aurora Roman

abcdefghijklmnopqrstuvwxyzABCDEFGHIJKLMNOPQRSTUVWXYZ1234567890&   442

News 706 Italic/Newstext — Aurora Italic

abcdefghijklmnopqrstuvwxyzABCDEFGHIJKLMNOPQRSTUVWXYZ1234567890&   443

News 706 Bold/Newstext — Aurora Bold

abcdefghijklmnopqrstuvwxyzABCDEFGHIJKLMNOPQRSTUVWX1234567890&   444

Candida, Humanist Slabserif 671 — Candida

abcdefghijklmnopqrstuvwxyzABCDEFGHIJKLMNOPQRSTUVWXYZ1234567890&   445

Candida Italic, Humanist Slabserif 671 — Candida Italic

abcdefghijklmnopqrstuvwxyzABCDEFGHIJKLMNOPQRSTUVWXYZ1234567890&   446

Candida Bold, Humanist Slabserif 671 — Candida Bold

abcdefghijklmnopqrstuvwxyzABCDEFGHIJKLMNOPQRSTUVWXY1234567890&   447

Cheltenham, Stubserif 205 — Cheltenham

abcdefghijklmnopqrstuvwxyzABCDEFGHIJKLMNOPQRSTUVWXYZ1234567890&   448

Cheltenham Italic, Stubserif 205 — Cheltenham Italic

abcdefghijklmnopqrstuvwxyzABCDEFGHIJKLMNOPQRSTUVWXYZ1234567890&   449

Cheltenham Bold/Head, Stubserif 205 — Cheltenham Bold/Head

abcdefghijklmnopqrstuvwxyzABCDEFGHIJKLMNOPQRSTUVWXYZ1234567890&   450

Cheltenham Bold Italic/Head, Stubserif 205 — Cheltenham Bold Italic /Head

abcdefghijklmnopqrstuvwxyzABCDEFGHIJKLMNOPQRSTUVWXYZ1234567890&   451

Cheltenham Bold, Stubserif 205 — Cheltenham Bold

abcdefghijklmnopqrstuvwxyzABCDEFGHIJKLMNOPQRSTUVWXYZ1234567890&   452

Cheltenham Bold Italic, Stubserif 205 — Cheltenham Bold Italic

abcdefghijklmnopqrstuvwxyzABCDEFGHIJKLMNOPQRSTUVWXYZ1234567890&   453

Cheltenham Bold Condensed, Stubserif 205 — Cheltenham Bold Condensed

abcdefghijklmnopqrstuvwxyzABCDEFGHIJKLMNOPQRSTUVWXYZ1234567890&

454

Cheltenham Bold Condensed Italic, Stubserif 205 — Cheltenham Bold Condensed Italic

abcdefghijklmnopqrstuvwxyzABCDEFGHIJKLMNOPQRSTUVWXYZ1234567890&

455

Cheltenham Bold Extra Condensed, Stubserif 205 — Cheltenham Bold Extra Condensed

abcdefghijklmnopqrstuvwxyzABCDEFGHIJKLMNOPQRSTUVWXYZ1234567890&

456

ITC Cheltenham Light, Stubserif 705 — ITC Cheltenham Light Roman

abcdefghijklmnopqrstuvwxyzABCDEFGHIJKLMNOPQRSTUVWXYZ1234567890&

457

ITC Cheltenham Light Italic, Stubserif 705 — ITC Cheltenham Light Italic

abcdefghijklmnopqrstuvwxyzABCDEFGHIJKLMNOPQRSTUVWXYZ1234567890&

458

ITC Cheltenham Book, Stubserif 705 — ITC Cheltenham Book

abcdefghijklmnopqrstuvwxyzABCDEFGHIJKLMNOPQRSTUVWXYZ1234567890&

459

ITC Cheltenham Book Italic, Stubserif 705 — ITC Cheltenham Book Italic

abcdefghijklmnopqrstuvwxyzABCDEFGHIJKLMNOPQRSTUVWXYZ1234567890&

460

ITC Cheltenham Bold, Stubserif 705 — ITC Cheltenham Bold

abcdefghijklmnopqrstuvwxyzABCDEFGHIJKLMNOPQRSTUVWXYZ1234567890&

461

ITC Cheltenham Bold Italic, Stubserif 705 — ITC Cheltenham Bold Italic

abcdefghijklmnopqrstuvwxyzABCDEFGHIJKLMNOPQRSTUVWXYZ1234567890&

462

ITC Cheltenham Ultra/Head, Stubserif 705 — ITC Cheltenham Ultra

abcdefghijklmnopqrstuvwxyzABCDEFGHIJKLMNOPQRSTUV1234567890&

463

ITC Cheltenham Ultra Italic/Head, Stubserif 705 — ITC Cheltenham Ultra Italic

abcdefghijklmnopqrstuvwxyzABCDEFGHIJKLMNOPQRSTUV1234567890&

464

Square Slabserif 711 Light — City Light

abcdefghijklmnopqrstuvwxyzABCDEFGHIJKLMNOPQRSTUVWXYZ1234567890&

465

Square Slabserif 711 Medium — City Medium

abcdefghijklmnopqrstuvwxyzABCDEFGHIJKLMNOPQRSTUVWXYZ1234567890&

466

Square Slabserif 711 Bold/Head — City Bold

abcdefghijklmnopqrstuvwxyzABCDEFGHIJKLMNOPQRSTUVWXYZ1234567890&

467

Clarendon Light, Clarendon 701 — Clarendon Light

abcdefghijklmnopqrstuvwxyzABCDEFGHIJKLMNOPQRSTUVW1234567890&

468

Clarendon, Clarendon 701 — Clarendon Roman

abcdefghijklmnopqrstuvwxyzABCDEFGHIJKLMNOPQRSTUV1234567890&

469

Clarendon Heavy, Clarendon 701 — Clarendon Heavy

abcdefghijklmnopqrstuvwxyzABCDEFGHIJKLMNOPQRSTUV1234567890&

470

Clarendon Bold, Clarendon 701 — Clarendon Bold

abcdefghijklmnopqrstuvwxyzABCDEFGHIJKLMNOPQRSTUV1234567890&

471

Clarendon Black, Clarendon 701 — Clarendon Black

abcdefghijklmnopqrstuvwxyzABCDEFGHIJKLMNOPQRSTU1234567890&

472

Clarendon Condensed, Clarendon 701 — Clarendon Condensed
abcdefghijklmnopqrstuvwxyzABCDEFGHIJKLMNOPQRSTUVWXYZ1234567890&   473

Clarendon Bold Condensed, Clarendon 701 — Clarendon Bold Condensed
abcdefghijklmnopqrstuvwxyzABCDEFGHIJKLMNOPQRSTUVWXYZ1234567890&   474

News 705/Newstext — Corona Roman
abcdefghijklmnopqrstuvwxyzABCDEFGHIJKLMNOPQRSTUVW1234567890&   475

News 705 Italic/Newstext — Corona Italic
abcdefghijklmnopqrstuvwxyzABCDEFGHIJKLMNOPQRSTUVWX1234567890&   476

News 705 Bold/Newstext — Corona Bold
abcdefghijklmnopqrstuvwxyzABCDEFGHIJKLMNOPQRSTUVW1234567890&   477

News 705 Bold Italic/Newstext — Corona Bold Italic
abcdefghijklmnopqrstuvwxyzABCDEFGHIJKLMNOPQRSTUVWX1234567890&   478

Courier 10 Pitch/Text, Fixed Pitch 810 — Courier 10 Pitch
abcdefghijklmnopqrstuvwxyzABCDEFGHIJKLMNOPQRSTUVWXYZ1234567890&   479

Courier Italic 10 Pitch/Text, Fixed Pitch 810 — Courier Italic 10 Pitch
abcdefghijklmnopqrstuvwxyzABCDEFGHIJKLMNOPQRSTUVWXYZ1234567890&   480

Courier Bold 10 Pitch/Text, Fixed Pitch 810 — Courier Bold 10 Pitch
abcdefghijklmnopqrstuvwxyzABCDEFGHIJKLMNOPQRSTUVWXYZ1234567890&   481

Courier Bold Italic 10 Pitch/Text, Fixed Pitch 810 — Courier Bold Italic 10 Pitch
abcdefghijklmnopqrstuvwxyzABCDEFGHIJKLMNOPQRSTUVWXYZ1234567890&   482

Egyptian 505 Light, Humanist Slabserif 715 — Egyptian 505 Light
abcdefghijklmnopqrstuvwxyzABCDEFGHIJKLMNOPQRSTUVWXYZ1234567890&   483

Egyptian 505, Humanist Slabserif 715 — Egyptian 505
abcdefghijklmnopqrstuvwxyzABCDEFGHIJKLMNOPQRSTUVWXYZ1234567890&   484

Egyptian 505 Medium, Humanist Slabserif 715 — Egyptian 505 Medium
abcdefghijklmnopqrstuvwxyzABCDEFGHIJKLMNOPQRSTUVWXYZ1234567890&   485

Egyptian 505 Bold, Humanist Slabserif 715 — Egyptian 505 Bold
abcdefghijklmnopqrstuvwxyzABCDEFGHIJKLMNOPQRSTUVWXYZ1234567890&   486

Humanist Slabserif 712 — Egyptienne 55
abcdefghijklmnopqrstuvwxyzABCDEFGHIJKLMNOPQRSTUVWXYZ1234567890&   487

Humanist Slabserif 712 Italic — Egyptienne Italic 56
abcdefghijklmnopqrstuvwxyzABCDEFGHIJKLMNOPQRSTUVWXYZ1234567890&   488

Humanist Slabserif 712 Bold — Egyptienne Bold 65
abcdefghijklmnopqrstuvwxyzABCDEFGHIJKLMNOPQRSTUVWXY1234567890&   489

Humanist Slabserif 712 Black — Egyptienne Black 75
abcdefghijklmnopqrstuvwxyzABCDEFGHIJKLMNOPQRSTUVW1234567890&   490

News 702/Newstext — Excelsior Roman
abcdefghijklmnopqrstuvwxyzABCDEFGHIJKLMNOPQRSTUVW1234567890&   491

News 702 Italic/Newstext — Excelsior Italic
abcdefghijklmnopqrstuvwxyzABCDEFGHIJKLMNOPQRSTUVW1234567890& 492

News 702 Bold/Newstext — Excelsior Bold
abcdefghijklmnopqrstuvwxyzABCDEFGHIJKLMNOPQRSTUV1234567890& 493

News 702 Bold Italic/Newstext — Excelsior Bold Italic
abcdefghijklmnopqrstuvwxyzABCDEFGHIJKLMNOPQRSTUV1234567890& 494

News 701/Newstext — Ionic No.5
abcdefghijklmnopqrstuvwxyzABCDEFGHIJKLMNOPQRSTU1234567890& 495

News 701 Italic/Newstext — Ionic No.5 Italic
abcdefghijklmnopqrstuvwxyzABCDEFGHIJKLMNOPQRSTUV1234567890& 496

News 701 Bold/Newstext — Ionic No.5 Bold
abcdefghijklmnopqrstuvwxyzABCDEFGHIJKLMNOPQRSTU1234567890& 497

ITC Italia Book, Revival 791 — ITC Italia Book
abcdefghijklmnopqrstuvwxyzABCDEFGHIJKLMNOPQRSTUVWXYZ1234567890& 498

ITC Italia Medium, Revival 791 — ITC Italia Medium
abcdefghijklmnopqrstuvwxyzABCDEFGHIJKLMNOPQRSTUVWXYZ1234567890& 499

ITC Italia Bold, Revival 791 — ITC Italia Bold
abcdefghijklmnopqrstuvwxyzABCDEFGHIJKLMNOPQRSTUVWXYZ1234567890& 500

ITC Lubalin Graph Extra Light, Geometric Slabserif 761 — ITC Lubalin Graph Extra Light
abcdefghijklmnopqrstuvwxyzABCDEFGHIJKLMNOPQRSTUVWXYZ1234567890& 501

ITC Lubalin Graph Extra Light Oblique, Geometric Slabserif 761 — ITC Lubalin Graph Extra Light Oblique
abcdefghijklmnopqrstuvwxyzABCDEFGHIJKLMNOPQRSTUVWXYZ1234567890& 502

ITC Lubalin Graph Book, Geometric Slabserif 761 — ITC Lubalin Graph Book
abcdefghijklmnopqrstuvwxyzABCDEFGHIJKLMNOPQRSTUVWXYZ1234567890& 503

ITC Lubalin Graph Book Oblique, Geometric Slabserif 761 — ITC Lubalin Graph Book Oblique
abcdefghijklmnopqrstuvwxyzABCDEFGHIJKLMNOPQRSTUVWXYZ1234567890& 504

ITC Lubalin Graph Medium, Geometric Slabserif 761 — ITC Lubalin Graph Medium
abcdefghijklmnopqrstuvwxyzABCDEFGHIJKLMNOPQRSTUVWXY1234567890& 505

ITC Lubalin Graph Medium Oblique, Geometric Slabserif 761 — ITC Lubalin Graph Medium Oblique
abcdefghijklmnopqrstuvwxyzABCDEFGHIJKLMNOPQRSTUVWXY1234567890& 506

ITC Lubalin Graph Demi, Geometric Slabserif 761 — ITC Lubalin Graph Demi
abcdefghijklmnopqrstuvwxyzABCDEFGHIJKLMNOPQRSTUVWX1234567890& 507

ITC Lubalin Graph Demi Oblique, Geometric Slabserif 761 — ITC Lubalin Graph Demi Oblique
abcdefghijklmnopqrstuvwxyzABCDEFGHIJKLMNOPQRSTUVWX1234567890& 508

ITC Lubalin Graph Bold, Geometric Slabserif 761 — ITC Lubalin Graph Bold
abcdefghijklmnopqrstuvwxyzABCDEFGHIJKLMNOPQRSTUVW1234567890& 509

ITC Lubalin Graph Bold Oblique, Geometric Slabserif 761 — ITC Lubalin Graph Bold Oblique
abcdefghijklmnopqrstuvwxyzABCDEFGHIJKLMNOPQRSTUVW1234567890& 510

Zapf Elliptical 711 — Melior Roman

abcdefghijklmnopqrstuvwxyzABCDEFGHIJKLMNOPQRSTUVWXYZ1234567890&

511

Zapf Elliptical 711 Italic — Melior Italic

abcdefghijklmnopqrstuvwxyzABCDEFGHIJKLMNOPQRSTUVWXYZ1234567890&

512

Zapf Elliptical 711 Bold — Melior Bold

abcdefghijklmnopqrstuvwxyzABCDEFGHIJKLMNOPQRSTUVWXYZ1234567890&

513

Zapf Elliptical 711 Bold Italic— Melior Bold Italic

abcdefghijklmnopqrstuvwxyzABCDEFGHIJKLMNOPQRSTUVWXYZ1234567890&

514

Geometric Slabserif 703 Light — Memphis Light

abcdefghijklmnopqrstuvwxyzABCDEFGHIJKLMNOPQRSTUVWXYZ1234567890&

515

Geometric Slabserif 703 Light Italic — Memphis Light Italic

abcdefghijklmnopqrstuvwxyzABCDEFGHIJKLMNOPQRSTUVWXYZ1234567890&

516

Geometric Slabserif 703 Medium — Memphis Medium

abcdefghijklmnopqrstuvwxyzABCDEFGHIJKLMNOPQRSTUVWXYZ1234567890&

517

Geometric Slabserif 703 Medium Italic — Memphis Medium Italic

abcdefghijklmnopqrstuvwxyzABCDEFGHIJKLMNOPQRSTUVWXYZ1234567890&

518

Geometric Slabserif 703 Bold — Memphis Bold

abcdefghijklmnopqrstuvwxyzABCDEFGHIJKLMNOPQRSTUVWXYZ1234567890&

519

Geometric Slabserif 703 Bold Italic — Memphis Bold Italic

abcdefghijklmnopqrstuvwxyzABCDEFGHIJKLMNOPQRSTUVWXYZ1234567890&

520

Geometric Slabserif 703 Extra Bold — Memphis Extra Bold

abcdefghijklmnopqrstuvwxyzABCDEFGHIJKLMNOPQRSTUVWX1234567890&

521

Geometric Slabserif 703 Extra Bold Italic — Memphis Extra Bold Italic

abcdefghijklmnopqrstuvwxyzABCDEFGHIJKLMNOPQRSTUVWXY1234567890&

522

Geometric Slabserif 703 Medium Condensed — Memphis Medium Condensed

abcdefghijklmnopqrstuvwxyzABCDEFGHIJKLMNOPQRSTUVWXYZ1234567890&

523

Geometric Slabserif 703 Bold Condensed — Memphis Bold Condensed

abcdefghijklmnopqrstuvwxyzABCDEFGHIJKLMNOPQRSTUVWXYZ1234567890&

524

Geometric Slabserif 703 Extra Bold Condensed — Memphis Extra Bold Condensed

abcdefghijklmnopqrstuvwxyzABCDEFGHIJKLMNOPQRSTUVWXYZ1234567890&

525

Pica 10 Pitch, Fixed Pitch 760 — Pica 10 Pitch

abcdefghijklmnopqrstuvwxyzABCDEFGHIJKLMNOPQRSTUVWXYZ1234567890&

526

Playbill/Head, Circus 721 — Playbill

abcdefghijklmnopqrstuvwxyzABCDEFGHIJKLMNOPQRSTUVWXYZ1234567890&

527

Prestige 12 Pitch/Text, Fixed Pitch 800 — Prestige 12 Pitch

abcdefghijklmnopqrstuvwxyzABCDEFGHIJKLMNOPQRSTUVWXYZ1234567890&

528

Prestige Italic 12 Pitch/Text, Fixed Pitch 800 — Prestige Italic 12 Pitch

abcdefghijklmnopqrstuvwxyzABCDEFGHIJKLMNOPQRSTUVWXYZ1234567890&

529

Prestige Bold 12 Pitch/Text, Fixed Pitch 800 — Prestige Bold 12 Pitch

abcdefghijklmnopqrstuvwxyzABCDEFGHIJKLMNOPQRSTUVWXYZ1234567890& 530

Prestige Bold Italic 12 Pitch/Text, Fixed Pitch 800 — Prestige Bold Italic 12 Pitch

abcdefghijklmnopqrstuvwxyzABCDEFGHIJKLMNOPQRSTUVWXYZ1234567890& 531

P.T.Barnum/Head, Circus 711 — P.T.Barnum

abcdefghijklmnopqrstuvwxyzABCDEFGHIJKLMNOPQRSTUVWXYZ1234567890& 532

Geometric Slabserif 712 Light — Rockwell Light Roman

abcdefghijklmnopqrstuvwxyzABCDEFGHIJKLMNOPQRSTUVWXYZ1234567890& 533

Geometric Slabserif 712 Light Italic — Rockwell Light Italic

abcdefghijklmnopqrstuvwxyzABCDEFGHIJKLMNOPQRSTUVWXYZ1234567890& 534

Geometric Slabserif 712 Medium — Rockwell Medium

abcdefghijklmnopqrstuvwxyzABCDEFGHIJKLMNOPQRSTUVWXYZ1234567890& 535

Geometric Slabserif 712 Medium Italic — Rockwell Medium Italic

abcdefghijklmnopqrstuvwxyzABCDEFGHIJKLMNOPQRSTUVWXYZ1234567890& 536

Geometric Slabserif 712 Bold — Rockwell Bold

abcdefghijklmnopqrstuvwxyzABCDEFGHIJKLMNOPQRSTUVWXYZ1234567890& 537

Geometric Slabserif 712 Extra Bold/Head — Rockwell Extra Bold

abcdefghijklmnopqrstuvwxyzABCDEFGHIJKLMNOPQRSTU1234567890& 538

Serifa Thin, Swiss Slabserif 722 — Serifa Thin 35

abcdefghijklmnopqrstuvwxyzABCDEFGHIJKLMNOPQRSTUVWXYZ1234567890& 539

Serifa Thin Italic, Swiss Slabserif 722 — Serifa Thin Italic 36

abcdefghijklmnopqrstuvwxyzABCDEFGHIJKLMNOPQRSTUVWXYZ1234567890& 540

Serifa Light, Swiss Slabserif 722 — Serifa Light 45

abcdefghijklmnopqrstuvwxyzABCDEFGHIJKLMNOPQRSTUVWXYZ1234567890& 541

Serifa Light Italic, Swiss Slabserif 722 — Serifa Light Italic 46

abcdefghijklmnopqrstuvwxyzABCDEFGHIJKLMNOPQRSTUVWXYZ1234567890& 542

Serifa, Swiss Slabserif 722 — Serifa 55

abcdefghijklmnopqrstuvwxyzABCDEFGHIJKLMNOPQRSTUVWXYZ1234567890& 543

Serifa Italic, Swiss Slabserif 722 — Serifa Italic 56

abcdefghijklmnopqrstuvwxyzABCDEFGHIJKLMNOPQRSTUVWXYZ1234567890& 544

Serifa Bold Swiss Slabserif 722 — Serifa Bold 65

abcdefghijklmnopqrstuvwxyzABCDEFGHIJKLMNOPQRSTUVWXYZ1234567890& 545

Serifa Black, Swiss Slabserif 722 — Serifa Black75

abcdefghijklmnopqrstuvwxyzABCDEFGHIJKLMNOPQRSTUVWX1234567890& 546

Serifa Bold Condensed, Swiss Slabserif 722 — Serifa Bold Condensed 67

abcdefghijklmnopqrstuvwxyzABCDEFGHIJKLMNOPQRSTUVWXYZ1234567890& 547

Stymie Light, Geometric Slabserif 711 — Stymie Light Roman

abcdefghijklmnopqrstuvwxyzABCDEFGHIJKLMNOPQRSTUVWXYZ1234567890& 548

Stymie Light Italic, Geometric Slabserif 711 — Stymie Light Italic

abcdefghijklmnopqrstuvwxyzABCDEFGHIJKLMNOPQRSTUVWXYZ1234567890&   549

Stymie Medium, Geometric Slabserif 711 — Stymie Medium

abcdefghijklmnopqrstuvwxyzABCDEFGHIJKLMNOPQRSTUVWXYZ1234567890&   550

Stymie Medium Italic, Geometric Slabserif 711 — Stymie Medium Italic

abcdefghijklmnopqrstuvwxyzABCDEFGHIJKLMNOPQRSTUVWXYZ1234567890&   551

Stymie Bold, Geometric Slabserif 711 — Stymie Bold

abcdefghijklmnopqrstuvwxyzABCDEFGHIJKLMNOPQRSTUVWXYZ1234567890&   552

Stymie Bold Italic, Geometric Slabserif 711 — Stymie Bold Italic

abcdefghijklmnopqrstuvwxyzABCDEFGHIJKLMNOPQRSTUVWXYZ1234567890&   553

Stymie Extra Bold/Head, Geometric Slabserif 711 — Stymie Extra Bold

abcdefghijklmnopqrstuvwxyzABCDEFGHIJKLMNOPQRSTUVWXYZ1234567890&   554

Stymie Extra Bold Condensed, Geometric Slabserif 711 — Stymie Extra Bold Condensed

abcdefghijklmnopqrstuvwxyzABCDEFGHIJKLMNOPQRSTUVWXYZ1234567890&   555

Century 731/Text — Textype Roman

abcdefghijklmnopqrstuvwxyzABCDEFGHIJKLMNOPQRSTUVWXY1234567890&   556

Century 731 Italic/Text — Textype Italic

abcdefghijklmnopqrstuvwxyzABCDEFGHIJKLMNOPQRSTUVWXYZ1234567890&   557

Century 731 Bold/Text — Textype Bold

abcdefghijklmnopqrstuvwxyzABCDEFGHIJKLMNOPQRSTUVWX1234567890&   558

Century 731 Bold Italic/Text — Textype Bold Italic

abcdefghijklmnopqrstuvwxyzABCDEFGHIJKLMNOPQRSTUVWXYZ1234567890&   559

Page

New Aster Roman
abcdefghijklmnopqrstuvwxyzABCDEFGHIJKLMNOPQRSTUVWXYZ1234567890& 560

New Aster Italic
abcdefghijklmnopqrstuvwxyzABCDEFGHIJKLMNOPQRSTUVWXYZ1234567890& 561

New Aster Semi Bold
abcdefghijklmnopqrstuvwxyzABCDEFGHIJKLMNOPQRSTUVWX1234567890& 562

New Aster Semi Bold Italic
abcdefghijklmnopqrstuvwxyzABCDEFGHIJKLMNOPQRSTUVWXYZ1234567890& 563

New Aster Bold
abcdefghijklmnopqrstuvwxyzABCDEFGHIJKLMNOPQRSTUVW1234567890& 564

New Aster Bold Italic
abcdefghijklmnopqrstuvwxyzABCDEFGHIJKLMNOPQRSTUVWX1234567890& 565

New Aster Black
abcdefghijklmnopqrstuvwxyzABCDEFGHIJKLMNOPQRSTU1234567890& 566

New Aster Black Italic
abcdefghijklmnopqrstuvwxyzABCDEFGHIJKLMNOPQRSTUV1234567890& 567

ITC Berkeley Oldstyle Book
abcdefghijklmnopqrstuvwxyzABCDEFGHIJKLMNOPQRSTUVWXYZ1234567890& 568

ITC Berkeley Oldstyle Book Italic
abcdefghijklmnopqrstuvwxyzABCDEFGHIJKLMNOPQRSTUVWXYZ1234567890& 569

ITC Berkeley Oldstyle Medium
abcdefghijklmnopqrstuvwxyzABCDEFGHIJKLMNOPQRSTUVWXYZ1234567890& 570

ITC Berkeley Oldstyle Medium Italic
abcdefghijklmnopqrstuvwxyzABCDEFGHIJKLMNOPQRSTUVWXYZ1234567890& 571

ITC Berkeley Oldstyle Bold
abcdefghijklmnopqrstuvwxyzABCDEFGHIJKLMNOPQRSTUVWXYZ1234567890& 572

ITC Berkeley Oldstyle Bold Italic
abcdefghijklmnopqrstuvwxyzABCDEFGHIJKLMNOPQRSTUVWXYZ1234567890& 573

ITC Berkeley Oldstyle Black
abcdefghijklmnopqrstuvwxyzABCDEFGHIJKLMNOPQRSTUVWXYZ1234567890& 574

ITC Berkeley Oldstyle Black Italic
abcdefghijklmnopqrstuvwxyzABCDEFGHIJKLMNOPQRSTUVWXYZ1234567890& 575

ITC Galliard Roman
abcdefghijklmnopqrstuvwxyzABCDEFGHIJKLMNOPQRSTUVWXYZ1234567890& 576

ITC Galliard Italic
abcdefghijklmnopqrstuvwxyzABCDEFGHIJKLMNOPQRSTUVWXYZ1234567890& 577

ITC Galliard Bold
abcdefghijklmnopqrstuvwxyzABCDEFGHIJKLMNOPQRSTUVWXYZ123456789 578

ITC Galliard Bold Italic
abcdefghijklmnopqrstuvwxyzABCDEFGHIJKLMNOPQRSTUVWXYZ1234567890&   579

Adobe Garamond Regular
abcdefghijklmnopqrstuvwxyzABCDEFGHIJKLMNOPQRSTUVWXYZ1234567890&   580

Adobe Garamond Italic
abcdefghijklmnopqrstuvwxyzABCDEFGHIJKLMNOPQRSTUVWXYZ1234567890&   581

Adobe Garamond Semi Bold
abcdefghijklmnopqrstuvwxyzABCDEFGHIJKLMNOPQRSTUVWXYZ1234567890&   582

Adobe Garamond Semi Bold Italic
abcdefghijklmnopqrstuvwxyzABCDEFGHIJKLMNOPQRSTUVWXYZ1234567890&   583

Adobe Garamond Bold
abcdefghijklmnopqrstuvwxyzABCDEFGHIJKLMNOPQRSTUVWXYZ1234567890&   584

Adobe Garamond Bold Italic
abcdefghijklmnopqrstuvwxyzABCDEFGHIJKLMNOPQRSTUVWXYZ1234567890&   585

Stempel Garamond Roman
abcdefghijklmnopqrstuvwxyzABCDEFGHIJKLMNOPQRSTUVWXYZ1234567890&   586

Stempel Garamond Italic
abcdefghijklmnopqrstuvwxyzABCDEFGHIJKLMNOPQRSTUVWXYZ1234567890&   587

Stempel Garamond Bold
abcdefghijklmnopqrstuvwxyzABCDEFGHIJKLMNOPQRSTUVWXYZ1234567890&   588

Stempel Garamond Bold Italic
abcdefghijklmnopqrstuvwxyzABCDEFGHIJKLMNOPQRSTUVWXYZ1234567890&   589

Garamond 3 Roman
abcdefghijklmnopqrstuvwxyzABCDEFGHIJKLMNOPQRSTUVWXYZ1234567890&   590

Garamond 3 Italic
abcdefghijklmnopqrstuvwxyzABCDEFGHIJKLMNOPQRSTUVWXYZ1234567890&   591

Garamond 3 Bold
abcdefghijklmnopqrstuvwxyzABCDEFGHIJKLMNOPQRSTUVWXYZ1234567890&   592

Garamond 3 Bold Italic
abcdefghijklmnopqrstuvwxyzABCDEFGHIJKLMNOPQRSTUVWXYZ1234567890&   593

ITC Garamond Light
abcdefghijklmnopqrstuvwxyzABCDEFGHIJKLMNOPQRSTUVWXYZ1234567890&   594

ITC Garamond Light Italic
abcdefghijklmnopqrstuvwxyzABCDEFGHIJKLMNOPQRSTUVWXYZ1234567890&   595

ITC Garamond Bold
abcdefghijklmnopqrstuvwxyzABCDEFGHIJKLMNOPQRSTUVWXYZ1234567890&   596

ITC Garamond Bold Italic
abcdefghijklmnopqrstuvwxyzABCDEFGHIJKLMNOPQRSTUVWXYZ1234567890&   597

Goudy Old Style Roman
abcdefghijklmnopqrstuvwxyzABCDEFGHIJKLMNOPQRSTUVWXYZ1234567890& 598

Goudy Old Style Italic
abcdefghijklmnopqrstuvwxyzABCDEFGHIJKLMNOPQRSTUVWXYZ1234567890& 599

Goudy Bold
abcdefghijklmnopqrstuvwxyzABCDEFGHIJKLMNOPQRSTUVWXYZ1234567890& 600

Goudy Bold Italic
abcdefghijklmnopqrstuvwxyzABCDEFGHIJKLMNOPQRSTUVWXYZ1234567890& 601

Goudy Extra Bold
abcdefghijklmnopqrstuvwxyzABCDEFGHIJKLMNOPQRSTUVWXYZ1234567890& 602

Goudy Heavyface
abcdefghijklmnopqrstuvwxyzABCDEFGHIJKLMNOPQRSTU1234567890& 603

Goudy Heavyface Italic
abcdefghijklmnopqrstuvwxyzABCDEFGHIJKLMNOPQRSTU1234567890& 604

Hiroshige Book
abcdefghijklmnopqrstuvwxyzABCDEFGHIJKLMNOPQRSTUVWXYZ1234567890& 605

Hiroshige Book Italic
abcdefghijklmnopqrstuvwxyzABCDEFGHIJKLMNOPQRSTUVWXYZ1234567890& 606

Hiroshige Medium
abcdefghijklmnopqrstuvwxyzABCDEFGHIJKLMNOPQRSTUVWXY1234567890& 607

Hiroshige Medium Italic
abcdefghijklmnopqrstuvwxyzABCDEFGHIJKLMNOPQRSTUVWXYZ1234567890& 608

Hiroshige Bold
abcdefghijklmnopqrstuvwxyzABCDEFGHIJKLMNOPQRSTUVW1234567890& 609

Hiroshige Bold Italic
abcdefghijklmnopqrstuvwxyzABCDEFGHIJKLMNOPQRSTUVW1234567890& 610

Hiroshige Black
abcdefghijklmnopqrstuvwxyzABCDEFGHIJKLMNOPQRST1234567890& 611

Hiroshige Black Italic
abcdefghijklmnopqrstuvwxyzABCDEFGHIJKLMNOPQRST1234567890& 612

Palatino Roman
abcdefghijklmnopqrstuvwxyzABCDEFGHIJKLMNOPQRSTUVWXYZ1234567890& 613

Palatino Italic
abcdefghijklmnopqrstuvwxyzABCDEFGHIJKLMNOPQRSTUVWXYZ1234567890& 614

Palatino Bold
abcdefghijklmnopqrstuvwxyzABCDEFGHIJKLMNOPQRSTUVWXYZ1234567890& 615

Palatino Bold Italic
abcdefghijklmnopqrstuvwxyzABCDEFGHIJKLMNOPQRSTUVWXYZ1234567890& 616

Sabon Roman
abcdefghijklmnopqrstuvwxyzABCDEFGHIJKLMNOPQRSTUVWXYZ1234567890& 617

Sabon Italic
abcdefghijklmnopqrstuvwxyzABCDEFGHIJKLMNOPQRSTUVWXYZ1234567890& 618

Sabon Bold
abcdefghijklmnopqrstuvwxyzABCDEFGHIJKLMNOPQRSTUVWXYZ1234567890& 619

Sabon Bold Italic
abcdefghijklmnopqrstuvwxyzABCDEFGHIJKLMNOPQRSTUVWXYZ1234567890& 620

Trump Mediaeval Roman
abcdefghijklmnopqrstuvwxyzABCDEFGHIJKLMNOPQRSTUVWXY1234567890& 621

Trump Mediaeval Italic
abcdefghijklmnopqrstuvwxyzABCDEFGHIJKLMNOPQRSTUVWXY1234567890& 622

Trump Mediaeval Bold
abcdefghijklmnopqrstuvwxyzABCDEFGHIJKLMNOPQRSTUVWXY1234567890& 623

Trump Mediaeval Bold Italic
abcdefghijklmnopqrstuvwxyzABCDEFGHIJKLMNOPQRSTUVWX1234567890& 624

Weiss Roman
abcdefghijklmnopqrstuvwxyzABCDEFGHIJKLMNOPQRSTUVWXYZ1234567890& 625

Weiss Italic
abcdefghijklmnopqrstuvwxyzABCDEFGHIJKLMNOPQRSTUVWXYZ1234567890& 626

Weiss Bold
abcdefghijklmnopqrstuvwxyzABCDEFGHIJKLMNOPQRSTUVWXYZ1234567890& 627

Weiss Extra Bold
abcdefghijklmnopqrstuvwxyzABCDEFGHIJKLMNOPQRSTUVWXYZ1234567890& 628

Americana Roman
abcdefghijklmnopqrstuvwxyzABCDEFGHIJKLMNOPQRSTUV1234567890& 629

Americana Italic
abcdefghijklmnopqrstuvwxyzABCDEFGHIJKLMNOPQRSTUV1234567890& 630

Americana Bold
abcdefghijklmnopqrstuvwxyzABCDEFGHIJKLMNOPQRSTUV1234567890& 631

Americana Extra Bold
abcdefghijklmnopqrstuvwxyzABCDEFGHIJKLMNOPQRST1234567890& 632

ITC New Baskerville Roman
abcdefghijklmnopqrstuvwxyzABCDEFGHIJKLMNOPQRSTUVWXYZ1234567890& 633

ITC New Baskerville Italic
abcdefghijklmnopqrstuvwxyzABCDEFGHIJKLMNOPQRSTUVWXYZ1234567890& 634

ITC New Baskerville Bold
abcdefghijklmnopqrstuvwxyzABCDEFGHIJKLMNOPQRSTUVWXYZ1234567890& 635

ITC New Baskerville Bold Italic
abcdefghijklmnopqrstuvwxyzABCDEFGHIJKLMNOPQRSTUVWXYZ1234567890&   636

ITC Bookman Light
abcdefghijklmnopqrstuvwxyzABCDEFGHIJKLMNOPQRSTUVWX1234567890&   637

ITC Bookman Light Italic
abcdefghijklmnopqrstuvwxyzABCDEFGHIJKLMNOPQRSTUVWXY1234567890&   638

ITC Bookman Demi
abcdefghijklmnopqrstuvwxyzABCDEFGHIJKLMNOPQRSTUV1234567890&   639

ITC Bookman Demi Italic
abcdefghijklmnopqrstuvwxyzABCDEFGHIJKLMNOPQRSTU1234567890&   640

Caslon 3 Roman
abcdefghijklmnopqrstuvwxyzABCDEFGHIJKLMNOPQRSTUVW1234567890&   641

Caslon 3 Italic
abcdefghijklmnopqrstuvwxyzABCDEFGHIJKLMNOPQRSTUVWXYZ1234567890&   642

Caslon 540 Roman
abcdefghijklmnopqrstuvwxyzABCDEFGHIJKLMNOPQRSTUVWXYZ1234567890&   643

Caslon 540 Italic
abcdefghijklmnopqrstuvwxyzABCDEFGHIJKLMNOPQRSTUVWXYZ1234567890&   644

Caslon Open Face
abcdefghijklmnopqrstuvwxyzABCDEFGHIJKLMNOPQRSTUVWXYZ1234567890&   645

Century Old Style Roman
abcdefghijklmnopqrstuvwxyzABCDEFGHIJKLMNOPQRSTUVWXYZ1234567890&   646

Century Old Style Italic
abcdefghijklmnopqrstuvwxyzABCDEFGHIJKLMNOPQRSTUVWXYZ1234567890&   647

Century Old Style Bold
abcdefghijklmnopqrstuvwxyzABCDEFGHIJKLMNOPQRSTUVWX1234567890&   648

ITC Clearface Regular
abcdefghijklmnopqrstuvwxyzABCDEFGHIJKLMNOPQRSTUVWXYZ1234567890&   649

ITC Clearface Regular Italic
abcdefghijklmnopqrstuvwxyzABCDEFGHIJKLMNOPQRSTUVWXYZ1234567890&   650

ITC Clearface Bold
abcdefghijklmnopqrstuvwxyzABCDEFGHIJKLMNOPQRSTUVWXYZ1234567890&   651

ITC Clearface Bold Italic
abcdefghijklmnopqrstuvwxyzABCDEFGHIJKLMNOPQRSTUVWXYZ1234567890&   652

ITC Clearface Heavy
abcdefghijklmnopqrstuvwxyzABCDEFGHIJKLMNOPQRSTUVWXYZ1234567890&   653

ITC Clearface Heavy Italic
abcdefghijklmnopqrstuvwxyzABCDEFGHIJKLMNOPQRSTUVWXYZ1234567890&   654

ITC Clearface Black
abcdefghijklmnopqrstuvwxyzABCDEFGHIJKLMNOPQRSTUVWXYZ1234567890&   655

ITC Clearface Black Italic
abcdefghijklmnopqrstuvwxyzABCDEFGHIJKLMNOPQRSTUVWXYZ1234567890&   656

Cochin Roman
abcdefghijklmnopqrstuvwxyzABCDEFGHIJKLMNOPQRSTUVWXYZ1234567890&   657

Cochin Italic
abcdefghijklmnopqrstuvwxyzABCDEFGHIJKLMNOPQRSTUVWXYZ1234567890&   658

Cochin Bold
abcdefghijklmnopqrstuvwxyzABCDEFGHIJKLMNOPQRSTUVWXYZ1234567890&   659

Cochin Bold Italic
abcdefghijklmnopqrstuvwxyzABCDEFGHIJKLMNOPQRSTUVWXYZ1234567890&   660

Concorde Roman
abcdefghijklmnopqrstuvwxyzABCDEFGHIJKLMNOPQRSTUVWXY1234567890&   661

Concorde Italic
abcdefghijklmnopqrstuvwxyzABCDEFGHIJKLMNOPQRSTUVWX1234567890&   662

Concorde Bold
abcdefghijklmnopqrstuvwxyzABCDEFGHIJKLMNOPQRSTUVWX1234567890&   663

Concorde Bold Italic
abcdefghijklmnopqrstuvwxyzABCDEFGHIJKLMNOPQRSTUVWXY1234567890&   664

Janson Text Roman
abcdefghijklmnopqrstuvwxyzABCDEFGHIJKLMNOPQRSTUVWXYZ1234567890&   665

Janson Text Italic
abcdefghijklmnopqrstuvwxyzABCDEFGHIJKLMNOPQRSTUVWXYZ1234567890&   666

Janson Text Bold
abcdefghijklmnopqrstuvwxyzABCDEFGHIJKLMNOPQRSTUVWXY1234567890&   667

Janson Text Bold Italic
abcdefghijklmnopqrstuvwxyzABCDEFGHIJKLMNOPQRSTUVWXYZ1234567890&   668

Life Roman
abcdefghijklmnopqrstuvwxyzABCDEFGHIJKLMNOPQRSTUVWXYZ1234567890&   669

Life Italic
abcdefghijklmnopqrstuvwxyzABCDEFGHIJKLMNOPQRSTUVWXYZ1234567890&   670

Life Bold
abcdefghijklmnopqrstuvwxyzABCDEFGHIJKLMNOPQRSTUVWXYZ1234567890&   671

Meridien Roman
abcdefghijklmnopqrstuvwxyzABCDEFGHIJKLMNOPQRSTUVWXYZ1234567890&   672

Meridien Italic
abcdefghijklmnopqrstuvwxyzABCDEFGHIJKLMNOPQRSTUVWXYZ1234567890&   673

Meridien Medium
abcdefghijklmnopqrstuvwxyzABCDEFGHIJKLMNOPQRSTUVWXYZ1234567890& 674

Meridien Medium Italic
abcdefghijklmnopqrstuvwxyzABCDEFGHIJKLMNOPQRSTUVWXYZ1234567890& 675

Meridien Bold
abcdefghijklmnopqrstuvwxyzABCDEFGHIJKLMNOPQRSTUVW1234567890& 676

Meridien Bold Italic
abcdefghijklmnopqrstuvwxyzABCDEFGHIJKLMNOPQRSTUVWXYZ1234567890& 677

Stone Serif Medium
abcdefghijklmnopqrstuvwxyzABCDEFGHIJKLMNOPQRSTUVWXYZ1234567890& 678

Stone Serif Medium Italic
abcdefghijklmnopqrstuvwxyzABCDEFGHIJKLMNOPQRSTUVWXYZ1234567890& 679

Stone Serif Semi Bold
abcdefghijklmnopqrstuvwxyzABCDEFGHIJKLMNOPQRSTUVWX1234567890& 680

Stone Serif Semi Bold Italic
abcdefghijklmnopqrstuvwxyzABCDEFGHIJKLMNOPQRSTUVWXY1234567890& 681

Stone Serif Bold
abcdefghijklmnopqrstuvwxyzABCDEFGHIJKLMNOPQRST1234567890& 682

Stone Serif Bold Italic
abcdefghijklmnopqrstuvwxyzABCDEFGHIJKLMNOPQRSTU1234567890& 683

ITC Tiffany Medium
abcdefghijklmnopqrstuvwxyzABCDEFGHIJKLMNOPQRSTUVW1234567890& 684

ITC Tiffany Medium Italic
abcdefghijklmnopqrstuvwxyzABCDEFGHIJKLMNOPQRSTUVW1234567890& 685

ITC Tiffany Demi
abcdefghijklmnopqrstuvwxyzABCDEFGHIJKLMNOPQRSTUVW1234567890& 686

ITC Tiffany Demi Italic
abcdefghijklmnopqrstuvwxyzABCDEFGHIJKLMNOPQRSTUV1234567890& 687

ITC Tiffany Heavy
abcdefghijklmnopqrstuvwxyzABCDEFGHIJKLMNOP1234567890& 688

ITC Tiffany Heavy Italic
abcdefghijklmnopqrstuvwxyzABCDEFGHIJKLMNO1234567890& 689

Times Roman (10pt.)
abcdefghijklmnopqrstuvwxyzABCDEFGHIJKLMNOPQRSTUVWXYZ1234567890& 690

Times Italic (10pt.)
abcdefghijklmnopqrstuvwxyzABCDEFGHIJKLMNOPQRSTUVWXYZ1234567890& 691

Times Bold (10pt.)
abcdefghijklmnopqrstuvwxyzABCDEFGHIJKLMNOPQRSTUVWXYZ1234567890& 692

Times Bold Italic (10pt.)
abcdefghijklmnopqrstuvwxyzABCDEFGHIJKLMNOPQRSTUVWXYZ1234567890& 693

Bauer Bodoni Roman
abcdefghijklmnopqrstuvwxyzABCDEFGHIJKLMNOPQRSTUVWXYZ1234567890& 694

Bauer Bodoni Italic
abcdefghijklmnopqrstuvwxyzABCDEFGHIJKLMNOPQRSTUVWXYZ1234567890& 695

Bauer Bodoni Bold
abcdefghijklmnopqrstuvwxyzABCDEFGHIJKLMNOPQRSTUVWXYZ1234567890& 696

Bauer Bodoni Bold Italic
abcdefghijklmnopqrstuvwxyzABCDEFGHIJKLMNOPQRSTUVWXYZ1234567890& 697

Bodoni Roman
abcdefghijklmnopqrstuvwxyzABCDEFGHIJKLMNOPQRSTUVWXYZ1234567890& 698

Bodoni Italic
abcdefghijklmnopqrstuvwxyzABCDEFGHIJKLMNOPQRSTUVWXYZ1234567890& 699

Bodoni Bold
abcdefghijklmnopqrstuvwxyzABCDEFGHIJKLMNOPQRSTUVWXYZ1234567890& 700

Bodoni Bold Italic
abcdefghijklmnopqrstuvwxyzABCDEFGHIJKLMNOPQRSTUVWXYZ1234567890& 701

Poster Bodoni Black
abcdefghijklmnopqrstuvwxyzABCDEFGHIJKLMNOPQR1234567890& 702

New Caledonia Roman
abcdefghijklmnopqrstuvwxyzABCDEFGHIJKLMNOPQRSTUVWXYZ1234567890& 703

New Caledonia Italic
abcdefghijklmnopqrstuvwxyzABCDEFGHIJKLMNOPQRSTUVWXYZ1234567890& 704

New Caledonia Semi Bold
abcdefghijklmnopqrstuvwxyzABCDEFGHIJKLMNOPQRSTUVWXYZ1234567890& 705

New Caledonia Semi Bold Italic
abcdefghijklmnopqrstuvwxyzABCDEFGHIJKLMNOPQRSTUVWXYZ1234567890& 706

New Caledonia Bold
abcdefghijklmnopqrstuvwxyzABCDEFGHIJKLMNOPQRSTUVWXYZ1234567890& 707

New Caledonia Bold Italic
abcdefghijklmnopqrstuvwxyzABCDEFGHIJKLMNOPQRSTUVWXYZ1234567890& 708

New Caledonia Black
abcdefghijklmnopqrstuvwxyzABCDEFGHIJKLMNOPQRSTUVW1234567890& 709

New Caledonia Black Italic
abcdefghijklmnopqrstuvwxyzABCDEFGHIJKLMNOPQRSTUVW1234567890& 710

Linotype Centennial 45 Light
abcdefghijklmnopqrstuvwxyzABCDEFGHIJKLMNOPQRSTUVWXYZ1234567890& 711

Linotype Centennial 46 Light Italic
abcdefghijklmnopqrstuvwxyzABCDEFGHIJKLMNOPQRSTUVWXYZ1234567890& 712

Linotype Centennial 55 Roman
abcdefghijklmnopqrstuvwxyzABCDEFGHIJKLMNOPQRSTUVWXYZ1234567890& 713

Linotype Centennial 56 Italic
abcdefghijklmnopqrstuvwxyzABCDEFGHIJKLMNOPQRSTUVWXYZ1234567890& 714

Linotype Centennial 75 Bold
abcdefghijklmnopqrstuvwxyzABCDEFGHIJKLMNOPQRSTUVWX1234567890& 715

Linotype Centennial 76 Bold Italic
abcdefghijklmnopqrstuvwxyzABCDEFGHIJKLMNOPQRSTUVWXY1234567890& 716

Linotype Centennial 95 Black
abcdefghijklmnopqrstuvwxyzABCDEFGHIJKLMNOPQRSTUVWXY1234567890& 717

Linotype Centennial 96 Black Italic
abcdefghijklmnopqrstuvwxyzABCDEFGHIJKLMNOPQRSTUVWXY1234567890& 718

Century Expanded Roman
abcdefghijklmnopqrstuvwxyzABCDEFGHIJKLMNOPQRSTUVWXYZ1234567890& 719

Century Expanded Italic
abcdefghijklmnopqrstuvwxyzABCDEFGHIJKLMNOPQRSTUVWXYZ1234567890& 720

New Century Schoolbook Roman
abcdefghijklmnopqrstuvwxyzABCDEFGHIJKLMNOPQRSTUVWXY1234567890& 721

New Century Schoolbook Italic
abcdefghijklmnopqrstuvwxyzABCDEFGHIJKLMNOPQRSTUVWXY1234567890& 722

New Century Schoolbook Bold
abcdefghijklmnopqrstuvwxyzABCDEFGHIJKLMNOPQRSTU1234567890& 723

New Century Schoolbook Bold Italic
abcdefghijklmnopqrstuvwxyzABCDEFGHIJKLMNOPQRSTUV1234567890& 724

Utopia Regular
abcdefghijklmnopqrstuvwxyzABCDEFGHIJKLMNOPQRSTUVWXYZ1234567890& 725

Utopia Italic
abcdefghijklmnopqrstuvwxyzABCDEFGHIJKLMNOPQRSTUVWXYZ1234567890& 726

Utopia Semi Bold
abcdefghijklmnopqrstuvwxyzABCDEFGHIJKLMNOPQRSTUVWXYZ1234567890& 727

Utopia Semi Bold Itaic
abcdefghijklmnopqrstuvwxyzABCDEFGHIJKLMNOPQRSTUVWXYZ1234567890& 728

Utopia Bold
abcdefghijklmnopqrstuvwxyzABCDEFGHIJKLMNOPQRSTUVWXYZ1234567890& 729

Utopia Bold Italic
abcdefghijklmnopqrstuvwxyzABCDEFGHIJKLMNOPQRSTUVWXYZ1234567890& 730

Utopia Black
abcdefghijklmnopqrstuvwxyzABCDEFGHIJKLMNOPQRSTUVW1234567890& 731

Walbaum Roman
abcdefghijklmnopqrstuvwxyzABCDEFGHIJKLMNOPQRSTUVWXYZ1234567890& 732

Walbaum Italic
abcdefghijklmnopqrstuvwxyzABCDEFGHIJKLMNOPQRSTUVWXYZ1234567890& 733

Walbaum Bold
abcdefghijklmnopqrstuvwxyzABCDEFGHIJKLMNOPQRSTUV1234567890& 734

Walbaum Bold Italic
abcdefghijklmnopqrstuvwxyzABCDEFGHIJKLMNOPQRSTUV1234567890& 735

Aachen Bold
abcdefghijklmnopqrstuvwxyzABCDEFGHIJKLMNOPQRSTUVI1234567890G 736

ITC American Typewriter Medium
abcdefghijklmnopqrstuvwxyzABCDEFGHIJKLMNOPQRSTUVW1234567890& 737

ITC American Typewriter Bold
abcdefghijklmnopqrstuvwxyzABCDEFGHIJKLMNOPQRSTU1234567890& 738

Candida Roman
abcdefghijklmnopqrstuvwxyzABCDEFGHIJKLMNOPQRSTUVWXY1234567890& 739

Candida Italic
abcdefghijklmnopqrstuvwxyzABCDEFGHIJKLMNOPQRSTUVWXY1234567890& 740

Candida Bold
abcdefghijklmnopqrstuvwxyzABCDEFGHIJKLMNOPQRSTUVWX1234567890& 741

ITC Cheltenham Book
abcdefghijklmnopqrstuvwxyzABCDEFGHIJKLMNOPQRSTUVWXYZ1234567890& 742

ITC Cheltenham Book Italic
abcdefghijklmnopqrstuvwxyzABCDEFGHIJKLMNOPQRSTUVWXYZ1234567890& 743

ITC Cheltenham Bold
abcdefghijklmnopqrstuvwxyzABCDEFGHIJKLMNOPQRSTUVWXYZ1234567890& 744

ITC Cheltenham Bold Italic
abcdefghijklmnopqrstuvwxyzABCDEFGHIJKLMNOPQRSTUVWXYZ1234567890& 745

Clarendon Light
abcdefghijklmnopqrstuvwxyzABCDEFGHIJKLMNOPQRSTUVW1234567890& 746

Clarendon Roman
abcdefghijklmnopqrstuvwxyzABCDEFGHIJKLMNOPQRSTUV1234567890& 747

Clarendon Bold
abcdefghijklmnopqrstuvwxyzABCDEFGHIJKLMNOPQRSTU1234567890& 748

Corona Roman
abcdefghijklmnopqrstuvwxyzABCDEFGHIJKLMNOPQRSTUV1234567890& 749

Corona Italic
abcdefghijklmnopqrstuvwxyzABCDEFGHIJKLMNOPQRSTUVWX1234567890&   750

Corona Bold Face 2
abcdefghijklmnopqrstuvwxyzABCDEFGHIJKLMNOPQRSTUV1234567890&   751

Excelsior Roman
abcdefghijklmnopqrstuvwxyzABCDEFGHIJKLMNOPQRSTUVWX1234567890&   752

Excelsior Italic
abcdefghijklmnopqrstuvwxyzABCDEFGHIJKLMNOPQRSTUVWX1234567890&   753

Excelsior Bold
abcdefghijklmnopqrstuvwxyzABCDEFGHIJKLMNOPQRSTUV1234567890&   754

Glypha Roman
abcdefghijklmnopqrstuvwxyzABCDEFGHIJKLMNOPQRSTUVWXYZ1234567890&   755

Glypha Oblique
abcdefghijklmnopqrstuvwxyzABCDEFGHIJKLMNOPQRSTUVWXYZ1234567890&   756

Glypha Bold
abcdefghijklmnopqrstuvwxyzABCDEFGHIJKLMNOPQRSTUVWXY1234567890&   757

Glypha Bold Oblique
abcdefghijklmnopqrstuvwxyzABCDEFGHIJKLMNOPQRSTUVWXY1234567890&   758

Impressum Roman
abcdefghijklmnopqrstuvwxyzABCDEFGHIJKLMNOPQRSTUV1234567890&   759

Impressum Italic
abcdefghijklmnopqrstuvwxyzABCDEFGHIJKLMNOPQRSTUVW1234567890&   760

Impressum Bold
abcdefghijklmnopqrstuvwxyzABCDEFGHIJKLMNOPQRSTUV1234567890&   761

ITC Italia Book
abcdefghijklmnopqrstuvwxyzABCDEFGHIJKLMNOPQRSTUVWXYZ1234567890&   762

ITC Italia Medium
abcdefghijklmnopqrstuvwxyzABCDEFGHIJKLMNOPQRSTUVWXYZ1234567890&   763

ITC Italia Bold
abcdefghijklmnopqrstuvwxyzABCDEFGHIJKLMNOPQRSTUVWXYZ1234567890&   764

ITC Lubalin Graph Book
abcdefghijklmnopqrstuvwxyzABCDEFGHIJKLMNOPQRSTUVWXY1234567890&   765

ITC Lubalin Graph Book Oblique
abcdefghijklmnopqrstuvwxyzABCDEFGHIJKLMNOPQRSTUVWXY1234567890&   766

ITC Lubalin Graph Demi
abcdefghijklmnopqrstuvwxyzABCDEFGHIJKLMNOPQRSTUVWXY1234567890&   767

ITC Lubalin Graph Demi Oblique
abcdefghijklmnopqrstuvwxyzABCDEFGHIJKLMNOPQRSTUVWXY1234567890&   768

Melior Roman

abcdefghijklmnopqrstuvwxyzABCDEFGHIJKLMNOPQRSTUVWXYZ1234567890& 769

Melior Italic

abcdefghijklmnopqrstuvwxyzABCDEFGHIJKLMNOPQRSTUVWXYZ1234567890& 770

Melior Bold

abcdefghijklmnopqrstuvwxyzABCDEFGHIJKLMNOPQRSTUVWXYZ1234567890& 771

Melior Bold Italic

abcdefghijklmnopqrstuvwxyzABCDEFGHIJKLMNOPQRSTUVWXY1234567890& 772

Memphis Light

abcdefghijklmnopqrstuvwxyzABCDEFGHIJKLMNOPQRSTUVWXYZ1234567890& 773

Memphis Light Italic

abcdefghijklmnopqrstuvwxyzABCDEFGHIJKLMNOPQRSTUVWXYZ1234567890& 774

Memphis Medium

abcdefghijklmnopqrstuvwxyzABCDEFGHIJKLMNOPQRSTUVWXYZ1234567890& 775

Memphis Medium Italic

abcdefghijklmnopqrstuvwxyzABCDEFGHIJKLMNOPQRSTUVWXYZ1234567890& 776

Memphis Bold

abcdefghijklmnopqrstuvwxyzABCDEFGHIJKLMNOPQRSTUVWXYZ1234567890& 777

Memphis Bold Italic

abcdefghijklmnopqrstuvwxyzABCDEFGHIJKLMNOPQRSTUVWXYZ1234567890& 778

Memphis Extra Bold

abcdefghijklmnopqrstuvwxyzABCDEFGHIJKLMNOPQ1234567890& 779

Prestige Elite Roman

abcdefghijklmnopqrstuvwxyzABCDEFGHIJKLMNOPQRSTUVWXYZ1234567890& 780

Prestige Elite Slanted

abcdefghijklmnopqrstuvwxyzABCDEFGHIJKLMNOPQRSTUVWXYZ1234567890& 781

Prestige Elite Bold

abcdefghijklmnopqrstuvwxyzABCDEFGHIJKLMNOPQRSTUVWXYZ1234567890& 782

Prestige Elite Bold Slanted

abcdefghijklmnopqrstuvwxyzABCDEFGHIJKLMNOPQRSTUVWXYZ1234567890& 783

Serifa 45 Light

abcdefghijklmnopqrstuvwxyzABCDEFGHIJKLMNOPQRSTUVWXYZ1234567890& 784

Serifa 46 Light Italic

abcdefghijklmnopqrstuvwxyzABCDEFGHIJKLMNOPQRSTUVWXYZ1234567890& 785

Serifa 55 Roman

abcdefghijklmnopqrstuvwxyzABCDEFGHIJKLMNOPQRSTUVWXYZ1234567890& 786

Serifa 56 Italic

abcdefghijklmnopqrstuvwxyzABCDEFGHIJKLMNOPQRSTUVWXYZ1234567890& 787

Serifa 65 Bold

abcdefghijklmnopqrstuvwxyzABCDEFGHIJKLMNOPQRSTUVWX1234567890& 788

Serifa 75 Black

abcdefghijklmnopqrstuvwxyzABCDEFGHIJKLMNOPQRSTUVW1234567890& 789

Serif

Old Face
Transitional
Modern Face
Slab Serif

Typeface Library
Bitstream Fonts   74
Linotype Fonts   560

ABCDEFGHIJKL
MNOPQRSTU
VWXYZ
abcdefghijklmnopq
rstuvwxyz
1234567890&$¢£¥
fiflæœÆŒÅßÇÌÎÍÏã
§†-–—/()''""'.,!¡?¿

10/11

In our house we had a cat with the grandiose name of Gonnosuke. Usually with cats and dogs we know who the mother is but not the father. A cat with a large belly wondered into the house of m y younger sister and her husband and gave birth to five kittens. While the mother was a pure whit e thoroughbred Chinchila, the kittens were black and white tabbies of mixed breed. One of these came to our house about two weeks after its birth and was given the name Gonnosuke. At that ti me we already had one female Shiba dog and one female brown tabby cat in our house comprisi

16/17

In our house we had a cat with the grandiose name of Gonn osuke. Usually with cats and dogs we know who the mother is but not the father. A cat with a large belly wondered into t he house of my younger sister and her husband and gave birt

24/25

In our house we had a cat with the gran diose name of Gonnosuke. Usually with cats and dogs we know who the mother

ABCDEFGHIJKLM NOPQRSTUVWXYZ abcdefghijklmnopq rstuvwxyz 1234567890&$¢£¥ fiflæœÆŒÅßÇÌÎÍÏã §†-–—/()''""":;.,!¡?¿

10/11

In our house we had a cat with the grandiose name of Gonnosuke. Usually with cats and dogs we k now who the mother is but not the father. A cat with a large belly wondered into the house of my yo unger sister and her husband and gave birth to five kittens. While the mother was a pure white thoro ughbred Chinchila, the kittens were black and white tabbies of mixed breed. One of these came to ou r house about two weeks after its birth and was given the name Gonnosuke. At that time we already had one female Shiba dog and one female brown tabby cat in our house comprising only 13 thubo.

16/17

In our house we had a cat with the grandiose name of Gonnos uke. Usually with cats and dogs we know who the mother is b ut not the father. A cat with a large belly wondered into the ho use of my younger sister and her husband and gave birth to fiv

24/25

In our house we had a cat with the grand iose name of Gonnosuke. Usually with ca ts and dogs we know who the mother is b

Like **Aster Bold**

ABCDEFGHIJKL MNOPQRSTU VWXYZ abcdefghijklmnopq rstuvwxyz 1234567890&$¢£¥ fiflæœÆŒÅßÇÌÎÍÏ ã§†-–—/()''""";.,!¡?¿

10/11

In our house we had a cat with the grandiose name of Gonnosuke. Usually with cats and dogs w e know who the mother is but not the father. A cat with a large belly wondered into the house of my younger sister and her husband and gave birth to five kittens. While the mother was a pure white thoroughbred Chinchila, the kittens were black and white tabbies of mixed breed. One of t hese came to our house about two weeks after its birth and was given the name Gonnosuke. At t hat time we already had one female Shiba dog and one female brown tabby cat in our house com

16/17

In our house we had a cat with the grandiose name of Gonn osuke. Usually with cats and dogs we know who the mother is but not the father. A cat with a large belly wondered into t he house of my younger sister and her husband and gave bir

24/25

In our house we had a cat with the gran diose name of Gonnosuke. Usually with cats and dogs we know who the mother

Like **Aster Bold Italic**

ABCDEFGHIJKL MNOPQRSTU VWXYZ
abcdefghijklmnopq rstuvwxyz
1234567890&$¢£¥ fiflæœÆŒÅßÇÌÎÍÏã §†----/()''""";.,!¡?¿

10/11

In our house we had a cat with the grandiose name of Gonnosuke. Usually with cats and dogs we know who the mother is but not the father. A cat with a large belly wondered into the house of my younger sister and her husband and gave birth to five kittens. While the mother was a pu re white thoroughbred Chinchila, the kittens were black and white tabbies of mixed breed. One o f these came to our house about two weeks after its birth and was given the name Gonnosuke. A t that time we already had one female Shiba dog and one female brown tabby cat in our house

16/17

In our house we had a cat with the grandiose name of Gon nosuke. Usually with cats and dogs we know who the mothe r is but not the father. A cat with a large belly wondered int o the house of my younger sister and her husband and gave

24/25

In our house we had a cat with the gra ndiose name of Gonnosuke. Usually wit h cats and dogs we know who the moth

ABCDEFGHIJK
LMNOPQRSTU
VWXYZ
abcdefghijklmnopq
rstuvwxyz
1234567890&$¢£¥
fiflæœÆŒÅßÇÌÎÍÏã§†
–——/()''""":;.,!¡?¿

10/11

In our house we had a cat with the grandiose name of Gonnosuke. Usually with cats and dogs we know who t he mother is but not the father. A cat with a large belly wondered into the house of my younger sister and her husband and gave birth to five kittens. While the mother was a pure white thoroughbred Chinchila, the kitten s were black and white tabbies of mixed breed. One of these came to our house about two weeks after its birth and was given the name Gonnosuke. At that time we already had one female Shiba dog and one female brown tabby cat in our house comprising only 13 thubo. The dog was called Momo and the cat Mii. My wife, who w

16/17

In our house we had a cat with the grandiose name of Gonnosuke. Usually with cats and dogs we know who the mother is but not the f ather. A cat with a large belly wondered into the house of my young er sister and her husband and gave birth to five kittens. While the m

24/25

In our house we had a cat with the grandiose name of Gonnosuke. Usually with cats and d ogs we know who the mother is but not the f

ABCDEFGHIJK LMNOPQRSTU VWXYZ

abcdefghijklmnopq rstuvwxyz

1234567890&$¢£¥ fiflæœÆŒÅßÇÌÎÍÏã§† –——/()''""".;.,!¡?¿

10/11

In our house we had a cat with the grandiose name of Gonnosuke. Usually with cats and dogs we know who the mother is b ut not the father. A cat with a large belly wondered into the house of my younger sister and her husband and gave birth to five kittens. While the mother was a pure white thoroughbred Chinchila, the kittens were black and white tabbies of mixed breed. One of these came to our house about two weeks after its birth and was given the name Gonnosuke. At that time we already had one female Shiba dog and one female brown tabby cat in our house comprising only 13 thubo. The dog was called Momo and the cat Mii. My wife, who was very much opposed to keeping cats and dogs, instantaneously fell for its shaggy appearance

16/17

In our house we had a cat with the grandiose name of Gonnosuke. Usually w ith cats and dogs we know who the mother is but not the father. A cat with a l arge belly wondered into the house of my younger sister and her husband and g ave birth to five kittens. While the mother was a pure white thoroughbred Ch

24/25

In our house we had a cat with the grandiose name of Gonnosuke. Usually with cats and dogs we kno w who the mother is but not the father. A cat with a

Like **Bembo Bold**

ABCDEFGHIJK LMNOPQRSTU VWXYZ

abcdefghijklmnopq rstuvwxyz

1234567890&$¢£¥

fiflæœÆŒÅßÇÌÎÍÏã

§†-–—/()''""".;.,!¡?¿

10/11

In our house we had a cat with the grandiose name of Gonnosuke. Usually with cats and dogs we k now who the mother is but not the father. A cat with a large belly wondered into the house of my y ounger sister and her husband and gave birth to five kittens. While the mother was a pure white th oroughbred Chinchila, the kittens were black and white tabbies of mixed breed. One of these cam e to our house about two weeks after its birth and was given the name Gonnosuke. At that time we already had one female Shiba dog and one female brown tabby cat in our house comprising only 1

16/17

In our house we had a cat with the grandiose name of Gonno suke. Usually with cats and dogs we know who the mother is but not the father. A cat with a large belly wondered into the house of my younger sister and her husband and gave birth to

24/25

In our house we had a cat with the grand iose name of Gonnosuke. Usually with ca ts and dogs we know who the mother is b

ABCDEFGHIJK LMNOPQRSTU VWXYZ

abcdefghijklmnopq rstuvwxyz 1234567890&$¢£¥ fiflæœÆŒÅßÇÌÎÍÏã§ †-–—/()''""".;.,!¡?¿

10/11

In our house we had a cat with the grandiose name of Gonnosuke. Usually with cats and dogs we know who the mother is but not the father. A cat with a large belly wondered into the house of my younger sister and her husban d and gave birth to five kittens. While the mother was a pure white thoroughbred Chinchila, the kittens were bla ck and white tabbies of mixed breed. One of these came to our house about two weeks after its birth and was given the name Gonnosuke. At that time we already had one female Shiba dog and one female brown tabby cat in our h ouse comprising only 13 thubo. The dog was called Momo and the cat Mii. My wife, who was very much opposed

16/17

In our house we had a cat with the grandiose name of Gonnosuke. Us ually with cats and dogs we know who the mother is but not the father. A cat with a large belly wondered into the house of my younger sister a nd her husband and gave birth to five kittens. While the mother was a

24/25

In our house we had a cat with the grandiose n ame of Gonnosuke. Usually with cats and dogs we know who the mother is but not the father.

81

ABCDEFGHIJKLMNO
PQRSTUVWXYZ
abcdefghijklmnopq
rstuvwxyz
1234567890&$¢£¥
fiflæœÆŒÅßÇÌÎÍÏã§†
——/()''""":;.,!¡?¿

10/11

In our house we had a cat with the grandiose name of Gonnosuke. Usually with cats and dogs we know who the m other is but not the father. A cat with a large belly wondered into the house of my younger sister and her husband a nd gave birth to five kittens. While the mother was a pure white thoroughbred Chinchila, the kittens were black an d white tabbies of mixed breed. One of these came to our house about two weeks after its birth and was given the n ame Gonnosuke. At that time we already had one female Shiba dog and one female brown tabby cat in our house c omprising only 13 tubo. The dog was called Momo and the cat Mii. My wife, who was very much opposed to keepi

16/17

In our house we had a cat with the grandiose name of Gonnosuke. Usu ally with cats and dogs we know who the mother is but not the father. A cat with a large belly wondered into the house of my younger sister and her husband and gave birth to five kittens. While the mother was a pure

24/25

In our house we had a cat with the grandiose na me of Gonnosuke. Usually with cats and dogs we know who the mother is but not the father.

ABCDEFGHIJKLMNO

PQRSTUVWXYZ

abcdefghijklmnopq

rstuvwxyz

1234567890&$¢£¥

fiflæœÆŒÅßÇÌÎÍÏã§†

——/()''""":;.,!¡?¿

10/11

In our house we had a cat with the grandiose name of Gonnosuke. Usually with cats and dogs we know who the mother is but not the father. A cat with a large belly wondered into the house of my younger sister and her husband and gave birth to five kitt ens. While the mother was a pure white thoroughbred Chinchila, the kittens were black and white tabbies of mixed breed. One of these came to our house about two weeks after its birth and was given the name Gonnosuke. At that time we already had on e female Shiba dog and one female brown tabby cat in our house comprising only 13 tubo. The dog was called Momo and the cat Mii. My wife, who was very much opposed to keeping cats and dogs, instantaneously fell for its shaggy appearance and the

16/17

In our house we had a cat with the grandiose name of Gonnosuke. Usuall y with cats and dogs we know who the mother is but not the father. A cat with a large belly wondered into the house of my younger sister and her hu sband and gave birth to five kittens. While the mother was a pure white th

24/25

In our house we had a cat with the grandiose name of Gonnosuke. Usually with cats and dogs we know who the mother is but not the father. A cat with a la

ABCDEFGHIJKLMNO
PQRSTUVWXYZ
abcdefghijklmnopq
rstuvwxyz
1234567890&$¢£¥
fiflæœÆŒÅßÇÌÎÍÏã§†
——/()''""":;.,!¡?¿

10/11

In our house we had a cat with the grandiose name of Gonnosuke. Usually with cats and dogs we know who the mother is but not the father. A cat with a large belly wondered into the house of my younger sister and her husband and gave birth to five kittens. While the mother was a pure white thoroughbred Chinchila, the kittens were black and white tabbies of mixed breed. One of these came to our house about two weeks after its birth and was given the name Gonnosuke. At that time we already had one female Shiba dog and one female brown tabby cat in our house comprising only 13 tubo. The dog was called Momo and the cat Mii. My wife, who was very much

16/17

In our house we had a cat with the grandiose name of Gonnosuke. Us ually with cats and dogs we know who the mother is but not the fathe r. A cat with a large belly wondered into the house of my younger siste r and her husband and gave birth to five kittens. While the mother wa

24/25

In our house we had a cat with the grandiose name of Gonnosuke. Usually with cats and do gs we know who the mother is but not the fath

ABCDEFGHIJKLMNO
PQRSTUVWXYZ
abcdefghijklmnopq
rstuvwxyz
1234567890&$¢£¥
fiflæœÆŒÅßÇÌÎÍÏã§†
———/()''""".;.,!¡?¿

10/11

In our house we had a cat with the grandiose name of Gonnosuke. Usually with cats and dogs we know who the mother is but not the father. A cat with a large belly wondered into the house of my younger sister and her husband and gave bir th to five kittens. While the mother was a pure white thoroughbred Chinchila, the kittens were black and white tabbies of mixed breed. One of these came to our house about two weeks after its birth and was given the name Gonnosuke. At that time we already had one female Shiba dog and one female brown tabby cat in our house comprising only 13 tubo. The do g was called Momo and the cat Mii. My wife, who was very much opposed to keeping cats and dogs, instantaneously fell

16/17

In our house we had a cat with the grandiose name of Gonnosuke. Usually with cats and dogs we know who the mother is but not the father. A cat wit h a large belly wondered into the house of my younger sister and her husba nd and gave birth to five kittens. While the mother was a pure white thorou

24/25

In our house we had a cat with the grandiose nam e of Gonnosuke. Usually with cats and dogs we kn ow who the mother is but not the father. A cat wit

ABCDEFGHIJKLMNO
PQRSTUVWXYZ
abcdefghijklmnopq
rstuvwxyz
1234567890&$¢£¥
fiflæœÆŒÅßÇÌÎÍÏã§†
——/()''""":;.,!¡?¿

10/11

In our house we had a cat with the grandiose name of Gonnosuke. Usually with cats and dogs we know who the mother is but not the father. A cat with a large belly wondered into the house of my younger sister and her husband and gave birth to five kittens. While the mother was a pure white thoroughbred Chinchila, the kittens were black and white tabbies of mixed breed. One of these came to our house about two weeks after its birth and was given the name Gonnosuke. At that time we already had one female Shiba dog and one female brown tabby cat in our house comprising only 13 tubo. The dog was called Momo and the cat Mii. My wife, w

16/17

In our house we had a cat with the grandiose name of Gonnosuke. Usually with cats and dogs we know who the mother is but not the father. A cat with a large belly wondered into the house of my younger sister and her husband and gave birth to five kittens. While the

24/25

In our house we had a cat with the grandiose name of Gonnosuke. Usually with cats and dogs we know who the mother is but not the f

ABCDEFGHIJKLMNO
PQRSTUVWXYZ
abcdefghijklmnopq
rstuvwxyz
1234567890&$¢£¥
fiflæœÆŒÅßÇÌÎÍÏã§†
———/()''""":;.,!¡?¿

10/11

In our house we had a cat with the grandiose name of Gonnosuke. Usually with cats and dogs we know who the m
other is but not the father. A cat with a large belly wondered into the house of my younger sister and her husband
and gave birth to five kittens. While the mother was a pure white thoroughbred Chinchila, the kittens were black a
nd white tabbies of mixed breed. One of these came to our house about two weeks after its birth and was given the
name Gonnosuke. At that time we already had one female Shiba dog and one female brown tabby cat in our house
comprising only 13 tubo. The dog was called Momo and the cat Mii. My wife, who was very much opposed to keepi

16/17

In our house we had a cat with the grandiose name of Gonnosuke. Usu
ally with cats and dogs we know who the mother is but not the father. A
cat with a large belly wondered into the house of my younger sister and
her husband and gave birth to five kittens. While the mother was a pur

24/25

In our house we had a cat with the grandiose n
ame of Gonnosuke. Usually with cats and dogs
we know who the mother is but not the father. A

ABCDEFGHIJKLMN
OPQRSTUVWXYZ
abcdefghijklmnopq
rstuvwxyz
1234567890&$¢£¥
fiflæœÆŒÅßÇÌÎÍÏã§
†-——/()''""":;.,!¡?¿

10/11

In our house we had a cat with the grandiose name of Gonnosuke. Usually with cats and dogs we know who the mother is but not the father. A cat with a large belly wondered into the house of my younger sis ter and her husband and gave birth to five kittens. While the mother was a pure white thoroughbred Ch inchila, the kittens were black and white tabbies of mixed breed. One of these came to our house about two weeks after its birth and was given the name Gonnosuke. At that time we already had one female S hiba dog and one female brown tabby cat in our house comprising only 13 tubo. The dog was called Mo

16/17

In our house we had a cat with the grandiose name of Gonnosuk e. Usually with cats and dogs we know who the mother is but no t the father. A cat with a large belly wondered into the house of my younger sister and her husband and gave birth to five kittens

24/25

In our house we had a cat with the grandio se name of Gonnosuke. Usually with cats a nd dogs we know who the mother is but no

ABCDEFGHIJKLMN
OPQRSTUVWXYZ
abcdefghijklmnopq
rstuvwxyz
1234567890&$¢£¥
fiflæœÆŒÅßÇÌÎÍÏã§
†-–—/()''""":;.,!¡?¿

10/11

In our house we had a cat with the grandiose name of Gonnosuke. Usually with cats and dogs we know wh o the mother is but not the father. A cat with a large belly wondered into the house of my younger sister an d her husband and gave birth to five kittens. While the mother was a pure white thoroughbred Chinchila, t he kittens were black and white tabbies of mixed breed. One of these came to our house about two weeks a fter its birth and was given the name Gonnosuke. At that time we already had one female Shiba dog and o ne female brown tabby cat in our house comprising only 13 tubo. The dog was called Momo and the cat M

16/17

In our house we had a cat with the grandiose name of Gonnosuke. Usually with cats and dogs we know who the mother is but not the father. A cat with a large belly wondered into the house of my you nger sister and her husband and gave birth to five kittens. While t

24/25

In our house we had a cat with the grandios e name of Gonnosuke. Usually with cats an d dogs we know who the mother is but not t

ABCDEFGHIJKL
MNOPQRSTUVW
XYZ
abcdefghijklmnopqrst
uvwxyz
1234567890&$¢£¥
fiflæœÆŒÅßÇÌÎÍÏã§
†-–—/()'’“”:;.,!¡?¿

10/11

In our house we had a cat with the grandiose name of Gonnosuke. Usually with cats and dogs we know w
ho the mother is but not the father. A cat with a large belly wondered into the house of my younger sister
and her husband and gave birth to five kittens. While the mother was a pure white thoroughbred Chinchil
a, the kittens were black and white tabbies of mixed breed. One of these came to our house about two w
eeks after its birth and was given the name Gonnosuke. At that time we already had one female Shiba do
g and one female brown tabby cat in our house comprising only 13 tubo. The dog was called Momo and

16/17

In our house we had a cat with the grandiose name of Gonnosuke.
Usually with cats and dogs we know who the mother is but not th
e father. A cat with a large belly wondered into the house of my y
ounger sister and her husband and gave birth to five kittens. Whil

24/25

In our house we had a cat with the grandios
e name of Gonnosuke. Usually with cats an
d dogs we know who the mother is but not

ABCDEFGHIJKL
MNOPQRSTUVW
XYZ
abcdefghijklmnopq
rstuvwxyz
1234567890&$¢£¥
fiflæœÆŒÅßÇÌÎÍÏã§
†-––—/()''""·;·,!¡?¿

10/11

In our house we had a cat with the grandiose name of Gonnosuke. Usually with cats and dogs we know who the mother is but not the father. A cat with a large belly wondered into the house of my younger sister and h er husband and gave birth to five kittens. While the mother was a pure white thoroughbred Chinchila, the k ittens were black and white tabbies of mixed breed. One of these came to our house about two weeks after it s birth and was given the name Gonnosuke. At that time we already had one female Shiba dog and one fem ale brown tabby cat in our house comprising only 13 tubo. The dog was called Momo and the cat Mii. My

16/17

In our house we had a cat with the grandiose name of Gonnosuke. Usually with cats and dogs we know who the mother is but not the father. A cat with a large belly wondered into the house of my youn ger sister and her husband and gave birth to five kittens. While the

24/25

In our house we had a cat with the grandiose name of Gonnosuke. Usually with cats and dogs we know who the mother is but not the

ABCDEFGHIJKL
MNOPQRSTUVW
XYZ
abcdefghijklmnopq
rstuvwxyz
1234567890&$¢£¥
fiflæœÆŒÅßÇÌÎÍÏã
§†-–—/()''""":;.,!¡?¿

10/11

In our house we had a cat with the grandiose name of Gonnosuke. Usually with cats and dogs we know
who the mother is but not the father. A cat with a large belly wondered into the house of my younger si
ster and her husband and gave birth to five kittens. While the mother was a pure white thoroughbred
Chinchila, the kittens were black and white tabbies of mixed breed. One of these came to our house ab
out two weeks after its birth and was given the name Gonnosuke. At that time we already had one fem
ale Shiba dog and one female brown tabby cat in our house comprising only 13 tubo. The dog was calle

16/17

In our house we had a cat with the grandiose name of Gonnosu
ke. Usually with cats and dogs we know who the mother is but n
ot the father. A cat with a large belly wondered into the house of
my younger sister and her husband and gave birth to five kittens

24/25

In our house we had a cat with the grandio
se name of Gonnosuke. Usually with cats a
nd dogs we know who the mother is but n

ABCDEFGHIJKL MNOPQRSTUVW XYZ
abcdefghijklmnopq rstuvwxyz
1234567890&$¢£¥
fiflæœÆŒÅßÇÌÎÍÏã
§†--—/()'’"“”:;.,!¡?¿

10/11

In our house we had a cat with the grandiose name of Gonnosuke. Usually with cats and dogs we kn ow who the mother is but not the father. A cat with a large belly wondered into the house of my youn ger sister and her husband and gave birth to five kittens. While the mother was a pure white thorou ghbred Chinchila, the kittens were black and white tabbies of mixed breed. One of these came to ou r house about two weeks after its birth and was given the name Gonnosuke. At that time we already had one female Shiba dog and one female brown tabby cat in our house comprising only 13 tubo. Th

16/17

In our house we had a cat with the grandiose name of Gonnos uke. Usually with cats and dogs we know who the mother is bu t not the father. A cat with a large belly wondered into the hou se of my younger sister and her husband and gave birth to five

24/25

In our house we had a cat with the grand iose name of Gonnosuke. Usually with ca ts and dogs we know who the mother is b

ABCDEFGHIJKLMN
OPQRSTUVWXYZ
abcdefghijklmnopq
rstuvwxyz
1234567890&$¢£¥
fiflæœÆŒÅßÇÌÎÍÏã§
+-——/()''""":;.,!¡?¿

10/11

In our house we had a cat with the grandiose name of Gonnosuke. Usually with cats and dogs we k now who the mother is but not the father. A cat with a large belly wondered into the house of my y ounger sister and her husband and gave birth to five kittens. While the mother was a pure white tho roughbred Chinchila, the kittens were black and white tabbies of mixed breed. One of these came to o ur house about two weeks after its birth and was given the name Gonnosuke. At that time we alread y had one female Shiba dog and one female brown tabby cat in our house comprising only 13 thub

16/17

In our house we had a cat with the grandiose name of Gonnos uke. Usually with cats and dogs we know who the mother is but not the father. A cat with a large belly wondered into the h ouse of my younger sister and her husband and gave birth to

24/25

In our house we had a cat with the grand iose name of Gonnosuke. Usually with ca ts and dogs we know who the mother is

ABCDEFGHIJKLMNO
PQRSTUVWXYZ
abcdefghijklmnopq
rstuvwxyz
1234567890&$¢£¥
fiflæœÆŒÅßÇÌÎÍÏã§†
——/()''""":;.,!¡?¿

10/11

In our house we had a cat with the grandiose name of Gonnosuke. Usually with cats and dogs we know wh o the mother is but not the father. A cat with a large belly wondered into the house of my younger sister an d her husband and gave birth to five kittens. While the mother was a pure white thoroughbred Chinchila, t he kittens were black and white tabbies of mixed breed. One of these came to our house about two weeks aft er its birth and was given the name Gonnosuke. At that time we already had one female Shiba dog and one female brown tabby cat in our house comprising only 13 thubo. The dog was called Momo and the cat Mii.

16/17

In our house we had a cat with the grandiose name of Gonnosuke. Usually with cats and dogs we know who the mother is but not th e father. A cat with a large belly wondered into the house of my yo unger sister and her husband and gave birth to five kittens. While

24/25

In our house we had a cat with the grandios e name of Gonnosuke. Usually with cats an d dogs we know who the mother is but not t

ABCDEFGHIJKLMN
OPQRSTUVWXYZ
abcdefghijklmnopq
rstuvwxyz
1234567890&$¢£¥
fiflæœÆŒÅßÇÌÎÍÏã§
†---—/()''""":;.,!¡?¿

10/11

In our house we had a cat with the grandiose name of Gonnosuke. Usually with cats and dogs w
e know who the mother is but not the father. A cat with a large belly wondered into the house of
my younger sister and her husband and gave birth to five kittens. While the mother was a pure
white thoroughbred Chinchila, the kittens were black and white tabbies of mixed breed. One of t
hese came to our house about two weeks after its birth and was given the name Gonnosuke. At t
hat time we already had one female Shiba dog and one female brown tabby cat in our house com

16/17

In our house we had a cat with the grandiose name of Gonn
osuke. Usually with cats and dogs we know who the
mother is but not the father. A cat with a large belly
wondered into the house of my younger sister and her

24/25

In our house we had a cat with the gran
diose name of Gonnosuke. Usually with
cats and dogs we know who the mother

ABCDEFGHIJKLMN
OPQRSTUVWXYZ
abcdefghijklmno
pqrstuvwxyz
1234567890&$¢£¥
fiflæœÆŒÅßÇÌÎÍÏã§
+———/()''""":;.,!¡?¿

10/11

In our house we had a cat with the grandiose name of Gonnosuke. Usually with cats and dogs we know who the mother is but not the father. A cat with a large belly wondered into the house of my younger sister and her husband and gave birth to five kittens. While the mother was a pure white thoroughbred Chinchila, the kittens were black and white tabbies of mixed breed. One of these came to our house about two weeks after its birth and was given the name Gonnosuke. At that time we already had one female Shiba dog and one female brown tabby cat in our house comprising only 13 thubo. The dog was

16/17

In our house we had a cat with the grandiose name of Gonnosuke. Usually with cats and dogs we know who the mother is but not the father. A cat with a large belly wondered into the house of my younger sister and her husband and gave birth to five kit

24/25

In our house we had a cat with the grandiose name of Gonnosuke. Usually with cats and dogs we know who the mother is but

ABCDEFGHIJKLM
NOPQRSTUVWXY
Zabcdefghijklmno
pqrstuvwxyz
1234567890&$¢£¥
fiflæœÆŒÅßÇÌÎÍÏ
ã§†-–—/()''""·,.,!¡?¿

10/11

In our house we had a cat with the grandiose name of Gonnosuke. Usually with cats and dogs we know who the mother is but not the father. A cat with a large belly wondered int o the house of my younger sister and her husband and gave birth to five kittens. While th e mother was a pure white thoroughbred Chinchila, the kittens were black and white tab bies of mixed breed. One of these came to our house about two weeks after its birth and was given the name Gonnosuke. At that time we already had one female Shiba dog and o

16/17

In our house we had a cat with the grandiose name of G onnosuke. Usually with cats and dogs we know who the mother is but not the father. A cat with a large belly wo ndered into the house of my younger sister and her hus

24/25

In our house we had a cat with the g randiose name of Gonnosuke. Usuall y with cats and dogs we know who t

ABCDEFGHIJKLM
NOPQRSTUVWXY
Zabcdefghijklmno
pqrstuvwxyz
1234567890&$¢£
¥fiflæœÆŒÅßÇÌÎÍÏ
ã§†----——/()''""'':;.,!¡?¿

10/11

In our house we had a cat with the grandiose name of Gonnosuke. Usually with cats and do gs we know who the mother is but not the father. A cat with a large belly wondered into the house of my younger sister and her husband and gave birth to five kittens. While the mother was a pure white thoroughbred Chinchila, the kittens were black and white tabbies of mixe d breed. One of these came to our house about two weeks after its birth and was given the n ame Gonnosuke. At that time we already had one female Shiba dog and one female brown t

16/17

In our house we had a cat with the grandiose name of Go nnosuke. Usually with cats and dogs we know who the m other is but not the father. A cat with a large belly wonde red into the house of my younger sister and her husband

24/25

In our house we had a cat with the gr andiose name of Gonnosuke. Usually with cats and dogs we know who the

Bitstream Carmina Black

ABCDEFGHIJKLM
NOPQRSTUVWXY
Zabcdefghijklmn
opqrstuvwxyz123
4567890&$¢£¥fifl
æœÆŒÅßÇÌÎÍÏïã§
✝-–—/()''''""":;.,!¡?¿

10/11

In our house we had a cat with the grandiose name of Gonnosuke. Usually with cat
s and dogs we know who the mother is but not the father. A cat with a large belly
wondered into the house of my younger sister and her husband and gave birth to fi
ve kittens. While the mother was a pure white thoroughbred Chinchila, the kittens
were black and white tabbies of mixed breed. One of these came to our house abou
t two weeks after its birth and was given the name Gonnosuke. At that time we alr

16/17

In our house we had a cat with the grandiose name
of Gonnosuke. Usually with cats and dogs we know
who the mother is but not the father. A cat with a
large belly wondered into the house of my younger

24/25

In our house we had a cat with th
e grandiose name of Gonnosuke.
Usually with cats and dogs we kno

ABCDEFGHIJKLM

NOPQRSTUVWX

YZabcdefghijklm

nopqrstuvwxyz

1234567890&$¢

£¥fiflæœÆŒ

ÅßçÌÎÍÏã§†

———/()''''""":;.,!¡?¿

10/11

In our house we had a cat with the grandiose name of Gonnosuke. Usually with cat
s and dogs we know who the mother is but not the father. A cat with a large belly
wondered into the house of my younger sister and her husband and gave birth to fi
ve kittens. While the mother was a pure white thoroughbred Chinchila, the kittens
were black and white tabbies of mixed breed. One of these came to our house abou
t two weeks after its birth and was given the name Gonnosuke. At that time we alr

16/17

In our house we had a cat with the grandiose name
of Gonnosuke. Usually with cats and dogs we know
who the mother is but not the father. A cat with a l
arge belly wondered into the house of my younger si

24/25

In our house we had a cat with th
e grandiose name of Gonnosuke. U
sually with cats and dogs we kno

ABCDEFGHIJKLMN
OPQRSTUVWXYZ
abcdefghijklmnopq
rstuvwxyz
1234567890&$¢£¥
fiflæœÆŒÅßçÌÎÍÏã§†
———/()''""":;.,!¡?¿

10/11

In our house we had a cat with the grandiose name of Gonnosuke. Usually with cats and dogs we know w
ho the mother is but not the father. A cat with a large belly wondered into the house of my younger sister
and her husband and gave birth to five kittens. While the mother was a pure white thoroughbred Chinchil
a, the kittens were black and white tabbies of mixed breed. One of these came to our house about two wee
ks after its birth and was given the name Gonnosuke. At that time we already had one female Shiba dog a
nd one female brown tabby cat in our house comprising only 13 thubo. The dog was called Momo and the

16/17

In our house we had a cat with the grandiose name of Gonnosuke.
Usually with cats and dogs we know who the mother is but not th
e father. A cat with a large belly wondered into the house of my yo
unger sister and her husband and gave birth to five kittens. While

24/25

In our house we had a cat with the grandios
e name of Gonnosuke. Usually with cats an
d dogs we know who the mother is but not

ABCDEFGHIJKLMNOP
QRSTUVWXYZ
abcdefghijklmnopq
rstuvwxyz
1234567890&$¢£¥
fiflæœÆŒÅßÇÌÎÍÏã§†
——/()''""":;.,!¡?¿

10/11

In our house we had a cat with the grandiose name of Gonnosuke. Usually with cats and dogs we know wh o the mother is but not the father. A cat with a large belly wondered into the house of my younger sister an d her husband and gave birth to five kittens. While the mother was a pure white thoroughbred Chinchila, th e kittens were black and white tabbies of mixed breed. One of these came to our house about two weeks afte r its birth and was given the name Gonnosuke. At that time we already had one female Shiba dog and one female brown tabby cat in our house comprising only 13 thubo. The dog was called Momo and the cat Mii.

16/17

In our house we had a cat with the grandiose name of Gonnosuke. Usually with cats and dogs we know who the mother is but not the father. A cat with a large belly wondered into the house of my youn ger sister and her husband and gave birth to five kittens. While th

24/25

In our house we had a cat with the grandios e name of Gonnosuke. Usually with cats an d dogs we know who the mother is but not t

ABCDEFGHIJKLMNO
PQRSTUVWXYZ
abcdefghijklmnopq
rstuvwxyz
1234567890&$¢£¥
fiflæœÆŒÅßÇÌÎÍÏÃ§†
——––/()''""":;.,!¡?¿

10/11

In our house we had a cat with the grandiose name of Gonnosuke. Usually with cats and dogs we kno w who the mother is but not the father. A cat with a large belly wondered into the house of my younger sister and her husband and gave birth to five kittens. While the mother was a pure white thoroughbred Chinchila, the kittens were black and white tabbies of mixed breed. One of these came to our house ab out two weeks after its birth and was given the name Gonnosuke. At that time we already had one fem ale Shiba dog and one female brown tabby cat in our house comprising only 13 thubo. The dog was cal

16/17

In our house we had a cat with the grandiose name of Gonnosu ke. Usually with cats and dogs we know who the mother is but not the father. A cat with a large belly wondered into the house of my younger sister and her husband and gave birth to five kitt

24/25

In our house we had a cat with the grandi ose name of Gonnosuke. Usually with cats and dogs we know who the mother is but

ABCDEFGHIJKLMNO PQRSTUVWXYZ abcdefghijklmnopq rstuvwxyz 1234567890&$¢£¥ fiflœœÆŒÅßÇÌÎÍÏã§† ——/()''""":;.,!¡?¿

10/11

In our house we had a cat with the grandiose name of Gonnosuke. Usually with cats and dogs we kno
w who the mother is but not the father. A cat with a large belly wondered into the house of my younger
sister and her husband and gave birth to five kittens. While the mother was a pure white thoroughbred
Chinchila, the kittens were black and white tabbies of mixed breed. One of these came to our house abo
ut two weeks after its birth and was given the name Gonnosuke. At that time we already had one fema
le Shiba dog and one female brown tabby cat in our house comprising only 13 thubo. The dog was call

16/17

In our house we had a cat with the grandiose name of Gonnosu
ke. Usually with cats and dogs we know who the mother is but
not the father. A cat with a large belly wondered into the house
of my younger sister and her husband and gave birth to five kit

24/25

In our house we had a cat with the grandi
ose name of Gonnosuke. Usually with cats
and dogs we know who the mother is but

ABCDEFGHIJKLMNO
PQRSTUVWXYZ
abcdefghijklmnopq
rstuvwxyz
1234567890&$¢£¥
fiflæœÆŒÅßÇÌÎÍÏã§
†-——/()''""":;.,!¡?¿

10/11

In our house we had a cat with the grandiose name of Gonnosuke. Usually with cats and dogs we know who the mother is but not the father. A cat with a large belly wondered into the house of m y younger sister and her husband and gave birth to five kittens. While the mother was a pure whi te thoroughbred Chinchila, the kittens were black and white tabbies of mixed breed. One of these came to our house about two weeks after its birth and was given the name Gonnosuke. At that ti me we already had one female Shiba dog and one female brown tabby cat in our house comprisin

16/17

In our house we had a cat with the grandiose name of Gonno suke. Usually with cats and dogs we know who the mother is but not the father. A cat with a large belly wondered into the house of my younger sister and her husband and gave

24/25

In our house we had a cat with the gran diose name of Gonnosuke. Usually with cats and dogs we know who the mother

A BCDEFGHIJKLMN

OPQRSTUVWXYZ

abcdefghijklmnopq

rstuvwxyz

1234567890&$¢£¥

fiflæœÆŒÅßÇÌÎÍÏã

§†-–—/()''""":;.,!¡?¿

10/11

In our house we had a cat with the grandiose name of Gonnosuke. Usually with cats and dogs w
e know who the mother is but not the father. A cat with a large belly wondered into the house of
my younger sister and her husband and gave birth to five kittens. While the mother was a pure
white thoroughbred Chinchila, the kittens were black and white tabbies of mixed breed. One of
these came to our house about two weeks after its birth and was given the name Gonnosuke. At
that time we already had one female Shiba dog and one female brown tabby cat in our house co

16/17

In our house we had a cat with the grandiose name of Gonn
osuke. Usually with cats and dogs we know who the mother
is but not the father. A cat with a large belly wondered into
the house of my younger sister and her husband and gave b

24/25

In our house we had a cat with the gra
ndiose name of Gonnosuke. Usually wit
h cats and dogs we know who the moth

ABCDEFGHIJKLM
NOPQRSTUVWXYZ
abcdefghijklmnopq
rstuvwxyz
1234567890&$¢£¥
fiflæœÆŒÅßÇÌÎÍÏã§†
⌐——/()''''''',,,,!¡?¿

10/11

In our house we had a cat with the grandiose name of Gonnosuke. Usually with cats and dogs we know who the mother is but not the father. A cat with a large belly wondered into the house of my younger sister and her husb and and gave birth to five kittens. While the mother was a pure white thoroughbred Chinchila, the kittens wer e black and white tabbies of mixed breed. One of these came to our house about two weeks after its birth and wa s given the name Gonnosuke. At that time we already had one female Shiba dog and one female brown tabby cat in our house comprising only 13 thubo. The dog was called Momo and the cat Mii. My wife, who was very muc

16/17

In our house we had a cat with the grandiose name of Gonnosuke. Us ually with cats and dogs we know who the mother is but not the fathe r. A cat with a large belly wondered into the house of my younger siste r and her husband and gave birth to five kittens. While the mother w

24/25

In our house we had a cat with the grandiose name of Gonnosuke. Usually with cats and do gs we know who the mother is but not the fath

ABCDEFGHIJKLMN
OPQRSTUVWXYZ
abcdefghijklmnop
qrstuvwxyz
1234567890&$¢£¥
fiflæœÆŒÅßÇÌÎÍÏã
§†-–—/()''""":;.,!¡?¿

10/11

In our house we had a cat with the grandiose name of Gonnosuke. Usually with cats and dogs we know who the mother is but not the father. A cat with a large belly wondered int o the house of my younger sister and her husband and gave birth to five kittens. While th e mother was a pure white thoroughbred Chinchila, the kittens were black and white tabb ies of mixed breed. One of these came to our house about two weeks after its birth and w as given the name Gonnosuke. At that time we already had one female Shiba dog and one

16/17

In our house we had a cat with the grandiose name of G onnosuke. Usually with cats and dogs we know who th e mother is but not the father. A cat with a large belly w ondered into the house of my younger sister and her h

24/25

In our house we had a cat with the g randiose name of Gonnosuke. Usuall y with cats and dogs we know who t

ABCDEFGHIJKLMN

OPQRSTUVWXYZ

abcdefghijklmnopq

rstuvwxyz

1234567890&$¢£¥

fiflæœÆŒÅßÇÌÎÍÏã§†

———/()'""":;.,!¡?¿

10/11

In our house we had a cat with the grandiose name of Gonnosuke. Usually with cats and dogs we know who the mother is but not the father. A cat with a large belly wondered into the house of my younger sister and her husband and gave birth to five kittens. While the mother was a pure white thoroughbred Chinchila, the kittens were black and white tabbies of mixed breed. One of these came to our house about two weeks after its birth and was given the name Gonnosuke. At that time we already had one female Shiba dog and one female brown tabby cat in our house comprising only 13 thubo. The dog was called Momo and the cat Mii. My wife, who was very much oppo

16/17

In our house we had a cat with the grandiose name of Gonnosuke. Usually with cats and dogs we know who the mother is but not the father. A cat with a large belly wondered into the house of my younger sister and her husband and gave birth to five kittens. While the mother wa

24/25

In our house we had a cat with the grandiose name of Gonnosuke. Usually with cats and dogs we know who the mother is but not the fath

ITC Galliard Roman

ABCDEFGHIJKL
MNOPQRSTUVW
XYZabcdefghijklmn
opqrstuvwxyz
1234567890&$¢£¥
fiflæœÆŒÅßÇÌÎÍÏĩã
§†--——/()''""·:;.,!¡?¿

10/11

In our house we had a cat with the grandiose name of Gonnosuke. Usually with cats and dogs we know w
ho the mother is but not the father. A cat with a large belly wondered into the house of my younger sister
and her husband and gave birth to five kittens. While the mother was a pure white thoroughbred Chinchil
a, the kittens were black and white tabbies of mixed breed. One of these came to our house about two wee
ks after its birth and was given the name Gonnosuke. At that time we already had one female Shiba dog an
d one female brown tabby cat in our house comprising only 13 tubo. The dog was called Momo and the

16/17

In our house we had a cat with the grandiose name of Gonnosuke.
Usually with cats and dogs we know who the mother is but not th
e father. A cat with a large belly wondered into the house of my yo
unger sister and her husband and gave birth to five kittens. While

24/25

In our house we had a cat with the grandios
e name of Gonnosuke. Usually with cats an
d dogs we know who the mother is but not

ITC Galliard Italic

ABCDEFGHIJKL
MNOPQRSTUVW
XYZabcdefghijklmnop
qrstuvwxyz
1234567890&$¢£¥
fiflæœÆŒÅßÇÌÎÍÏã§
†-——/()°''""·,·.,!¡?¿

10/11

In our house we had a cat with the grandiose name of Gonnosuke. Usually with cats and dogs we know who the mo
ther is but not the father. A cat with a large belly wondered into the house of my younger sister and her husband an
d gave birth to five kittens. While the mother was a pure white thoroughbred Chinchila, the kittens were black and
white tabbies of mixed breed. One of these came to our house about two weeks after its birth and was given the nam
e Gonnosuke. At that time we already had one female Shiba dog and one female brown tabby cat in our house com
prising only 13 tubo. The dog was called Momo and the cat Mii. My wife, who was very much opposed to keeping c

16/17

In our house we had a cat with the grandiose name of Gonnosuke. Usu
ally with cats and dogs we know who the mother is but not the father. A
cat with a large belly wondered into the house of my younger sister and
her husband and gave birth to five kittens. While the mother was a pur

24/25

In our house we had a cat with the grandiose n
ame of Gonnosuke. Usually with cats and dogs
we know who the mother is but not the father. A

ABCDEFGHIJKL
MNOPQRSTUV
WXYZabcdefghijkl
mnopqrstuvwxyz12
34567890&$¢£¥
fiflæœÆŒÅßÇÌÎÍÏã
§†-–—/()''""".:;.,!¡?¿

10/11

In our house we had a cat with the grandiose name of Gonnosuke. Usually with cats and dogs we k now who the mother is but not the father. A cat with a large belly wondered into the house of my younger sister and her husband and gave birth to five kittens. While the mother was a pure white t horoughbred Chinchila, the kittens were black and white tabbies of mixed breed. One of these cam e to our house about two weeks after its birth and was given the name Gonnosuke. At that time we already had one female Shiba dog and one female brown tabby cat in our house comprising only 13

16/17

In our house we had a cat with the grandiose name of Gonno suke. Usually with cats and dogs we know who the mother is but not the father. A cat with a large belly wondered into the house of my younger sister and her husband and gave birth to

24/25

In our house we had a cat with the grand iose name of Gonnosuke. Usually with ca ts and dogs we know who the mother is

113

ABCDEFGHIJKL MNOPQRSTUVW XYZabcdefghijklmno pqrstuvwxyz 1234567890&$¢£¥ fiflæœÆŒÅßÇÌÎÍÏã §†-–——/()°""":;.,!¡?¿

10/11

In our house we had a cat with the grandiose name of Gonnosuke. Usually with cats and dogs we know who the mother is but not the father. A cat with a large belly wondered into the house of my younger sister and he r husband and gave birth to five kittens. While the mother was a pure white thoroughbred Chinchila, the k ittens were black and white tabbies of mixed breed. One of these came to our house about two weeks after its birth and was given the name Gonnosuke. At that time we already had one female Shiba dog and one femal e brown tabby cat in our house comprising only 13 tubo. The dog was called Momo and the cat Mii. My wif

16/17

In our house we had a cat with the grandiose name of Gonnosuke. Usually with cats and dogs we know who the mother is but not the f ather. A cat with a large belly wondered into the house of my young er sister and her husband and gave birth to five kittens. While the

24/25

In our house we had a cat with the grandiose name of Gonnosuke. Usually with cats and dogs we know who the mother is but not the f

ITC Galliard Black

ABCDEFGHIJKL
MNOPQRSTUVW
XYZabcdefghijklm
nopqrstuvwxyz12
34567890&$¢£¥fi
flæœÆŒÅßÇÌÎÍÏã
§†-–—/()'' "" ".,;.,!¡?¿

10/11

In our house we had a cat with the grandiose name of Gonnosuke. Usually with cats and dogs we know who the mother is but not the father. A cat with a large belly wondered into the hous e of my younger sister and her husband and gave birth to five kittens. While the mother was a pure white thoroughbred Chinchila, the kittens were black and white tabbies of mixed breed. One of these came to our house about two weeks after its birth and was given the name Gonno suke. At that time we already had one female Shiba dog and one female brown tabby cat in our

16/17

In our house we had a cat with the grandiose name of Gon nosuke. Usually with cats and dogs we know who the moth er is but not the father. A cat with a large belly wondered i nto the house of my younger sister and her husband and ga

24/25

In our house we had a cat with the gra ndiose name of Gonnosuke. Usually wi th cats and dogs we know who the mot

ABCDEFGHIJKL
MNOPQRSTUV
WXYZabcdefghijkl
mnopqrstuvwxyz12
34567890&$¢£¥fifl
æœÆŒÅßÇÌÎÍÏãß†
---—/()''""'.;.,!¡?¿

10/11

In our house we had a cat with the grandiose name of Gonnosuke. Usually with cats and dogs we kno
w who the mother is but not the father. A cat with a large belly wondered into the house of my younge
r sister and her husband and gave birth to five kittens. While the mother was a pure white thoroughb
red Chinchila, the kittens were black and white tabbies of mixed breed. One of these came to our hous
e about two weeks after its birth and was given the name Gonnosuke. At that time we already had on
e female Shiba dog and one female brown tabby cat in our house comprising only 13 tubo. The dog wa

16/17

In our house we had a cat with the grandiose name of Gonnosu
ke. Usually with cats and dogs we know who the mother is but n
ot the father. A cat with a large belly wondered into the house o
f my younger sister and her husband and gave birth to five kitt

24/25

In our house we had a cat with the grandi
ose name of Gonnosuke. Usually with cats
and dogs we know who the mother is but n

ITC Galliard Ultra

ABCDEFGHIJK LMNOPQRSTU VWXYZabcdefgh ijklmnopqrstuvw xyz1234567890& $¢£¥fiflæœÆŒ ÅßÇÌÎÍÏãã§† ----/()''''''''';.,,!¡?¿

10/11

In our house we had a cat with the grandiose name of Gonnosuke. Usually with cats and dogs we know who the mother is but not the father. A cat with a large belly wondered in to the house of my younger sister and her husband and gave birth to five kittens. While the mother was a pure white thoroughbred Chinchila, the kittens were black and white tabbies of mixed breed. One of these came to our house about two weeks after its birth a nd was given the name Gonnosuke. At that time we already had one female Shiba dog an

16/17

In our house we had a cat with the grandiose name of Gonnosuke. Usually with cats and dogs we know who t he mother is but not the father. A cat with a large belly wondered into the house of my younger sister and her

24/25

In our house we had a cat with the gra ndiose name of Gonnosuke. Usually wi th cats and dogs we know who the mot

ABCDEFGHIJKL MNOPQRSTUV WXYZabcdefghijk lmnopqrstuvwxyz 1234567890& $¢£¥fiflæœÆŒ ÅßÇÌÍÎÏãß† ---—/()''""·;.,!¡?¿

10/11

In our house we had a cat with the grandiose name of Gonnosuke. Usually with cats and dogs we know who the mother is but not the father. A cat with a large belly wondered into the house of my younger sister and her husband and gave birth to five kittens. While the mother was a pu re white thoroughbred Chinchila, the kittens were black and white tabbies of mixed breed. One of these came to our house about two weeks after its birth and was given the name Gonnosuke. At that time we already had one female Shiba dog and one female brown tabby cat in our hous

16/17

In our house we had a cat with the grandiose name of Gon nosuke. Usually with cats and dogs we know who the mothe r is but not the father. A cat with a large belly wondered in to the house of my younger sister and her husband and gave

24/25

In our house we had a cat with the gra ndiose name of Gonnosuke. Usually wit h cats and dogs we know who the mothe

ABCDEFGHIJKL
MNOPQRSTUVW
XYZabcdefghijklmno
pqrstuvwxyz
1234567890&$¢£¥
fiflæœÆŒÅßÇÌÎÍÏã§
†-——/()''""":;.,!¡?¿

10/11

In our house we had a cat with the grandiose name of Gonnosuke. Usually with cats and dogs we know wh
o the mother is but not the father. A cat with a large belly wondered into the house of my younger sister an
d her husband and gave birth to five kittens. While the mother was a pure white thoroughbred Chinchila, t
he kittens were black and white tabbies of mixed breed. One of these came to our house about two weeks a
fter its birth and was given the name Gonnosuke. At that time we already had one female Shiba dog and on
e female brown tabby cat in our house comprising only 13 tubo. The dog was called Momo and the cat Mii.

16/17

In our house we had a cat with the grandiose name of Gonnosuke.
Usually with cats and dogs we know who the mother is but not the
father. A cat with a large belly wondered into the house of my you
nger sister and her husband and gave birth to five kittens. While th

24/25

In our house we had a cat with the grandiose
name of Gonnosuke. Usually with cats and
dogs we know who the mother is but not th

ABCDEFGHIJKL
MNOPQRSTUVW
XYZabcdefghijklmnop
qrstuvwxyz
1234567890&$¢£¥
fiflæœÆŒÅßÇÌÎÍÏã§
†–——/() ''""":.;.,!¡?¿

10/11

In our house we had a cat with the grandiose name of Gonnosuke. Usually with cats and dogs we know who the mother is but not the father. A cat with a large belly wondered into the house of my younger sister and her husband and gave birth to five kittens. While the mother was a pure white thoroughbred Chinchila, the kittens were black and white tabbies of mixed breed. One of these came to our house about two weeks after its birth and was given the name Gonnosuke. At that time we already had one female Shiba dog and one female brown tabby cat in our house comprising only 13 tubo. The dog was called Momo and the cat Mii. My wife, who was very much op

16/17

In our house we had a cat with the grandiose name of Gonnosuke. Usually with cats and dogs we know who the mother is but not the father. A cat with a large belly wondered into the house of my younger sister

24/25

In our house we had a cat with the grandiose name of Gonnosuke. Usually with cats and dogs we know who the mother is but not the fath

ABCDEFGHIJKL
MNOPQRSTUVW
XYZabcdefghijklmn
opqrstuvwxyz
1234567890&$¢£¥
fiflæœÆŒÅßÇÌÎÍÏã§
†-–——/()'’“”:;.,!¡?¿

10/11

In our house we had a cat with the grandiose name of Gonnosuke. Usually with cats and dogs we know who the mother is but not the father. A cat with a large belly wondered into the house of my younger s ister and her husband and gave birth to five kittens. While the mother was a pure white thoroughbred Chinchila, the kittens were black and white tabbies of mixed breed. One of these came to our house abo ut two weeks after its birth and was given the name Gonnosuke. At that time we already had one femal e Shiba dog and one female brown tabby cat in our house comprising only 13 tubo. The dog was called

16/17

In our house we had a cat with the grandiose name of Gonnosuk e. Usually with cats and dogs we know who the mother is but no t the father. A cat with a large belly wondered into the house of my younger sister and her husband and gave birth to five kitten

24/25

In our house we had a cat with the grandio se name of Gonnosuke. Usually with cats a nd dogs we know who the mother is but n

Like **Stempel Garamond Bold Italic**

ABCDEFGHIJKL
MNOPQRSTUVW
XYZabcdefghijklmno
pqrstuvwxyz
1234567890&$¢£¥
fiflæœÆŒÅßÇÌÎÍÏã§
†–——/()'''""·:;·.,!¡?¿

10/11

In our house we had a cat with the grandiose name of Gonnosuke. Usually with cats and dogs we know who the mother is but not the father. A cat with a large belly wondered into the house of my younger sister and he r husband and gave birth to five kittens. While the mother was a pure white thoroughbred Chinchila, the ki ttens were black and white tabbies of mixed breed. One of these came to our house about two weeks after its birth and was given the name Gonnosuke. At that time we already had one female Shiba dog and one femal e brown tabby cat in our house comprising only 13 tubo. The dog was called Momo and the cat Mii. My wif

16/17

In our house we had a cat with the grandiose name of Gonnosuke. Usually with cats and dogs we know who the mother is but not the father. A cat with a large belly wondered into the house of my youn ger sister and her husband and gave birth to five kittens. While the

24/25

In our house we had a cat with the grandiose name of Gonnosuke. Usually with cats and dogs we know who the mother is but not the

ABCDEFGHIJKLMNO
PQRSTUVWXYZ
abcdefghijklmnopqrst
uvwxyz
1234567890&$¢£¥
fiflæœÆŒÅßÇÌÎÍÏã§†
——/()'’“”:;.,!¡?¿

10/11

In our house we had a cat with the grandiose name of Gonnosuke. Usually with cats and dogs we know who the moth er is but not the father. A cat with a large belly wondered into the house of my younger sister and her husband and ga ve birth to five kittens. While the mother was a pure white thoroughbred Chinchila, the kittens were black and white tabbies of mixed breed. One of these came to our house about two weeks after its birth and was given the name Gonn osuke. At that time we already had one female Shiba dog and one female brown tabby cat in our house comprising on ly 13 thubo. The dog was called Momo and the cat Mii. My wife, who was very much opposed to keeping cats and do

16/17

In our house we had a cat with the grandiose name of Gonnosuke. Usuall y with cats and dogs we know who the mother is but not the father. A cat with a large belly wondered into the house of my younger sister and her h usband and gave birth to five kittens. While the mother was a pure white

24/25

In our house we had a cat with the grandiose na me of Gonnosuke. Usually with cats and dogs we know who the mother is but not the father. A cat

ABCDEFGHIJKLMNO
PQRSTUVWXYZ
abcdefghijklmnopqrst
uvwxyz
1234567890&$¢£¥
fiflæœÆŒÅßÇÌÎÍÏã§†
———/()''""":;.,!¡?¿

10/11

In our house we had a cat with the grandiose name of Gonnosuke. Usually with cats and dogs we know who the mother is but not the father. A cat with a large belly wondered into the house of my younger sister and her husband and gave birth to five kittens. While t he mother was a pure white thoroughbred Chinchila, the kittens were black and white tabbies of mixed breed. One of these came to ou r house about two weeks after its birth and was given the name Gonnosuke. At that time we already had one female Shiba dog and o ne female brown tabby cat in our house comprising only 13 thubo. The dog was called Momo and the cat Mii. My wife, who was ver y much opposed to keeping cats and dogs, instantaneously fell for its shaggy appearance and the black tip of its nose and decided on its

16/17

In our house we had a cat with the grandiose name of Gonnosuke. Usually with ca ts and dogs we know who the mother is but not the father. A cat with a large belly wondered into the house of my younger sister and her husband and gave birth to fiv e kittens. While the mother was a pure white thoroughbred Chinchila, the kittens

24/25

In our house we had a cat with the grandiose name of Gonnosuke. Usually with cats and dogs we know who the mother is but not the father. A cat with a large bell

ABCDEFGHIJKLMN
OPQRSTUVWXYZ
abcdefghijklmnopqrst
uvwxyz
1234567890&$¢£¥
fiflæœÆŒÅßÇÌÎÍÏã§†
——/()"""":;.,!¡?¿

10/11

In our house we had a cat with the grandiose name of Gonnosuke. Usually with cats and dogs we know who the mother is but not the father. A cat with a large belly wondered into the house of my younger sister and he r husband and gave birth to five kittens. While the mother was a pure white thoroughbred Chinchila, the kitt ens were black and white tabbies of mixed breed. One of these came to our house about two weeks after its b irth and was given the name Gonnosuke. At that time we already had one female Shiba dog and one female b rown tabby cat in our house comprising only 13 thubo. The dog was called Momo and the cat Mii. My wife,

16/17

In our house we had a cat with the grandiose name of Gonnosuke. Usually with cats and dogs we know who the mother is but not the father. A cat with a large belly wondered into the house of my youn ger sister and her husband and gave birth to five kittens. While the

24/25

In our house we had a cat with the grandiose name of Gonnosuke. Usually with cats and d ogs we know who the mother is but not the f

ABCDEFGHIJKLMN
OPQRSTUVWXYZ

abcdefghijklmnopqrst
uvwxyz
1234567890&$¢£¥
fiflæœÆŒÅßÇÌÎÍÏã§†
——/()""'':;.,!¡?¿

10/11

In our house we had a cat with the grandiose name of Gonnosuke. Usually with cats and dogs we know who the mot her is but not the father. A cat with a large belly wondered into the house of my younger sister and her husband and gave birth to five kittens. While the mother was a pure white thoroughbred Chinchila, the kittens were black and wh ite tabbies of mixed breed. One of these came to our house about two weeks after its birth and was given the name G onnosuke. At that time we already had one female Shiba dog and one female brown tabby cat in our house comprisi ng only 13 thubo. The dog was called Momo and the cat Mii. My wife, who was very much opposed to keeping cats an

16/17

In our house we had a cat with the grandiose name of Gonnosuke. Usual ly with cats and dogs we know who the mother is but not the father. A ca t with a large belly wondered into the house of my younger sister and her husband and gave birth to five kittens. While the mother was a pure whi

24/25

In our house we had a cat with the grandiose na me of Gonnosuke. Usually with cats and dogs we know who the mother is but not the father. A cat

ABCDEFGHIJKLM
NOPQRSTUVWXYZ

abcdefghijklmnopq
rstuvwxyz
1234567890&$¢£¥
fiflæœÆŒÅßÇÌÎÍÏã§
†-–—/()''""·;·,!¡?¿

10/11

In our house we had a cat with the grandiose name of Gonnosuke. Usually with cats and dogs we know who the mother is but not the father. A cat with a large belly wondered into the house of my younger sister and her husb and and gave birth to five kittens. While the mother was a pure white thoroughbred Chinchila, the kittens were black and white tabbies of mixed breed. One of these came to our house about two weeks after its birth and wa s given the name Gonnosuke. At that time we already had one female Shiba dog and one female brown tabby c at in our house comprising only 13 tubo. The dog was called Momo and the cat Mii. My wife, who was very mu

16/17

In our house we had a cat with the grandiose name of Gonnosuke. U sually with cats and dogs we know who the mother is but not the fath er. A cat with a large belly wondered into the house of my younger sis ter and her husband and gave birth to five kittens. While the mother

24/25

In our house we had a cat with the grandiose name of Gonnosuke. Usually with cats and do gs we know who the mother is but not the fath

ABCDEFGHIJKLMN
OPQRSTUVWXYZ
abcdefghijklmnopq
rstuvwxyz
1234567890&$¢£¥
fiflæœÆŒÅßÇÌÎÍÏã§†
——/()''""";.,!¡?¿

10/11

In our house we had a cat with the grandiose name of Gonnosuke. Usually with cats and dogs we know who the mother is but not the father. A cat with a large belly wondered into the house of my younger sister and her husband and gave birth to five kittens. While the mother was a pure white thoroughbred Chinchila, the kittens were black and white tabbies of mixed breed. One of these came to our house about two weeks after its birth and was given the name Gonnosuke. At that time we already had one female Shiba dog and one female brown tabby cat in our house comprising only 13 tubo. The dog was called Momo and the cat Mii. My wife, who was very much opposed to keeping cats and dogs, instant

16/17

In our house we had a cat with the grandiose name of Gonnosuke. Usually with cats and dogs we know who the mother is but not the father. A cat with a large belly wondered into the house of my younger sister and her husband and gave birth to five kittens. While the mother was a pure white t

24/25

In our house we had a cat with the grandiose name of Gonnosuke. Usually with cats and dogs we know who the mother is but not the father. A cat

Like **Simoncini Garamond Bold**

ABCDEFGHIJKL MNOPQRSTUV WXYZ

abcdefghijklmnopq rstuvwxyz 1234567890&$¢£¥ fiflæœÆŒÅßÇÌÎÍÏã§ †-–—/()''""".;.,!¡?¿

10/11

In our house we had a cat with the grandiose name of Gonnosuke. Usually with cats and dogs we know w
ho the mother is but not the father. A cat with a large belly wondered into the house of my younger sister
and her husband and gave birth to five kittens. While the mother was a pure white thoroughbred Chinchi
la, the kittens were black and white tabbies of mixed breed. One of these came to our house about two we
eks after its birth and was given the name Gonnosuke. At that time we already had one female Shiba dog
and one female brown tabby cat in our house comprising only 13 tubo. The dog was called Momo and the

16/17

In our house we had a cat with the grandiose name of Gonnosuk
e. Usually with cats and dogs we know who the mother is but not
the father. A cat with a large belly wondered into the house of my
younger sister and her husband and gave birth to five kittens. Wh

24/25

In our house we had a cat with the grandios
e name of Gonnosuke. Usually with cats an
d dogs we know who the mother is but not t

ABCDEFGHIJKLMNO
PQRSTUVWXYZ
abcdefghijklmnopq
rstuvwxyz
1234567890&$¢£¥
fiflæœÆŒÅßÇÌÎÍÏã§†
–——/()''""":;.,!¡?¿

10/11

In our house we had a cat with the grandiose name of Gonnosuke. Usually with cats and dogs we know w
ho the mother is but not the father. A cat with a large belly wondered into the house of my younger sister
and her husband and gave birth to five kittens. While the mother was a pure white thoroughbred Chinchil
a, the kittens were black and white tabbies of mixed breed. One of these came to our house about two we
eks after its birth and was given the name Gonnosuke. At that time we already had one female Shiba dog a
nd one female brown tabby cat in our house comprising only 13 tubo. The dog was called Momo and the

16/17

In our house we had a cat with the grandiose name of Gonnosuk
e. Usually with cats and dogs we know who the mother is but not t
he father. A cat with a large belly wondered into the house of my y
ounger sister and her husband and gave birth to five kittens. While

24/25

In our house we had a cat with the grandios
e name of Gonnosuke. Usually with cats and
dogs we know who the mother is but not th

*ABCDEFGHIJKLMNO
PQRSTUVWXYZ
abcdefghijklmnopq
rstuvwxyz
1234567890&$¢£¥
fiflæœÆŒÅßÇÌÎÍÏã§†
–——/()''""":;.,!¡?¿*

10/11

In our house we had a cat with the grandiose name of Gonnosuke. Usually with cats and dogs we know who the mother is but not the father. A cat with a large belly wondered into the house of my younger siste r and her husband and gave birth to five kittens. While the mother was a pure white thoroughbred Chin chila, the kittens were black and white tabbies of mixed breed. One of these came to our house about tw o weeks after its birth and was given the name Gonnosuke. At that time we already had one female Shib a dog and one female brown tabby cat in our house comprising only 13 tubo. The dog was called Momo

16/17

In our house we had a cat with the grandiose name of Gonnosu ke. Usually with cats and dogs we know who the mother is but no t the father. A cat with a large belly wondered into the house of m y younger sister and her husband and gave birth to five kittens.

24/25

In our house we had a cat with the grandio se name of Gonnosuke. Usually with cats a nd dogs we know who the mother is but no

ABCDEFGHIJKLMN
OPQRSTUVWXYZ
abcdefghijklmnopq
rstuvwxyz
1234567890&$¢£¥
fiflæœÆŒÅßÇÌÎÍÏã§
†-–—/()''""":;.,!¡?¿

10/11

In our house we had a cat with the grandiose name of Gonnosuke. Usually with cats and dogs we kno
w who the mother is but not the father. A cat with a large belly wondered into the house of my young
er sister and her husband and gave birth to five kittens. While the mother was a pure white thoroughb
red Chinchila, the kittens were black and white tabbies of mixed breed. One of these came to our hou
se about two weeks after its birth and was given the name Gonnosuke. At that time we already had on
e female Shiba dog and one female brown tabby cat in our house comprising only 13 tubo. The dog w

16/17

In our house we had a cat with the grandiose name of Gonnosu
ke. Usually with cats and dogs we know who the mother is but
not the father. A cat with a large belly wondered into the house
of my younger sister and her husband and gave birth to five kitt

24/25

In our house we had a cat with the grandi
ose name of Gonnosuke. Usually with cats
and dogs we know who the mother is but

ABCDEFGHIJKLMN
OPQRSTUVWXYZ
abcdefghijklmnopq
rstuvwxyz
1234567890&$¢£¥
fiflæœÆŒÅßÇÌÎÍÏã§
†-——/()'’“”:;.,!¡?¿

10/11

In our house we had a cat with the grandiose name of Gonnosuke. Usually with cats and dogs we k now who the mother is but not the father. A cat with a large belly wondered into the house of my yo unger sister and her husband and gave birth to five kittens. While the mother was a pure white thor oughbred Chinchila, the kittens were black and white tabbies of mixed breed. One of these came to our house about two weeks after its birth and was given the name Gonnosuke. At that time we alre ady had one female Shiba dog and one female brown tabby cat in our house comprising only 13 tub

16/17

In our house we had a cat with the grandiose name of Gonnos uke. Usually with cats and dogs we know who the mother is b ut not the father. A cat with a large belly wondered into the ho use of my younger sister and her husband and gave birth to fi

24/25

In our house we had a cat with the grand iose name of Gonnosuke. Usually with ca ts and dogs we know who the mother is b

ABCDEFGHIJKLMN
OPQRSTUVWXYZ
abcdefghijklmnop
qrstuvwxyz
1234567890&$¢£¥
fiflæœÆŒÅßÇÌÎÍÏã
§†-–—/()'’“”:;.,!¡?¿

10/11

In our house we had a cat with the grandiose name of Gonnosuke. Usually with cats and dogs we know who the mother is but not the father. A cat with a large belly wondered into the hou se of my younger sister and her husband and gave birth to five kittens. While the mother was a pure white thoroughbred Chinchila, the kittens were black and white tabbies of mixed bree d. One of these came to our house about two weeks after its birth and was given the name Go nnosuke. At that time we already had one female Shiba dog and one female brown tabby cat

16/17

In our house we had a cat with the grandiose name of Gon nosuke. Usually with cats and dogs we know who the mot her is but not the father. A cat with a large belly wondered into the house of my younger sister and her husband and

24/25

In our house we had a cat with the gra ndiose name of Gonnosuke. Usually wi th cats and dogs we know who the mot

ABCDEFGHIJKLMN
OPQRSTUVWXYZ
abcdefghijklmnop
qrstuvwxyz
1234567890&$¢£¥
fiflæœÆŒÅßÇÌÎÍÏã
§†-–—/()''""";:.,!¡?¿

10/11

In our house we had a cat with the grandiose name of Gonnosuke. Usually with cats and do gs we know who the mother is but not the father. A cat with a large belly wondered into the house of my younger sister and her husband and gave birth to five kittens. While the mother was a pure white thoroughbred Chinchila, the kittens were black and white tabbies of mixe d breed. One of these came to our house about two weeks after its birth and was given the n ame Gonnosuke. At that time we already had one female Shiba dog and one female brown t

16/17

In our house we had a cat with the grandiose name of Go nnosuke. Usually with cats and dogs we know who the m other is but not the father. A cat with a large belly wonde red into the house of my younger sister and her husband

24/25

In our house we had a cat with the gr andiose name of Gonnosuke. Usually with cats and dogs we know who the

135

ABCDEFGHIJKL
MNOPQRSTUVW
XYZabcdefghijkl
mnopqrstuvwxyz
1234567890&
$¢£¥fiflæœÆŒ
ÅßÇÌÎÍÏÏÄÃ§†
——/()''""":;.,!¡?¿

10/11

In our house we had a cat with the grandiose name of Gonnosuke. Usually with cats and dogs we know who the mother is but not the father. A cat with a large belly wondered in to the house of my younger sister and her husband and gave birth to five kittens. While the mother was a pure white thoroughbred Chinchila, the kittens were black and white tabbies of mixed breed. One of these came to our house about two weeks after its birth and was given the name Gonnosuke. At that time we already had one female Shiba dog a

16/17

In our house we had a cat with the grandiose name of Gonnosuke. Usually with cats and dogs we know who t he mother is but not the father. A cat with a large belly wondered into the house of my younger sister and her

24/25

In our house we had a cat with the g randiose name of Gonnosuke. Usuall y with cats and dogs we know who t

ABCDEFGHIJKLM NOPQRSTUVWX YZabcdefghijklmn opqrstuvwxyz 1234567890& $¢£¥fiflæœÆŒ ÅßÇÌÎÍÏã§† ——/() ''""":;.,!¡?¿

10/11

In our house we had a cat with the grandiose name of Gonnosuke. Usually with cats an
d dogs we know who the mother is but not the father. A cat with a large belly wondered i
nto the house of my younger sister and her husband and gave birth to five kittens. While
the mother was a pure white thoroughbred Chinchila, the kittens were black and white t
abbies of mixed breed. One of these came to our house about two weeks after its birth a
nd was given the name Gonnosuke. At that time we already had one female Shiba dog a

16/17

In our house we had a cat with the grandiose name of
Gonnosuke. Usually with cats and dogs we know who t
he mother is but not the father. A cat with a large belly
wondered into the house of my younger sister and her

24/25

In our house we had a cat with the g
randiose name of Gonnosuke. Usual
ly with cats and dogs we know who t

ABCDEFGHIJKLMNOPQ RSTUVWXYZ

abcdefghijklmnopqrstuvwxyz

1234567890&$¢£¥ fiflæœÆŒÅßÇÌÎÍÏïã§† -——/()''""":;.,!¡?¿

10/11

In our house we had a cat with the grandiose name of Gonnosuke. Usually with cats and dogs we know who the mother is but not the father. A c at with a large belly wondered into the house of my younger sister and her husband and gave birth to five kittens. While the mother was a pure w hite thoroughbred Chinchila, the kittens were black and white tabbies of mixed breed. One of these came to our house about two weeks after its b irth and was given the name Gonnosuke. At that time we already had one female Shiba dog and one female brown tabby cat in our house compr ising only 13 tubo. The dog was called Momo and the cat Mii. My wife, who was very much opposed to keeping cats and dogs, instantaneously fe ll for its shaggy appearance and the black tip of its nose and decided on its name, crying this dog's name is Momo. Mii is a stray cat which my d

16/17

In our house we had a cat with the grandiose name of Gonnosuke. Usually with cats and d ogs we know who the mother is but not the father. A cat with a large belly wondered into t he house of my younger sister and her husband and gave birth to five kittens. While the m other was a pure white thoroughbred Chinchila, the kittens were black and white tabbies o

24/25

In our house we had a cat with the grandiose name of Gonn osuke. Usually with cats and dogs we know who the mother is but not the father. A cat with a large belly wondered into

ABCDEFGHIJKLMNOPQ
RSTUVWXYZ
abcdefghijklmnopq
rstuvwxyz
1234567890&$¢£¥
fiflæœÆŒÅßÇÌÎÍÏã§†
-–—/() ' ' " ":;.,!¡?¿

10/11

In our house we had a cat with the grandiose name of Gonnosuke. Usually with cats and dogs we know who the mother is but not the father. A cat with a large belly wondered into the house of my younger sister and her husband and gave birth to five kittens. While the mother was a pure white thoroughbred Chinchila, the kittens were black and white tabbies of mixed breed. One of these came to our h ouse about two weeks after its birth and was given the name Gonnosuke. At that time we already had one female Shiba dog and one female brown tabby cat in our house comprising only 13 tubo. The dog was called Momo and the cat Mii. My wife, who was very muc h opposed to keeping cats and dogs, instantaneously fell for its shaggy appearance and the black tip of its nose and decided on its na

16/17

In our house we had a cat with the grandiose name of Gonnosuke. Usually with cat s and dogs we know who the mother is but not the father. A cat with a large belly wo ndered into the house of my younger sister and her husband and gave birth to five kittens. While the mother was a pure white thoroughbred Chinchila, the kittens were

24/25

In our house we had a cat with the grandiose name of Gonnosuke. Usually with cats and dogs we know who t he mother is but not the father. A cat with a large belly

ABCDEFGHIJKLMNOPQ RSTUVWXYZ
abcdefghijklmnopq rstuvwxyz
1234567890&$¢£¥ fiflæœÆŒÅßÇÌÎÍÏã§†
----——/()''""":;.,!¡?¿

10/11

In our house we had a cat with the grandiose name of Gonnosuke. Usually with cats and dogs we know who the mother is but not th
e father. A cat with a large belly wondered into the house of my younger sister and her husband and gave birth to five kittens. While
the mother was a pure white thoroughbred Chinchila, the kittens were black and white tabbies of mixed breed. One of these came t
o our house about two weeks after its birth and was given the name Gonnosuke. At that time we already had one female Shiba dog a
nd one female brown tabby cat in our house comprising only 13 tubo. The dog was called Momo and the cat Mii. My wife, who was v
ery much opposed to keeping cats and dogs, instantaneously fell for its shaggy appearance and the black tip of its nose and decided

16/17

In our house we had a cat with the grandiose name of Gonnosuke. Usually with ca
ts and dogs we know who the mother is but not the father. A cat with a large belly
wondered into the house of my younger sister and her husband and gave birth to f
ive kittens. While the mother was a pure white thoroughbred Chinchila, the kittens

24/25

In our house we had a cat with the grandiose name of
Gonnosuke. Usually with cats and dogs we know who t
he mother is but not the father. A cat with a large belly

ABCDEFGHIJKLMNOP

QRSTUVWXYZ

abcdefghijklmnopq

rstuvwxyz

1234567890&$¢£¥

fiflæœÆŒÅßçÌÎÍÏã§†

-–—/()''""":;.,!¡?¿

10/11

In our house we had a cat with the grandiose name of Gonnosuke. Usually with cats and dogs we know who the mother is but not the father. A cat with a large belly wondered into the house of my younger sister and her husband and gave birth to five kitt ens. While the mother was a pure white thoroughbred Chinchila, the kittens were black and white tabbies of mixed breed. One of these came to our house about two weeks after its birth and was given the name Gonnosuke. At that time we already had on e female Shiba dog and one female brown tabby cat in our house comprising only 13 tubo. The dog was called Momo and the c at Mii. My wife, who was very much opposed to keeping cats and dogs, instantaneously fell for its shaggy appearance and the

16/17

In our house we had a cat with the grandiose name of Gonnosuke. Usually wit h cats and dogs we know who the mother is but not the father. A cat with a larg e belly wondered into the house of my younger sister and her husband and gav e birth to five kittens. While the mother was a pure white thoroughbred Chinchi

24/25

In our house we had a cat with the grandiose name of Gonnosuke. Usually with cats and dogs we know who the mother is but not the father. A cat with a lar

ABCDEFGHIJKLMN
OPQRSTUVWXYZ
abcdefghijklmnopq
rstuvwxyz
1234567890&$¢£¥
fiflæœÆŒÅßçÌÎÍÏïã§†
-–—/()''""":;.,!¡?¿

10/11

In our house we had a cat with the grandiose name of Gonnosuke. Usually with cats and dogs we know who the mother is but not the father. A cat with a large belly wondered into the house of my younger sister and her husband and gave birth to five kittens. While the mother was a pure white thoroughbred Chinchila, the kittens were black and white tabbies of mixed breed. One of these came to our house about two weeks after its birth and was given the name Gonnosuke. At that time we already had one female Shiba dog and one female brown tabby cat in our house comprising only 13 tubo. The dog was called Momo and the cat Mii. My wife, who was very much opposed to keeping cats and dogs, insta

16/17

In our house we had a cat with the grandiose name of Gonnosuke. Usually with cats and dogs we know who the mother is but not the father. A cat with a large belly wondered into the house of my younger sister and her husband and gave birth to five kittens. While the mother was a pure white th

24/25

In our house we had a cat with the grandiose name of Gonnosuke. Usually with cats and dogs we know who the mother is but not the father. A cat

ABCDEFGHIJKLMN
OPQRSTUVWXYZ
abcdefghijklmnopq
rstuvwxyz
1234567890&$¢£¥
fiflæœÆŒÅßÇÌÎÍÏã§
†-–——/()''"":;.,!¡?¿

10/11

In our house we had a cat with the grandiose name of Gonnosuke. Usually with cats and dogs we know who the mother is but not the father. A cat with a large belly wondered into the house of my younger sister and her husb and and gave birth to five kittens. While the mother was a pure white thoroughbred Chinchila, the kittens were black and white tabbies of mixed breed. One of these came to our house about two weeks after its birth and wa s given the name Gonnosuke. At that time we already had one female Shiba dog and one female brown tabby ca t in our house comprising only 13 tubo. The dog was called Momo and the cat Mii. My wife, who was very much

16/17

In our house we had a cat with the grandiose name of Gonnosuke. Us ually with cats and dogs we know who the mother is but not the fathe r. A cat with a large belly wondered into the house of my younger sist er and her husband and gave birth to five kittens. While the mother

24/25

In our house we had a cat with the grandiose name of Gonnosuke. Usually with cats and dog s we know who the mother is but not the fathe

ABCDEFGHIJKLMNO
PQRSTUVWXYZ
abcdefghijklmnop
qrstuvwxyz
1234567890&$¢£¥
fiflæœÆŒÅßÇÌÎÍÏã§
†-–—/()''""":;.,!¡?¿

10/11

In our house we had a cat with the grandiose name of Gonnosuke. Usually with cats and dogs we know who t he mother is but not the father. A cat with a large belly wondered into the house of my younger sister and h er husband and gave birth to five kittens. While the mother was a pure white thoroughbred Chinchila, the k ittens were black and white tabbies of mixed breed. One of these came to our house about two weeks after it s birth and was given the name Gonnosuke. At that time we already had one female Shiba dog and one femal e brown tabby cat in our house comprising only 13 tubo. The dog was called Momo and the cat Mii. My wife,

16/17

In our house we had a cat with the grandiose name of Gonnosuke. Usually with cats and dogs we know who the mother is but not the f ather. A cat with a large belly wondered into the house of my young er sister and her husband and gave birth to five kittens. While the

24/25

In our house we had a cat with the grandiose name of Gonnosuke. Usually with cats and do gs we know who the mother is but not the fat

ABCDEFGHIJKLMN
OPQRSTUVWXYZ
abcdefghijklmnop
qrstuvwxyz
1234567890&
$¢£¥fiflæœÆŒ
ÅßÇÌÎÍÏã§†
-–—/()''""";.,!¡?¿

10/11

In our house we had a cat with the grandiose name of Gonnosuke. Usually with cats and dogs we know who the mother is but not the father. A cat with a large belly wondered into the house of my younger sis ter and her husband and gave birth to five kittens. While the mother was a pure white thoroughbred Ch inchila, the kittens were black and white tabbies of mixed breed. One of these came to our house about two weeks after its birth and was given the name Gonnosuke. At that time we already had one female S hiba dog and one female brown tabby cat in our house comprising only 13 tubo. The dog was called Mo

16/17

In our house we had a cat with the grandiose name of Gonnosuk e. Usually with cats and dogs we know who the mother is but not the father. A cat with a large belly wondered into the house of m y younger sister and her husband and gave birth to five kittens.

24/25

In our house we had a cat with the grandio se name of Gonnosuke. Usually with cats a nd dogs we know who the mother is but not

145

ABCDEFGHIJKLMN
OPQRSTUVWXYZ
abcdefghijklmnopq
rstuvwxyz
1234567890&$¢£¥
fiflæœÆŒÅßÇÌÎÍÏã§†
⸗——/()''""":;.,!¡?¿

10/11

In our house we had a cat with the grandiose name of Gonnosuke. Usually with cats and dogs we know who the mother is but not the father. A cat with a large belly wondered into the house of my younger sister and her husba nd and gave birth to five kittens. While the mother was a pure white thoroughbred Chinchila, the kittens were b lack and white tabbies of mixed breed. One of these came to our house about two weeks after its birth and was gi ven the name Gonnosuke. At that time we already had one female Shiba dog and one female brown tabby cat in our house comprising only 13 tubo. The dog was called Momo and the cat Mii. My wife, who was very much opp

16/17

In our house we had a cat with the grandiose name of Gonnosuke. Us ually with cats and dogs we know who the mother is but not the fathe r. A cat with a large belly wondered into the house of my younger siste r and her husband and gave birth to five kittens. While the mother wa

24/25

In our house we had a cat with the grandiose n ame of Gonnosuke. Usually with cats and dogs we know who the mother is but not the father.

ABCDEFGHIJKLMN
OPQRSTUVWXYZ
abcdefghijklmnopq
rstuvwxyz
1234567890&$¢£¥
fiflæœÆŒÅßÇÌÎÍÏã§†
-——/()''""·:;.,!¡?¿

10/11

In our house we had a cat with the grandiose name of Gonnosuke. Usually with cats and dogs we know who the mother is but not the father. A cat with a large belly wondered into the house of my younger sister and her husband and gave birt h to five kittens. While the mother was a pure white thoroughbred Chinchila, the kittens were black and white tabbies of mixed breed. One of these came to our house about two weeks after its birth and was given the name Gonnosuke. At that time we already had one female Shiba dog and one female brown tabby cat in our house comprising only 13 tubo. The do g was called Momo and the cat Mii. My wife, who was very much opposed to keeping cats and dogs, instantaneously fell

16/17

In our house we had a cat with the grandiose name of Gonnosuke. Us ually with cats and dogs we know who the mother is but not the fathe r. A cat with a large belly wondered into the house of my younger siste r and her husband and gave birth to five kittens. While the mother wa

24/25

In our house we had a cat with the grandiose n ame of Gonnosuke. Usually with cats and dogs we know who the mother is but not the father.

ABCDEFGHIJKLMN
OPQRSTUVWXYZ
abcdefghijklmnopq
rstuvwxyz
1234567890&$¢£¥
fiflæœÆŒÅßÇÌÎÍÏã§
†-——/()""""·;·,·!¡?¿

10/11

In our house we had a cat with the grandiose name of Gonnosuke. Usually with cats and dogs we know wh o the mother is but not the father. A cat with a large belly wondered into the house of my younger sister an d her husband and gave birth to five kittens. While the mother was a pure white thoroughbred Chinchila, t he kittens were black and white tabbies of mixed breed. One of these came to our house about two weeks a fter its birth and was given the name Gonnosuke. At that time we already had one female Shiba dog and on e female brown tabby cat in our house comprising only 13 tubo. The dog was called Momo and the cat Mii.

16/17

In our house we had a cat with the grandiose name of Gonnosuke. Usually with cats and dogs we know who the mother is but not the father. A cat with a large belly wondered into the house of my you nger sister and her husband and gave birth to five kittens. While th

24/25

In our house we had a cat with the grandios e name of Gonnosuke. Usually with cats and dogs we know who the mother is but not the

ABCDEFGHIJKL MNOPQRSTU VWXYZ

abcdefghijklmnopq rstuvwxyz 1234567890&$¢£¥ fiflæœÆŒÅßÇÌÎÍÏã§ †-——/()''""".;.,!¡?¿

10/11

In our house we had a cat with the grandiose name of Gonnosuke. Usually with cats and dogs we know who th e mother is but not the father. A cat with a large belly wondered into the house of my younger sister and her hus band and gave birth to five kittens. While the mother was a pure white thoroughbred Chinchila, the kittens were black and white tabbies of mixed breed. One of these came to our house about two weeks after its birth and was given the name Gonnosuke. At that time we already had one female Shiba dog and one female brown tabby cat in our house comprising only 13 tubo. The dog was called Momo and the cat Mii. My wife, who was very muc

16/17

In our house we had a cat with the grandiose name of Gonnosuke. Usually with cats and dogs we know who the mother is but not the father. A cat with a large belly wondered into the house of my you nger sister and her husband and gave birth to five kittens. While th

24/25

In our house we had a cat with the grandios e name of Gonnosuke. Usually with cats and dogs we know who the mother is but not the

ABCDEFGHIJKL
MNOPQRSTU
VWXYZ
abcdefghijklmnopq
rstuvwxyz
1234567890&$¢£¥
fiflæœÆŒÅßÇÌÎÍÏã§
†-–—/()''""•:;.,!¡?¿

10/11

In our house we had a cat with the grandiose name of Gonnosuke. Usually with cats and dogs we kno
w who the mother is but not the father. A cat with a large belly wondered into the house of my younge
r sister and her husband and gave birth to five kittens. While the mother was a pure white thoroughbr
ed Chinchila, the kittens were black and white tabbies of mixed breed. One of these came to our hous
e about two weeks after its birth and was given the name Gonnosuke. At that time we already had one
female Shiba dog and one female brown tabby cat in our house comprising only 13 tubo. The dog was

16/17

In our house we had a cat with the grandiose name of Gonnosu
ke. Usually with cats and dogs we know who the mother is but
not the father. A cat with a large belly wondered into the house
of my younger sister and her husband and gave birth to five kitt

24/25

In our house we had a cat with the grandi
ose name of Gonnosuke. Usually with cats
and dogs we know who the mother is but

ABCDEFGHIJKLMN
OPQRSTUVWXYZ
abcdefghijklmnopq
rstuvwxyz
1234567890&$¢£¥
fiflæœÆŒÅßÇÌÎÍÏã§†
-——/()''""":;.,!¡?¿

10/11

In our house we had a cat with the grandiose name of Gonnosuke. Usually with cats and dogs we know who the mother is but not the father. A cat with a large belly wondered into the house of my younger sister and he r husband and gave birth to five kittens. While the mother was a pure white thoroughbred Chinchila, the kitt ens were black and white tabbies of mixed breed. One of these came to our house about two weeks after its bi rth and was given the name Gonnosuke. At that time we already had one female Shiba dog and one female br own tabby cat in our house comprising only 13 tubo. The dog was called Momo and the cat Mii. My wife, who

16/17

In our house we had a cat with the grandiose name of Gonnosuke. Usually with cats and dogs we know who the mother is but not the f ather. A cat with a large belly wondered into the house of my young er sister and her husband and gave birth to five kittens. While the m

24/25

In our house we had a cat with the grandiose name of Gonnosuke. Usually with cats and d ogs we know who the mother is but not the f

ABCDEFGHIJKLMN
OPQRSTUVWXYZ
abcdefghijklmnopq
rstuvwxyz
1234567890&$¢£¥
fiflæœÆŒÅßÇÌÎÍÏã§
†-——/()''"''".:;.,!¡?¿

10/11

In our house we had a cat with the grandiose name of Gonnosuke. Usually with cats and dogs we know wh o the mother is but not the father. A cat with a large belly wondered into the house of my younger sister an d her husband and gave birth to five kittens. While the mother was a pure white thoroughbred Chinchila, t he kittens were black and white tabbies of mixed breed. One of these came to our house about two weeks a fter its birth and was given the name Gonnosuke. At that time we already had one female Shiba dog and on e female brown tabby cat in our house comprising only 13 tubo. The dog was called Momo and the cat Mii.

16/17

In our house we had a cat with the grandiose name of Gonnosuke. Usually with cats and dogs we know who the mother is but not the father. A cat with a large belly wondered into the house of my you nger sister and her husband and gave birth to five kittens. While th

24/25

In our house we had a cat with the grandios e name of Gonnosuke. Usually with cats and dogs we know who the mother is but not the

ABCDEFGHIJKL
MNOPQRSTUVW
XYZabcdefghijkl
mnopqrstuvwx
yz1234567890&
$¢£¥fiflæœÆŒ
ÅßçÌÎÍÏïã§†
‘—/()‘’“”:;.,!¡?¿

10/11

In our house we had a cat with the grandiose name of Gonnosuke. Usually with cats and dogs we know who the mother is but not the father. A cat with a large belly wo ndered into the house of my younger sister and her husband and gave birth to five k ittens. While the mother was a pure white thoroughbred Chinchila, the kittens were black and white tabbies of mixed breed. One of these came to our house about two weeks after its birth and was given the name Gonnosuke. At that time we already h

16/17

In our house we had a cat with the grandiose name of Gonnosuke. Usually with cats and dogs we know who the mother is but not the father. A cat with a la rge belly wondered into the house of my younger sis

24/25

In our house we had a cat with the grandiose name of Gonnosuke. Usu ally with cats and dogs we know w

ABCDEFGHIJKLMNOP
QRSTUVWXYZ
abcdefghijklmnopq
rstuvwxyz
1234567890&$¢£¥
fiflæœÆŒÅßçÌÎÍÏïã§†
·——/()''""""·;·,!¡?¿

10/11

In our house we had a cat with the grandiose name of Gonnosuke. Usually with cats and dogs we know who the mother is but not the father. A cat with a large belly wondered into the house of my younger sis ter and her husband and gave birth to five kittens. While the mother was a pure white thoroughbred Chi nchila, the kittens were black and white tabbies of mixed breed. One of these came to our house about t wo weeks after its birth and was given the name Gonnosuke. At that time we already had one female Shi ba dog and one female brown tabby cat in our house comprising only 13 tubo. The dog was called Momo a

16/17

In our house we had a cat with the grandiose name of Gonnosuke. Usually with cats and dogs we know who the mother is but not t he father. A cat with a large belly wondered into the house of my younger sister and her husband and gave birth to five kittens. W

24/25

In our house we had a cat with the grandio se name of Gonnosuke. Usually with cats an d dogs we know who the mother is but not

ABCDEFGHIJKLMN
OPQRSTUVWXYZ
abcdefghijklmnopq
rstuvwxyz
1234567890&$¢£¥
fiflæœÆŒÅßÇÌÎÍÏã§†
-——/()''""":;.,!¡?¿

10/11

In our house we had a cat with the grandiose name of Gonnosuke. Usually with cats and dogs we know who the mo
ther is but not the father. A cat with a large belly wondered into the house of my younger sister and her husband and
gave birth to five kittens. While the mother was a pure white thoroughbred Chinchila, the kittens were black and whi
te tabbies of mixed breed. One of these came to our house about two weeks after its birth and was given the name Go
nnosuke. At that time we already had one female Shiba dog and one female brown tabby cat in our house comprising
only 13 thubo. The dog was called Momo and the cat Mii. My wife, who was very much opposed to keeping cats and

16/17

In our house we had a cat with the grandiose name of Gonnosuke. Usual
ly with cats and dogs we know who the mother is but not the father. A ca
t with a large belly wondered into the house of my younger sister and her
husband and gave birth to five kittens. While the mother was a pure whit

24/25

In our house we had a cat with the grandiose na
me of Gonnosuke. Usually with cats and dogs w
e know who the mother is but not the father. A

ABCDEFGHIJKLMN
OPQRSTUVWXYZ
abcdefghijklmnopq
rstuvwxyz
1234567890&$¢£¥
fiflæœÆŒÅßÇÌÎÍÏã§†
——/()''""":;.,!¡?¿

10/11

In our house we had a cat with the grandiose name of Gonnosuke. Usually with cats and dogs we know who the mother is b ut not the father. A cat with a large belly wondered into the house of my younger sister and her husband and gave birth to fi ve kittens. While the mother was a pure white thoroughbred Chinchila, the kittens were black and white tabbies of mixed b reed. One of these came to our house about two weeks after its birth and was given the name Gonnosuke. At that time we al eady had one female Shiba dog and one female brown tabby cat in our house comprising only 13 thubo. The dog was called Momo and the cat Mii. My wife, who was very much opposed to keeping cats and dogs, instantaneously fell for its shaggy ap

16/17

In our house we had a cat with the grandiose name of Gonnosuke. Usually w ith cats and dogs we know who the mother is but not the father. A cat with a large belly wondered into the house of my younger sister and her husband an d gave birth to five kittens. While the mother was a pure white thoroughbred

24/25

In our house we had a cat with the grandiose name of Gonnosuke. Usually with cats and dogs we kno w who the mother is but not the father. A cat with

ABCDEFGHIJKLMN
OPQRSTUVWXYZ
abcdefghijklmnopq
rstuvwxyz
1234567890&$¢£¥
fiflæœÆŒÅßÇÌÎÍÏã§†
-——/()''"""':;.,!¡?¿

10/11

In our house we had a cat with the grandiose name of Gonnosuke. Usually with cats and dogs we know who the mother is but not the father. A cat with a large belly wondered into the house of my younger sister and her husband and gave birth to five kittens. While the mother was a pure white thoroughbred Chinchila, the kittens were black and white tabbies of mixed breed. One of these came to our house about two weeks after its birth and was given the name Gonnosuke. At that time we already had one female Shiba dog and one female brown tabby cat in our house comprising only 13 thubo. The dog was called Momo and the cat Mii. My wife, who was very much opposed

16/17

In our house we had a cat with the grandiose name of Gonnosuke. Usually with cats and dogs we know who the mother is but not the father. A cat with a large belly wondered into the house of my younger sister and her husband and gave birth to five kittens. While the mother was a

24/25

In our house we had a cat with the grandiose name of Gonnosuke. Usually with cats and dogs we know who the mother is but not the father.

ABCDEFGHIJKL
MNOPQRSTU
VWXYZ
abcdefghijklmnopq
rstuvwxyz
1234567890&$¢£¥
fiflæœÆŒÅßÇÌÎÍÏ
ã§†-–—/()''""":;.,!¡?¿

10/11

In our house we had a cat with the grandiose name of Gonnosuke. Usually with cats and dogs we know who the mother is but not the father. A cat with a large belly wondered into the hous e of my younger sister and her husband and gave birth to five kittens. While the mother was a pure white thoroughbred Chinchila, the kittens were black and white tabbies of mixed breed. One of these came to our house about two weeks after its birth and was given the name Gonn osuke. At that time we already had one female Shiba dog and one female brown tabby cat in

16/17

In our house we had a cat with the grandiose name of Gon nosuke. Usually with cats and dogs we know who the mot her is but not the father. A cat with a large belly wondered into the house of my younger sister and her husband and

24/25

In our house we had a cat with the gra ndiose name of Gonnosuke. Usually wi th cats and dogs we know who the mot

ABCDEFGHIJKL MNOPQRSTU VWXYZ
abcdefghijklmnopq rstuvwxyz
1234567890&$¢£¥ fiflœœÆŒÅßÇÌÎÍÏã §†-–—/() '’“”:;.,!¡?¿

10/11

In our house we had a cat with the grandiose name of Gonnosuke. Usually with cats and dogs we know who the mother is but not the father. A cat with a large belly wondered into the hous e of my younger sister and her husband and gave birth to five kittens. While the mother was a pure white thoroughbred Chinchila, the kittens were black and white tabbies of mixed breed. One of these came to our house about two weeks after its birth and was given the name Gonn osuke. At that time we already had one female Shiba dog and one female brown tabby cat in

16/17

In our house we had a cat with the grandiose name of Gon nosuke. Usually with cats and dogs we know who the mot her is but not the father. A cat with a large belly wondered into the house of my younger sister and her husband and

24/25

In our house we had a cat with the gra ndiose name of Gonnosuke. Usually wi th cats and dogs we know who the mot

ABCDEFGHIJKL MNOPQRSTU VWXYZ

abcdefghijklmno pqrstuvwxyz 1234567890&$¢£¥ fiflæœÆŒÅßÇÌÎÍÏ ã§†--——/()''""";.,!¡?¿

10/11

In our house we had a cat with the grandiose name of Gonnosuke. Usually with cats and d ogs we know who the mother is but not the father. A cat with a large belly wondered into t he house of my younger sister and her husband and gave birth to five kittens. While the m other was a pure white thoroughbred Chinchila, the kittens were black and white tabbies o f mixed breed. One of these came to our house about two weeks after its birth and was give n the name Gonnosuke. At that time we already had one female Shiba dog and one female

16/17

In our house we had a cat with the grandiose name of G onnosuke. Usually with cats and dogs we know who the mother is but not the father. A cat with a large belly won dered into the house of my younger sister and her husba

24/25

In our house we had a cat with the gr andiose name of Gonnosuke. Usually with cats and dogs we know who the

ABCDEFGHIJKLM
NOPQRSTUVWXYZ
abcdefghijklmnopq
rstuvwxyz
1234567890&$¢£¥
fiflæœÆŒÅßÇÌÎÍÏã§†
——/()''""":;.,!¡?¿

10/11

In our house we had a cat with the grandiose name of Gonnosuke. Usually with cats and dogs we know who the mother is but not the father. A cat with a large belly wondered into the house of my younger sister and h er husband and gave birth to five kittens. While the mother was a pure white thoroughbred Chinchila, the ki ttens were black and white tabbies of mixed breed. One of these came to our house about two weeks after its birth and was given the name Gonnosuke. At that time we already had one female Shiba dog and one female brown tabby cat in our house comprising only 13 thubo. The dog was called Momo and the cat Mii. My wife,

16/17

In our house we had a cat with the grandiose name of Gonnosuke. Usually with cats and dogs we know who the mother is but not the father. A cat with a large belly wondered into the house of my young er sister and her husband and gave birth to five kittens. While the

24/25

In our house we had a cat with the grandiose name of Gonnosuke. Usually with cats and d ogs we know who the mother is but not the f

ABCDEFGHIJKLM
NOPQRSTUVWXYZ
abcdefghijklmnopq
rstuvwxyz
1234567890&$¢£¥
fiflœœÆŒÅßÇÌÎÍÏã§
†-——/() '’"":;.,!¡?¿

10/11

In our house we had a cat with the grandiose name of Gonnosuke. Usually with cats and dogs we know who t
he mother is but not the father. A cat with a large belly wondered into the house of my younger sister and her
husband and gave birth to five kittens. While the mother was a pure white thoroughbred Chinchila, the kittens
were black and white tabbies of mixed breed. One of these came to our house about two weeks after its birth a
nd was given the name Gonnosuke. At that time we already had one female Shiba dog and one female brown
tabby cat in our house comprising only 13 thubo. The dog was called Momo and the cat Mii. My wife, who was

16/17

In our house we had a cat with the grandiose name of Gonnosuke. U
sually with cats and dogs we know who the mother is but not the fath
er. A cat with a large belly wondered into the house of my younger si
ster and her husband and gave birth to five kittens. While the mothe

24/25

In our house we had a cat with the grandiose
name of Gonnosuke. Usually with cats and d
ogs we know who the mother is but not the fat

ABCDEFGHIJKL MNOPQRSTU VWXYZ

abcdefghijklmnopq rstuvwxyz 1234567890&$¢£¥ fiflæœÆŒÅßÇÌÎÍÏã §†--——/()""""·:;.,!¡?¿

10/11

In our house we had a cat with the grandiose name of Gonnosuke. Usually with cats and dogs we know who the mother is but not the father. A cat with a large belly wondered into the house of my younger sister and her husband and gave birth to five kittens. While the mother was a pure white thoroughbred Chinchila, the kittens were black and white tabbies of mixed breed. One of these c ame to our house about two weeks after its birth and was given the name Gonnosuke. At that tim e we already had one female Shiba dog and one female brown tabby cat in our house comprising

16/17

In our house we had a cat with the grandiose name of Gonn osuke. Usually with cats and dogs we know who the mother is but not the father. A cat with a large belly wondered into th e house of my younger sister and her husband and gave birt

24/25

In our house we had a cat with the gran diose name of Gonnosuke. Usually with cats and dogs we know who the mother

ABCDEFGHIJKLMNO
PQRSTUVWXYZ
abcdefghijklmnopq
rstuvwxyz
1234567890&$¢£¥
fiflæœÆŒÅßÇÌÎÍÏã§
†-–—/()''""":;.,!¡?¿

10/11

In our house we had a cat with the grandiose name of Gonnosuke. Usually with cats and dogs we kno
w who the mother is but not the father. A cat with a large belly wondered into the house of my young
r sister and her husband and gave birth to five kittens. While the mother was a pure white thoroughbr
ed Chinchila, the kittens were black and white tabbies of mixed breed. One of these came to our hous
e about two weeks after its birth and was given the name Gonnosuke. At that time we already had one
female Shiba dog and one female brown tabby cat in our house comprising only 13 tubo. The dog was

16/17

In our house we had a cat with the grandiose name of Gonnosu
ke. Usually with cats and dogs we know who the mother is but
not the father. A cat with a large belly wondered into the house
of my younger sister and her husband and gave birth to five kitt

24/25

In our house we had a cat with the grandi
ose name of Gonnosuke. Usually with cats
and dogs we know who the mother is but

ITC Leawood Book Italic

ABCDEFGHIJKLMNO
PQRSTUVWXYZ
abcdefghijklmnopq
rstuvwxyz
1234567890&$¢£¥
fiflœœÆŒÅßÇÌÎÍÏĨã§
†-–——/()""'"":;.,¡i?¿

10/11

In our house we had a cat with the grandiose name of Gonnosuke. Usually with cats and dogs we know who the mother is but not the father. A cat with a large belly wondered into the house of my younger si ster and her husband and gave birth to five kittens. While the mother was a pure white thoroughbred C hinchila, the kittens were black and white tabbies of mixed breed. One of these came to our house abo ut two weeks after its birth and was given the name Gonnosuke. At that time we already had one femal e Shiba dog and one female brown tabby cat in our house comprising only 13 tubo. The dog was called

16/17

In our house we had a cat with the grandiose name of Gonnosu ke. Usually with cats and dogs we know who the mother is but n ot the father. A cat with a large belly wondered into the house of my younger sister and her husband and gave birth to five kittens

24/25

In our house we had a cat with the grandi ose name of Gonnosuke. Usually with cats and dogs we know who the mother is but

ABCDEFGHIJKLMN
OPQRSTUVWXYZ
abcdefghijklmnopq
rstuvwxyz
1234567890&$¢£¥
fiflæœÆŒÅßÇÌÎÍÏã
§†-–——/()''""":;.,!¡?¿

10/11

In our house we had a cat with the grandiose name of Gonnosuke. Usually with cats and dogs we know who the mother is but not the father. A cat with a large belly wondered into the house of my younger sister and her husband and gave birth to five kittens. While the mother was a pu re white thoroughbred Chinchila, the kittens were black and white tabbies of mixed breed. One of these came to our house about two weeks after its birth and was given the name Gonnosuk e. At that time we already had one female Shiba dog and one female brown tabby cat in our ho

16/17

In our house we had a cat with the grandiose name of Gon nosuke. Usually with cats and dogs we know who the moth er is but not the father. A cat with a large belly wondered in to the house of my younger sister and her husband and gav

24/25

In our house we had a cat with the gra ndiose name of Gonnosuke. Usually wi th cats and dogs we know who the mot

ABCDEFGHIJKLMN
OPQRSTUVWXYZ
abcdefghijklmnopq
rstuvwxyz
1234567890&$¢£¥
fiflœœÆŒÅßÇÌÎÍÏãã§
†-–——/()''""":;.,!¡?¿

10/11

In our house we had a cat with the grandiose name of Gonnosuke. Usually with cats and dogs we know who the mother is but not the father. A cat with a large belly wondered into the house of my younger sister and her husband and gave birth to five kittens. While the mother was a pure white thoroughbred Chinchila, the kittens were black and white tabbies of mixed breed. One of these ca me to our house about two weeks after its birth and was given the name Gonnosuke. At that time we already had one female Shiba dog and one female brown tabby cat in our house comprising on

16/17

In our house we had a cat with the grandiose name of Gonno suke. Usually with cats and dogs we know who the mother is but not the father. A cat with a large belly wondered into the house of my younger sister and her husband and gave birth t

24/25

In our house we had a cat with the gran diose name of Gonnosuke. Usually with cats and dogs we know who the mother

ABCDEFGHIJKLMN
OPQRSTUVWXYZ
abcdefghijklmnop
qrstuvwxyz
1234567890&
$¢£¥fiflæœÆŒ
ÅßçÌÎÍÏã§†
-–—/()''""·;·,!¡?¿

10/11

In our house we had a cat with the grandiose name of Gonnosuke. Usually with cats and dogs we know who the mother is but not the father. A cat with a large belly wondered int o the house of my younger sister and her husband and gave birth to five kittens. While t he mother was a pure white thoroughbred Chinchila, the kittens were black and white ta bbies of mixed breed. One of these came to our house about two weeks after its birth an d was given the name Gonnosuke. At that time we already had one female Shiba dog and

16/17

In our house we had a cat with the grandiose name of Gonnosuke. Usually with cats and dogs we know who t he mother is but not the father. A cat with a large belly wondered into the house of my younger sister and her

24/25

In our house we had a cat with the g randiose name of Gonnosuke. Usuall y with cats and dogs we know who t

A B C D E F G H I J K L M N O P Q R S T U V W X Y Z a b c d e f g h i j k l m n o p q r s t u v w x y z 1 2 3 4 5 6 7 8 9 0 &

$ ¢ £ ¥ fi fl æ œ Æ Œ Å ß ç ì î í ï ã § †

- - — / ( ) " " " " : ; . , ! ¡ ? ¿

10/11

In our house we had a cat with the grandiose name of Gonnosuke. Usually with cats and dogs we know who the mother is but not the father. A cat with a large belly wondered into the hou se of my younger sister and her husband and gave birth to five kittens. While the mother was a pure white thoroughbred Chinchila, the kittens were black and white tabbies of mixed bree d. One of these came to our house about two weeks after its birth and was given the name Go nnosuke. At that time we already had one female Shiba dog and one female brown tabby cat

16/17

In our house we had a cat with the grandiose name of Gon nosuke. Usually with cats and dogs we know who the mot her is but not the father. A cat with a large belly wondered into the house of my younger sister and her husband and

24/25

In our house we had a cat with the gra ndiose name of Gonnosuke. Usually wi th cats and dogs we know who the mot

ITC Leawood Black

ABCDEFGHIJKLM NOPQRSTUVWX YZabcdefghijklm nopqrstuvwxyz 1234567890& $¢£¥fiflæœÆŒ Åßçìîíïã§† --——/()''""":;.,!¡?¿

10/11

In our house we had a cat with the grandiose name of Gonnosuke. Usually with cats a
nd dogs we know who the mother is but not the father. A cat with a large belly wonder
ed into the house of my younger sister and her husband and gave birth to five kittens.
While the mother was a pure white thoroughbred Chinchila, the kittens were black an
d white tabbies of mixed breed. One of these came to our house about two weeks afte
r its birth and was given the name Gonnosuke. At that time we already had one femal

16/17

In our house we had a cat with the grandiose name of
Gonnosuke. Usually with cats and dogs we know who
the mother is but not the father. A cat with a large be
lly wondered into the house of my younger sister and

24/25

In our house we had a cat with the
grandiose name of Gonnosuke. Usu
ally with cats and dogs we know wh

ITC Leawood Black Italic

ABCDEFGHIJKL MNOPQRSTUVW XYZabcdefghijklm nopqrstuvwxyz 1234567890&

$¢£¥fiflæœÆŒ ÅßçÌÎÍÏã§†ー――/()""""'':;.,!¡?¿

10/11

In our house we had a cat with the grandiose name of Gonnosuke. Usually with cats and d ogs we know who the mother is but not the father. A cat with a large belly wondered into t he house of my younger sister and her husband and gave birth to five kittens. While the mo ther was a pure white thoroughbred Chinchila, the kittens were black and white tabbies of mixed breed. One of these came to our house about two weeks after its birth and was given the name Gonnosuke. At that time we already had one female Shiba dog and one female br

16/17

In our house we had a cat with the grandiose name of G onnosuke. Usually with cats and dogs we know who the mother is but not the father. A cat with a large belly won dered into the house of my younger sister and her husba

24/25

In our house we had a cat with the gr andiose name of Gonnosuke. Usually with cats and dogs we know who the

ABCDEFGHIJKLMN
OPQRSTUVWXYZ
abcdefghijklmnopq
rstuvwxyz
1234567890&
$¢£¥fiflæœÆŒ
ÅßÇÌÎÍÏã§†
——/()''""".;.,!¡?¿

10/11

In our house we had a cat with the grandiose name of Gonnosuke. Usually with cats and dogs we know who the mother is but not the father. A cat with a large belly wondered into the house of my younger sister and her husband and gave birth to five kittens. While the mother was a pure white t horoughbred Chinchila, the kittens were black and white tabbies of mixed breed. One of these cam e to our house about two weeks after its birth and was given the name Gonnosuke. At that time we already had one female Shiba dog and one female brown tabby cat in our house comprising only 1

16/17

In our house we had a cat with the grandiose name of Gonno suke. Usually with cats and dogs we know who the mother is but not the father. A cat with a large belly wondered into the house of my younger sister and her husband and gave birth to

24/25

In our house we had a cat with the grand iose name of Gonnosuke. Usually with ca ts and dogs we know who the mother is

ABCDEFGHIJKLMN
OPQRSTUVWXYZ
abcdefghijklmnopq
rstuvwxyz
1234567890&
$¢£¥fiflœœÆŒ
ÅßÇÌÎÍÏã§†
——/()''""":;.,!¡?¿

10/11

In our house we had a cat with the grandiose name of Gonnosuke. Usually with cats and dogs we kn ow who the mother is but not the father. A cat with a large belly wondered into the house of my youn ger sister and her husband and gave birth to five kittens. While the mother was a pure white thoroug hbred Chinchila, the kittens were black and white tabbies of mixed breed. One of these came to our ho use about two weeks after its birth and was given the name Gonnosuke. At that time we already had one female Shiba dog and one female brown tabby cat in our house comprising only 13 tubo. The dog

16/17

In our house we had a cat with the grandiose name of Gonnosu ke. Usually with cats and dogs we know who the mother is but not the father. A cat with a large belly wondered into the house of my younger sister and her husband and gave birth to five kit

24/25

In our house we had a cat with the grandi ose name of Gonnosuke. Usually with cat s and dogs we know who the mother is bu

ABCDEFGHIJKLM
NOPQRSTUVWX
YZabcdefghijklmno
pqrstuvwxyz
1234567890&
$¢£¥fiflæœÆŒ
ÅßÇÌÎÍÏã§†
--——/()''""".;.,!¡?¿

10/11

In our house we had a cat with the grandiose name of Gonnosuke. Usually with cats and dogs w e know who the mother is but not the father. A cat with a large belly wondered into the house of my younger sister and her husband and gave birth to five kittens. While the mother was a pure white thoroughbred Chinchila, the kittens were black and white tabbies of mixed breed. One of t hese came to our house about two weeks after its birth and was given the name Gonnosuke. At t hat time we already had one female Shiba dog and one female brown tabby cat in our house com

16/17

In our house we had a cat with the grandiose name of Gonn osuke. Usually with cats and dogs we know who the mother is but not the father. A cat with a large belly wondered into the house of my younger sister and her husband and gave bi

24/25

In our house we had a cat with the gran diose name of Gonnosuke. Usually with cats and dogs we know who the mother

ABCDEFGHIJKLMNOP
QRSTUVWXYZ
abcdefghijklmnopq
rstuvwxyz
1234567890&$¢£¥
fiflæœÆŒÅßçÌÎÍÏã§†
‑——/()''""":;.,!¡?¿

10/11

In our house we had a cat with the grandiose name of Gonnosuke. Usually with cats and dogs we know who the mother is but not the father. A cat with a large belly wondered into the house of my younger sister and her husband and gave birth to five kittens. While the mother was a pure white thoroughbred Chinchila, the kittens were black and white tabbies of mixed breed. One of these came to our house about two weeks after its birth and was given the name Gonnosuke. At that time we already had one female Shiba dog and one female brown tabby cat in our house comprising only 13 tubo. The dog was called Momo and the cat Mii. My wif

16/17

In our house we had a cat with the grandiose name of Gonnosuke. Usually with cats and dogs we know who the mother is but not the father. A cat with a large belly wondered into the house of my younger sister and her husband and gave birth to five kittens. While the m

24/25

In our house we had a cat with the grandiose name of Gonnosuke. Usually with cats and dogs we know who the mother is but not the

ABCDEFGHIJKLMNOP
QRSTUVWXYZ
abcdefghijklmnopq
rstuvwxyz
1234567890&$¢£¥
fiflæœÆŒÅßÇÌÎÍÏã§†
-——/()''""":;.,!¡?¿

10/11

In our house we had a cat with the grandiose name of Gonnosuke. Usually with cats and dogs we know who the mother is but not the father. A cat with a large belly wondered into the house of my younger sister and her husband and gave birth to five ki ttens. While the mother was a pure white thoroughbred Chinchila, the kittens were black and white tabbies of mixed breed. O ne of these came to our house about two weeks after its birth and was given the name Gonnosuke. At that time we already had one female Shiba dog and one female brown tabby cat in our house comprising only 13 tubo. The dog was called Momo and t he cat Mii. My wife, who was very much opposed to keeping cats and dogs, instantaneously fell for its shaggy appearance and

16/17

In our house we had a cat with the grandiose name of Gonnosuke. Usually wit h cats and dogs we know who the mother is but not the father. A cat with a lar ge belly wondered into the house of my younger sister and her husband and ga ve birth to five kittens. While the mother was a pure white thoroughbred Chinc

24/25

In our house we had a cat with the grandiose name of Gonnosuke. Usually with cats and dogs we know who the mother is but not the father. A cat with a la

ABCDEFGHIJKLMNO
PQRSTUVWXYZ
abcdefghijklmnopq
rstuvwxyz
1234567890&$¢£¥
fiflæœÆŒÅßÇÌÎÍÏã§†
-–——/()''""":;.,!¡?¿

10/11

In our house we had a cat with the grandiose name of Gonnosuke. Usually with cats and dogs we know who the mother is but not the father. A cat with a large belly wondered into the house of my younger sist er and her husband and gave birth to five kittens. While the mother was a pure white thoroughbred Chin chila, the kittens were black and white tabbies of mixed breed. One of these came to our house about t wo weeks after its birth and was given the name Gonnosuke. At that time we already had one female Shi ba dog and one female brown tabby cat in our house comprising only 13 tubo. The dog was called Mom

16/17

In our house we had a cat with the grandiose name of Gonnosuk e. Usually with cats and dogs we know who the mother is but not the father. A cat with a large belly wondered into the house of my younger sister and her husband and gave birth to five kittens. Wh

24/25

In our house we had a cat with the grandio se name of Gonnosuke. Usually with cats a nd dogs we know who the mother is but no

ABCDEFGHIJKLMNO
PQRSTUVWXYZ

abcdefghijklmnopq
rstuvwxyz
1234567890&$¢£¥
fiflæœÆŒÅßÇÌÎÍÏã§†
-–—/()'' ""·:;.,!¡?¿

10/11

In our house we had a cat with the grandiose name of Gonnosuke. Usually with cats and dogs we know who the mother is but not the father. A cat with a large belly wondered into the house of my younger sister and her husband and gave birth to five kittens. While the mother was a pure white thoroughbred Chinchila, the kittens were black and white tabbies of mixed breed. One of these came to our house about two weeks after its birth and was given the name Gonnosuke. At that time we already had one female Shiba dog and one female brown tabby cat in our house comprising only 13 tubo. The dog was called Momo and the cat Mii. My wife, who was very much opposed to keeping cats and dogs, instantaneo

16/17

In our house we had a cat with the grandiose name of Gonnosuke. Usually with cats and dogs we know who the mother is but not the father. A cat with a large belly wondered into the house of my younger sister and her husband and gave birth to five kittens. While the mother was a pure white thor

24/25

In our house we had a cat with the grandiose name of Gonnosuke. Usually with cats and dogs we know who the mother is but not the father. A cat

ABCDEFGHIJKLMN
OPQRSTUVWXYZ
abcdefghijklmnopq
rstuvwxyz
1234567890&$¢£¥
fiflæœÆŒÅßÇÌÎÍÏã§
†-–—/()''""":;.,!¡?¿

10/11

In our house we had a cat with the grandiose name of Gonnosuke. Usually with cats and dogs we know who the mother is but not the father. A cat with a large belly wondered into the house of my younger sister and her husband and gave birth to five kittens. While the mother was a pure white t horoughbred Chinchila, the kittens were black and white tabbies of mixed breed. One of these ca me to our house about two weeks after its birth and was given the name Gonnosuke. At that time we already had one female Shiba dog and one female brown tabby cat in our house comprising o

16/17

In our house we had a cat with the grandiose name of Gonno suke. Usually with cats and dogs we know who the mother is but not the father. A cat with a large belly wondered into the house of my younger sister and her husband and gave birth t

24/25

In our house we had a cat with the gran diose name of Gonnosuke. Usually with cats and dogs we know who the mother

ABCDEFGHIJKLMN
OPQRSTUVWXYZ

abcdefghijklmnopq
rstuvwxyz

1234567890&$¢£¥
fiflæœÆŒÅßÇÌÎÍÏĨã§†
'-—/()''""":;.,!¡?¿

10/11

In our house we had a cat with the grandiose name of Gonnosuke. Usually with cats and dogs we know who t
he mother is but not the father. A cat with a large belly wondered into the house of my younger sister and he
r husband and gave birth to five kittens. While the mother was a pure white thoroughbred Chinchila, the kitt
ens were black and white tabbies of mixed breed. One of these came to our house about two weeks after its b
irth and was given the name Gonnosuke. At that time we already had one female Shiba dog and one female
brown tabby cat in our house comprising only 13 tubo. The dog was called Momo and the cat Mii. My wife,

16/17

In our house we had a cat with the grandiose name of Gonnosuke.
Usually with cats and dogs we know who the mother is but not the f
ather. A cat with a large belly wondered into the house of my young
er sister and her husband and gave birth to five kittens. While the

24/25

In our house we had a cat with the grandiose
name of Gonnosuke. Usually with cats and d
ogs we know who the mother is but not the fa

ABCDEFGHIJKLMN
OPQRSTUVWXYZ
abcdefghijklmn
opqrstuvwxyz
1234567890&
$¢£¥fiflæœÆŒ
Åßçìîíïã§†
⌐-—/()˘˘""˝:;.,!¡?¿

10/11

In our house we had a cat with the grandiose name of Gonnosuke. Usually with cats an
d dogs we know who the mother is but not the father. A cat with a large belly wondere
d into the house of my younger sister and her husband and gave birth to five kittens.
While the mother was a pure white thoroughbred Chinchila, the kittens were black an
d white tabbies of mixed breed. One of these came to our house about two weeks afte
r its birth and was given the name Gonnosuke. At that time we already had one female

16/17

In our house we had a cat with the grandiose name of
Gonnosuke. Usually with cats and dogs we know who
the mother is but not the father. A cat with a large be
lly wondered into the house of my younger sister and

24/25

In our house we had a cat with the
grandiose name of Gonnosuke. Usu
ally with cats and dogs we know wh

ABCDEFGHIJKLMN
OPQRSTUVWXYZ
abcdefghijklmnopq
rstuvwxyz
1234567890&$¢£¥
fiflæœÆŒÅßÇÌÎÍÏã§
†-——/()''""":;.,!¡?¿

10/11

In our house we had a cat with the grandiose name of Gonnosuke. Usually with cats and dogs we kno w who the mother is but not the father. A cat with a large belly wondered into the house of my young er sister and her husband and gave birth to five kittens. While the mother was a pure white thoroughb red Chinchila, the kittens were black and white tabbies of mixed breed. One of these came to our hous e about two weeks after its birth and was given the name Gonnosuke. At that time we already had one female Shiba dog and one female brown tabby cat in our house comprising only 13 tubo. The dog was

16/17

In our house we had a cat with the grandiose name of Gonnosu ke. Usually with cats and dogs we know who the mother is but not the father. A cat with a large belly wondered into the house of my younger sister and her husband and gave birth to five kitt

24/25

In our house we had a cat with the grandi ose name of Gonnosuke. Usually with cats and dogs we know who the mother is but

ABCDEFGHIJKLMN
OPQRSTUVWXYZ
abcdefghijklmnopq
rstuvwxyz
1234567890&$¢£¥
fiflæœÆŒÅßÇÌÎÍÏã§†
——/()''""":;.,!¡?¿

10/11

In our house we had a cat with the grandiose name of Gonnosuke. Usually with cats and dogs we know who the mother is but not the father. A cat with a large belly wondered into the house of my younger sister and her husband and gave birth to five kittens. While the mother was a pure white thoroughbred Chinchila, the kittens were black and white tabbies of mixed breed. One of these came to our house about two weeks after its birth and was given the name Gonnosuke. At that time we already had one female Shiba dog and one female brown tabby cat in our house comprising only 13 tubo. The dog was called Momo and the cat Mii. My wife, who was very much opposed to k

16/17

In our house we had a cat with the grandiose name of Gonnosuke. Usually with cats and dogs we know who the mother is but not the father. A cat with a large belly wondered into the house of my younger sister and her husband and gave birth to five kittens. While the mother was a

24/25

In our house we had a cat with the grandiose name of Gonnosuke. Usually with cats and dogs we know who the mother is but not the father.

Like **Palatino Bold**

ABCDEFGHIJKL MNOPQRSTUVW XYZ

abcdefghijklmnopqr stuvwxyz

1234567890&$¢£¥

fiflæœÆŒÅßÇÌÎÍÏã

§†-–—/()''""·;.,!¡?¿

10/11

In our house we had a cat with the grandiose name of Gonnosuke. Usually with cats and dogs we kn ow who the mother is but not the father. A cat with a large belly wondered into the house of my you nger sister and her husband and gave birth to five kittens. While the mother was a pure white thoro ughbred Chinchila, the kittens were black and white tabbies of mixed breed. One of these came to o ur house about two weeks after its birth and was given the name Gonnosuke. At that time we alread y had one female Shiba dog and one female brown tabby cat in our house comprising only 13 tubo.

16/17

In our house we had a cat with the grandiose name of Gonnos uke. Usually with cats and dogs we know who the mother is b ut not the father. A cat with a large belly wondered into the ho use of my younger sister and her husband and gave birth to fiv

24/25

In our house we had a cat with the grandi ose name of Gonnosuke. Usually with cat s and dogs we know who the mother is b

Like **Palatino Bold Italic**

ABCDEFGHIJKLMN
OPQRSTUVWXYZ
abcdefghijklmnopq
rstuvwxyz
1234567890&$¢£¥
fiflæœÆŒÅßÇÌÎÍÏã§
†-——/()""""·;·.,!¡?¿

10/11

In our house we had a cat with the grandiose name of Gonnosuke. Usually with cats and dogs we know who the mother is but not the father. A cat with a large belly wondered into the house of my younger sist er and her husband and gave birth to five kittens. While the mother was a pure white thoroughbred Chinc hila, the kittens were black and white tabbies of mixed breed. One of these came to our house about two weeks after its birth and was given the name Gonnosuke. At that time we already had one female Shiba d og and one female brown tabby cat in our house comprising only 13 tubo. The dog was called Momo and

16/17

In our house we had a cat with the grandiose name of Gonnosuke. Usually with cats and dogs we know who the mother is but not t he father. A cat with a large belly wondered into the house of my younger sister and her husband and gave birth to five kittens. Wh

24/25

In our house we had a cat with the grandios e name of Gonnosuke. Usually with cats an d dogs we know who the mother is but not

ABCDEFGHIJKLM
NOPQRSTUVWXYZ
abcdefghijklmnopqrs
tuvwxyz
1234567890&$¢£¥
fiflæœÆŒÅßÇÌÎÍÏã
§†-–—/()''""".;.,!¡?¿

10/11

In our house we had a cat with the grandiose name of Gonnosuke. Usually with cats and dogs we know w
ho the mother is but not the father. A cat with a large belly wondered into the house of my younger sister
and her husband and gave birth to five kittens. While the mother was a pure white thoroughbred Chinchi
la, the kittens were black and white tabbies of mixed breed. One of these came to our house about two we
eks after its birth and was given the name Gonnosuke. At that time we already had one female Shiba dog
and one female brown tabby cat in our house comprising only 13 thubo. The dog was called Momo and th

16/17

In our house we had a cat with the grandiose name of Gonnosuke.
Usually with cats and dogs we know who the mother is but not th
e father. A cat with a large belly wondered into the house of my yo
unger sister and her husband and gave birth to five kittens. While

24/25

In our house we had a cat with the grandios
e name of Gonnosuke. Usually with cats an
d dogs we know who the mother is but not

Aldine 721 Light Italic
Like **Plantin Light Italic**

ABCDEFGHIJKLM
NOPQRSTUVWXYZ
abcdefghijklmnopqrstu
vwxyz
1234567890&$¢£¥
fiflæœÆŒÅßÇÌÎÍÏã§†
———/()''""";.,!¡?¿

10/11

In our house we had a cat with the grandiose name of Gonnosuke. Usually with cats and dogs we know who the m other is but not the father. A cat with a large belly wondered into the house of my younger sister and her husband a nd gave birth to five kittens. While the mother was a pure white thoroughbred Chinchila, the kittens were black an d white tabbies of mixed breed. One of these came to our house about two weeks after its birth and was given the na me Gonnosuke. At that time we already had one female Shiba dog and one female brown tabby cat in our house co mprising only 13 thubo. The dog was called Momo and the cat Mii. My wife, who was very much opposed to keepi

16/17

In our house we had a cat with the grandiose name of Gonnosuke. Usu ally with cats and dogs we know who the mother is but not the father. A cat with a large belly wondered into the house of my younger sister and her husband and gave birth to five kittens. While the mother was a pure

24/25

In our house we had a cat with the grandiose n ame of Gonnosuke. Usually with cats and dogs we know who the mother is but not the father.

ABCDEFGHIJ KLMNOPQRSTU VWXYZ

abcdefghijklmnopq rstuvwxyz

1234567890&$¢£¥

fiflæœÆŒÅßÇÌÎÍÏã§

†-–—/()''""":;.,!¡?¿

10/11

In our house we had a cat with the grandiose name of Gonnosuke. Usually with cats and dogs we know wh o the mother is but not the father. A cat with a large belly wondered into the house of my younger sister a nd her husband and gave birth to five kittens. While the mother was a pure white thoroughbred Chinchil a, the kittens were black and white tabbies of mixed breed. One of these came to our house about two wee ks after its birth and was given the name Gonnosuke. At that time we already had one female Shiba dog an d one female brown tabby cat in our house comprising only 13 thubo. The dog was called Momo and the

16/17

In our house we had a cat with the grandiose name of Gonnosuke. Usually with cats and dogs we know who the mother is but not th e father. A cat with a large belly wondered into the house of my yo unger sister and her husband and gave birth to five kittens. While

24/25

In our house we had a cat with the grandios e name of Gonnosuke. Usually with cats an d dogs we know who the mother is but not t

ABCDEFGHIJK LMNOPQRSTU VWXYZ

abcdefghijklmnopq rstuvwxyz

1234567890&$¢£¥ fiflæœÆŒÅßÇÌÎÍÏãß†
—/()''""""·;·,!¡?¿

10/11

In our house we had a cat with the grandiose name of Gonnosuke. Usually with cats and dogs we know who the mo ther is but not the father. A cat with a large belly wondered into the house of my younger sister and her husband and gave birth to five kittens. While the mother was a pure white thoroughbred Chinchila, the kittens were black and whi te tabbies of mixed breed. One of these came to our house about two weeks after its birth and was given the name Gon nosuke. At that time we already had one female Shiba dog and one female brown tabby cat in our house comprising o nly 13 thubo. The dog was called Momo and the cat Mii. My wife, who was very much opposed to keeping cats and

16/17

In our house we had a cat with the grandiose name of Gonnosuke. Usua lly with cats and dogs we know who the mother is but not the father. A c at with a large belly wondered into the house of my younger sister and he r husband and gave birth to five kittens. While the mother was a pure w

24/25

In our house we had a cat with the grandiose na me of Gonnosuke. Usually with cats and dogs w e know who the mother is but not the father. A c

ABCDEFGHIJK
LMNOPQRSTU
VWXYZ
abcdefghijklmnopq
rstuvwxyz
1234567890&$¢£¥
fiflæœÆŒÅßÇÌÎÍÏã
§†‒–—/()''""".;.,!¡?¿

10/11

In our house we had a cat with the grandiose name of Gonnosuke. Usually with cats and dogs we kno
w who the mother is but not the father. A cat with a large belly wondered into the house of my young
er sister and her husband and gave birth to five kittens. While the mother was a pure white thorough
bred Chinchila, the kittens were black and white tabbies of mixed breed. One of these came to our ho
use about two weeks after its birth and was given the name Gonnosuke. At that time we already had o
ne female Shiba dog and one female brown tabby cat in our house comprising only 13 thubo. The dog

16/17

In our house we had a cat with the grandiose name of Gonnosu
ke. Usually with cats and dogs we know who the mother is but
not the father. A cat with a large belly wondered into the house
of my younger sister and her husband and gave birth to five kitt

24/25

In our house we had a cat with the grandi
ose name of Gonnosuke. Usually with cat
s and dogs we know who the mother is but

Aldine 721 Bold Italic
Like **Plantin Bold Italic**

ABCDEFGHIƷK
LMNOPQRSTU
VWXYZ
abcdefghijklmnopq
rstuvwxyz
1234567890&$¢£¥
fiflæœÆŒÅßÇÌÎÍÏã
§†-——/()''""";.,!¡?¿

10/11

In our house we had a cat with the grandiose name of Gonnosuke. Usually with cats and dogs we know w ho the mother is but not the father. A cat with a large belly wondered into the house of my younger sister a nd her husband and gave birth to five kittens. While the mother was a pure white thoroughbred Chinchila, the kittens were black and white tabbies of mixed breed. One of these came to our house about two weeks a fter its birth and was given the name Gonnosuke. At that time we already had one female Shiba dog and o ne female brown tabby cat in our house comprising only 13 thubo. The dog was called Momo and the cat

16/17

In our house we had a cat with the grandiose name of Gonnosuke. Usually with cats and dogs we know who the mother is but not th e father. A cat with a large belly wondered into the house of my yo unger sister and her husband and gave birth to five kittens. While

24/25

In our house we had a cat with the grandio se name of Gonnosuke. Usually with cats a nd dogs we know who the mother is but not

Like **Plantin Bold Condensed**

ABCDEFGHIJKLMNOPQ
RSTUVWXYZ
abcdefghijklmnopq
rstuvwxyz
1234567890&$¢£¥
fiflæœÆŒÅßÇÌÎÍÏã§†
–––—/()'""'":;.,!¡?¿

10/11

In our house we had a cat with the grandiose name of Gonnosuke. Usually with cats and dogs we know who the mother i s but not the father. A cat with a large belly wondered into the house of my younger sister and her husband and gave bir th to five kittens. While the mother was a pure white thoroughbred Chinchila, the kittens were black and white tabbies of mixed breed. One of these came to our house about two weeks after its birth and was given the name Gonnosuke. At t hat time we already had one female Shiba dog and one female brown tabby cat in our house comprising only 13 thubo. The dog was called Momo and the cat Mii. My wife, who was very much opposed to keeping cats and dogs, instantaneou

16/17

In our house we had a cat with the grandiose name of Gonnosuke. Usually with cats and dogs we know who the mother is but not the father. A cat wit h a large belly wondered into the house of my younger sister and her husb and and gave birth to five kittens. While the mother was a pure white thor

24/25

In our house we had a cat with the grandiose nam e of Gonnosuke. Usually with cats and dogs we kn ow who the mother is but not the father. A cat wit

Like **Sabon Roman**

ABCDEFGHIJKLMN
OPQRSTUVWXYZ
abcdefghijklmnopq
rstuvwxyz
1234567890&$¢£¥
fiflæœÆŒÅßÇÌÎÍÏã§†
——–/()''""":;.,!¡?¿

10/11

In our house we had a cat with the grandiose name of Gonnosuke. Usually with cats and dogs we know who the mother is but not the father. A cat with a large belly wondered into the house of my younger sist er and her husband and gave birth to five kittens. While the mother was a pure white thoroughbred Chin chila, the kittens were black and white tabbies of mixed breed. One of these came to our house about tw o weeks after its birth and was given the name Gonnosuke. At that time we already had one female Shiba dog and one female brown tabby cat in our house comprising only 13 thubo. The dog was called Momo

16/17

In our house we had a cat with the grandiose name of Gonnosuk e. Usually with cats and dogs we know who the mother is but not the father. A cat with a large belly wondered into the house of my younger sister and her husband and gave birth to five kittens. Wh

24/25

In our house we had a cat with the grandios e name of Gonnosuke. Usually with cats an d dogs we know who the mother is but not

ABCDEFGHIJKLM NOPQRSTUVWXYZ
abcdefghijklmnopq rstuvwxyz
1234567890&$¢£¥ fiflæœÆŒÅßÇÌÎÍÏãß †-––—/()''""":;.,!¡?¿

10/11

In our house we had a cat with the grandiose name of Gonnosuke. Usually with cats and dogs we know w ho the mother is but not the father. A cat with a large belly wondered into the house of my younger sister and her husband and gave birth to five kittens. While the mother was a pure white thoroughbred Chinchil a, the kittens were black and white tabbies of mixed breed. One of these came to our house about two wee ks after its birth and was given the name Gonnosuke. At that time we already had one female Shiba dog and one female brown tabby cat in our house comprising only 13 thubo. The dog was called Momo and

16/17

In our house we had a cat with the grandiose name of Gonnosuke. Usually with cats and dogs we know who the mother is but not th e father. A cat with a large belly wondered into the house of my y ounger sister and her husband and gave birth to five kittens. While

24/25

In our house we had a cat with the grandios e name of Gonnosuke. Usually with cats an d dogs we know who the mother is but not

ABCDEFGHIJKLM
NOPQRSTUVWX
YZabcdefghijklmnop
qrstuvwxyz
1234567890&$¢£¥
fiflæœÆŒÅßÇÌÎÍÏã§
†----——/()''""":;.,!¡?¿

10/11

In our house we had a cat with the grandiose name of Gonnosuke. Usually with cats and dogs we know who the mother is but not the father. A cat with a large belly wondered into the house of my younger sis ter and her husband and gave birth to five kittens. While the mother was a pure white thoroughbred Ch inchila, the kittens were black and white tabbies of mixed breed. One of these came to our house about two weeks after its birth and was given the name Gonnosuke. At that time we already had one female Sh iba dog and one female brown tabby cat in our house comprising only 13 thubo. The dog was called Mo

16/17

In our house we had a cat with the grandiose name of Gonnosuk e. Usually with cats and dogs we know who the mother is but no t the father. A cat with a large belly wondered into the house of my younger sister and her husband and gave birth to five kittens.

24/25

In our house we had a cat with the grandio se name of Gonnosuke. Usually with cats a nd dogs we know who the mother is but no

ABCDEFGHIJKL
MNOPQRSTU
VWXYZ
abcdefghijklmnopq
rstuvwxyz
1234567890&$¢£¥
fiflæœÆŒÅßÇÌÎÍÏãS
†-——/()''""";.,!¡?¿

10/11

In our house we had a cat with the grandiose name of Gonnosuke. Usually with cats and dogs we know who the mother is but not the father. A cat with a large belly wondered into the house of my younger sis ter and her husband and gave birth to five kittens. While the mother was a pure white thoroughbred Ch inchila, the kittens were black and white tabbies of mixed breed. One of these came to our house about t wo weeks after its birth and was given the name Gonnosuke. At that time we already had one female Sh iba dog and one female brown tabby cat in our house comprising only 13 thubo. The dog was called Mo

16/17

In our house we had a cat with the grandiose name of Gonnosuk e. Usually with cats and dogs we know who the mother is but no t the father. A cat with a large belly wondered into the house of my younger sister and her husband and gave birth to five kittens.

24/25

In our house we had a cat with the grandio se name of Gonnosuke. Usually with cats a nd dogs we know who the mother is but no

ABCDEFGHIJKLMN
OPQRSTUVWXYZ
abcdefghijklmnopq
rstuvwxyz
1234567890&$¢£¥
fiflæœÆŒÅßÇÌÎÍÏā§†
——/()''""".;.,!¡¿?

10/11

In our house we had a cat with the grandiose name of Gonnosuke. Usually with cats and dogs we know w
ho the mother is but not the father. A cat with a large belly wondered into the house of my younger sister
and her husband and gave birth to five kittens. While the mother was a pure white thoroughbred Chinchil
a, the kittens were black and white tabbies of mixed breed. One of these came to our house about two wee
ks after its birth and was given the name Gonnosuke. At that time we already had one female Shiba dog a
nd one female brown tabby cat in our house comprising only 13 tubo. The dog was called Momo and the c

16/17

In our house we had a cat with the grandiose name of Gonnosuke.
Usually with cats and dogs we know who the mother is but not t
he father. A cat with a large belly wondered into the house of my
younger sister and her husband and gave birth to five kittens. Whi

24/25

In our house we had a cat with the grandios
e name of Gonnosuke. Usually with cats an
d dogs we know who the mother is but not

ABCDEFGHIJKLMN
OPQRSTUVWXYZ
abcdefghijklmnopq
rstuvwxyz
1234567890&$¢£¥
fiflæœÆŒÅßÇÌÎÍÏã§†
——/()''""":;.,!¡¿?

10/11

In our house we had a cat with the grandiose name of Gonnosuke. Usually with cats and dogs we know who the mothe r is but not the father. A cat with a large belly wondered into the house of my younger sister and her husband and gave birth to five kittens. While the mother was a pure white thoroughbred Chinchila, the kittens were black and white tabb ies of mixed breed. One of these came to our house about two weeks after its birth and was given the name Gonnosuke. At that time we already had one female Shiba dog and one female brown tabby cat in our house comprising only 13 tub o. The dog was called Momo and the cat Mii. My wife, who was very much opposed to keeping cats and dogs, instant

16/17

In our house we had a cat with the grandiose name of Gonnosuke. Usuall y with cats and dogs we know who the mother is but not the father. A cat with a large belly wondered into the house of my younger sister and her hu sband and gave birth to five kittens. While the mother was a pure white th

24/25

In our house we had a cat with the grandiose na me of Gonnosuke. Usually with cats and dogs we know who the mother is but not the father. A cat

ABCDEFGHIJKLMN
OPQRSTUVWXYZ
abcdefghijklmnopq
rstuvwxyz
1234567890&$¢£¥
fiflæœÆŒÅßÇÌÎÍÏãŞ
†--——/()''""":;.,!¡¿?

10/11

In our house we had a cat with the grandiose name of Gonnosuke. Usually with cats and dogs we know who the mother is but not the father. A cat with a large belly wondered into the house of my younger si ster and her husband and gave birth to five kittens. While the mother was a pure white thoroughbred C hinchila, the kittens were black and white tabbies of mixed breed. One of these came to our house about two weeks after its birth and was given the name Gonnosuke. At that time we already had one female S hiba dog and one female brown tabby cat in our house comprising only 13 tubo. The dog was called Mo

16/17

In our house we had a cat with the grandiose name of Gonnosuk e. Usually with cats and dogs we know who the mother is but n ot the father. A cat with a large belly wondered into the house of my younger sister and her husband and gave birth to five kittens.

24/25

In our house we had a cat with the grandio se name of Gonnosuke. Usually with cats a nd dogs we know who the mother is but n

ABCDEFGHIJKLMN
OPQRSTUVWXYZ
abcdefghijklmnopq
rstuvwxyz
1234567890&$¢£¥
fiflæœÆŒÅßÇÌÎÍÏã§†
——/()''""".;.,!¡¿?

10/11

In our house we had a cat with the grandiose name of Gonnosuke. Usually with cats and dogs we know who the mother is but not the father. A cat with a large belly wondered into the house of my younger sister and her husband and gave birth to five kittens. While the mother was a pure white thoroughbred Chinchila, the kittens were black and white tabbies of mixed breed. One of these came to our house about two weeks after its birth and was given the name Gonnosuke. At that time we already had one female Shiba dog and one female brown tabby cat in our house comprising only 13 tubo. The dog was called Momo and the cat Mii. My wife, who was very much opposed to keeping

16/17

In our house we had a cat with the grandiose name of Gonnosuke. Usually with cats and dogs we know who the mother is but not the father. A cat with a large belly wondered into the house of my younger sister and her husband and gave birth to five kittens. While the mother was a pure

24/25

In our house we had a cat with the grandiose name of Gonnosuke. Usually with cats and dogs we know who the mother is but not the father. A

ABCDEFGHIJKLMN
OPQRSTUVWXYZ
abcdefghijklmnopq
rstuvwxyz
1234567890&$¢£¥
fiflæœÆŒÅßÇÌÎÍÏã§
†-–—/()''""".;.,!¡¿?

10/11

In our house we had a cat with the grandiose name of Gonnosuke. Usually with cats and dogs we kn
ow who the mother is but not the father. A cat with a large belly wondered into the house of my yo
unger sister and her husband and gave birth to five kittens. While the mother was a pure white thor
oughbred Chinchila, the kittens were black and white tabbies of mixed breed. One of these came to o
ur house about two weeks after its birth and was given the name Gonnosuke. At that time we alread
y had one female Shiba dog and one female brown tabby cat in our house comprising only 13 tubo. T

16/17

In our house we had a cat with the grandiose name of Gonnos
uke. Usually with cats and dogs we know who the mother is b
ut not the father. A cat with a large belly wondered into the ho
use of my younger sister and her husband and gave birth to fiv

24/25

In our house we had a cat with the grandi
ose name of Gonnosuke. Usually with cat
s and dogs we know who the mother is b

ABCDEFGHIJKLM
NOPQRSTUVWX
YZabcdefghijklmnopq
rstuvwxyz
1234567890&$¢£¥
fiflæœÆŒÅßÇÌÎÍÏã§
†––——/()''""''":;.,!¡¿?

10/11

In our house we had a cat with the grandiose name of Gonnosuke. Usually with cats and dogs we know who t
he mother is but not the father. A cat with a large belly wondered into the house of my younger sister and her
husband and gave birth to five kittens. While the mother was a pure white thoroughbred Chinchila, the kitten
s were black and white tabbies of mixed breed. One of these came to our house about two weeks after its birth
and was given the name Gonnosuke. At that time we already had one female Shiba dog and one female brow
n tabby cat in our house comprising only 13 tubo. The dog was called Momo and the cat Mii. My wife, who w

16/17

In our house we had a cat with the grandiose name of Gonnosuke. U
sually with cats and dogs we know who the mother is but not the fat
her. A cat with a large belly wondered into the house of my younger s
ister and her husband and gave birth to five kittens. While the moth

24/25

In our house we had a cat with the grandiose
name of Gonnosuke. Usually with cats and d
ogs we know who the mother is but not the fa

ABCDEFGHIJKLM
NOPQRSTUVWX
YZabcdefghijklmn
opqrstuvwxyz
1234567890&$¢£¥
fiflæœÆŒÅßÇÌÎÍÏã
§†-–—/()''""":;.,!¡?¿

10/11

In our house we had a cat with the grandiose name of Gonnosuke. Usually with cats and dogs we know who the mother is but not the father. A cat with a large belly wondered into the ho use of my younger sister and her husband and gave birth to five kittens. While the mother wa s a pure white thoroughbred Chinchila, the kittens were black and white tabbies of mixed bre ed. One of these came to our house about two weeks after its birth and was given the name G onnosuke. At that time we already had one female Shiba dog and one female brown tabby cat

16/17

In our house we had a cat with the grandiose name of Gon nosuke. Usually with cats and dogs we know who the mot her is but not the father. A cat with a large belly wondered into the house of my younger sister and her husband and g

24/25

In our house we had a cat with the gra ndiose name of Gonnosuke. Usually wi th cats and dogs we know who the mo

ABCDEFGHIJKL
MNOPQRSTUVW
XYZabcdefghijklmn
opqrstuvwxyz
1234567890&$¢£¥
fiflæœÆŒÅßÇÌÎÍÏã
§†-––—/()''""'';:;.,!¡?¿

10/11

In our house we had a cat with the grandiose name of Gonnosuke. Usually with cats and dogs we kn
ow who the mother is but not the father. A cat with a large belly wondered into the house of my youn
ger sister and her husband and gave birth to five kittens. While the mother was a pure white thorou
ghbred Chinchila, the kittens were black and white tabbies of mixed breed. One of these came to our
house about two weeks after its birth and was given the name Gonnosuke. At that time we already h
ad one female Shiba dog and one female brown tabby cat in our house comprising only 13 tubo. The

16/17

In our house we had a cat with the grandiose name of Gonnos
uke. Usually with cats and dogs we know who the mother is b
ut not the father. A cat with a large belly wondered into the ho
use of my younger sister and her husband and gave birth to fiv

24/25

In our house we had a cat with the grand
iose name of Gonnosuke. Usually with ca
ts and dogs we know who the mother is b

Schneidler Black

ABCDEFGHIJKL
MNOPQRSTUV
WXYZabcdefghijk
lmnopqrstuvwxyz
1234567890&
$¢£¥fiflæœÆŒ
ÅßÇÌÎÍÏã§†
——/()""""".;.,!¡¿?

10/11

In our house we had a cat with the grandiose name of Gonnosuke. Usually with cats and d ogs we know who the mother is but not the father. A cat with a large belly wondered into the house of my younger sister and her husband and gave birth to five kittens. While the mother was a pure white thoroughbred Chinchila, the kittens were black and white tabbie s of mixed breed. One of these came to our house about two weeks after its birth and was given the name Gonnosuke. At that time we already had one female Shiba dog and one fe

16/17

In our house we had a cat with the grandiose name of G onnosuke. Usually with cats and dogs we know who the mother is but not the father. A cat with a large belly wo ndered into the house of my younger sister and her hus

24/25

In our house we had a cat with the gr andiose name of Gonnosuke. Usually with cats and dogs we know who the

ABCDEFGHIJKL
MNOPQRSTUVW
XYZabcdefghijklm
nopqrstuvwxyz123
4567890&$¢£¥fifl
æœÆŒÅßÇÌÎÍÏã
§†---——/()'''"""";,.,!¡?¿

10/11

In our house we had a cat with the grandiose name of Gonnosuke. Usually with cats and dogs we know who the mother is but not the father. A cat with a large belly wondered into the house of my younger sister and her husband and gave birth to five kittens. While the mother was a p ure white thoroughbred Chinchila, the kittens were black and white tabbies of mixed breed. On e of these came to our house about two weeks after its birth and was given the name Gonnosuk e. At that time we already had one female Shiba dog and one female brown tabby cat in our ho

16/17

In our house we had a cat with the grandiose name of Gon nosuke. Usually with cats and dogs we know who the moth er is but not the father. A cat with a large belly wondered i nto the house of my younger sister and her husband and ga

24/25

In our house we had a cat with the gra ndiose name of Gonnosuke. Usually wi th cats and dogs we know who the mot

ABCDEFGHIJKLMN
OPQRSTUVWXYZ
abcdefghijklmnopq
rstuvwxyz
1234567890&$¢£¥
fiflæœÆŒÅßçÌÎÍÏã§
†-–—/()'''""•:;.,!¡?¿

10/11

In our house we had a cat with the grandiose name of Gonnosuke. Usually with cats and dogs we know who the mother is but not the father. A cat with a large belly wondered into the house of my younger si ster and her husband and gave birth to five kittens. While the mother was a pure white thoroughbred C hinchila, the kittens were black and white tabbies of mixed breed. One of these came to our house abou t two weeks after its birth and was given the name Gonnosuke. At that time we already had one female Shiba dog and one female brown tabby cat in our house comprising only 13 tubo. The dog was called M

16/17

In our house we had a cat with the grandiose name of Gonnosuk e. Usually with cats and dogs we know who the mother is but no t the father. A cat with a large belly wondered into the house of my younger sister and her husband and gave birth to five kittens

24/25

In our house we had a cat with the grandio se name of Gonnosuke. Usually with cats a nd dogs we know who the mother is but no

ABCDEFGHIJKLM
NOPQRSTUVWX
YZabcdefghijklmn
opqrstuvwxyz
1234567890&$¢£¥
fiflæœÆŒÅßÇÌÎÍÏã
§†-–——/()''""":;.,!¡?¿

10/11

In our house we had a cat with the grandiose name of Gonnosuke. Usually with cats and dogs we kn ow who the mother is but not the father. A cat with a large belly wondered into the house of my youn ger sister and her husband and gave birth to five kittens. While the mother was a pure white thoroug hbred Chinchila, the kittens were black and white tabbies of mixed breed. One of these came to our h ouse about two weeks after its birth and was given the name Gonnosuke. At that time we already had one female Shiba dog and one female brown tabby cat in our house comprising only 13 tubo. The dog

16/17

In our house we had a cat with the grandiose name of Gonnos uke. Usually with cats and dogs we know who the mother is bu t not the father. A cat with a large belly wondered into the hous e of my younger sister and her husband and gave birth to five k

24/25

In our house we had a cat with the grandi ose name of Gonnosuke. Usually with cat s and dogs we know who the mother is bu

Like **Trump Mediaeval Italic**

ABCDEFGHIJKLMN
OPQRSTUVWXYZ
abcdefghijklmnopq
rstuvwxyz
1234567890&$¢£¥
fiflæœÆŒÅßÇÌÎÍÏã§
†-——/()'''""":;.,!¡¿¿

10/11

*In our house we had a cat with the grandiose name of Gonnosuke. Usually with cats and dogs we kn
ow who the mother is but not the father. A cat with a large belly wondered into the house of my youn
ger sister and her husband and gave birth to five kittens. While the mother was a pure white thorough
bred Chinchila, the kittens were black and white tabbies of mixed breed. One of these came to our ho
use about two weeks after its birth and was given the name Gonnosuke. At that time we already had
one female Shiba dog and one female brown tabby cat in our house comprising only 13 tubo. The dog*

16/17

*In our house we had a cat with the grandiose name of Gonnos
uke. Usually with cats and dogs we know who the mother is b
ut not the father. A cat with a large belly wondered into the ho
use of my younger sister and her husband and gave birth to five*

24/25

*In our house we had a cat with the grand
iose name of Gonnosuke. Usually with ca
ts and dogs we know who the mother is b*

ABCDEFGHIJKLM
NOPQRSTUVWX
YZabcdefghijklmno
pqrstuvwxyz
1234567890&$¢£¥
fiflæœÆŒÅßÇÌÎÍÏã
§†-–—/()''""·;.,!¡?¿

10/11

In our house we had a cat with the grandiose name of Gonnosuke. Usually with cats and dogs we know who the mother is but not the father. A cat with a large belly wondered into the house of m y younger sister and her husband and gave birth to five kittens. While the mother was a pure whit e thoroughbred Chinchila, the kittens were black and white tabbies of mixed breed. One of these came to our house about two weeks after its birth and was given the name Gonnosuke. At that ti me we already had one female Shiba dog and one female brown tabby cat in our house comprising

16/17

In our house we had a cat with the grandiose name of Gonn osuke. Usually with cats and dogs we know who the mother is but not the father. A cat with a large belly wondered into t he house of my younger sister and her husband and gave birt

24/25

In our house we had a cat with the gran diose name of Gonnosuke. Usually with cats and dogs we know who the mother

ABCDEFGHIJKLM NOPQRSTUVWX YZabcdefghijklmno pqrstuvwxyz 1234567890&$¢£¥ fiflæœÆŒÅßÇÌÎÍÏã §†-–——/()''""":;.,!¡?¿

10/11

In our house we had a cat with the grandiose name of Gonnosuke. Usually with cats and dogs we know who the mother is but not the father. A cat with a large belly wondered into the house of my younger sister and her husband and gave birth to five kittens. While the mother was a pure white thoroughbred Chinchila, the kittens were black and white tabbies of mixed breed. One of these ca me to our house about two weeks after its birth and was given the name Gonnosuke. At that time we already had one female Shiba dog and one female brown tabby cat in our house comprising on

16/17

In our house we had a cat with the grandiose name of Gonno suke. Usually with cats and dogs we know who the mother is but not the father. A cat with a large belly wondered into the house of my younger sister and her husband and gave birth t

24/25

In our house we had a cat with the gran diose name of Gonnosuke. Usually with cats and dogs we know who the mother

ABCDEFGHIJK LMNOPQRST UVWXYZ abcdefghijklmno pqrstuvwxyz 1234567890&$¢£¥ fiflæœÆŒÅßÇÌÎÍÏ ã§†----/()''""":;.,!!?¿

10/11

In our house we had a cat with the grandiose name of Gonnosuke. Usually with cats a
nd dogs we know who the mother is but not the father. A cat with a large belly wonde
red into the house of my younger sister and her husband and gave birth to five kitten
s. While the mother was a pure white thoroughbred Chinchila, the kittens were black
and white tabbies of mixed breed. One of these came to our house about two weeks af
ter its birth and was given the name Gonnosuke. At that time we already had one fem

16/17

In our house we had a cat with the grandiose name of
Gonnosuke. Usually with cats and dogs we know who
the mother is but not the father. A cat with a large be
lly wondered into the house of my younger sister and

24/25

In our house we had a cat with the
grandiose name of Gonnosuke. Usu
ally with cats and dogs we know w

ABCDEFGHIJKLMN
OPQRSTUVWXYZ
abcdefghijklmnopq
rstuvwxyz
1234567890&$¢£¥
fiflæœÆŒÅßÇÌÎÍÏã§†
-——/()''""":;.,!¡?¿

10/11

In our house we had a cat with the grandiose name of Gonnosuke. Usually with cats and dogs we know who the mother is but not the father. A cat with a large belly wondered into the house of my younger sister and her husband and gave birth to five kittens. While the mother was a pure white thoroughbred Chinchila, the kittens were black and white tabbies of mixed breed. One of these came to our house about two weeks afte r its birth and was given the name Gonnosuke. At that time we already had one female Shiba dog and one f emale brown tabby cat in our house comprising only 13 tubo. The dog was called Momo and the cat Mii. M

16/17

In our house we had a cat with the grandiose name of Gonnosuke. Usually with cats and dogs we know who the mother is but not the father. A cat with a large belly wondered into the house of my youn ger sister and her husband and gave birth to five kittens. While the

24/25

In our house we had a cat with the grandios e name of Gonnosuke. Usually with cats and dogs we know who the mother is but not the

ABCDEFGHIJKL
MNOPQRSTUV
WXYZabcdefghijkl
mnopqrstuvwxyz
1234567890&
$¢£¥fiflæœÆŒ
ÅßÇÌÎÍÏã§†
-–——/()''""'':;.,!¡?¿

10/11

In our house we had a cat with the grandiose name of Gonnosuke. Usually with cats and do
gs we know who the mother is but not the father. A cat with a large belly wondered into the
house of my younger sister and her husband and gave birth to five kittens. While the mother
was a pure white thoroughbred Chinchila, the kittens were black and white tabbies of mixed
breed. One of these came to our house about two weeks after its birth and was given the na
me Gonnosuke. At that time we already had one female Shiba dog and one female brown ta

16/17

In our house we had a cat with the grandiose name of Go
nnosuke. Usually with cats and dogs we know who the m
other is but not the father. A cat with a large belly wonde
red into the house of my younger sister and her husband

24/25

In our house we had a cat with the gr
andiose name of Gonnosuke. Usually
with cats and dogs we know who the

214

ABCDEFGHIJKLMNOPQ RSTUVWXYZ

abcdefghijklmnopq rstuvwxyz
1234567890&$¢£¥
fiflæœÆŒÅßÇÌÎÍÏãṧ§†
-——/()''""":;.,!¡?¿

10/11

In our house we had a cat with the grandiose name of Gonnosuke. Usually with cats and dogs we know who the mother is but not the father. A cat with a large belly wondered into the house of my younger sister and her husband and gave birth to five kittens. While th e mother was a pure white thoroughbred Chinchila, the kittens were black and white tabbies of mixed breed. One of these came to ou r house about two weeks after its birth and was given the name Gonnosuke. At that time we already had one female Shiba dog and o ne female brown tabby cat in our house comprising only 13 tubo. The dog was called Momo and the cat Mii. My wife, who was very much opposed to keeping cats and dogs, instantaneously fell for its shaggy appearance and the black tip of its nose and decided on

16/17

In our house we had a cat with the grandiose name of Gonnosuke. Usually with cat s and dogs we know who the mother is but not the father. A cat with a large belly w ondered into the house of my younger sister and her husband and gave birth to five kittens. While the mother was a pure white thoroughbred Chinchila, the kittens we

24/25

In our house we had a cat with the grandiose name of Gonnosuke. Usually with cats and dogs we know who t he mother is but not the father. A cat with a large belly

ABCDEFGHIJKLMNOPQ
RSTUVWXYZ
abcdefghijklmnopqrstuvwxyz
1234567890&$¢£¥
fiflæœÆŒÅßçÌÎÍÏïã§†
-——/()''""":;.,!¡?¿

10/11

In our house we had a cat with the grandiose name of Gonnosuke. Usually with cats and dogs we know who the mother is but not the father. A cat with a large bel ly wondered into the house of my younger sister and her husband and gave birth to five kittens. While the mother was a pure white thoroughbred Chinchila, the ki ttens were black and white tabbies of mixed breed. One of these came to our house about two weeks after its birth and was given the name Gonnosuke. At that time we already had one female Shiba dog and one female brown tabby cat in our house comprising only 13 tubo. The dog was called Momo and the cat Mii. My wife, w ho was very much opposed to keeping cats and dogs, instantaneously fell for its shaggy appearance and the black tip of its nose and decided on its name, crying th is dog's name is Momo. Mii is a stray cat which my daughter picked up.It cried a lot making a sound like mil mil, so we were soon calling it Mii. Of course it was a

16/17

In our house we had a cat with the grandiose name of Gonnosuke. Usually with cats and dogs we kno w who the mother is but not the father. A cat with a large belly wondered into the house of my younge r sister and her husband and gave birth to five kittens. While the mother was a pure white thoroughb red Chinchila, the kittens were black and white tabbies of mixed breed. One of these came

24/25

In our house we had a cat with the grandiose name of Gonnosuke. Usually with cats and dogs we know who the mother is but not the father. A cat with a large belly wondered into the house of my young

ABCDEFGHIJKL
MNOPQRSTUVW
XYZabcdefghijklm
nopqrstuvwxyz
1234567890&
$¢£¥fiflæœÆŒ
ÅßÇÌÎÍÏã§†
-–—/()''""·;·,!¡?¿

10/11

In our house we had a cat with the grandiose name of Gonnosuke. Usually with cats and do
gs we know who the mother is but not the father. A cat with a large belly wondered into the
house of my younger sister and her husband and gave birth to five kittens. While the mother
was a pure white thoroughbred Chinchila, the kittens were black and white tabbies of mixed
breed. One of these came to our house about two weeks after its birth and was given the na
me Gonnosuke. At that time we already had one female Shiba dog and one female brown ta

16/17

In our house we had a cat with the grandiose name of Go
nnosuke. Usually with cats and dogs we know who the m
other is but not the father. A cat with a large belly wonde
red into the house of my younger sister and her husband

24/25

In our house we had a cat with the gr
andiose name of Gonnosuke. Usually
with cats and dogs we know who the

ABCDEFGHIJKLM
NOPQRSTUVWX
YZabcdefghijklmn
opqrstuvwxyz
1234567890
&$¢£¥
fiflæœÆŒÅßçÌÎÍÏã
§†-–—/()''""":;.,!¡?¿

10/11

In our house we had a cat with the grandiose name of Gonnosuke. Usually with cats and dogs we know who the mother is but not the father. A cat with a large belly wondered int o the house of my younger sister and her husband and gave birth to five kittens. While the mother was a pure white thoroughbred Chinchila, the kittens were black and white tabbie s of mixed breed. One of these came to our house about two weeks after its birth and wa s given the name Gonnosuke. At that time we already had one female Shiba dog and one

16/17

In our house we had a cat with the grandiose name of G onnosuke. Usually with cats and dogs we know who th e mother is but not the father. A cat with a large belly wo ndered into the house of my younger sister and her hus

24/25

In our house we had a cat with the gr andiose name of Gonnosuke. Usually with cats and dogs we know who th

ABCDEFGHIJKLM
NOPQRSTUVWX
YZabcdefghijklmn
opqrstuvwxyz
1234567890
&$¢£¥
fiflæœÆŒÅßÇÌÎÍÏã
§†-–——/()''""":;.,!¡?¿

10/11

In our house we had a cat with the grandiose name of Gonnosuke. Usually with cats and dogs we know who the mother is but not the father. A cat with a large belly wondered into the house of my younger sister and her husband and gave birth to five kittens. While the m other was a pure white thoroughbred Chinchila, the kittens were black and white tabbies of mixed breed. One of these came to our house about two weeks after its birth and was give n the name Gonnosuke. At that time we already had one female Shiba dog and one female

16/17

In our house we had a cat with the grandiose name of G onnosuke. Usually with cats and dogs we know who th e mother is but not the father. A cat with a large belly wo ndered into the house of my younger sister and her husb

24/25

In our house we had a cat with the gr andiose name of Gonnosuke. Usually with cats and dogs we know who th

ABCDEFGHIJKLM
NOPQRSTUVWX
YZabcdefghijklm
nopqrstuvwxyz
1234567890
&$¢£¥
fiflæœÆŒÅßÇÌÎÍÏ
ã§†-–—/()''""":;.,!¡?¿

10/11

In our house we had a cat with the grandiose name of Gonnosuke. Usually with cats and dogs we know who the mother is but not the father. A cat with a large belly wondered in to the house of my younger sister and her husband and gave birth to five kittens. While t he mother was a pure white thoroughbred Chinchila, the kittens were black and white ta bbies of mixed breed. One of these came to our house about two weeks after its birth an d was given the name Gonnosuke. At that time we already had one female Shiba dog an

16/17

In our house we had a cat with the grandiose name of Gonnosuke. Usually with cats and dogs we know who the mother is but not the father. A cat with a large belly wondered into the house of my younger sister and her

24/25

In our house we had a cat with the g randiose name of Gonnosuke. Usuall y with cats and dogs we know who

ABCDEFGHIJKL MNOPQRSTUVW XYZabcdefghijkl mnopqrstuvwxyz 1234567890 &$¢£¥fiflæœÆŒ ÅßÇÌÎÍÏã§† -–—/()''""":;.,!¡?¿

10/11

In our house we had a cat with the grandiose name of Gonnosuke. Usually with cats an
d dogs we know who the mother is but not the father. A cat with a large belly wondere
d into the house of my younger sister and her husband and gave birth to five kittens. W
hile the mother was a pure white thoroughbred Chinchila, the kittens were black and w
hite tabbies of mixed breed. One of these came to our house about two weeks after its
birth and was given the name Gonnosuke. At that time we already had one female Shib

16/17

In our house we had a cat with the grandiose name of
Gonnosuke. Usually with cats and dogs we know who
the mother is but not the father. A cat with a large bell
y wondered into the house of my younger sister and h

24/25

In our house we had a cat with the
grandiose name of Gonnosuke. Usu
ally with cats and dogs we know wh

ABCDEFGHIJKLMNOP
QRSTUVWXYZ
abcdefghijklmnopqr
stuvwxyz
1234567890&$¢£¥
fiflæœÆŒÅßçÌÎÍÏã§†
——/()''""":;.,!¡?¿

10/11

In our house we had a cat with the grandiose name of Gonnosuke. Usually with cats and dogs we know wh
o the mother is but not the father. A cat with a large belly wondered into the house of my younger sister an
d her husband and gave birth to five kittens. While the mother was a pure white thoroughbred Chinchila, th
e kittens were black and white tabbies of mixed breed. One of these came to our house about two weeks af
ter its birth and was given the name Gonnosuke. At that time we already had one female Shiba dog and on
e female brown tabby cat in our house comprising only 13 thubo. The dog was called Momo and the cat Mi

16/17

In our house we had a cat with the grandiose name of Gonnosuke.
Usually with cats and dogs we know who the mother is but not the
father. A cat with a large belly wondered into the house of my youn
ger sister and her husband and gave birth to five kittens. While the

24/25

In our house we had a cat with the grandios
e name of Gonnosuke. Usually with cats and
dogs we know who the mother is but not the

ABCDEFGHIJ
KLMNOPQR
STUVWXYZ
abcdefghijklmno
pqrstuvwxyz
1234567890&$¢£¥
fiflæœÆŒÅßÇÌÎÍÏã§
†–——/()''""":;.,!¡?¿

10/11

In our house we had a cat with the grandiose name of Gonnosuke. Usually with cats and dogs we kn ow who the mother is but not the father. A cat with a large belly wondered into the house of my youn ger sister and her husband and gave birth to five kittens. While the mother was a pure white thoroug hbred Chinchila, the kittens were black and white tabbies of mixed breed. One of these came to our house about two weeks after its birth and was given the name Gonnosuke. At that time we already ha d one female Shiba dog and one female brown tabby cat in our house comprising only 13 thubo. The

16/17

In our house we had a cat with the grandiose name of Gonnos uke. Usually with cats and dogs we know who the mother is bu t not the father. A cat with a large belly wondered into the hou se of my younger sister and her husband and gave birth to five

24/25

In our house we had a cat with the grandi ose name of Gonnosuke. Usually with cats and dogs we know who the mother is but

ABCDEFGHIJKLM
NOPQRSTUVWXYZ
abcdefghijklmnopq
rstuvwxyz
1234567890&$¢£¥
fiflæœÆŒÅßÇÌÎÍÏã§†
———/()''"":;.,!¡?¿

10/11

In our house we had a cat with the grandiose name of Gonnosuke. Usually with cats and dogs we know who the m
other is but not the father. A cat with a large belly wondered into the house of my younger sister and her husband a
nd gave birth to five kittens. While the mother was a pure white thoroughbred Chinchila, the kittens were black an
d white tabbies of mixed breed. One of these came to our house about two weeks after its birth and was given the n
ame Gonnosuke. At that time we already had one female Shiba dog and one female brown tabby cat in our house c
omprising only 13 thubo. The dog was called Momo and the cat Mii. My wife, who was very much opposed to kee

16/17

In our house we had a cat with the grandiose name of Gonnosuke. Usu
ally with cats and dogs we know who the mother is but not the father. A
cat with a large belly wondered into the house of my younger sister and
her husband and gave birth to five kittens. While the mother was a pur

24/25

In our house we had a cat with the grandiose n
ame of Gonnosuke. Usually with cats and dogs
we know who the mother is but not the father. A

ABCDEFGHIJ
KLMNOPQR
STUVWXYZ
abcdefghijklmno
pqrstuvwxyz
1234567890&$¢£¥
fiflæœÆŒÅßÇÌÎÍÏã
§†—-——/()''""'.,;.,!¡?¿

10/11

In our house we had a cat with the grandiose name of Gonnosuke. Usually with cats and dogs we k now who the mother is but not the father. A cat with a large belly wondered into the house of my y ounger sister and her husband and gave birth to five kittens. While the mother was a pure white th oroughbred Chinchila, the kittens were black and white tabbies of mixed breed. One of these came to our house about two weeks after its birth and was given the name Gonnosuke. At that time we alr eady had one female Shiba dog and one female brown tabby cat in our house comprising only 13 t

16/17

In our house we had a cat with the grandiose name of Gonnos uke. Usually with cats and dogs we know who the mother is b ut not the father. A cat with a large belly wondered into the h ouse of my younger sister and her husband and gave birth to

24/25

In our house we had a cat with the grand iose name of Gonnosuke. Usually with ca ts and dogs we know who the mother is b

ABCDEFGHIJKLM
NOPQRSTUVWXYZ
abcdefghijklmnopq
rstuvwxyz
1234567890&$¢£¥
fiflæœÆŒÅßÇÌÎÍÏã§
†-––——/()''""·;·,!¡?¿

10/11

In our house we had a cat with the grandiose name of Gonnosuke. Usually with cats and dogs we know who the mother is but not the father. A cat with a large belly wondered into the house of my younger siste r and her husband and gave birth to five kittens. While the mother was a pure white thoroughbred Chin chila, the kittens were black and white tabbies of mixed breed. One of these came to our house about two weeks after its birth and was given the name Gonnosuke. At that time we already had one female Shiba dog and one female brown tabby cat in our house comprising only 13 thubo. The dog was called Momo a

16/17

In our house we had a cat with the grandiose name of Gonnosuk e. Usually with cats and dogs we know who the mother is but not the father. A cat with a large belly wondered into the house of my younger sister and her husband and gave birth to five kittens. W

24/25

In our house we had a cat with the grandio se name of Gonnosuke. Usually with cats a nd dogs we know who the mother is but not

ABCDEFGHIJKLM
NOPQRSTUVWXYZ
abcdefghijklmnopq
rstuvwxyz
1234567890&$¢£¥
fiflæœÆŒÅßÇÌÎÍÏã§
†-–——/()''""":;.,!¡?¿

10/11

In our house we had a cat with the grandiose name of Gonnosuke. Usually with cats and dogs we know who the mother is but not the father. A cat with a large belly wondered into the house of my younger s ister and her husband and gave birth to five kittens. While the mother was a pure white thoroughbred Chinchila, the kittens were black and white tabbies of mixed breed. One of these came to our house a bout two weeks after its birth and was given the name Gonnosuke. At that time we already had one fe male Shiba dog and one female brown tabby cat in our house comprising only 13 tubo. The dog was c

16/17

In our house we had a cat with the grandiose name of Gonnosu ke. Usually with cats and dogs we know who the mother is but n ot the father. A cat with a large belly wondered into the house of my younger sister and her husband and gave birth to five kitten

24/25

In our house we had a cat with the grandi ose name of Gonnosuke. Usually with cats and dogs we know who the mother is but

ABCDEFGHIJKLMN
OPQRSTUVWXYZ
abcdefghijklmnopq
rstuvwxyz
1234567890&$¢£¥
fiflæœÆŒÅßÇÌÎÍÏ ã§†
——–/()""""'',.;:.,!¡?¿

10/11

In our house we had a cat with the grandiose name of Gonnosuke. Usually with cats and dogs we know who the m other is but not the father. A cat with a large belly wondered into the house of my younger sister and her husband a nd gave birth to five kittens. While the mother was a pure white thoroughbred Chinchila, the kittens were black an d white tabbies of mixed breed. One of these came to our house about two weeks after its birth and was given the na me Gonnosuke. At that time we already had one female Shiba dog and one female brown tabby cat in our house co mprising only 13 tubo. The dog was called Momo and the cat Mii. My wife, who was very much opposed to keepin

16/17

In our house we had a cat with the grandiose name of Gonnosuke. Usu ally with cats and dogs we know who the mother is but not the father. A cat with a large belly wondered into the house of my younger sister and her husband and gave birth to five kittens. While the mother was a pur

24/25

In our house we had a cat with the grandiose n ame of Gonnosuke. Usually with cats and dogs we know who the mother is but not the father. A

ABCDEFGHIJKLM
NOPQRSTUVWX
YZabcdefghijklmno
pqrstuvwxyz
1234567890&$¢£¥
fiflæœÆŒÅßÇÌÎÍÏã
§†-–——/()''""":;.,!¡?¿

10/11

In our house we had a cat with the grandiose name of Gonnosuke. Usually with cats and dogs we kno
w who the mother is but not the father. A cat with a large belly wondered into the house of my young
er sister and her husband and gave birth to five kittens. While the mother was a pure white thorough
bred Chinchila, the kittens were black and white tabbies of mixed breed. One of these came to our h
ouse about two weeks after its birth and was given the name Gonnosuke. At that time we already had
one female Shiba dog and one female brown tabby cat in our house comprising only 13 tubo. The do

16/17

In our house we had a cat with the grandiose name of Gonnos
uke. Usually with cats and dogs we know who the mother is but
not the father. A cat with a large belly wondered into the house
of my younger sister and her husband and gave birth to five kit

24/25

In our house we had a cat with the grandi
ose name of Gonnosuke. Usually with cats
and dogs we know who the mother is but

ABCDEFGHIJKLMN
OPQRSTUVWXYZ
abcdefghijklmnopq
rstuvwxyz
1234567890&$¢£¥
fiflæœÆŒÅßÇÌÎÍÏã§†
-——/()''""".,;.,!¡?¿

10/11

In our house we had a cat with the grandiose name of Gonnosuke. Usually with cats and dogs we know who th
e mother is but not the father. A cat with a large belly wondered into the house of my younger sister and her hu
sband and gave birth to five kittens. While the mother was a pure white thoroughbred Chinchila, the kittens w
ere black and white tabbies of mixed breed. One of these came to our house about two weeks after its birth and
was given the name Gonnosuke. At that time we already had one female Shiba dog and one female brown tabb
y cat in our house comprising only 13 tubo. The dog was called Momo and the cat Mii. My wife, who was very

16/17

In our house we had a cat with the grandiose name of Gonnosuke. U
sually with cats and dogs we know who the mother is but not the fath
er. A cat with a large belly wondered into the house of my younger sis
ter and her husband and gave birth to five kittens. While the mother

24/25

In our house we had a cat with the grandiose
name of Gonnosuke. Usually with cats and do
gs we know who the mother is but not the fath

ABCDEFGHIJKLM
NOPQRSTUVWX
YZabcdefghijklmno
pqrstuvwxyz
1234567890&$¢£¥
fiflæœÆŒÅßÇÌÎÍÏã
§†-–—/()''"":.;.,!¡?¿

10/11

In our house we had a cat with the grandiose name of Gonnosuke. Usually with cats and dogs we k
now who the mother is but not the father. A cat with a large belly wondered into the house of my y
ounger sister and her husband and gave birth to five kittens. While the mother was a pure white th
oroughbred Chinchila, the kittens were black and white tabbies of mixed breed. One of these came
to our house about two weeks after its birth and was given the name Gonnosuke. At that time we alr
eady had one female Shiba dog and one female brown tabby cat in our house comprising only 13

16/17

In our house we had a cat with the grandiose name of Gonno
suke. Usually with cats and dogs we know who the mother is
but not the father. A cat with a large belly wondered into the
house of my younger sister and her husband and gave birth t

24/25

In our house we had a cat with the grand
iose name of Gonnosuke. Usually with ca
ts and dogs we know who the mother is b

ABCDEFGHIJKLM
NOPQRSTUVWXYZ
abcdefghijklmnopq
rstuvwxyz
1234567890&$¢£¥
fiflœœÆŒÅßÇÌÎÍÏã§
†-——/()''"":;.,!¡?¿

10/11

In our house we had a cat with the grandiose name of Gonnosuke. Usually with cats and dogs we know who the mother is but not the father. A cat with a large belly wondered into the house of my younger siste r and her husband and gave birth to five kittens. While the mother was a pure white thoroughbred Chin chila, the kittens were black and white tabbies of mixed breed. One of these came to our house about two weeks after its birth and was given the name Gonnosuke. At that time we already had one female Shiba dog and one female brown tabby cat in our house comprising only 13 tubo. The dog was called Momo a

16/17

In our house we had a cat with the grandiose name of Gonnosuk e. Usually with cats and dogs we know who the mother is but not the father. A cat with a large belly wondered into the house of my younger sister and her husband and gave birth to five kittens. W

24/25

In our house we had a cat with the grandio se name of Gonnosuke. Usually with cats a nd dogs we know who the mother is but not

ABCDEFGHIJKLM
NOPQRSTUVWX
YZabcdefghijklmn
opqrstuvwxyz
1234567890&$¢£¥
fiflæœÆŒÅßÇÌÎÍÏ
ã§†‒–—/()""''":;.,!¡?¿

10/11

In our house we had a cat with the grandiose name of Gonnosuke. Usually with cats and dogs w
e know who the mother is but not the father. A cat with a large belly wondered into the house of
my younger sister and her husband and gave birth to five kittens. While the mother was a pure
white thoroughbred Chinchila, the kittens were black and white tabbies of mixed breed. One of
these came to our house about two weeks after its birth and was given the name Gonnosuke. At
that time we already had one female Shiba dog and one female brown tabby cat in our house co

16/17

In our house we had a cat with the grandiose name of Gonn
osuke. Usually with cats and dogs we know who the mother
is but not the father. A cat with a large belly wondered into
the house of my younger sister and her husband and gave b

24/25

In our house we had a cat with the gran
diose name of Gonnosuke. Usually with
cats and dogs we know who the mother

ABCDEFGHIJKLM
NOPQRSTUVWXYZ
abcdefghijklmnopq
rstuvwxyz
1234567890&$¢£¥
fiflæœÆŒÅßÇÌÎÍÏã
§†‡-–——/()''""":;.,!¡?¿

10/11

In our house we had a cat with the grandiose name of Gonnosuke. Usually with cats and dogs we k now who the mother is but not the father. A cat with a large belly wondered into the house of my yo unger sister and her husband and gave birth to five kittens. While the mother was a pure white tho roughbred Chinchila, the kittens were black and white tabbies of mixed breed. One of these came to our house about two weeks after its birth and was given the name Gonnosuke. At that time we alre ady had one female Shiba dog and one female brown tabby cat in our house comprising only 13 tub

16/17

In our house we had a cat with the grandiose name of Gonnos uke. Usually with cats and dogs we know who the mother is b ut not the father. A cat with a large belly wondered into the h ouse of my younger sister and her husband and gave birth to f

24/25

In our house we had a cat with the gran diose name of Gonnosuke. Usually with c ats and dogs we know who the mother is

ABCDEFGHIJKL
MNOPQRSTU
VWXYZ
abcdefghijklmnopq
rstuvwxyz
1234567890&$¢£¥
fiflæœÆŒÅßÇÌÎÍÏã§
†-——/()''""":;.,!¡?¿

10/11

In our house we had a cat with the grandiose name of Gonnosuke. Usually with cats and dogs we know who the mother is but not the father. A cat with a large belly wondered into the house of my younger sister and her husba nd and gave birth to five kittens. While the mother was a pure white thoroughbred Chinchila, the kittens were bla ck and white tabbies of mixed breed. One of these came to our house about two weeks after its birth and was give n the name Gonnosuke. At that time we already had one female Shiba dog and one female brown tabby cat in ou r house comprising only 13 thubo. The dog was called Momo and the cat Mii. My wife, who was very much oppo

16/17

In our house we had a cat with the grandiose name of Gonnosuke. Us ually with cats and dogs we know who the mother is but not the father. A cat with a large belly wondered into the house of my younger sister a nd her husband and gave birth to five kittens. While the mother was a

24/25

In our house we had a cat with the grandiose n ame of Gonnosuke. Usually with cats and dogs we know who the mother is but not the father.

ABCDEFGHIJKLM
NOPQRSTUVW
XYZabcdefghijklmn
opqrstuvwxyz
1234567890&$¢£¥
fiflœœÆŒÅßÇÌÎÍÏã§†
——/()''"":;.,!¡?¿

10/11

In our house we had a cat with the grandiose name of Gonnosuke. Usually with cats and dogs we know who the mothe
r is but not the father. A cat with a large belly wondered into the house of my younger sister and her husband and gave
birth to five kittens. While the mother was a pure white thoroughbred Chinchila, the kittens were black and white tabbie
s of mixed breed. One of these came to our house about two weeks after its birth and was given the name Gonnosuke.
At that time we already had one female Shiba dog and one female brown tabby cat in our house comprising only 13 th
ubo. The dog was called Momo and the cat Mii. My wife, who was very much opposed to keeping cats and dogs, insta

16/17

In our house we had a cat with the grandiose name of Gonnosuke. Usuall
y with cats and dogs we know who the mother is but not the father. A cat
with a large belly wondered into the house of my younger sister and her hu
sband and gave birth to five kittens. While the mother was a pure white th

24/25

In our house we had a cat with the grandiose na
me of Gonnosuke. Usually with cats and dogs we
know who the mother is but not the father. A cat

Bernhard Modern Bold

ABCDEFGHIJKLM
NOPQRSTUVWX
YZabcdefghijklmnop
qrstuvwxyz
1234567890&$¢£¥
fiflæœÆŒÅßÇÌÎÍÏã
§†-—––/()''"":;.,!¡?¿

10/11

In our house we had a cat with the grandiose name of Gonnosuke. Usually with cats and dogs we kno
w who the mother is but not the father. A cat with a large belly wondered into the house of my younger
sister and her husband and gave birth to five kittens. While the mother was a pure white thoroughbred
Chinchila, the kittens were black and white tabbies of mixed breed. One of these came to our house ab
out two weeks after its birth and was given the name Gonnosuke. At that time we already had one fem
ale Shiba dog and one female brown tabby cat in our house comprising only 13 thubo. The dog was cal

16/17

In our house we had a cat with the grandiose name of Gonnosu
ke. Usually with cats and dogs we know who the mother is but
not the father. A cat with a large belly wondered into the house
of my younger sister and her husband and gave birth to five kitt

24/25

In our house we had a cat with the grandio
se name of Gonnosuke. Usually with cats
and dogs we know who the mother is but

ABCDEFGHIJKLM NOPQRSTUVWX YZabcdefghijklmnopq rstuvwxyz 1234567890&$¢£¥ fiflæœÆŒÅßÇÌÎÍÏãS †-——/()''""":;.,!¡?¿

10/11

In our house we had a cat with the grandiose name of Gonnosuke. Usually with cats and dogs we know wh o the mother is but not the father. A cat with a large belly wondered into the house of my younger sister an d her husband and gave birth to five kittens. While the mother was a pure white thoroughbred Chinchila, th e kittens were black and white tabbies of mixed breed. One of these came to our house about two weeks afte r its birth and was given the name Gonnosuke. At that time we already had one female Shiba dog and one female brown tabby cat in our house comprising only 13 thubo. The dog was called Momo and the cat Mii.

16/17

In our house we had a cat with the grandiose name of Gonnosuke. Usually with cats and dogs we know who the mother is but not the father. A cat with a large belly wondered into the house of my youn ger sister and her husband and gave birth to five kittens. While the

24/25

In our house we had a cat with the grandios e name of Gonnosuke. Usually with cats an d dogs we know who the mother is but not t

ABCDEFGHIJKL
MNOPQRSTU
VWXYZ
abcdefghijklmno
pqrstuvwxyz
1234567890&$¢£¥
fiflæœÆŒÅßÇÌÍÎÏ
ã§†——/()'""":.,.,!¡?¿

10/11

In our house we had a cat with the grandiose name of Gonnosuke. Usually with cats and dogs we know w
ho the mother is but not the father. A cat with a large belly wondered into the house of my younger sister
and her husband and gave birth to five kittens. While the mother was a pure white thoroughbred Chinch
ila, the kittens were black and white tabbies of mixed breed. One of these came to our house about two
weeks after its birth and was given the name Gonnosuke. At that time we already had one female Shiba
dog and one female brown tabby cat in our house comprising only 13 thubo. The dog was called Momo a

16/17

In our house we had a cat with the grandiose name of Gonnosuk
e. Usually with cats and dogs we know who the mother is but not
the father. A cat with a large belly wondered into the house of my
younger sister and her husband and gave birth to five kittens. Wh

24/25

In our house we had a cat with the grandios
e name of Gonnosuke. Usually with cats an
d dogs we know who the mother is but not

ABCDEFGHIJKL MNOPQRSTU VWXYZ

abcdefghijklmno pqrstuvwxyz

1234567890&$¢£¥

fiflæœÆŒÅßÇÌÎÍÏã

§†–——/()''""";.,!¡?¿

10/11

In our house we had a cat with the grandiose name of Gonnosuke. Usually with cats and dogs we know who the mother is but not the father. A cat with a large belly wondered into the house of my younger sis ter and her husband and gave birth to five kittens. While the mother was a pure white thoroughbred C hinchila, the kittens were black and white tabbies of mixed breed. One of these came to our house abou t two weeks after its birth and was given the name Gonnosuke. At that time we already had one female Shiba dog and one female brown tabby cat in our house comprising only 13 thubo. The dog was called

16/17

In our house we had a cat with the grandiose name of Gonnosuk e. Usually with cats and dogs we know who the mother is but no t the father. A cat with a large belly wondered into the house of my younger sister and her husband and gave birth to five kitten

24/25

In our house we had a cat with the grandio se name of Gonnosuke. Usually with cats a nd dogs we know who the mother is but no

ABCDEFGHIJKL
MNOPQRSTU
VWXYZ
abcdefghijklmno
pqrstuvwxyz
1234567890&$¢£¥
fiflæœÆŒÅßÇÌÎÍÏ
ã§†——/()''""":;.,!¡?¿

10/11

In our house we had a cat with the grandiose name of Gonnosuke. Usually with cats and dogs we know who the mother is but not the father. A cat with a large belly wondered into the house of my younger sister and her husband and gave birth to five kittens. While the mother was a pure white thoroughbred Chinchila, the kittens were black and white tabbies of mixed breed. One of these ca me to our house about two weeks after its birth and was given the name Gonnosuke. At that time we already had one female Shiba dog and one female brown tabby cat in our house comprising on

16/17

In our house we had a cat with the grandiose name of Gonno suke. Usually with cats and dogs we know who the mother is but not the father. A cat with a large belly wondered into the house of my younger sister and her husband and gave birth t

24/25

In our house we had a cat with the grand iose name of Gonnosuke. Usually with c ats and dogs we know who the mother is

ABCDEFGHIJKL
MNOPQRSTU
VWXYZ

abcdefghijklmno
pqrstuvwxyz
1234567890&$¢£¥
fiflæœÆŒÅßÇÌÎÍÏ
ã§†——–/() '’“”:;.,!¡?¿

10/11

In our house we had a cat with the grandiose name of Gonnosuke. Usually with cats and dogs w e know who the mother is but not the father. A cat with a large belly wondered into the house of my younger sister and her husband and gave birth to five kittens. While the mother was a pure white thoroughbred Chinchila, the kittens were black and white tabbies of mixed breed. One of t hese came to our house about two weeks after its birth and was given the name Gonnosuke. At t hat time we already had one female Shiba dog and one female brown tabby cat in our house co

16/17

In our house we had a cat with the grandiose name of Gonn osuke. Usually with cats and dogs we know who the mother is but not the father. A cat with a large belly wondered into t he house of my younger sister and her husband and gave bi

24/25

In our house we had a cat with the grand iose name of Gonnosuke. Usually with c ats and dogs we know who the mother is

ABCDEFGHIJKLM
NOPQRSTUVWXYZ
abcdefghijklmnopq
rstuvwxyz
1234567890&$¢£¥
fiflæœÆŒÅßÇÌÎÍÏã
§†-–—/()''""":;.,!¡?¿

10/11

In our house we had a cat with the grandiose name of Gonnosuke. Usually with cats and dogs we know who the mother is but not the father. A cat with a large belly wondered into the house of my younger sister and her husband and gave birth to five kittens. While the mother was a pu re white thoroughbred Chinchila, the kittens were black and white tabbies of mixed breed. One of these came to our house about two weeks after its birth and was given the name Gonnosuke. At that time we already had one female Shiba dog and one female brown tabby cat in our house

16/17

In our house we had a cat with the grandiose name of Gon nosuke. Usually with cats and dogs we know who the moth er is but not the father. A cat with a large belly wondered in to the house of my younger sister and her husband and gav

24/25

In our house we had a cat with the gran diose name of Gonnosuke. Usually with cats and dogs we know who the mother

ITC Bookman Light Italic

ABCDEFGHIJKLM
NOPQRSTUVWXYZ
abcdefghijklmnop
qrstuvwxyz
1234567890&
$¢£¥fiflæœÆŒ
ÅßÇÌÎÍÏã§†
-–—/()""""::;.,!¡?¿

10/11

In our house we had a cat with the grandiose name of Gonnosuke. Usually with cats and do
gs we know who the mother is but not the father. A cat with a large belly wondered into the
house of my younger sister and her husband and gave birth to five kittens. While the mother
was a pure white thoroughbred Chinchila, the kittens were black and white tabbies of mixe
d breed. One of these came to our house about two weeks after its birth and was given the
name Gonnosuke. At that time we already had one female Shiba dog and one female brown

16/17

In our house we had a cat with the grandiose name of Go
nnosuke. Usually with cats and dogs we know who the m
other is but not the father. A cat with a large belly wonde
red into the house of my younger sister and her husband

24/25

In our house we had a cat with the gr
andiose name of Gonnosuke. Usually
with cats and dogs we know who the

ITC Bookman Medium

ABCDEFGHIJKL
MNOPQRSTUVWX
YZabcdefghijklmn
opqrstuvwxyz
1234567890&
$¢£¥fiflæœÆŒ
ÅßÇÌÎÍÏãã§†
––—/()""'''':;.,!¡?¿

10/11

In our house we had a cat with the grandiose name of Gonnosuke. Usually with cats and dogs we know who the mother is but not the father. A cat with a large belly wondered into the house of my younger sister and her husband and gave birth to five kittens. While the mother was a pure white thoroughbred Chinchila, the kittens were black and white tabbies of mixed breed. One of these came to our house about two weeks after its birth and was given the name Gonnosuke. At that time we already had one female Shiba dog and one female brown

16/17

In our house we had a cat with the grandiose name of Gonnosuke. Usually with cats and dogs we know who the mother is but not the father. A cat with a large belly wondered into the house of my younger sister and her husband

24/25

In our house we had a cat with the grandiose name of Gonnosuke. Usually with cats and dogs we know who the

ABCDEFGHIJKL MNOPQRSTUVWX YZabcdefghijklmn opqrstuvwxyz 1234567890& $¢£¥fiflæœÆŒ ÅßÇÌÎÍÏã§† ——/()''""":;.,!¡?¿

10/11

In our house we had a cat with the grandiose name of Gonnosuke. Usually with cats and dogs we know who the mother is but not the father. A cat with a large belly wondered into the house of my younger sister and her husband and gave birth to five kittens. While the mother was a pure white thoroughbred Chinchila, the kittens were black and white tabbies of mixed breed. One of these came to our house about two weeks after its birth and was given the name Gonnosuke. At that time we already had one female Shiba dog and one

16/17

In our house we had a cat with the grandiose name of Gonnosuke. Usually with cats and dogs we know who the mother is but not the father. A cat with a large belly wondered into the house of my younger sister and her h

24/25

In our house we had a cat with the g randiose name of Gonnosuke. Usuall y with cats and dogs we know who t

ABCDEFGHIJKL
MNOPQRSTUVWX
YZabcdefghijklmn
opqrstuvwxyz
1234567890&
$¢£¥fiflæœÆŒ
ÅßÇÌÎÍÏã§†
-–—/()''""";.,!¡?¿

10/11

In our house we had a cat with the grandiose name of Gonnosuke. Usually with cats and d
ogs we know who the mother is but not the father. A cat with a large belly wondered into t
he house of my younger sister and her husband and gave birth to five kittens. While the
mother was a pure white thoroughbred Chinchila, the kittens were black and white tabbie
s of mixed breed. One of these came to our house about two weeks after its birth and was
given the name Gonnosuke. At that time we already had one female Shiba dog and one fe

16/17

In our house we had a cat with the grandiose name of G
onnosuke. Usually with cats and dogs we know who the
mother is but not the father. A cat with a large belly wo
ndered into the house of my younger sister and her hus

24/25

In our house we had a cat with the gr
andiose name of Gonnosuke. Usually
with cats and dogs we know who the

ABCDEFGHIJKL
MNOPQRSTUVW
XYZabcdefghijkl
mnopqrstuvwxyz
1234567890&
$¢£¥fiflæœÆŒ
ÅßÇÌÎÍÏã§†
-–—/()'"""';.,!¡?¿

10/11

In our house we had a cat with the grandiose name of Gonnosuke. Usually with cats a
nd dogs we know who the mother is but not the father. A cat with a large belly wonder
ed into the house of my younger sister and her husband and gave birth to five kittens.
While the mother was a pure white thoroughbred Chinchila, the kittens were black an
d white tabbies of mixed breed. One of these came to our house about two weeks after
its birth and was given the name Gonnosuke. At that time we already had one female

16/17

In our house we had a cat with the grandiose name of
Gonnosuke. Usually with cats and dogs we know who
the mother is but not the father. A cat with a large bel
ly wondered into the house of my younger sister and

24/25

In our house we had a cat with the
grandiose name of Gonnosuke. Usu
ally with cats and dogs we know w

ABCDEFGHIJKL
MNOPQRSTUVW
XYZabcdefghijkl
mnopqrstuvwxyz
1234567890&
$¢£¥fiflæœÆŒ
ÅßÇÌÎÍÏãå§†
–—/()''""":;.,!¡?¿

10/11

In our house we had a cat with the grandiose name of Gonnosuke. Usually with cats
and dogs we know who the mother is but not the father. A cat with a large belly wond
ered into the house of my younger sister and her husband and gave birth to five kitt
ens. While the mother was a pure white thoroughbred Chinchila, the kittens were bla
ck and white tabbies of mixed breed. One of these came to our house about two week
s after its birth and was given the name Gonnosuke. At that time we already had one

16/17

In our house we had a cat with the grandiose name o
f Gonnosuke. Usually with cats and dogs we know wh
o the mother is but not the father. A cat with a large
belly wondered into the house of my younger sister a

24/25

In our house we had a cat with the
grandiose name of Gonnosuke. Usu
ally with cats and dogs we know wh

ABCDEFGHIJKL
MNOPQRSTUVW
XYZabcdefghijk
lmnopqrstuvwx
yz1234567890&
$¢£¥fiflæœÆŒ
ÅßÇÌÎÍÏãã§†
-–——/()""""";;..,!¡?¿

10/11

In our house we had a cat with the grandiose name of Gonnosuke. Usually with c
ats and dogs we know who the mother is but not the father. A cat with a large be
lly wondered into the house of my younger sister and her husband and gave birt
h to five kittens. While the mother was a pure white thoroughbred Chinchila, the
kittens were black and white tabbies of mixed breed. One of these came to our h
ouse about two weeks after its birth and was given the name Gonnosuke. At that

16/17

In our house we had a cat with the grandiose nam
e of Gonnosuke. Usually with cats and dogs we kn
ow who the mother is but not the father. A cat wit
h a large belly wondered into the house of my you

24/25

In our house we had a cat with th
e grandiose name of Gonnosuke.
Usually with cats and dogs we kn

ABCDEFGHIJKL
MNOPQRSTU
VWXYZ
abcdefghijklmno
pqrstuvwxyz
1234567890&$¢£¥
fiflæœÆŒÅßÇÌÎÍÏã
§†-–—/()''""":;.,!¡?¿

10/11

In our house we had a cat with the grandiose name of Gonnosuke. Usually with cats and dogs we kn ow who the mother is but not the father. A cat with a large belly wondered into the house of my you nger sister and her husband and gave birth to five kittens. While the mother was a pure white thoro ughbred Chinchila, the kittens were black and white tabbies of mixed breed. One of these came to ou r house about two weeks after its birth and was given the name Gonnosuke. At that time we already had one female Shiba dog and one female brown tabby cat in our house comprising only 13 thubo. T

16/17

In our house we had a cat with the grandiose name of Gonnos uke. Usually with cats and dogs we know who the mother is bu t not the father. A cat with a large belly wondered into the hou se of my younger sister and her husband and gave birth to five

24/25

In our house we had a cat with the grandi ose name of Gonnosuke. Usually with cat s and dogs we know who the mother is bu

ABCDEFGHIJKL
MNOPQRSTU
VWXYZabcdefghijkl
mnopqrstuvwxyz
1234567890
&$¢£¥fiflœœ
ÆŒÅßÇÌÎÍÏ㧆
———/()''""":;.,!¡?¿

10/11

In our house we had a cat with the grandiose name of Gonnosuke. Usually with cats and dogs we know who the mother is but not the father. A cat with a large belly wondered into the house of my younger sister and her husband and gave birth to five kittens. While the mother was a pure white thoroughbred Chinchila, the kittens were black and white tabbies of mixed breed. One of these came to our house about two weeks after its birth and was given the name Gonnosuke. At that time we already had one female Shiba dog and one female brown tabby cat in our house comprising only 13 thubo. The dog was called Momo and the cat Mii. My wif

16/17

In our house we had a cat with the grandiose name of Gonnosuke. Usually with cats and dogs we know who the mother is but not the father. A cat with a large belly wondered into the house of my younger sister and her husband and gave birth to five kittens. While the

24/25

In our house we had a cat with the grandiose name of Gonnosuke. Usually with cats and dogs we know who the mother is but not the f

ABCDEFGHIJKLM NOPQRSTUVWXYZ

abcdefghijklmnopq rstuvwxyz

1234567890&$¢£¥

fiflæœÆŒÅßÇÌÎÍÏã§†

——/()''""";.,!¡?¿

10/11

In our house we had a cat with the grandiose name of Gonnosuke. Usually with cats and dogs we know who the mother is but not the father. A cat with a large belly wondered into the house of my younger sister and her husband and gave birth to five kittens. While the mother was a pure white thoroughbred Chinchila, the kittens were black and white tabbies of mixed breed. One of these came to our house about two weeks after its birth and was given the name Gonnosuke. At that time we already had one female Shiba dog and one female brown tabby cat in our house comprising only 13 thubo. The dog was ca lled Momo and the cat Mii. My wife, who was very much opposed to keeping cats and dogs, instantaneously fell for its

16/17

In our house we had a cat with the grandiose name of Gonnosuke. Usually with cats and dogs we know who the mother is but not the father. A cat with a large belly wondered into the house of my younger sister and her husband and gave birth to five kittens. While the mother was a pure white thoroughb

24/25

In our house we had a cat with the grandiose name of Gonnosuke. Usually with cats and dogs we kno w who the mother is but not the father. A cat with

ABCDEFGHIJKLMN
OPQRSTUVWXYZ
abcdefghijklmnopq
rstuvwxyz
1234567890&$¢£¥
fiflæœÆŒÅßÇÌÎÍÏã§†
——/()''""":;.,!¡?¿

10/11

In our house we had a cat with the grandiose name of Gonnosuke. Usually with cats and dogs we know who the mother is but not the father. A cat with a large belly wondered into the house of my younger sister and her husband and gave birth to five kittens. While the mother was a pure white thoroughbred Chinchila, the kittens were black and white tabbies of mixed breed. One of these came to our house about two weeks after its birth and was given the name Gonnosuke. At that time we already had one female Shiba dog and one female brown tabby cat in our house comprising only 13 thubo. The dog was called Momo and the cat Mii. My wife, who was very much opposed to keeping cats and dogs, instantaneously fell for its shaggy appearance and the black tip of its nose and decided on its nam

16/17

In our house we had a cat with the grandiose name of Gonnosuke. Usually with cat s and dogs we know who the mother is but not the father. A cat with a large belly w ondered into the house of my younger sister and her husband and gave birth to five k ittens. While the mother was a pure white thoroughbred Chinchila, the kittens were

24/25

In our house we had a cat with the grandiose name of Gonnosuke. Usually with cats and dogs we know who t he mother is but not the father. A cat with a large belly

ABCDEFGHIJK
LMNOPQRSTU
VWXYZabcdefghij
klmnopqrstuvwxyz
1234567890&$¢£¥
fiflæœÆŒÅßÇÌÎÍÏã
§†---——/()''""".;.,!¡?¿

10/11

In our house we had a cat with the grandiose name of Gonnosuke. Usually with cats and dogs we kno
w who the mother is but not the father. A cat with a large belly wondered into the house of my young
er sister and her husband and gave birth to five kittens. While the mother was a pure white thorough
bred Chinchila, the kittens were black and white tabbies of mixed breed. One of these came to our h
ouse about two weeks after its birth and was given the name Gonnosuke. At that time we already had
one female Shiba dog and one female brown tabby cat in our house comprising only 13 thubo. The d

16/17

In our house we had a cat with the grandiose name of Gonnos
uke. Usually with cats and dogs we know who the mother is bu
t not the father. A cat with a large belly wondered into the hous
e of my younger sister and her husband and gave birth to five ki

24/25

In our house we had a cat with the grandi
ose name of Gonnosuke. Usually with cat
s and dogs we know who the mother is bu

ABCDEFGHIJKLMN
OPQRSTUVWXYZ
abcdefghijklmnopq
rstuvwxyz
1234567890&$¢£¥
fiflæœÆŒÅßÇÌÎÍÏã§
†-–——/()''""";.,!¡?¿

10/11

In our house we had a cat with the grandiose name of Gonnosuke. Usually with cats and dogs we know who t he mother is but not the father. A cat with a large belly wondered into the house of my younger sister and he r husband and gave birth to five kittens. While the mother was a pure white thoroughbred Chinchila, the kit tens were black and white tabbies of mixed breed. One of these came to our house about two weeks after its birth and was given the name Gonnosuke. At that time we already had one female Shiba dog and one female brown tabby cat in our house comprising only 13 thubo. The dog was called Momo and the cat Mii. My wife,

16/17

In our house we had a cat with the grandiose name of Gonnosuke. Usually with cats and dogs we know who the mother is but not the father. A cat with a large belly wondered into the house of my youn ger sister and her husband and gave birth to five kittens. While the

24/25

In our house we had a cat with the grandiose name of Gonnosuke. Usually with cats and d ogs we know who the mother is but not the f

ABCDEFGHIJKLMN
OPQRSTUVWXYZ
abcdefghijklmnopq
rstuvwxyz
1234567890&$¢£¥
fiflæœÆŒÅßÇÌÎÍÏã§†
-——/()''""".;.,!¡?¿

10/11

In our house we had a cat with the grandiose name of Gonnosuke. Usually with cats and dogs we know who the mother is but n
ot the father. A cat with a large belly wondered into the house of my younger sister and her husband and gave birth to five kitte
ns. While the mother was a pure white thoroughbred Chinchila, the kittens were black and white tabbies of mixed breed. One o
f these came to our house about two weeks after its birth and was given the name Gonnosuke. At that time we already had one f
emale Shiba dog and one female brown tabby cat in our house comprising only 13 thubo. The dog was called Momo and the ca
t Mii. My wife, who was very much opposed to keeping cats and dogs, instantaneously fell for its shaggy appearance and the bl

16/17

In our house we had a cat with the grandiose name of Gonnosuke. Usually wit
h cats and dogs we know who the mother is but not the father. A cat with a lar
ge belly wondered into the house of my younger sister and her husband and gav
e birth to five kittens. While the mother was a pure white thoroughbred Chinch

24/25

In our house we had a cat with the grandiose name o
f Gonnosuke. Usually with cats and dogs we know w
ho the mother is but not the father. A cat with a larg

Caslon Bold Roman

ABCDEFGHIJK LMNOPQRSTU VWXYZ

abcdefghijklmnopq
rstuvwxyz
1234567890&$¢£¥
fiflæœÆŒÅßÇÌÎÍÏ
ã§†-–—/()''""":;.,!¡?¿

10/11

In our house we had a cat with the grandiose name of Gonnosuke. Usually with cats and dogs we know who the mother is but not the father. A cat with a large belly wondered into the house of my younger sister and her husband and gave birth to five kittens. While the mother was a pure white t horoughbred Chinchila, the kittens were black and white tabbies of mixed breed. One of these cam e to our house about two weeks after its birth and was given the name Gonnosuke. At that time we already had one female Shiba dog and one female brown tabby cat in our house comprising only 13

16/17

In our house we had a cat with the grandiose name of Gonno suke. Usually with cats and dogs we know who the mother is but not the father. A cat with a large belly wondered into the house of my younger sister and her husband and gave birth to

24/25

In our house we had a cat with the grand iose name of Gonnosuke. Usually with c ats and dogs we know who the mother is

ABCDEFGHIJKL MNOPQRSTU VWXYZ

abcdefghijklmnopq rstuvwxyz

1234567890&$¢£¥

fiflæœÆŒÅßÇÌÎÍÏã

§†-——/()""""::;.,!¡?¿

10/11

In our house we had a cat with the grandiose name of Gonnosuke. Usually with cats and dogs we know who the mother is but not the father. A cat with a large belly wondered into the house of my younger sister and her husband and gave birth to five kittens. While the mother was a pure white thoroughbred Chinchilla, the kittens were black and white tabbies of mixed breed. One of these came to our house about two weeks after its birth and was given the name Gonnosuke. At that time we already had one female Shiba dog and one female brown tabby cat in our house comprising only 13 thubo. The dog was called Momo and the c

16/17

In our house we had a cat with the grandiose name of Gonnosuke. Usually with cats and dogs we know who the mother is but not the father. A cat with a large belly wondered into the house of my younger sister and her husband and gave birth to five kittens. While

24/25

In our house we had a cat with the grandio se name of Gonnosuke. Usually with cats a nd dogs we know who the mother is but not

ABCDEFGHIJK
LMNOPQRSTU
VWXYZ

abcdefghijklmnopq

rstuvwxyz

1234567890&$¢£¥

fiflæœÆŒÅßÇÌÎÍÏã§

†-——/()''""•;•,!¡?¿

10/11

In our house we had a cat with the grandiose name of Gonnosuke. Usually with cats and dogs we know who the moth er is but not the father. A cat with a large belly wondered into the house of my younger sister and her husband and ga ve birth to five kittens. While the mother was a pure white thoroughbred Chinchila, the kittens were black and white tabbies of mixed breed. One of these came to our house about two weeks after its birth and was given the name Gonn osuke. At that time we already had one female Shiba dog and one female brown tabby cat in our house comprising onl y 13 thubo. The dog was called Momo and the cat Mii. My wife, who was very much opposed to keeping cats and dog

16/17

In our house we had a cat with the grandiose name of Gonnosuke. Usuall y with cats and dogs we know who the mother is but not the father. A cat with a large belly wondered into the house of my younger sister and her h usband and gave birth to five kittens. While the mother was a pure white

24/25

In our house we had a cat with the grandiose na me of Gonnosuke. Usually with cats and dogs we know who the mother is but not the father. A ca

ABCDEFGHIJKLMN
OPQRSTUVWXYZ
abcdefghijklmnopq
rstuvwxyz
1234567890&$¢£¥
fiflæœÆŒÅßÇÌÎÍÏã§
†-——/()''""·;·,!¡?¿

10/11

In our house we had a cat with the grandiose name of Gonnosuke. Usually with cats and dogs we kno
w who the mother is but not the father. A cat with a large belly wondered into the house of my young
er sister and her husband and gave birth to five kittens. While the mother was a pure white thorough
bred Chinchila, the kittens were black and white tabbies of mixed breed. One of these came to our ho
use about two weeks after its birth and was given the name Gonnosuke. At that time we already had o
ne female Shiba dog and one female brown tabby cat in our house comprising only 13 tubo. The dog

16/17

In our house we had a cat with the grandiose name of Gonnosu
ke. Usually with cats and dogs we know who the mother is but
not the father. A cat with a large belly wondered into the house
of my younger sister and her husband and gave birth to five kitt

24/25

In our house we had a cat with the grandi
ose name of Gonnosuke. Usually with cats
and dogs we know who the mother is but

ABCDEFGHIJKLMN
OPQRSTUVWXYZ
abcdefghijklmnopq
rstuvwxyz
1234567890&$¢£¥
fiflæœÆŒÅßÇÌÎÍÏã§
†---——/()''""":;.,!¡?¿

10/11

In our house we had a cat with the grandiose name of Gonnosuke. Usually with cats and dogs we know who the mother is but not the father. A cat with a large belly wondered into the house of my younger sister and her husband and gave birth to five kittens. While the mother was a pure white thoroughbred Chinchila, the kittens were black and white tabbies of mixed breed. One of these came to our house about two weeks after its birth and was given the name Gonnosuke. At that time we already had one female Shiba dog and one female brown tabby cat in our house comprising only 13 tubo. The dog was calle

16/17

In our house we had a cat with the grandiose name of Gonnosu ke. Usually with cats and dogs we know who the mother is but not the father. A cat with a large belly wondered into the house o f my younger sister and her husband and gave birth to five kitte

24/25

In our house we had a cat with the grandi ose name of Gonnosuke. Usually with cats and dogs we know who the mother is but

ABCDEFGHIJKLMN
OPQRSTUVWXYZ
abcdefghijklmnopq
rstuvwxyz
1234567890&$¢£¥
fiflæœÆŒÅßÇÌÎÍÏã
§†-—––/()'’“”:;.,!¡?¿

10/11

In our house we had a cat with the grandiose name of Gonnosuke. Usually with cats and dogs we kn ow who the mother is but not the father. A cat with a large belly wondered into the house of my you nger sister and her husband and gave birth to five kittens. While the mother was a pure white thoro ughbred Chinchila, the kittens were black and white tabbies of mixed breed. One of these came to our house about two weeks after its birth and was given the name Gonnosuke. At that time we alre ady had one female Shiba dog and one female brown tabby cat in our house comprising only 13 tub

16/17

In our house we had a cat with the grandiose name of Gonnos uke. Usually with cats and dogs we know who the mother is b ut not the father. A cat with a large belly wondered into the h ouse of my younger sister and her husband and gave birth to fi

24/25

In our house we had a cat with the grandi ose name of Gonnosuke. Usually with cat s and dogs we know who the mother is bu

ABCDEFGHIJKLM
NOPQRSTUVWXYZ
abcdefghijklmnopq
rstuvwxyz
1234567890&$¢£¥
fiflæœÆŒÅßÇÌÎÍÏã
§†-–—/()''""":;.,!¡?¿

10/11

In our house we had a cat with the grandiose name of Gonnosuke. Usually with cats and dogs we kn ow who the mother is but not the father. A cat with a large belly wondered into the house of my youn ger sister and her husband and gave birth to five kittens. While the mother was a pure white thoroug hbred Chinchila, the kittens were black and white tabbies of mixed breed. One of these came to our h ouse about two weeks after its birth and was given the name Gonnosuke. At that time we already ha d one female Shiba dog and one female brown tabby cat in our house comprising only 13 tubo. The

16/17

In our house we had a cat with the grandiose name of Gonnos uke. Usually with cats and dogs we know who the mother is b ut not the father. A cat with a large belly wondered into the hou se of my younger sister and her husband and gave birth to five

24/25

In our house we had a cat with the grand iose name of Gonnosuke. Usually with ca ts and dogs we know who the mother is b

ABCDEFGHIJKLMN
OPQRSTUVWXYZ
abcdefghijklmnopq
rstuvwxyz
1234567890&$¢£¥
fiflæœÆŒÅßÇÌÎÍÏã
§†-——/()''""":;.,!¡?¿

10/11

In our house we had a cat with the grandiose name of Gonnosuke. Usually with cats and dogs we know who the mother is but not the father. A cat with a large belly wondered into the house of my younger sister and her husband and gave birth to five kittens. While the mother was a pure white thoroughbred Chinchila, the kittens were black and white tabbies of mixed breed. One of these came to our house about two weeks after its birth and was given the name Gonnosuke. At that time we already had one female Shiba dog and one female brown tabby cat in our house comprising

16/17

In our house we had a cat with the grandiose name of Gonnosuke. Usually with cats and dogs we know who the mother is but not the father. A cat with a large belly wondered into the house of my younger sister and her husband and gave birth

24/25

In our house we had a cat with the grandiose name of Gonnosuke. Usually with cats and dogs we know who the mother

ABCDEFGHIJKLM
NOPQRSTUVWXYZ
abcdefghijklmnopq
rstuvwxyz
1234567890&$¢£¥
fiflæœÆŒÅßÇÌÎÍÏã
§†-–——/()''""";.,!¡?¿

10/11

In our house we had a cat with the grandiose name of Gonnosuke. Usually with cats and dogs we know who the mother is but not the father. A cat with a large belly wondered into the house of my younger sister and her husband and gave birth to five kittens. While the mother was a pure white thoroughbred Chinchila, the kittens were black and white tabbies of mixed breed. One of these came to our house about two weeks after its birth and was given the name Gonnosuke. At that time we already had one female Shiba dog and one female brown tabby cat in our house comprising on

16/17

In our house we had a cat with the grandiose name of Gonno suke. Usually with cats and dogs we know who the mother is but not the father. A cat with a large belly wondered into the house of my younger sister and her husband and gave birth

24/25

In our house we had a cat with the gran diose name of Gonnosuke. Usually with cats and dogs we know who the mother

ABCDEFGHIJKL
MNOPQRSTUVW
XYZabcdefghijklm
nopqrstuvwxyz
1234567890&
$¢£¥fiflæœÆŒ
ÅßÇÌÎÍÏã§†
----—/()''"":;.,!¡?¿

10/11

In our house we had a cat with the grandiose name of Gonnosuke. Usually with cats and dogs
we know who the mother is but not the father. A cat with a large belly wondered into the hou
se of my younger sister and her husband and gave birth to five kittens. While the mother was
a pure white thoroughbred Chinchila, the kittens were black and white tabbies of mixed bree
d. One of these came to our house about two weeks after its birth and was given the name Go
nnosuke. At that time we already had one female Shiba dog and one female brown tabby cat

16/17

In our house we had a cat with the grandiose name of Gon
nosuke. Usually with cats and dogs we know who the mot
her is but not the father. A cat with a large belly wondered
into the house of my younger sister and her husband and

24/25

In our house we had a cat with the gra
ndiose name of Gonnosuke. Usually wi
th cats and dogs we know who the mot

ABCDEFGHIJKL
MNOPQRSTUVW
XYZabcdefghijklm
nopqrstuvwxyz
1234567890&
$¢£¥fiflæœÆŒ
ÅßÇÌÎÍÏã§†
-–—/()''""·;·,!¡?¿

10/11

In our house we had a cat with the grandiose name of Gonnosuke. Usually with cats and do
gs we know who the mother is but not the father. A cat with a large belly wondered into the
house of my younger sister and her husband and gave birth to five kittens. While the mother
was a pure white thoroughbred Chinchila, the kittens were black and white tabbies of mixed
breed. One of these came to our house about two weeks after its birth and was given the na
me Gonnosuke. At that time we already had one female Shiba dog and one female brown tab

16/17

In our house we had a cat with the grandiose name of Go
nnosuke. Usually with cats and dogs we know who the mo
ther is but not the father. A cat with a large belly wonder
ed into the house of my younger sister and her husband a

24/25

In our house we had a cat with the gr
andiose name of Gonnosuke. Usually
with cats and dogs we know who the

ABCDEFGHIJKLMN
OPQRSTUVWXYZ
abcdefghijklmnopq
rstuvwxyz
1234567890&$¢£¥
fiflæœÆŒÅßÇÌÎÍÏã§†
——/()'’“”:;.,!¡?¿

10/11

In our house we had a cat with the grandiose name of Gonnosuke. Usually with cats and dogs we know who the mother is but not the father. A cat with a large belly wondered into the house of my younger sister and her husband and gave birth to five kittens. While the mother was a pure white thoroughbred Chinchila, the kittens were black and white tabbies of mixed breed. One of these came to our house about two weeks after its birth and was given the name Gonnosuke. At that time we already had one female Shiba dog and one fem ale brown tabby cat in our house comprising only 13 thubo. The dog was called Momo and the cat Mii. My

16/17

In our house we had a cat with the grandiose name of Gonnosuke. Usually with cats and dogs we know who the mother is but not the father. A cat with a large belly wondered into the house of my youn ger sister and her husband and gave birth to five kittens. While the

24/25

In our house we had a cat with the grandiose name of Gonnosuke. Usually with cats and d ogs we know who the mother is but not the

ABCDEFGHIJKLMN
OPQRSTUVWXYZ
abcdefghijklmnopq
rstuvwxyz
1234567890&$¢£¥
fiflæœÆŒÅßÇÌÎÍÏã§†
-–—/()''""";:.,!¡?¿

10/11

In our house we had a cat with the grandiose name of Gonnosuke. Usually with cats and dogs we know who the mother is but not the father. A cat with a large belly wondered into the house of my younger sister and her husban d and gave birth to five kittens. While the mother was a pure white thoroughbred Chinchila, the kittens were blac k and white tabbies of mixed breed. One of these came to our house about two weeks after its birth and was given the name Gonnosuke. At that time we already had one female Shiba dog and one female brown tabby cat in our house comprising only 13 thubo. The dog was called Momo and the cat Mii. My wife, who was very much oppose

16/17

In our house we had a cat with the grandiose name of Gonnosuke. Us ually with cats and dogs we know who the mother is but not the father. A cat with a large belly wondered into the house of my younger sister and her husband and gave birth to five kittens. While the mother was

24/25

In our house we had a cat with the grandiose name of Gonnosuke. Usually with cats and do gs we know who the mother is but not the fathe

ABCDEFGHIJKL
MNOPQRSTU
VWXYZ
abcdefghijklmnopq
rstuvwxyz
1234567890&$¢£¥
fiflæœÆŒÅßÇÌÎÍÏã
§†----——/()'""",.;.,!¡?¿

10/11

In our house we had a cat with the grandiose name of Gonnosuke. Usually with cats and dogs we know who the mother is but not the father. A cat with a large belly wondered into the house of m y younger sister and her husband and gave birth to five kittens. While the mother was a pure wh ite thoroughbred Chinchila, the kittens were black and white tabbies of mixed breed. One of thes e came to our house about two weeks after its birth and was given the name Gonnosuke. At that time we already had one female Shiba dog and one female brown tabby cat in our house comprisi

16/17

In our house we had a cat with the grandiose name of Gonno suke. Usually with cats and dogs we know who the mother is but not the father. A cat with a large belly wondered into t he house of my younger sister and her husband and gave birt

24/25

In our house we had a cat with the gran diose name of Gonnosuke. Usually with cats and dogs we know who the mother

ABCDEFGHIJKLMN
OPQRSTUVWXYZ
abcdefghijklmno
pqrstuvwxyz
1234567890&$¢£¥
fiflæœÆŒÅßÇÌÎÍÏã§†
-–—/()'""":;.,!¡?¿

10/11

In our house we had a cat with the grandiose name of Gonnosuke. Usually with cats and dogs we know who the mother is but not the father. A cat with a large belly wondered into the house of my younger s ister and her husband and gave birth to five kittens. While the mother was a pure white thoroughbred Chinchila, the kittens were black and white tabbies of mixed breed. One of these came to our house ab out two weeks after its birth and was given the name Gonnosuke. At that time we already had one fem ale Shiba dog and one female brown tabby cat in our house comprising only 13 thubo. The dog was cal

16/17

In our house we had a cat with the grandiose name of Gonnosu ke. Usually with cats and dogs we know who the mother is but n ot the father. A cat with a large belly wondered into the house of my younger sister and her husband and gave birth to five kitten

24/25

In our house we had a cat with the grandi ose name of Gonnosuke. Usually with cats and dogs we know who the mother is but

ABCDEFGHIJKLMNO
PQRSTUVWXYZ
abcdefghijklmno
pqrstuvwxyz
1234567890&$¢£¥
fiflæœÆŒÅßÇÌÎÍÏïã§†
——––/()'"""·.;.,!¡?¿

10/11

In our house we had a cat with the grandiose name of Gonnosuke. Usually with cats and dogs we know wh
o the mother is but not the father. A cat with a large belly wondered into the house of my younger sister an
d her husband and gave birth to five kittens. While the mother was a pure white thoroughbred Chinchila, t
he kittens were black and white tabbies of mixed breed. One of these came to our house about two weeks af
ter its birth and was given the name Gonnosuke. At that time we already had one female Shiba dog and on
e female brown tabby cat in our house comprising only 13 thubo. The dog was called Momo and the cat Mi

16/17

In our house we had a cat with the grandiose name of Gonnosuke.
Usually with cats and dogs we know who the mother is but not the
father. A cat with a large belly wondered into the house of my you
nger sister and her husband and gave birth to five kittens. While t

24/25

In our house we had a cat with the grandios
e name of Gonnosuke. Usually with cats and
dogs we know who the mother is but not the

ABCDEFGHIJKLMN
OPQRSTUVWXYZ
abcdefghijklmno
pqrstuvwxyz
1234567890&$¢£¥
fiflæœÆŒÅßÇÌÎÍÏã§
†-–—/()''""":;.,!¡?¿

10/11

In our house we had a cat with the grandiose name of Gonnosuke. Usually with cats and dogs we know who the mother is but not the father. A cat with a large belly wondered into the house of m y younger sister and her husband and gave birth to five kittens. While the mother was a pure wh ite thoroughbred Chinchila, the kittens were black and white tabbies of mixed breed. One of thes e came to our house about two weeks after its birth and was given the name Gonnosuke. At that time we already had one female Shiba dog and one female brown tabby cat in our house compris

16/17

In our house we had a cat with the grandiose name of Gonn osuke. Usually with cats and dogs we know who the mother is but not the father. A cat with a large belly wondered into t he house of my younger sister and her husband and gave bir

24/25

In our house we had a cat with the gran diose name of Gonnosuke. Usually with cats and dogs we know who the mother

ABCDEFGHIJKLMN
OPQRSTUVWXYZ
abcdefghijklmno
pqrstuvwxyz
1234567890&$¢£¥
fiflæœÆŒÅßÇÌÎÍÏã§
†-–—/0''""·;·,!¡?¿

10/11

In our house we had a cat with the grandiose name of Gonnosuke. Usually with cats and dogs we know who the mother is but not the father. A cat with a large belly wondered into the house of my younger sister and her husband and gave birth to five kittens. While the mother was a pure white thoroughbred Chinchila, the kittens were black and white tabbies of mixed breed. One of these ca me to our house about two weeks after its birth and was given the name Gonnosuke. At that time we already had one female Shiba dog and one female brown tabby cat in our house comprising on

16/17

In our house we had a cat with the grandiose name of Gonno suke. Usually with cats and dogs we know who the mother is but not the father. A cat with a large belly wondered into the house of my younger sister and her husband and gave birth t

24/25

In our house we had a cat with the gran diose name of Gonnosuke. Usually with c ats and dogs we know who the mother is

ABCDEFGHIJKLM
NOPQRSTUVWX
YZabcdefghijklm
nopqrstuvwxyz
1234567890
&$¢£¥fiflæœÆŒ
ÅßçÌÎÍÏã§†
——/()''""·;·,!¡?¿

10/11

In our house we had a cat with the grandiose name of Gonnosuke. Usually with cats a
nd dogs we know who the mother is but not the father. A cat with a large belly wonde
red into the house of my younger sister and her husband and gave birth to five kitten
s. While the mother was a pure white thoroughbred Chinchila, the kittens were black
and white tabbies of mixed breed. One of these came to our house about two weeks af
ter its birth and was given the name Gonnosuke. At that time we already had one fem

16/17

In our house we had a cat with the grandiose name of
Gonnosuke. Usually with cats and dogs we know who
the mother is but not the father. A cat with a large bel
ly wondered into the house of my younger sister and

24/25

In our house we had a cat with the
grandiose name of Gonnosuke. Usu
ally with cats and dogs we know wh

ABCDEFGHIJKLM
NOPQRSTUVWXY
Zabcdefghijklmno
pqrstuvwxyz
1234567890
&$¢£¥fiflæœÆŒ
ÅßçÌÎÍÏã§†
——/()''""":;.,!¡?¿

10/11

In our house we had a cat with the grandiose name of Gonnosuke. Usually with cats an
d dogs we know who the mother is but not the father. A cat with a large belly wondered
into the house of my younger sister and her husband and gave birth to five kittens. Whi
le the mother was a pure white thoroughbred Chinchila, the kittens were black and whi
te tabbies of mixed breed. One of these came to our house about two weeks after its birt
h and was given the name Gonnosuke. At that time we already had one female Shiba do

16/17

In our house we had a cat with the grandiose name of
Gonnosuke. Usually with cats and dogs we know who t
he mother is but not the father. A cat with a large bell
y wondered into the house of my younger sister and he

24/25

In our house we had a cat with the
grandiose name of Gonnosuke. Usua
lly with cats and dogs we know who

ABCDEFGHIJKLMNO
PQRSTUVWXYZ
abcdefghijklmnopq
rstuvwxyz
1234567890&$¢£¥
fiflæœÆŒÅßÇÌÎÍÏã§†
-–——/()''""":;.,!¡?¿

10/11

In our house we had a cat with the grandiose name of Gonnosuke. Usually with cats and dogs we know who th e mother is but not the father. A cat with a large belly wondered into the house of my younger sister and her hu sband and gave birth to five kittens. While the mother was a pure white thoroughbred Chinchila, the kittens we re black and white tabbies of mixed breed. One of these came to our house about two weeks after its birth and was given the name Gonnosuke. At that time we already had one female Shiba dog and one female brown tabby cat in our house comprising only 13 tubo. The dog was called Momo and the cat Mii. My wife, who was very m

16/17

In our house we had a cat with the grandiose name of Gonnosuke. Us ually with cats and dogs we know who the mother is but not the fath er. A cat with a large belly wondered into the house of my younger sis ter and her husband and gave birth to five kittens. While the mother

24/25

In our house we had a cat with the grandiose name of Gonnosuke. Usually with cats and do gs we know who the mother is but not the fat

278

ABCDEFGHIJKLMNO
PQRSTUVWXYZ
abcdefghijklmnopq
rstuvwxyz
1234567890&$¢£¥
fiflœœÆŒÅßÇÌÎÍÏã§†
-–——/()''""":;.,!¡?¿

10/11

In our house we had a cat with the grandiose name of Gonnosuke. Usually with cats and dogs we know who t he mother is but not the father. A cat with a large belly wondered into the house of my younger sister and her husband and gave birth to five kittens. While the mother was a pure white thoroughbred Chinchila, the kittens were black and white tabbies of mixed breed. One of these came to our house about two weeks after its birth a nd was given the name Gonnosuke. At that time we already had one female Shiba dog and one female brown tabby cat in our house comprising only 13 tubo. The dog was called Momo and the cat Mii. My wife, who was

16/17

In our house we had a cat with the grandiose name of Gonnosuke. Usually with cats and dogs we know who the mother is but not the f ather. A cat with a large belly wondered into the house of my young er sister and her husband and gave birth to five kittens. While the m

24/25

In our house we had a cat with the grandiose name of Gonnosuke. Usually with cats and d ogs we know who the mother is but not the fa

279

ABCDEFGHIJKLMNO
PQRSTUVWXYZ
abcdefghijklmnopq
rstuvwxyz
1234567890&$¢£¥
fiflæœÆŒÅßÇÌÎÍÏã§†
-–—/()''""":;.,!¡?¿

10/11

In our house we had a cat with the grandiose name of Gonnosuke. Usually with cats and dogs we know who the mother is but not the father. A cat with a large belly wondered into the house of my younger sister and h er husband and gave birth to five kittens. While the mother was a pure white thoroughbred Chinchila, the ki ttens were black and white tabbies of mixed breed. One of these came to our house about two weeks after its birth and was given the name Gonnosuke. At that time we already had one female Shiba dog and one female brown tabby cat in our house comprising only 13 tubo. The dog was called Momo and the cat Mii. My wife,

16/17

In our house we had a cat with the grandiose name of Gonnosuke. Usually with cats and dogs we know who the mother is but not the father. A cat with a large belly wondered into the house of my youn ger sister and her husband and gave birth to five kittens. While the

24/25

In our house we had a cat with the grandiose name of Gonnosuke. Usually with cats and d ogs we know who the mother is but not the

ABCDEFGHIJKLMN
OPQRSTUVWXYZ
abcdefghijklmnopq
rstuvwxyz
1234567890&$¢£¥
fiflœœÆŒÅßÇÌÎÍÏã§†
---—/()''""".;.,!¡?¿

10/11

In our house we had a cat with the grandiose name of Gonnosuke. Usually with cats and dogs we know wh o the mother is but not the father. A cat with a large belly wondered into the house of my younger sister an d her husband and gave birth to five kittens. While the mother was a pure white thoroughbred Chinchila, t he kittens were black and white tabbies of mixed breed. One of these came to our house about two weeks a fter its birth and was given the name Gonnosuke. At that time we already had one female Shiba dog and o ne female brown tabby cat in our house comprising only 13 tubo. The dog was called Momo and the cat M

16/17

In our house we had a cat with the grandiose name of Gonnosuke. Usually with cats and dogs we know who the mother is but not the father. A cat with a large belly wondered into the house of my you nger sister and her husband and gave birth to five kittens. While th

24/25

In our house we had a cat with the grandios e name of Gonnosuke. Usually with cats an d dogs we know who the mother is but not t

ABCDEFGHIJKLMN
OPQRSTUVWXYZ
abcdefghijklmnopq
rstuvwxyz
1234567890&$¢£¥
fiflæœÆŒÅßÇÎÎÍÏã§†
-–—/()''""":;.,!¡?¿

10/11

In our house we had a cat with the grandiose name of Gonnosuke. Usually with cats and dogs we know w
ho the mother is but not the father. A cat with a large belly wondered into the house of my younger sister
and her husband and gave birth to five kittens. While the mother was a pure white thoroughbred Chinchi
la, the kittens were black and white tabbies of mixed breed. One of these came to our house about two we
eks after its birth and was given the name Gonnosuke. At that time we already had one female Shiba dog
and one female brown tabby cat in our house comprising only 13 tubo. The dog was called Momo and the

16/17

In our house we had a cat with the grandiose name of Gonnosuk
e. Usually with cats and dogs we know who the mother is but not
the father. A cat with a large belly wondered into the house of my
younger sister and her husband and gave birth to five kittens. Wh

24/25

In our house we had a cat with the grandio
se name of Gonnosuke. Usually with cats a
nd dogs we know who the mother is but no

ABCDEFGHIJKLMN OPQRSTUVWXYZ abcdefghijklmnopq rstuvwxyz 1234567890&$¢£¥ fiflæœÆŒÅßÇÌÎÍÏã§ †-––—/() ''""".;.,!¡?¿

10/11

In our house we had a cat with the grandiose name of Gonnosuke. Usually with cats and dogs we kno w who the mother is but not the father. A cat with a large belly wondered into the house of my younge r sister and her husband and gave birth to five kittens. While the mother was a pure white thoroughbr ed Chinchila, the kittens were black and white tabbies of mixed breed. One of these came to our house about two weeks after its birth and was given the name Gonnosuke. At that time we already had one f emale Shiba dog and one female brown tabby cat in our house comprising only 13 tubo. The dog was

16/17

In our house we had a cat with the grandiose name of Gonnosu ke. Usually with cats and dogs we know who the mother is but n ot the father. A cat with a large belly wondered into the house of my younger sister and her husband and gave birth to five kit

24/25

In our house we had a cat with the grandi ose name of Gonnosuke. Usually with cats and dogs we know who the mother is but

ABCDEFGHIJKLMN
OPQRSTUVWXYZ
abcdefghijklmnopq
rstuvwxyz
1234567890&$¢£¥
fiflæœÆŒÅßÇÌÎÍÏã
§†⸷--—/()''""·;·.,!¡?¿

10/11

In our house we had a cat with the grandiose name of Gonnosuke. Usually with cats and dogs we know who the mother is but not the father. A cat with a large belly wondered into the house of m y younger sister and her husband and gave birth to five kittens. While the mother was a pure wh ite thoroughbred Chinchila, the kittens were black and white tabbies of mixed breed. One of thes e came to our house about two weeks after its birth and was given the name Gonnosuke. At that t ime we already had one female Shiba dog and one female brown tabby cat in our house comprisi

16/17

In our house we had a cat with the grandiose name of Gonn osuke. Usually with cats and dogs we know who the mother is but not the father. A cat with a large belly wondered into the house of my younger sister and her husband and gave bi

24/25

In our house we had a cat with the gran diose name of Gonnosuke. Usually with cats and dogs we know who the mother

ABCDEFGHIJKLM
NOPQRSTUVWXYZ
abcdefghijklmnopq
rstuvwxyz
1234567890&$¢£¥
fiflœæÆŒÅßÇÌÎÍÏã
§†-–—/()''""""·;·.,!¡?¿

10/11

In our house we had a cat with the grandiose name of Gonnosuke. Usually with cats and dogs we know who the mother is but not the father. A cat with a large belly wondered into the house of my younger sister and her husband and gave birth to five kittens. While the mother was a pu re white thoroughbred Chinchila, the kittens were black and white tabbies of mixed breed. One of these came to our house about two weeks after its birth and was given the name Gonnosuke. At that time we already had one female Shiba dog and one female brown tabby cat in our hous

16/17

In our house we had a cat with the grandiose name of Gon nosuke. Usually with cats and dogs we know who the mothe r is but not the father. A cat with a large belly wondered in to the house of my younger sister and her husband and gav

24/25

In our house we had a cat with the gra ndiose name of Gonnosuke. Usually wit h cats and dogs we know who the moth

ABCDEFGHIJKLMN
OPQRSTUVWXYZ
abcdefghijklmnopq
rstuvwxyz
1234567890&$¢£¥
fiflæœÆŒÅßÇÎÎÎÎã
§†–-——/()''""·;.,!¡?¿

10/11

In our house we had a cat with the grandiose name of Gonnosuke. Usually with cats and dogs we kn
ow who the mother is but not the father. A cat with a large belly wondered into the house of my you
nger sister and her husband and gave birth to five kittens. While the mother was a pure white thoro
ughbred Chinchila, the kittens were black and white tabbies of mixed breed. One of these came to o
ur house about two weeks after its birth and was given the name Gonnosuke. At that time we alread
y had one female Shiba dog and one female brown tabby cat in our house comprising only 13 tubo.

16/17

In our house we had a cat with the grandiose name of Gonnos
uke. Usually with cats and dogs we know who the mother is b
ut not the father. A cat with a large belly wondered into the ho
use of my younger sister and her husband and gave birth to fiv

24/25

In our house we had a cat with the grand
iose name of Gonnosuke. Usually with ca
ts and dogs we know who the mother is b

ABCDEFGHIJKL
MNOPQRSTU
VWXYZ
abcdefghijklmnopq
rstuvwxyz
1234567890&$¢£¥
fiflæœÆŒÅßÇÌÎÍÏã
§†----——/()''""".;.,!¡?¿

10/11

In our house we had a cat with the grandiose name of Gonnosuke. Usually with cats and dogs we kn ow who the mother is but not the father. A cat with a large belly wondered into the house of my you nger sister and her husband and gave birth to five kittens. While the mother was a pure white thorou ghbred Chinchila, the kittens were black and white tabbies of mixed breed. One of these came to our house about two weeks after its birth and was given the name Gonnosuke. At that time we already h ad one female Shiba dog and one female brown tabby cat in our house comprising only 13 thubo. Th

16/17

In our house we had a cat with the grandiose name of Gonnos uke. Usually with cats and dogs we know who the mother is b ut not the father. A cat with a large belly wondered into the ho use of my younger sister and her husband and gave birth to fiv

24/25

In our house we had a cat with the grandi ose name of Gonnosuke. Usually with cat s and dogs we know who the mother is b

ABCDEFGHIJKL
MNOPQRSTU
VWXYZ
abcdefghijklmnopq
rstuvwxyz
1234567890&$¢£¥
fiflæœÆŒÅßÇÌÎÍÏã
§†-–—/() ''""".,.,!¡?¿

10/11

In our house we had a cat with the grandiose name of Gonnosuke. Usually with cats and dogs we know who the mother is but not the father. A cat with a large belly wondered into the house of my younger sister and her husband and gave birth to five kittens. While the mother was a pure white thoroughbred Chinchila, the kittens were black and white tabbies of mixed breed. One of these came to our house about two weeks after its birth and was given the name Gonnosuke. At that time we already had one female Shiba dog and one female brown tabby cat in our house comprising on

16/17

In our house we had a cat with the grandiose name of Gonno suke. Usually with cats and dogs we know who the mother is but not the father. A cat with a large belly wondered into the house of my younger sister and her husband and gave birth t

24/25

In our house we had a cat with the gran diose name of Gonnosuke. Usually with cats and dogs we know who the mother

ABCDEFGHIJKL
MNOPQRSTU
VWXYZ
abcdefghijklmnopq
rstuvwxyz
1234567890&$¢£¥
fiflæœÆŒÅßÇÌÎÍÏ
ã§†-–——/()''""":;.,!¡?¿

10/11

In our house we had a cat with the grandiose name of Gonnosuke. Usually with cats and dogs we k now who the mother is but not the father. A cat with a large belly wondered into the house of my y ounger sister and her husband and gave birth to five kittens. While the mother was a pure white th oroughbred Chinchila, the kittens were black and white tabbies of mixed breed. One of these came to our house about two weeks after its birth and was given the name Gonnosuke. At that time we a lready had one female Shiba dog and one female brown tabby cat in our house comprising only 13

16/17

In our house we had a cat with the grandiose name of Gonnos uke. Usually with cats and dogs we know who the mother is b ut not the father. A cat with a large belly wondered into the h ouse of my younger sister and her husband and gave birth to f

24/25

In our house we had a cat with the grand iose name of Gonnosuke. Usually with c ats and dogs we know who the mother is

ABCDEFGHIJKLMNO
PQRSTUVWXYZ
abcdefghijklmnopq
rstuvwxyz
1234567890&$¢£¥
fiflæœÆŒÅßÇÌÎÍÏã§†
--——/()''""":;.,!¡?¿

10/11

In our house we had a cat with the grandiose name of Gonnosuke. Usually with cats and dogs we know who t he mother is but not the father. A cat with a large belly wondered into the house of my younger sister and her husband and gave birth to five kittens. While the mother was a pure white thoroughbred Chinchila, the kitten s were black and white tabbies of mixed breed. One of these came to our house about two weeks after its birt h and was given the name Gonnosuke. At that time we already had one female Shiba dog and one female bro wn tabby cat in our house comprising only 13 tubo. The dog was called Momo and the cat Mii. My wife, who

16/17

In our house we had a cat with the grandiose name of Gonnosuke. U sually with cats and dogs we know who the mother is but not the fat her. A cat with a large belly wondered into the house of my younger sister and her husband and gave birth to five kittens. While the moth

24/25

In our house we had a cat with the grandiose name of Gonnosuke. Usually with cats and do gs we know who the mother is but not the fat

ABCDEFGHIJKLMNO
PQRSTUVWXYZ
abcdefghijklmnopq
rstuvwxyz
1234567890&$¢£¥
fiflœœÆŒÅßÇÌÎÍÏã§†
-–—/()''""":;.,!¡?¿

10/11

In our house we had a cat with the grandiose name of Gonnosuke. Usually with cats and dogs we know who the mot her is but not the father. A cat with a large belly wondered into the house of my younger sister and her husband and gave birth to five kittens. While the mother was a pure white thoroughbred Chinchila, the kittens were black and whi te tabbies of mixed breed. One of these came to our house about two weeks after its birth and was given the name G onnosuke. At that time we already had one female Shiba dog and one female brown tabby cat in our house comprisin g only 13 tubo. The dog was called Momo and the cat Mii. My wife, who was very much opposed to keeping cats an

16/17

In our house we had a cat with the grandiose name of Gonnosuke. Usual ly with cats and dogs we know who the mother is but not the father. A c at with a large belly wondered into the house of my younger sister and h er husband and gave birth to five kittens. While the mother was a pure

24/25

In our house we had a cat with the grandiose na me of Gonnosuke. Usually with cats and dogs w e know who the mother is but not the father. A

ABCDEFGHIJKLMNO
PQRSTUVWXYZ
abcdefghijklmnopq
rstuvwxyz
1234567890&$¢£¥
fiflæœÆŒÅßÇÌÎÍÏã§†
-–—/()''""":;.,!¡?¿

10/11

In our house we had a cat with the grandiose name of Gonnosuke. Usually with cats and dogs we know who the mother is but not the father. A cat with a large belly wondered into the house of my younger sister and her husband and gave birth to five kittens. While the mother was a pure white thoroughbred Chinchila, the kittens were black and white tabbies of mixed breed. One of these came to our house about two weeks after its birth and was given the name Gonnosuke. At that time we already had one female Shiba dog and one fe male brown tabby cat in our house comprising only 13 tubo. The dog was called Momo and the cat Mii. My

16/17

In our house we had a cat with the grandiose name of Gonnosuke. Usually with cats and dogs we know who the mother is but not the father. A cat with a large belly wondered into the house of my youn ger sister and her husband and gave birth to five kittens. While the

24/25

In our house we had a cat with the grandios e name of Gonnosuke. Usually with cats and dogs we know who the mother is but not the

ITC Cushing Medium Italic

ABCDEFGHIJKLMNO
PQRSTUVWXYZ
abcdefghijklmnopq
rstuvwxyz
1234567890&$¢£¥
fiflæœÆŒÅßÇÌÎÍÏã§†
-----—/()''""":;.,!¡?¿

10/11

In our house we had a cat with the grandiose name of Gonnosuke. Usually with cats and dogs we know who the m other is but not the father. A cat with a large belly wondered into the house of my younger sister and her husband and gave birth to five kittens. While the mother was a pure white thoroughbred Chinchila, the kittens were black a nd white tabbies of mixed breed. One of these came to our house about two weeks after its birth and was given the name Gonnosuke. At that time we already had one female Shiba dog and one female brown tabby cat in our house comprising only 13 tubo. The dog was called Momo and the cat Mii. My wife, who was very much opposed to kee

16/17

In our house we had a cat with the grandiose name of Gonnosuke. Usu ally with cats and dogs we know who the mother is but not the father. A cat with a large belly wondered into the house of my younger sister a nd her husband and gave birth to five kittens. While the mother was a

24/25

In our house we had a cat with the grandiose n ame of Gonnosuke. Usually with cats and dogs we know who the mother is but not the father.

293

ABCDEFGHIJKLMNO
PQRSTUVWXYZ
abcdefghijklmnopq
rstuvwxyz
1234567890&$¢£¥
fiflæœÆŒÅßÇÌÎÍÏã§†
-–—/()''""":;.,!¡?¿

10/11

In our house we had a cat with the grandiose name of Gonnosuke. Usually with cats and dogs we know who the mother is but not the father. A cat with a large belly wondered into the house of my younger sis ter and her husband and gave birth to five kittens. While the mother was a pure white thoroughbred Chi nchila, the kittens were black and white tabbies of mixed breed. One of these came to our house about t wo weeks after its birth and was given the name Gonnosuke. At that time we already had one female Sh iba dog and one female brown tabby cat in our house comprising only 13 tubo. The dog was called Momo

16/17

In our house we had a cat with the grandiose name of Gonnosuk e. Usually with cats and dogs we know who the mother is but not the father. A cat with a large belly wondered into the house of m y younger sister and her husband and gave birth to five kittens.

24/25

In our house we had a cat with the grandio se name of Gonnosuke. Usually with cats a nd dogs we know who the mother is but not

ITC Cushing Bold Italic

ABCDEFGHIJKLMN
OPQRSTUVWXYZ
abcdefghijklmnopq
rstuvwxyz
1234567890&$¢£¥
fiflæœÆŒÅßÇÌÎÍÏ㧠†
——–/()''""":;.,!¡?¿

10/11

In our house we had a cat with the grandiose name of Gonnosuke. Usually with cats and dogs we know who th
e mother is but not the father. A cat with a large belly wondered into the house of my younger sister and her hu
sband and gave birth to five kittens. While the mother was a pure white thoroughbred Chinchila, the kittens we
re black and white tabbies of mixed breed. One of these came to our house about two weeks after its birth and
was given the name Gonnosuke. At that time we already had one female Shiba dog and one female brown tabby
cat in our house comprising only 13 tubo. The dog was called Momo and the cat Mii. My wife, who was very

16/17

In our house we had a cat with the grandiose name of Gonnosuke. Us
ually with cats and dogs we know who the mother is but not the fathe
r. A cat with a large belly wondered into the house of my younger sis
ter and her husband and gave birth to five kittens. While the mother

24/25

In our house we had a cat with the grandiose
name of Gonnosuke. Usually with cats and do
gs we know who the mother is but not the fat

ABCDEFGHIJKLMN
OPQRSTUVWXYZ
abcdefghijklmnopq
rstuvwxyz
1234567890&$¢£¥
fiflæœÆŒÅßÇÌÎÍÏã§
†-–—/()''""";.,!¡?¿

10/11

In our house we had a cat with the grandiose name of Gonnosuke. Usually with cats and dogs we kn ow who the mother is but not the father. A cat with a large belly wondered into the house of my you nger sister and her husband and gave birth to five kittens. While the mother was a pure white thoro ughbred Chinchila, the kittens were black and white tabbies of mixed breed. One of these came to ou r house about two weeks after its birth and was given the name Gonnosuke. At that time we already had one female Shiba dog and one female brown tabby cat in our house comprising only 13 tubo. The

16/17

In our house we had a cat with the grandiose name of Gonnosu ke. Usually with cats and dogs we know who the mother is but not the father. A cat with a large belly wondered into the hous e of my younger sister and her husband and gave birth to five

24/25

In our house we had a cat with the grandi ose name of Gonnosuke. Usually with cats and dogs we know who the mother is but

ABCDEFGHIJKLM
NOPQRSTUVWXYZ
abcdefghijklmnopq
rstuvwxyz
1234567890&
$¢£¥fiflœœÆŒ
ÅßÇÌÎÍÏã§†
———/O''""·;·,!¡?¿

10/11

In our house we had a cat with the grandiose name of Gonnosuke. Usually with cats and dogs we know who the mother is but not the father. A cat with a large belly wondered into the house of my younger sister and her husband and gave birth to five kittens. While the mother was a pure white thoroughbred Chinchila, the kittens were black and white tabbies of mixed breed. One of these came to our house about two weeks after its birth and was given the name Gonnosuke. At that time we already had one female Shiba dog and one female brown tabby cat in our house comprising only 13 tubo. The dog was called Momo and the cat

16/17

In our house we had a cat with the grandiose name of Gonnosuke. Usually with cats and dogs we know who the mother is but not the father. A cat with a large belly wondered into the house of my younger sister and her husband and gave birth to five kittens. While

24/25

In our house we had a cat with the grandiose name of Gonnosuke. Usually with cats and dogs we know who the mother is but not t

ABCDEFGHIJKLMN
OPQRSTUVWXYZ
abcdefghijklmnopq
rstuvwxyz
1234567890&$¢£¥
fiflæœÆŒÅßÇÌÎÍÏã§†
-——/()''""";.,!¡?¿

10/11

In our house we had a cat with the grandiose name of Gonnosuke. Usually with cats and dogs we know who t he mother is but not the father. A cat with a large belly wondered into the house of my younger sister and he r husband and gave birth to five kittens. While the mother was a pure white thoroughbred Chinchila, the kit tens were black and white tabbies of mixed breed. One of these came to our house about two weeks after its birth and was given the name Gonnosuke. At that time we already had one female Shiba dog and one female brown tabby cat in our house comprising only 13 tubo. The dog was called Momo and the cat Mii. My wife,

16/17

In our house we had a cat with the grandiose name of Gonnosuke. Usually with cats and dogs we know who the mother is but not the f ather. A cat with a large belly wondered into the house of my young er sister and her husband and gave birth to five kittens. While the

24/25

In our house we had a cat with the grandiose name of Gonnosuke. Usually with cats and d ogs we know who the mother is but not the f

ABCDEFGHIJKLMN
OPQRSTUVWXYZ
abcdefghijklmnopq
rstuvwxyz
1234567890&$¢£¥
fiflæœÆŒÅßÇÌÎÍÏãß†
——/()''""":;.,!¡?¿

10/11

In our house we had a cat with the grandiose name of Gonnosuke. Usually with cats and dogs we know who the mother is but not the father. A cat with a large belly wondered into the house of my younger sister and her husb and and gave birth to five kittens. While the mother was a pure white thoroughbred Chinchila, the kittens were black and white tabbies of mixed breed. One of these came to our house about two weeks after its birth and was given the name Gonnosuke. At that time we already had one female Shiba dog and one female brown tabby cat in our house comprising only 13 tubo. The dog was called Momo and the cat Mii. My wife, who was very much

16/17

In our house we had a cat with the grandiose name of Gonnosuke. Us ually with cats and dogs we know who the mother is but not the fathe r. A cat with a large belly wondered into the house of my younger siste r and her husband and gave birth to five kittens. While the mother wa

24/25

In our house we had a cat with the grandiose n ame of Gonnosuke. Usually with cats and dogs we know who the mother is but not the father.

ABCDEFGHIJKL
MNOPQRSTUVW
XYZabcdefghijklmno
pqrstuvwxyz
1234567890&$¢£¥
fiflæœÆŒÅßÇÌÎÍÏã§
†-–—/()''""":;.,!¡?¿

10/11

In our house we had a cat with the grandiose name of Gonnosuke. Usually with cats and dogs we know who the mother is but not the father. A cat with a large belly wondered into the house of my younger sister and her husband and gave birth to five kittens. While the mother was a pure white thoroughbred Chinchila, th e kittens were black and white tabbies of mixed breed. One of these came to our house about two weeks aft er its birth and was given the name Gonnosuke. At that time we already had one female Shiba dog and one female brown tabby cat in our house comprising only 13 tubo. The dog was called Momo and the cat Mii.

16/17

In our house we had a cat with the grandiose name of Gonnosuke. Usually with cats and dogs we know who the mother is but not the father. A cat with a large belly wondered into the house of my you nger sister and her husband and gave birth to five kittens. While th

24/25

In our house we had a cat with the grandiose name of Gonnosuke. Usually with cats and dogs we know who the mother is but not the

ITC Grouch

ABCDEFGHIJKLM
NOPQRSTUVWXYZ
abcdefghijklmnop
qrstuvwxyz
1234567890&
$¢£¥fiflæœÆŒ
ÅßÇÌÎÍÏã§†
——/()''""·:;.,!¡?¿

10/11

In our house we had a cat with the grandiose name of Gonnosuke. Usually with cats and dogs we know who the mother is but not the father. A cat with a large belly wondered into the house of my younger sister and her husband and gave birth to five kittens. While the mother was a pure white thoroughbred Chinchila, the kittens were black and white tabbie s of mixed breed. One of these came to our house about two weeks after its birth and was given the name Gonnosuke. At that time we already had one female Shiba dog and one fe

16/17

In our house we had a cat with the grandiose name of G onnosuke. Usually with cats and dogs we know who the mother is but not the father. A cat with a large belly wo ndered into the house of my younger sister and her hus

24/25

In our house we had a cat with the gr andiose name of Gonnosuke. Usually with cats and dogs we know who the

Kis Roman, Dutch 721
Like **Janson Roman**

ABCDEFGHIJKLM
NOPQRSTUVWX
YZabcdefghijklmnop
qrstuvwxyz
1234567890&$¢£¥
fiflæœÆŒÅßÇÌÎÍÏã§
†-——/()''""":;.,!¡?¿

10/11

In our house we had a cat with the grandiose name of Gonnosuke. Usually with cats and dogs we know who the mother is but not the father. A cat with a large belly wondered into the house of my younger sister and h er husband and gave birth to five kittens. While the mother was a pure white thoroughbred Chinchila, the ki ttens were black and white tabbies of mixed breed. One of these came to our house about two weeks after its birth and was given the name Gonnosuke. At that time we already had one female Shiba dog and one female brown tabby cat in our house comprising only 13 tubo. The dog was called Momo and the cat Mii. My wife,

16/17

In our house we had a cat with the grandiose name of Gonnosuke. Usually with cats and dogs we know who the mother is but not the father. A cat with a large belly wondered into the house of my youn ger sister and her husband and gave birth to five kittens. While the

24/25

In our house we had a cat with the grandiose name of Gonnosuke. Usually with cats and d ogs we know who the mother is but not the

ABCDEFGHIJKLMN
OPQRSTUVWXYZ
abcdefghijklmnopq
rstuvwxyz
1234567890&$¢£¥
fiflæœÆŒÅßÇÌÎÍÏã§†
——/()'"""'.;.,!¡?¿

10/11

In our house we had a cat with the grandiose name of Gonnosuke. Usually with cats and dogs we know who the mother is but not the father. A cat with a large belly wondered into the house of my younger sister and her husband and gave birth to five kittens. While the mother was a pure white thoroughbred Chinchila, the kittens were black and white tabbies of mixed breed. One of these came to our house about two weeks after its birth and was given the name Gonnosuke. At that time we already had one female Shiba dog and one female brown tabby cat in our house comprising only 13 tubo. The dog was called Momo and the cat Mii. My wife, who was very much opposed to keeping cats and dogs, instantaneously fell for its sha

16/17

In our house we had a cat with the grandiose name of Gonnosuke. Usually with cats and dogs we know who the mother is but not the father. A cat with a large belly wondered into the house of my younger sister and her husband and gave birth to five kittens. While the mother was a pure white thoroughb

24/25

In our house we had a cat with the grandiose name of Gonnosuke. Usually with cats and dogs we know who the mother is but not the father. A cat with

ABCDEFGHIJKLMN
OPQRSTUVWXYZ
abcdefghijklmnopq
rstuvwxyz
1234567890&$¢£¥
fiflæœÆŒÅßÇÌÎÍÏã§
†-–—/()''""".;.,!¡?¿

10/11

In our house we had a cat with the grandiose name of Gonnosuke. Usually with cats and dogs we know w
ho the mother is but not the father. A cat with a large belly wondered into the house of my younger sister
and her husband and gave birth to five kittens. While the mother was a pure white thoroughbred Chinchil
a, the kittens were black and white tabbies of mixed breed. One of these came to our house about two we
eks after its birth and was given the name Gonnosuke. At that time we already had one female Shiba dog
and one female brown tabby cat in our house comprising only 13 tubo. The dog was called Momo and th

16/17

In our house we had a cat with the grandiose name of Gonnosuk
e. Usually with cats and dogs we know who the mother is but not
the father. A cat with a large belly wondered into the house of my
younger sister and her husband and gave birth to five kittens. Whi

24/25

In our house we had a cat with the grandios
e name of Gonnosuke. Usually with cats an
d dogs we know who the mother is but not

ABCDEFGHIJKLMN
OPQRSTUVWXYZ
abcdefghijklmnopq
rstuvwxyz
1234567890&$¢£¥
fiflæœÆŒÅßÇÌÎÍÏã§
†-———/()''""".;.,!¡?¿

10/11

In our house we had a cat with the grandiose name of Gonnosuke. Usually with cats and dogs we know who the mother is but not the father. A cat with a large belly wondered into the house of my younger sister and her husband and gave birth to five kittens. While the mother was a pure white thoroughbred Chinchila, the kittens were black and white tabbies of mixed breed. One of these came to our house about two weeks after its birth and was given the name Gonnosuke. At that time we already had one female Shiba dog and one female brown tabby cat in our house comprising only 13 tubo. The dog was called Momo and the cat Mii. M

16/17

In our house we had a cat with the grandiose name of Gonnosuke. Usually with cats and dogs we know who the mother is but not the father. A cat with a large belly wondered into the house of my younger sister and her husband and gave birth to five kittens. While the

24/25

In our house we had a cat with the grandiose name of Gonnosuke. Usually with cats and dogs we know who the mother is but not t

ABCDEFGHIJKL
MNOPQRSTUVW
XYZabcdefghijklmn
opqrstuvwxyz
1234567890&$¢£¥
fiflæœÆŒÅßÇÌÎÍÏã
§†----——/()''""";.,!¡?¿

10/11

In our house we had a cat with the grandiose name of Gonnosuke. Usually with cats and dogs we kn ow who the mother is but not the father. A cat with a large belly wondered into the house of my youn ger sister and her husband and gave birth to five kittens. While the mother was a pure white thoroug hbred Chinchila, the kittens were black and white tabbies of mixed breed. One of these came to our h ouse about two weeks after its birth and was given the name Gonnosuke. At that time we already had one female Shiba dog and one female brown tabby cat in our house comprising only 13 tubo. The do

16/17

In our house we had a cat with the grandiose name of Gonnos uke. Usually with cats and dogs we know who the mother is bu t not the father. A cat with a large belly wondered into the hous e of my younger sister and her husband and gave birth to five k

24/25

In our house we had a cat with the grandi ose name of Gonnosuke. Usually with cat s and dogs we know who the mother is bu

ABCDEFGHIJKL
MNOPQRSTUVW
XYZabcdefghijklmn
opqrstuvwxyz
1234567890&$¢£¥
fiflæœÆŒÅßÇÌÎÍÏã
§†-–——/()''""".;.,!¡?¿

10/11

In our house we had a cat with the grandiose name of Gonnosuke. Usually with cats and dogs we know who the mother is but not the father. A cat with a large belly wondered into the house of my younger sister and her husband and gave birth to five kittens. While the mother was a pure white thoroughbred Chinchila, the kittens were black and white tabbies of mixed breed. One of these came to our house about two weeks after its birth and was given the name Gonnosuke. At that time we already had one female Shiba dog and one female brown tabby cat in our house comprising on

16/17

In our house we had a cat with the grandiose name of Gonn osuke. Usually with cats and dogs we know who the mother i s but not the father. A cat with a large belly wondered into th e house of my younger sister and her husband and gave birth

24/25

In our house we had a cat with the gran diose name of Gonnosuke. Usually with cats and dogs we know who the mother i

ABCDEFGHIJKLMN
OPQRSTUVWXYZ
abcdefghijklmnopq
rstuvwxyz
1234567890&$¢£¥
fiflæœÆŒÅßÇÌÎÍÏã§
†-–——/()''""":;.,!¡?¿

10/11

In our house we had a cat with the grandiose name of Gonnosuke. Usually with cats and dogs we know who the mother is but not the father. A cat with a large belly wondered into the house of my younger si ster and her husband and gave birth to five kittens. While the mother was a pure white thoroughbred C hinchila, the kittens were black and white tabbies of mixed breed. One of these came to our house abou t two weeks after its birth and was given the name Gonnosuke. At that time we already had one female Shiba dog and one female brown tabby cat in our house comprising only 13 tubo. The dog was called M

16/17

In our house we had a cat with the grandiose name of Gonnosuk e. Usually with cats and dogs we know who the mother is but no t the father. A cat with a large belly wondered into the house of my younger sister and her husband and gave birth to five kitten

24/25

In our house we had a cat with the grandio se name of Gonnosuke. Usually with cats a nd dogs we know who the mother is but n

ABCDEFGHIJKLMNO
PQRSTUVWXYZ
abcdefghijklmnopq
rstuvwxyz
1234567890&$¢£¥
fiflæœÆŒÅßçÌÎÍÏã§†
-–——/()''""":;.,!¡?¿

10/11

In our house we had a cat with the grandiose name of Gonnosuke. Usually with cats and dogs we know who the mot her is but not the father. A cat with a large belly wondered into the house of my younger sister and her husband and g ave birth to five kittens. While the mother was a pure white thoroughbred Chinchila, the kittens were black and whit e tabbies of mixed breed. One of these came to our house about two weeks after its birth and was given the name Gonn osuke. At that time we already had one female Shiba dog and one female brown tabby cat in our house comprising on ly 13 tubo. The dog was called Momo and the cat Mii. My wife, who was very much opposed to keeping cats and dogs,

16/17

In our house we had a cat with the grandiose name of Gonnosuke. Usual ly with cats and dogs we know who the mother is but not the father. A ca t with a large belly wondered into the house of my younger sister and her husband and gave birth to five kittens. While the mother was a pure whi

24/25

In our house we had a cat with the grandiose na me of Gonnosuke. Usually with cats and dogs we know who the mother is but not the father. A cat

ABCDEFGHIJKLM
NOPQRSTUVWXYZ
abcdefghijklmnopq
rstuvwxyz
1234567890&$¢£¥
fiflæœÆŒÅßÇÌÎÍÏã
§†--—/()''"":;.,!¡?¿

10/11

In our house we had a cat with the grandiose name of Gonnosuke. Usually with cats and dogs we k now who the mother is but not the father. A cat with a large belly wondered into the house of my yo unger sister and her husband and gave birth to five kittens. While the mother was a pure white thor oughbred Chinchila, the kittens were black and white tabbies of mixed breed. One of these came to our house about two weeks after its birth and was given the name Gonnosuke. At that time we alrea dy had one female Shiba dog and one female brown tabby cat in our house comprising only 13 tubo.

16/17

In our house we had a cat with the grandiose name of Gonnos uke. Usually with cats and dogs we know who the mother is b ut not the father. A cat with a large belly wondered into the ho use of my younger sister and her husband and gave birth to fiv

24/25

In our house we had a cat with the grandi ose name of Gonnosuke. Usually with cat s and dogs we know who the mother is b

ABCDEFGHIJKLMN
OPQRSTUVWXYZ
abcdefghijklmnopq
rstuvwxyz
1234567890⍵$¢£¥
fiflæœÆŒÅßçÌÎÍÏ㧠
-–——/()''""",.,!¡?¿

10/11

In our house we had a cat with the grandiose name of Gonnosuke. Usually with cats and dogs we know who the mother is but not the father. A cat with a large belly wondered into the house of my younger sister and her husband and gave birth to five kittens. While the mother was a pure white thoroughbred Chinchila, the kittens were black and white tabbies of mixed breed. One of these came to our house about two weeks after its birth and was given the name Gonnosuke. At that time we already had one female Shiba dog and one female brown tabby cat in our house comprising only 13 tubo. The dog was called Momo and the cat Mii. My wife, who was very much oppos

16/17

In our house we had a cat with the grandiose name of Gonnosuke. Usually with cats and dogs we know who the mother is but not the father. A cat with a large belly wondered into the house of my younger sister and her husband and gave birth to five kittens. While the mother was

24/25

In our house we had a cat with the grandiose name of Gonnosuke. Usually with cats and dogs we know who the mother is but not the fath

ABCDEFGHIJKL MNOPQRSTUVW XYZabcdefghijklm nopqrstuvwxyz 1234567890&$¢£¥ fiflæœÆŒÅßÇÌÎÍÏ ã§†-–——/()''""":;.,!¡?¿

10/11

In our house we had a cat with the grandiose name of Gonnosuke. Usually with cats and dog
s we know who the mother is but not the father. A cat with a large belly wondered into the
house of my younger sister and her husband and gave birth to five kittens. While the mother
was a pure white thoroughbred Chinchila, the kittens were black and white tabbies of mixe
d breed. One of these came to our house about two weeks after its birth and was given the n
ame Gonnosuke. At that time we already had one female Shiba dog and one female brown t

16/17

In our house we had a cat with the grandiose name of Go
nnosuke. Usually with cats and dogs we know who the m
other is but not the father. A cat with a large belly wonde
red into the house of my younger sister and her husband

24/25

In our house we had a cat with the gra
ndiose name of Gonnosuke. Usually w
ith cats and dogs we know who the m

ABCDEFGHIJKLM NOPQRSTUVWXYZ abcdefghijklmnopq rstuvwxyz 1234567890&$¢£¥ fiflæœÆŒÅßÇÌÎÍÏã§ †-–—/()''""":;.,!¡?¿

10/11

In our house we had a cat with the grandiose name of Gonnosuke. Usually with cats and dogs we know who the mother is but not the father. A cat with a large belly wondered into the house of my younger sis ter and her husband and gave birth to five kittens. While the mother was a pure white thoroughbred Ch inchila, the kittens were black and white tabbies of mixed breed. One of these came to our house about t wo weeks after its birth and was given the name Gonnosuke. At that time we already had one female Sh iba dog and one female brown tabby cat in our house comprising only 13 tubo. The dog was called Mo

16/17

In our house we had a cat with the grandiose name of Gonnosuk e. Usually with cats and dogs we know who the mother is but no t the father. A cat with a large belly wondered into the house of my younger sister and her husband and gave birth to five kittens

24/25

In our house we had a cat with the grandio se name of Gonnosuke. Usually with cats a nd dogs we know who the mother is but no

ABCDEFGHIJKLMNOP
QRSTUVWXYZ
abcdefghijklmnopq
rstuvwxyz
1234567890&$¢£¥
fiflæœÆŒÅßÇÌÎÍÏã§†
–——/()''""":;.,!¡?¿

10/11

In our house we had a cat with the grandiose name of Gonnosuke. Usually with cats and dogs we know who the mother is but not the father. A cat with a large belly wondered into the house of my younger sister and her husband and gave birth to five kit tens. While the mother was a pure white thoroughbred Chinchila, the kittens were black and white tabbies of mixed breed. O ne of these came to our house about two weeks after its birth and was given the name Gonnosuke. At that time we already had one female Shiba dog and one female brown tabby cat in our house comprising only 13 tubo. The dog was called Momo and t he cat Mii. My wife, who was very much opposed to keeping cats and dogs, instantaneously fell for its shaggy appearance and t

16/17

In our house we had a cat with the grandiose name of Gonnosuke. Usually wit h cats and dogs we know who the mother is but not the father. A cat with a lar ge belly wondered into the house of my younger sister and her husband and ga ve birth to five kittens. While the mother was a pure white thoroughbred Chin

24/25

In our house we had a cat with the grandiose name of Gonnosuke. Usually with cats and dogs we know who the mother is but not the father. A cat with a la

ABCDEFGHIJKLMNOPQR STUVWXYZ

abcdefghijklmnopqrstuvwxyz

1234567890&$¢£¥

fiflœœÆŒÅßçÌÎÍÏã§†

———/()''""":;.,!¡?¿

10/11

In our house we had a cat with the grandiose name of Gonnosuke. Usually with cats and dogs we know who the mother is but not the father. A cat with a large belly wondered into the house of my younger sister and her husband and gave birth to five kittens. While the mother was a pure white thoroughbred Chinchila, the kittens were black and white tabbies of mixed breed. One of these came to our house about two weeks after its birth and was given the name Gonnosuke. At that time we already had one female Shiba dog and one female brown tabby cat in our house comp rising only 13 tubo. The dog was called Momo and the cat Mii. My wife, who was very much opposed to keeping cats and dogs, instantaneously fell for its shaggy appearance and the black tip of its nose and decided on its name, crying this dog's name is Momo. Mii is a stray cat which my

16/17

In our house we had a cat with the grandiose name of Gonnosuke. Usually with cats and dogs we know who the mother is but not the father. A cat with a large belly wondered into the house of my younger sister and her husband and gave birth to five kittens. While the mother was a pure white thoroughbred Chinchila, the kittens were black and white tabbies

24/25

In our house we had a cat with the grandiose name of Gon nosuke. Usually with cats and dogs we know who the mothe r is but not the father. A cat with a large belly wondered int

ABCDEFGHIJKLMNO
PQRSTUVWXYZ
abcdefghijklmnopq
rstuvwxyz
1234567890&$¢£¥
fiflæœÆŒÅßçÌÎÍÏã§†
----—/()'"""·;·,!¡?¿

10/11

In our house we had a cat with the grandiose name of Gonnosuke. Usually with cats and dogs we know who the mother is but not the father. A cat with a large belly wondered into the house of my younger sister and her husband and gave birth to five kittens. While the mother was a pure white thoroughbred Chinchila, the kittens were black and white tabbies of mixed breed. One of these came to our house about two weeks after its birth and was given the name Gonnosuke. At that time we already had one female Shiba dog and one female brown tabby cat in our house comprising only 13 tubo. The dog was called Momo and the cat Mii. My wife, who was ver

16/17

In our house we had a cat with the grandiose name of Gonnosuke. Usually with cats and dogs we know who the mother is but not the father. A cat with a large belly wondered into the house of my younger sister and her husband and gave birth to five kittens. While the mother

24/25

In our house we had a cat with the grandiose name of Gonnosuke. Usually with cats and dogs we know who the mother is but not the fat

ABCDEFGHIJKLMNOP
QRSTUVWXYZ
abcdefghijklmnopq
rstuvwxyz
1234567890&$¢£¥
fiflæœÆŒÅßÇÌÎÍÏã§†
-–——/()''""":;.,!¡?¿

10/11

In our house we had a cat with the grandiose name of Gonnosuke. Usually with cats and dogs we know who the mother is b ut not the father. A cat with a large belly wondered into the house of my younger sister and her husband and gave birth to fi ve kittens. While the mother was a pure white thoroughbred Chinchila, the kittens were black and white tabbies of mixed bre ed. One of these came to our house about two weeks after its birth and was given the name Gonnosuke. At that time we alrea dy had one female Shiba dog and one female brown tabby cat in our house comprising only 13 tubo. The dog was called Mo mo and the cat Mii. My wife, who was very much opposed to keeping cats and dogs, instantaneously fell for its shaggy appea

16/17

In our house we had a cat with the grandiose name of Gonnosuke. Usually wi th cats and dogs we know who the mother is but not the father. A cat with a l arge belly wondered into the house of my younger sister and her husband and gave birth to five kittens. While the mother was a pure white thoroughbred C

24/25

In our house we had a cat with the grandiose name of Gonnosuke. Usually with cats and dogs we know who the mother is but not the father. A cat with a l

Lapidary 333 Black/Head
Like **Perpetua Black**

ABCDEFGHIJKL MNOPQRSTUVW XYZabcdefghijkl mnopqrstuvwxyz 1234567890&$¢£¥ fiflæœÆŒÅßÇÌÎÍÏ ã§†-–—/()''""";.,!¡?¿

10/11

In our house we had a cat with the grandiose name of Gonnosuke. Usually with cats and d ogs we know who the mother is but not the father. A cat with a large belly wondered into t he house of my younger sister and her husband and gave birth to five kittens. While the m other was a pure white thoroughbred Chinchila, the kittens were black and white tabbies of mixed breed. One of these came to our house about two weeks after its birth and was gi ven the name Gonnosuke. At that time we already had one female Shiba dog and one femal

16/17

In our house we had a cat with the grandiose name of G onnosuke. Usually with cats and dogs we know who the mother is but not the father. A cat with a large belly wo ndered into the house of my younger sister and her husb

24/25

In our house we had a cat with the gr andiose name of Gonnosuke. Usually with cats and dogs we know who the

ABCDEFGHIJKLMNO
PQRSTUVWXYZ
abcdefghijklmnopq
rstuvwxyz
1234567890&$¢£¥
fiflæœÆŒÅßÇÌÎÍÏĩã§†
——/()''""":;.,!¡?¿

10/11

In our house we had a cat with the grandiose name of Gonnosuke. Usually with cats and dogs we know who the m other is but not the father. A cat with a large belly wondered into the house of my younger sister and her husband a nd gave birth to five kittens. While the mother was a pure white thoroughbred Chinchila, the kittens were black and white tabbies of mixed breed. One of these came to our house about two weeks after its birth and was given the na me Gonnosuke. At that time we already had one female Shiba dog and one female brown tabby cat in our house co mprising only 13 tubo. The dog was called Momo and the cat Mii. My wife, who was very much opposed to keepin

16/17

In our house we had a cat with the grandiose name of Gonnosuke. Usua lly with cats and dogs we know who the mother is but not the father. A cat with a large belly wondered into the house of my younger sister and her husband and gave birth to five kittens. While the mother was a pure

24/25

In our house we had a cat with the grandiose na me of Gonnosuke. Usually with cats and dogs w e know who the mother is but not the father. A

ABCDEFGHIJKLMN
OPQRSTUVWXYZ
abcdefghijklmnopq
rstuvwxyz
1234567890&$¢£¥
fiflæœÆŒÅßÇÌÎÍÏã§
†-–—/()''""":;.,!¡?¿

10/11

In our house we had a cat with the grandiose name of Gonnosuke. Usually with cats and dogs we know who the mother is but not the father. A cat with a large belly wondered into the house of my younger sis ter and her husband and gave birth to five kittens. While the mother was a pure white thoroughbred Ch inchila, the kittens were black and white tabbies of mixed breed. One of these came to our house about two weeks after its birth and was given the name Gonnosuke. At that time we already had one female S hiba dog and one female brown tabby cat in our house comprising only 13 tubo. The dog was called Mo

16/17

In our house we had a cat with the grandiose name of Gonnosuk e. Usually with cats and dogs we know who the mother is but not the father. A cat with a large belly wondered into the house of m y younger sister and her husband and gave birth to five kittens.

24/25

In our house we had a cat with the grandio se name of Gonnosuke. Usually with cats a nd dogs we know who the mother is but no

ITC Tiffany Light

ABCDEFGHIJKL
MNOPQRSTUVW
XYZabcdefghijklm
nopqrstuvwxyz
1234567890&
$¢£¥fiflæœÆŒ
ÅßÇÌÎÍÏã§†
-––—/()''""":;.,!¡?¿

10/11

In our house we had a cat with the grandiose name of Gonnosuke. Usually with cats and dogs we know who the mother is but not the father. A cat with a large belly wondered into the house of m y younger sister and her husband and gave birth to five kittens. While the mother was a pure whi te thoroughbred Chinchila, the kittens were black and white tabbies of mixed breed. One of these came to our house about two weeks after its birth and was given the name Gonnosuke. At that ti me we already had one female Shiba dog and one female brown tabby cat in our house comprisin

16/17

In our house we had a cat with the grandiose name of Gonn osuke. Usually with cats and dogs we know who the mother is but not the father. A cat with a large belly wondered into t he house of my younger sister and her husband and gave bir

24/25

In our house we had a cat with the gran diose name of Gonnosuke. Usually with cats and dogs we know who the mother

ABCDEFGHIJKL
MNOPQRSTUVW
XYZabcdefghijklmn
opqrstuvwxyz
1234567890&
$¢£¥fiflæœÆŒ
ÅßÇÌÎÍÏã§†
–––—/O''""":;.,!¡?¿

10/11

In our house we had a cat with the grandiose name of Gonnosuke. Usually with cats and dogs we know who the mother is but not the father. A cat with a large belly wondered into the house of my younger sister and her husband and gave birth to five kittens. While the mother was a pure white thoroughbred Chinchila, the kittens were black and white tabbies of mixed breed. One of these came to our house about two weeks after its birth and was given the name Gonnosuke. At that time we already had one female Shiba dog and one female brown tabby cat in our house comprising on

16/17

In our house we had a cat with the grandiose name of Gonno suke. Usually with cats and dogs we know who the mother i s but not the father. A cat with a large belly wondered into th e house of my younger sister and her husband and gave birt

24/25

In our house we had a cat with the gran diose name of Gonnosuke. Usually with cats and dogs we know who the mother

ABCDEFGHIJKL
MNOPQRSTUVW
XYZabcdefghijklm
nopqrstuvwxyz
1234567890&
$¢£¥fiflæœÆŒ
ÅßÇÌÎÍÏãã§†
-——/O'''""":;.,!¡?¿

10/11

In our house we had a cat with the grandiose name of Gonnosuke. Usually with cats and dogs
we know who the mother is but not the father. A cat with a large belly wondered into the hou
se of my younger sister and her husband and gave birth to five kittens. While the mother was
a pure white thoroughbred Chinchila, the kittens were black and white tabbies of mixed bree
d. One of these came to our house about two weeks after its birth and was given the name Go
nnosuke. At that time we already had one female Shiba dog and one female brown tabby cat

16/17

In our house we had a cat with the grandiose name of Gon
nosuke. Usually with cats and dogs we know who the mot
her is but not the father. A cat with a large belly wondered
into the house of my younger sister and her husband and

24/25

In our house we had a cat with the gra
ndiose name of Gonnosuke. Usually wi
th cats and dogs we know who the mot

ABCDEFGHIJKL
MNOPQRSTUVW
XYZabcdefghijklmn
opqrstuvwxyz
1234567890&
$¢£¥fiflæœÆŒ
ÅßÇÌÎÍÏã§†
-–—/O''""":;.,!¡?¿

10/11

In our house we had a cat with the grandiose name of Gonnosuke. Usually with cats and dogs we know who the mother is but not the father. A cat with a large belly wondered into the house of my younger sister and her husband and gave birth to five kittens. While the mother was a pu re white thoroughbred Chinchila, the kittens were black and white tabbies of mixed breed. One of these came to our house about two weeks after its birth and was given the name Gonnosuke. At that time we already had one female Shiba dog and one female brown tabby cat in our hous

16/17

In our house we had a cat with the grandiose name of Gon nosuke. Usually with cats and dogs we know who the moth er is but not the father. A cat with a large belly wondered i nto the house of my younger sister and her husband and ga

24/25

In our house we had a cat with the gra ndiose name of Gonnosuke. Usually wi th cats and dogs we know who the mot

ITC Tiffany Demi

ABCDEFGHIJKL
MNOPQRSTUVW
XYZabcdefghijkl
mnopqrstuvwxyz
1234567890&
$¢£¥fiflæœÆŒ
ÅßÇÌÎÍÏã§†
-–—/0''""".:;.,!¡?¿

10/11

In our house we had a cat with the grandiose name of Gonnosuke. Usually with cats and do
gs we know who the mother is but not the father. A cat with a large belly wondered into the
house of my younger sister and her husband and gave birth to five kittens. While the mothe
r was a pure white thoroughbred Chinchila, the kittens were black and white tabbies of mi
xed breed. One of these came to our house about two weeks after its birth and was given th
e name Gonnosuke. At that time we already had one female Shiba dog and one female bro

16/17

In our house we had a cat with the grandiose name of Go
nnosuke. Usually with cats and dogs we know who the m
other is but not the father. A cat with a large belly wonde
red into the house of my younger sister and her husband

24/25

In our house we had a cat with the gr
andiose name of Gonnosuke. Usually
with cats and dogs we know who the

ABCDEFGHIJKL
MNOPQRSTUVW
XYZabcdefghijklm
nopqrstuvwxyz
1234567890&
$¢£¥fiflæœÆŒ
ÅßÇÌÎÍÏã§†
––—/()''""":;.,!¡?¿

10/11

In our house we had a cat with the grandiose name of Gonnosuke. Usually with cats and dog
s we know who the mother is but not the father. A cat with a large belly wondered into the ho
use of my younger sister and her husband and gave birth to five kittens. While the mother wa
s a pure white thoroughbred Chinchila, the kittens were black and white tabbies of mixed bree
d. One of these came to our house about two weeks after its birth and was given the name Go
nnosuke. At that time we already had one female Shiba dog and one female brown tabby cat

16/17

In our house we had a cat with the grandiose name of Go
nnosuke. Usually with cats and dogs we know who the mo
ther is but not the father. A cat with a large belly wondere
d into the house of my younger sister and her husband an

24/25

In our house we had a cat with the gra
ndiose name of Gonnosuke. Usually w
ith cats and dogs we know who the mo

ITC Tiffany Heavy

ABCDEFGHIJK
LMNOPQRSTU
VWXYZabcdefg
hijklmnopqrstu
vwxyz12345678
90&$¢£¥fiflæœ
ÆŒÅßÇÌÎÍÏã§†
——/()''""•:;.,!¿?¡

10/11

In our house we had a cat with the grandiose name of Gonnosuke. Usually with cats and dogs we know who the mother is but not the father. A cat with a large belly wondered into the house of my younger sister and her husband and gave birth to five kittens. While the mother was a pure white thoroughbred Chinchil a, the kittens were black and white tabbies of mixed breed. One of these came to our house about two weeks after its birth and was given the name Gonnosuk

16/17

In our house we had a cat with the grandiose na me of Gonnosuke. Usually with cats and dogs we know who the mother is but not the father. A cat with a large belly wondered into the house of my

24/25

In our house we had a cat with t he grandiose name of Gonnosuk e. Usually with cats and dogs we

ABCDEFGHIJK
LMNOPQRSTU
VWXYZ
abcdefghijklmn
opqrstuvwxyz
1234567890&$
¢£¥fiflæœÆŒ
ÅßÇÌÎÍÏãã§†
–‒—/()'''"""..,,,;;!¡?¿

16/17

In our house we had a cat with the grandiose n
ame of Gonnosuke. Usually with cats and dogs
we know who the mother is but not the father. A
cat with a large belly wondered into the house o

24/25

In our house we had a cat with
the grandiose name of Gonnosu
ke. Usually with cats and dogs

ABCDEFGHIJKLM
NOPQRSTUVWXYZ
abcdefghijklmnopq
rstuvwxyz
1234567890&$¢£¥
fiflæœÆŒÅßÇÌÎÍÏã§†
----—/()''""".:;.,!¡?¿

10/11

In our house we had a cat with the grandiose name of Gonnosuke. Usually with cats and dogs we know who the mother is but not the father. A cat with a large belly wondered into the house of my younger sister and her husband and gave birth to five kittens. While the mother was a pure white thoroughbred Chinchila, the kittens were black and white tabbies of mixed breed. One of these came to our house about two weeks after its birth and was given the name Gonnosuke. At that time we already had one female Shiba dog and one female brown tabby cat in our house comprising only 13 thubo. The dog was called Momo and the cat Mii. My wif

16/17

In our house we had a cat with the grandiose name of Gonnosuke. Usually with cats and dogs we know who the mother is but not the father. A cat with a large belly wondered into the house of my younger sister and her husband and gave birth to five kittens. While the

24/25

In our house we had a cat with the grandiose name of Gonnosuke. Usually with cats and dogs we know who the mother is but not the f

ABCDEFGHIJKLMN
OPQRSTUVWXYZ
abcdefghijklmnopq
rstuvwxyz
1234567890&$¢£¥
fiflœœÆŒÅßÇÌÎÍÏã§†
———/() '’“”:;.,!¡?¿

10/11

In our house we had a cat with the grandiose name of Gonnosuke. Usually with cats and dogs we know who the mother is but not the father. A cat with a large belly wondered into the house of my younger sister and her husband and gave birth to five kittens. While the mother was a pure white thoroughbred Chinchila, the kittens were black and white tabbies of mixed breed. One of these came to our house about two weeks after its birth and was given the name Gonnosuke. At that time we already had one female Shiba dog and one female brown tabby cat in our house comprising only 13 thubo. The dog was called Momo and the cat Mii. My wife, who was very much opposed to

16/17

In our house we had a cat with the grandiose name of Gonnosuke. Usually with cats and dogs we know who the mother is but not the father. A cat with a large belly wondered into the house of my younger sister and her husband and gave birth to five kittens. While the mother was a

24/25

In our house we had a cat with the grandiose name of Gonnosuke. Usually with cats and dogs we know who the mother is but not the father.

ABCDEFGHIJKL MNOPQRSTU VWXYZ

abcdefghijklmnopq rstuvwxyz 1234567890&$¢£¥fifl æœÆŒÅßÇÌÎÍÏã§† ——/()''""".:;.,!¡?¿

10/11

In our house we had a cat with the grandiose name of Gonnosuke. Usually with cats and dogs we know who the mother is but not the father. A cat with a large belly wondered into the house of my younger sister and her husband and gave birth to five kittens. While the mother was a pure white thoroughbred Chinchilla, the kittens were black and white tabbies of mixed breed. One of these came to our house about two weeks after its birth and was given the name Gonnosuke. At that time we already had one female Shiba dog and one female brown tabby cat in our house comprising only 13 thubo. The dog was called Momo and the

16/17

In our house we had a cat with the grandiose name of Gonnosuke. Usually with cats and dogs we know who the mother is but not the father. A cat with a large belly wondered into the house of my younger sister and her husband and gave birth to five kittens. While t

24/25

In our house we had a cat with the grandiose name of Gonnosuke. Usually with cats and d dogs we know who the mother is but not t

ABCDEFGHIJKLM NOPQRSTUVWXYZ abcdefghijklmnopq rstuvwxyz 1234567890&$¢£¥ fiflœœÆŒÅßÇÌÎÍÏã§ †-–—/()'’“”:;.,!¡?¿

10/11

In our house we had a cat with the grandiose name of Gonnosuke. Usually with cats and dogs we know who t he mother is but not the father. A cat with a large belly wondered into the house of my younger sister and her h usband and gave birth to five kittens. While the mother was a pure white thoroughbred Chinchila, the kittens w ere black and white tabbies of mixed breed. One of these came to our house about two weeks after its birth and was given the name Gonnosuke. At that time we already had one female Shiba dog and one female brown tab by cat in our house comprising only 13 thubo. The dog was called Momo and the cat Mii. My wife, who was ve

16/17

In our house we had a cat with the grandiose name of Gonnosuke. Usually with cats and dogs we know who the mother is but not the fa ther. A cat with a large belly wondered into the house of my younger s ister and her husband and gave birth to five kittens. While the mother

24/25

In our house we had a cat with the grandiose name of Gonnosuke. Usually with cats and d ogs we know who the mother is but not the fat

ABCDEFGHIJKLM
NOPQRSTUVWXYZ
abcdefghijklmnopq
rstuvwxyz
1234567890&$¢£¥
fiflæœÆŒÅßÇÌÎÍÏã§
†-–—/()''""";.,!¡?¿

10/11

In our house we had a cat with the grandiose name of Gonnosuke. Usually with cats and dogs we know wh
o the mother is but not the father. A cat with a large belly wondered into the house of my younger sister an
d her husband and gave birth to five kittens. While the mother was a pure white thoroughbred Chinchila,
the kittens were black and white tabbies of mixed breed. One of these came to our house about two weeks
after its birth and was given the name Gonnosuke. At that time we already had one female Shiba dog and
one female brown tabby cat in our house comprising only 13 thubo. The dog was called Momo and the cat

16/17

In our house we had a cat with the grandiose name of Gonnosuke.
Usually with cats and dogs we know who the mother is but not the
father. A cat with a large belly wondered into the house of my you
nger sister and her husband and gave birth to five kittens. While t

24/25

In our house we had a cat with the grandios
e name of Gonnosuke. Usually with cats an
d dogs we know who the mother is but not

ABCDEFGHIJKLM
NOPQRSTUVWXYZ
abcdefghijklmnopq
rstuvwxyz
1234567890&$¢£¥
fiflœœÆŒÅßÇÌÎÍÏã§†
———/()''""";.,!¡?¿

10/11

In our house we had a cat with the grandiose name of Gonnosuke. Usually with cats and dogs we know who the mother is but not the father. A cat with a large belly wondered into the house of my younger sister and her husb and and gave birth to five kittens. While the mother was a pure white thoroughbred Chinchila, the kittens were black and white tabbies of mixed breed. One of these came to our house about two weeks after its birth and was given the name Gonnosuke. At that time we already had one female Shiba dog and one female brown tabby cat in our house comprising only 13 thubo. The dog was called Momo and the cat Mii. My wife, who was very much

16/17

In our house we had a cat with the grandiose name of Gonnosuke. Us ually with cats and dogs we know who the mother is but not the fathe r. A cat with a large belly wondered into the house of my younger siste r and her husband and gave birth to five kittens. While the mother w

24/25

In our house we had a cat with the grandiose name of Gonnosuke. Usually with cats and do gs we know who the mother is but not the fath

ABCDEFGHIJKLM
NOPQRSTUVWXYZ
abcdefghijklmnopq
rstuvwxyz
1234567890&$¢£¥
fiflæœÆŒÅßÇÌÎÍÏã§
†-–—/()''""'.;.,!¡?¿

10/11

In our house we had a cat with the grandiose name of Gonnosuke. Usually with cats and dogs we know w
ho the mother is but not the father. A cat with a large belly wondered into the house of my younger sister
and her husband and gave birth to five kittens. While the mother was a pure white thoroughbred Chinchi
la, the kittens were black and white tabbies of mixed breed. One of these came to our house about two wee
ks after its birth and was given the name Gonnosuke. At that time we already had one female Shiba dog a
nd one female brown tabby cat in our house comprising only 13 thubo. The dog was called Momo and the

16/17

In our house we had a cat with the grandiose name of Gonnosuke.
Usually with cats and dogs we know who the mother is but not the
father. A cat with a large belly wondered into the house of my you
nger sister and her husband and gave birth to five kittens. While

24/25

In our house we had a cat with the grandios
e name of Gonnosuke. Usually with cats an
d dogs we know who the mother is but not t

ABCDEFGHIJKLM
NOPQRSTUVWXYZ
abcdefghijklmnopq
rstuvwxyz
1234567890&$¢£¥
fiflœœÆŒÅßÇÌÎÍÏã§†
-–——/() ''""':;.,!¡?¿

10/11

In our house we had a cat with the grandiose name of Gonnosuke. Usually with cats and dogs we know who the mother is but not the father. A cat with a large belly wondered into the house of my younger sister and her husba nd and gave birth to five kittens. While the mother was a pure white thoroughbred Chinchila, the kittens were bla rck and white tabbies of mixed breed. One of these came to our house about two weeks after its birth and was give n the name Gonnosuke. At that time we already had one female Shiba dog and one female brown tabby cat in ou r house comprising only 13 thubo. The dog was called Momo and the cat Mii. My wife, who was very much oppos

16/17

In our house we had a cat with the grandiose name of Gonnosuke. Us ually with cats and dogs we know who the mother is but not the father. A cat with a large belly wondered into the house of my younger sister a nd her husband and gave birth to five kittens. While the mother was a

24/25

In our house we had a cat with the grandiose n ame of Gonnosuke. Usually with cats and dogs we know who the mother is but not the father.

ABCDEFGHIJKL MNOPQRSTU VWXYZabcdefghijk lmnopqrstuvwxyz 1234567890&$¢£¥ fiflæœÆŒÅßÇÌÎÍÏã §†--——/()''""".:;.,!¡?¿

10/11

In our house we had a cat with the grandiose name of Gonnosuke. Usually with cats and dogs we k
now who the mother is but not the father. A cat with a large belly wondered into the house of my yo
unger sister and her husband and gave birth to five kittens. While the mother was a pure white tho
roughbred Chinchila, the kittens were black and white tabbies of mixed breed. One of these came t
o our house about two weeks after its birth and was given the name Gonnosuke. At that time we alr
eady had one female Shiba dog and one female brown tabby cat in our house comprising only 13 th

16/17

In our house we had a cat with the grandiose name of Gonnos
uke. Usually with cats and dogs we know who the mother is b
ut not the father. A cat with a large belly wondered into the h
ouse of my younger sister and her husband and gave birth to

24/25

In our house we had a cat with the grand
iose name of Gonnosuke. Usually with ca
ts and dogs we know who the mother is b

ABCDEFGHIJKLMNO
PQRSTUVWXYZ
abcdefghijklmnopq
rstuvwxyz
1234567890&$¢£¥
fiflæœÆŒÅßÇÌÎÍÏã
§†-–——/()'""":;.,!¡?¿

10/11

In our house we had a cat with the grandiose name of Gonnosuke. Usually with cats and dogs we know wh o the mother is but not the father. A cat with a large belly wondered into the house of my younger sister an d her husband and gave birth to five kittens. While the mother was a pure white thoroughbred Chinchila, t he kittens were black and white tabbies of mixed breed. One of these came to our house about two weeks a fter its birth and was given the name Gonnosuke. At that time we already had one female Shiba dog and on e female brown tabby cat in our house comprising only 13 tubo. The dog was called Momo and the cat Mii.

16/17

In our house we had a cat with the grandiose name of Gonnosuke. Usually with cats and dogs we know who the mother is but not the father. A cat with a large belly wondered into the house of my you nger sister and her husband and gave birth to five kittens. While th

24/25

In our house we had a cat with the grandios e name of Gonnosuke. Usually with cats and dogs we know who the mother is but not th

ABCDEFGHIJKLMN OPQRSTUVWXYZ abcdefghijklmnopq rstuvwxyz 1234567890&$¢£¥ fiflæœÆŒÅßÇÌÎÍÏã §†-–——/()'''""':;.,!¡?¿

10/11

In our house we had a cat with the grandiose name of Gonnosuke. Usually with cats and dogs we know who the mother is but not the father. A cat with a large belly wondered into the house of my younger sister and he r husband and gave birth to five kittens. While the mother was a pure white thoroughbred Chinchila, the kit tens were black and white tabbies of mixed breed. One of these came to our house about two weeks after its birth and was given the name Gonnosuke. At that time we already had one female Shiba dog and one femal e brown tabby cat in our house comprising only 13 tubo. The dog was called Momo and the cat Mii. My wife

16/17

In our house we had a cat with the grandiose name of Gonnosuke. Usually with cats and dogs we know who the mother is but not the father. A cat with a large belly wondered into the house of my youn ger sister and her husband and gave birth to five kittens. While the

24/25

In our house we had a cat with the grandios e name of Gonnosuke. Usually with cats and dogs we know who the mother is but not the

ABCDEFGHIJKLMN
OPQRSTUVWXYZ
abcdefghijklmnopq
rstuvwxyz
1234567890&$¢£¥
fiflæœÆŒÅßÇÌÎÍÏã
§†-–——/O''""":;.,!¡?¿

10/11

In our house we had a cat with the grandiose name of Gonnosuke. Usually with cats and dogs we know who the mother is but not the father. A cat with a large belly wondered into the house of my younger si ster and her husband and gave birth to five kittens. While the mother was a pure white thoroughbred C hinchila, the kittens were black and white tabbies of mixed breed. One of these came to our house abo ut two weeks after its birth and was given the name Gonnosuke. At that time we already had one femal e Shiba dog and one female brown tabby cat in our house comprising only 13 tubo. The dog was called

16/17

In our house we had a cat with the grandiose name of Gonnosu ke. Usually with cats and dogs we know who the mother is but n ot the father. A cat with a large belly wondered into the house of my younger sister and her husband and gave birth to five kittens

24/25

In our house we had a cat with the grandi ose name of Gonnosuke. Usually with cats and dogs we know who the mother is but

ABCDEFGHIJKLMN
OPQRSTUVWXYZ
abcdefghijklmnopq
rstuvwxyz
1234567890&$¢£¥
fiflæœÆŒÅßÇÌÎÍÏã§
†-——/()''""";.,!¡?¿

10/11

In our house we had a cat with the grandiose name of Gonnosuke. Usually with cats and dogs we kno
w who the mother is but not the father. A cat with a large belly wondered into the house of my younge
r sister and her husband and gave birth to five kittens. While the mother was a pure white thoroughb
red Chinchila, the kittens were black and white tabbies of mixed breed. One of these came to our hou
se about two weeks after its birth and was given the name Gonnosuke. At that time we already had o
ne female Shiba dog and one female brown tabby cat in our house comprising only 13 tubo. The dog

16/17

In our house we had a cat with the grandiose name of Gonnosu
ke. Usually with cats and dogs we know who the mother is but
not the father. A cat with a large belly wondered into the house
of my younger sister and her husband and gave birth to five kit

24/25

In our house we had a cat with the grandi
ose name of Gonnosuke. Usually with cats
and dogs we know who the mother is but

ABCDEFGHIJKLM
NOPQRSTUVWXY
Zabcdefghijklmnop
qrstuvwxyz
1234567890&$¢£¥
fiflæœÆŒÅßÇÌÎÍÏã
§†-–—/O'''""":;.,!¡?¿

10/11

In our house we had a cat with the grandiose name of Gonnosuke. Usually with cats and dogs w e know who the mother is but not the father. A cat with a large belly wondered into the house of my younger sister and her husband and gave birth to five kittens. While the mother was a pure white thoroughbred Chinchila, the kittens were black and white tabbies of mixed breed. One of these came to our house about two weeks after its birth and was given the name Gonnosuke. At that time we already had one female Shiba dog and one female brown tabby cat in our house co

16/17

In our house we had a cat with the grandiose name of Gonn osuke. Usually with cats and dogs we know who the mother is but not the father. A cat with a large belly wondered into t he house of my younger sister and her husband and gave bi

24/25

In our house we had a cat with the gran diose name of Gonnosuke. Usually with cats and dogs we know who the mother

ABCDEFGHIJKLM
NOPQRSTUVWXY
Zabcdefghijklmnop
qrstuvwxyz
1234567890&$¢£¥
fiflæœÆŒÅßÇÌÎÍÏã
§†-–——/O'’“”'.,;.,!¡?¿

10/11

In our house we had a cat with the grandiose name of Gonnosuke. Usually with cats and dogs
we know who the mother is but not the father. A cat with a large belly wondered into the house
of my younger sister and her husband and gave birth to five kittens. While the mother was a p
ure white thoroughbred Chinchila, the kittens were black and white tabbies of mixed breed. O
ne of these came to our house about two weeks after its birth and was given the name Gonnos
uke. At that time we already had one female Shiba dog and one female brown tabby cat in our

16/17

In our house we had a cat with the grandiose name of Gon
nosuke. Usually with cats and dogs we know who the moth
er is but not the father. A cat with a large belly wondered i
nto the house of my younger sister and her husband and g

24/25

In our house we had a cat with the gra
ndiose name of Gonnosuke. Usually wit
h cats and dogs we know who the moth

ABCDEFGHIJKL
MNOPQRSTUVW
XYZabcdefghijkl
mnopqrstuvwxyz
1234567890&
$¢£¥fiflæœÆŒ
Åßçìîíïã§†
‒–—/()''""".;,.,!¡?¿

10/11

In our house we had a cat with the grandiose name of Gonnosuke. Usually with cats an
d dogs we know who the mother is but not the father. A cat with a large belly wondered
into the house of my younger sister and her husband and gave birth to five kittens. Whil
e the mother was a pure white thoroughbred Chinchila, the kittens were black and whi
te tabbies of mixed breed. One of these came to our house about two weeks after its bir
th and was given the name Gonnosuke. At that time we already had one female Shiba d

16/17

In our house we had a cat with the grandiose name of
Gonnosuke. Usually with cats and dogs we know who
the mother is but not the father. A cat with a large bell
y wondered into the house of my younger sister and he

24/25

In our house we had a cat with the g
randiose name of Gonnosuke. Usual
ly with cats and dogs we know who

ABCDEFGHIJKL
MNOPQRSTUVW
XYZabcdefghijkl
mnopqrstuvwxyz
1234567890&
$¢£¥fiflæœÆŒ
ÅßÇÌÎÍÏã§†
‒–—/O''""·;.,!¡?¿

10/11

In our house we had a cat with the grandiose name of Gonnosuke. Usually with cats an
d dogs we know who the mother is but not the father. A cat with a large belly wondered
into the house of my younger sister and her husband and gave birth to five kittens. Whi
le the mother was a pure white thoroughbred Chinchila, the kittens were black and wh
ite tabbies of mixed breed. One of these came to our house about two weeks after its bi
rth and was given the name Gonnosuke. At that time we already had one female Shiba

16/17

In our house we had a cat with the grandiose name of
Gonnosuke. Usually with cats and dogs we know who t
he mother is but not the father. A cat with a large bell
y wondered into the house of my younger sister and he

24/25

In our house we had a cat with the
grandiose name of Gonnosuke. Usu
ally with cats and dogs we know wh

ABCDEFGHIJKLMNO
PQRSTUVWXYZ
abcdefghijklmnopqr
stuvwxyz
1234567890&$¢£¥
fiflæœÆŒÅßÇÌÎÍÏã§†
———/()''""":;.,!¡?¿

10/11

In our house we had a cat with the grandiose name of Gonnosuke. Usually with cats and dogs we know who the mother is but not the father. A cat with a large belly wondered into the house of my younger sister and her husband and gave birth to five kittens. While the mother was a pure white thoroughbred Chinchila, the kittens were black and white tabbies of mixed breed. One of these came to our house about two weeks after its birth and was given the name Gonnosuke. At that time we already had one female Shiba dog and one female brown tabby cat in our house comprising only 13 thubo. The dog was called Momo and the cat Mii. My wife, who was very much opposed to keeping cats and dogs, instantaneously fe

16/17

In our house we had a cat with the grandiose name of Gonnosuke. Usually with cats and dogs we know who the mother is but not the father. A cat with a large belly wondered into the house of my younger sister and her husband and gave birth to five kittens. While the mother was a pure white thorou

24/25

In our house we had a cat with the grandiose name of Gonnosuke. Usually with cats and dogs we know who the mother is but not the father. A cat wit

ABCDEFGHIJKLMN
OPQRSTUVWXYZ
abcdefghijklmnopq
rstuvwxyz
1234567890&$¢£¥
fiflæœÆŒÅßÇÌÎÍÏã§†
----/() '' "" .:;.,!¡?¿

10/11

In our house we had a cat with the grandiose name of Gonnosuke. Usually with cats and dogs we know who the mother is but not the father. A cat with a large belly wondered into the house of my younger sister and her husband and gave birth t o five kittens. While the mother was a pure white thoroughbred Chinchila, the kittens were black and white tabbies of mixe d breed. One of these came to our house about two weeks after its birth and was given the name Gonnosuke. At that time w e already had one female Shiba dog and one female brown tabby cat in our house comprising only 13 thubo. The dog was called Momo and the cat Mü. My wife, who was very much opposed to keeping cats and dogs, instantaneously fell for its

16/17

In our house we had a cat with the grandiose name of Gonnosuke. Usually with cats and dogs we know who the mother is but not the father. A cat with a large belly wondered into the house of my younger sister and her husband and gave birth to five kittens. While the mother was a pure white thoroughbr

24/25

In our house we had a cat with the grandiose nam e of Gonnosuke. Usually with cats and dogs we kn ow who the mother is but not the father. A cat with

ABCDEFGHIJKLMN
OPQRSTUVWXYZ
abcdefghijklmnopq
rstuvwxyz
1234567890&$¢£¥
fiflæœÆŒÅßÇÌÎÍÏã
§†-–—/()''""":;.,!¡?¿

10/11

In our house we had a cat with the grandiose name of Gonnosuke. Usually with cats and dogs we know wh o the mother is but not the father. A cat with a large belly wondered into the house of my younger sister and her husband and gave birth to five kittens. While the mother was a pure white thoroughbred Chinchila, the kittens were black and white tabbies of mixed breed. One of these came to our house about two weeks after its birth and was given the name Gonnosuke. At that time we already had one female Shiba dog and one fe male brown tabby cat in our house comprising only 13 thubo. The dog was called Momo and the cat Mii.

16/17

In our house we had a cat with the grandiose name of Gonnosuke. Usually with cats and dogs we know who the mother is but not the father. A cat with a large belly wondered into the house of my youn ger sister and her husband and gave birth to five kittens. While the

24/25

In our house we had a cat with the grandios e name of Gonnosuke. Usually with cats and dogs we know who the mother is but not the

ABCDEFGHIJKLM
NOPQRSTUVWXYZ
abcdefghijklmnopq
rstuvwxyz
1234567890&$¢£¥
fiflæœÆŒÅßÇÌÎÍÏã
§†-–——/() ' ' " ":.;.,!¡?¿

10/11

In our house we had a cat with the grandiose name of Gonnosuke. Usually with cats and dogs we know who the mother is but not the father. A cat with a large belly wondered into the house of my younger siste r and her husband and gave birth to five kittens. While the mother was a pure white thoroughbred Chinc hila, the kittens were black and white tabbies of mixed breed. One of these came to our house about two weeks after its birth and was given the name Gonnosuke. At that time we already had one female Shiba dog and one female brown tabby cat in our house comprising only 13 thubo. The dog was called Momo

16/17

In our house we had a cat with the grandiose name of Gonnosuk e. Usually with cats and dogs we know who the mother is but not the father. A cat with a large belly wondered into the house of my younger sister and her husband and gave birth to five kittens. Wh

24/25

In our house we had a cat with the grandio se name of Gonnosuke. Usually with cats a nd dogs we know who the mother is but not

Bauer Bodoni Black

ABCDEFGHIJKLMN
OPQRSTUVWXYZ
abcdefghijklmno
pqrstuvwxyz
1234567890&$¢£¥
fiflæœÆŒÅßÇÌÎÍÏã§
✝-–—/()''""::.,!¡?¿

10/11

In our house we had a cat with the grandiose name of Gonnosuke. Usually with cats and dogs we kn ow who the mother is but not the father. A cat with a large belly wondered into the house of my you nger sister and her husband and gave birth to five kittens. While the mother was a pure white thoro ughbred Chinchila, the kittens were black and white tabbies of mixed breed. One of these came to our house about two weeks after its birth and was given the name Gonnosuke. At that time we alrea dy had one female Shiba dog and one female brown tabby cat in our house comprising only 13 thu

16/17

In our house we had a cat with the grandiose name of Gonnos uke. Usually with cats and dogs we know who the mother is bu t not the father. A cat with a large belly wondered into the hou se of my younger sister and her husband and gave birth to five

24/25

In our house we had a cat with the grand iose name of Gonnosuke. Usually with cat s and dogs we know who the mother is b

ABCDEFGHIJKLM
NOPQRSTUVWXYZ
abcdefghijklmnopq
rstuvwxyz
1234567890&$¢£¥
fiflæœÆŒÅßÇÌÎÍÏã
§†----—/() '''"";.,,!¡?¿

10/11

In our house we had a cat with the grandiose name of Gonnosuke. Usually with cats and dogs we know who the mother is but not the father. A cat with a large belly wondered into the house of my younger sister and her husband and gave birth to five kittens. While the mother was a pure white thoroughbred Chinchila, the kittens were black and white tabbies of mixed breed. One of these came to our house about two weeks after its birth and was given the name Gonnosuke. At that time we already had one female Shiba dog and one female brown tabby cat in our house comprising o

16/17

In our house we had a cat with the grandiose name of Gonnosuke. Usually with cats and dogs we know who the mother is but not the father. A cat with a large belly wondered into the house of my younger sister and her husband and gave birth t

24/25

In our house we had a cat with the grandiose name of Gonnosuke. Usually with cats and dogs we know who the mother

ABCDEFGHIJKLMNO
PQRSTUVWXYZ
abcdefghijklmnopq
rstuvwxyz
1234567890&$¢£¥
fiflæœÆŒÅßçÌÎÍÏã§✝
--——/()''""":;.,!¡?¿

10/11

In our house we had a cat with the grandiose name of Gonnosuke. Usually with cats and dogs we know who the mother i
s but not the father. A cat with a large belly wondered into the house of my younger sister and her husband and gave bir
th to five kittens. While the mother was a pure white thoroughbred Chinchila, the kittens were black and white tabbies o
f mixed breed. One of these came to our house about two weeks after its birth and was given the name Gonnosuke. At th
at time we already had one female Shiba dog and one female brown tabby cat in our house comprising only 13 thubo. T
he dog was called Momo and the cat Mii. My wife, who was very much opposed to keeping cats and dogs, instantaneousl

16/17

In our house we had a cat with the grandiose name of Gonnosuke. Usually
with cats and dogs we know who the mother is but not the father. A cat wit
h a large belly wondered into the house of my younger sister and her husb
and and gave birth to five kittens. While the mother was a pure white thoro

24/25

In our house we had a cat with the grandiose nam
e of Gonnosuke. Usually with cats and dogs we kn
ow who the mother is but not the father. A cat wit

ABCDEFGHIJKLMNO
PQRSTUVWXYZ
abcdefghijklmnopq
rstuvwxyz
1234567890&$¢£¥
fiflæœÆŒÅßÇÌÎÍÏã§✝
-–—/()''""":;.,!¡?¿

10/11

In our house we had a cat with the grandiose name of Gonnosuke. Usually with cats and dogs we know who the m
other is but not the father. A cat with a large belly wondered into the house of my younger sister and her husband
and gave birth to five kittens. While the mother was a pure white thoroughbred Chinchila, the kittens were black
and white tabbies of mixed breed. One of these came to our house about two weeks after its birth and was given t
he name Gonnosuke. At that time we already had one female Shiba dog and one female brown tabby cat in our ho
use comprising only 13 thubo. The dog was called Momo and the cat Mii. My wife, who was very much opposed to

16/17

In our house we had a cat with the grandiose name of Gonnosuke. Usua
lly with cats and dogs we know who the mother is but not the father. A
cat with a large belly wondered into the house of my younger sister an
d her husband and gave birth to five kittens. While the mother was a p

24/25

In our house we had a cat with the grandiose n
ame of Gonnosuke. Usually with cats and dogs
we know who the mother is but not the father.

ABCDEFGHIJKLMNO
PQRSTUVWXYZ
abcdefghijklmnopq
rstuvwxyz
1234567890&$¢£¥
fiflæœÆŒÅßÇÌÎÍÏã§†
-–——/()''""::.,!¡?¿

10/11

In our house we had a cat with the grandiose name of Gonnosuke. Usually with cats and dogs we know who the moth er is but not the father. A cat with a large belly wondered into the house of my younger sister and her husband and ga ve birth to five kittens. While the mother was a pure white thoroughbred Chinchila, the kittens were black and white tabbies of mixed breed. One of these came to our house about two weeks after its birth and was given the name Gonn osuke. At that time we already had one female Shiba dog and one female brown tabby cat in our house comprising on ly 13 thubo. The dog was called Momo and the cat Mii. My wife, who was very much opposed to keeping cats and do

16/17

In our house we had a cat with the grandiose name of Gonnosuke. Usuall y with cats and dogs we know who the mother is but not the father. A cat with a large belly wondered into the house of my younger sister and her husband and gave birth to five kittens. While the mother was a pure whit

24/25

In our house we had a cat with the grandiose na me of Gonnosuke. Usually with cats and dogs we know who the mother is but not the father. A cat

ABCDEFGHIJKLMNO
PQRSTUVWXYZ
abcdefghijklmnopq
rstuvwxyz
1234567890&$¢£¥
fiflœœÆŒÅßÇÌÎÍÏã§†
———/() '"''";.,!¡?¿

10/11

In our house we had a cat with the grandiose name of Gonnosuke. Usually with cats and dogs we know who the mothe r is but not the father. A cat with a large belly wondered into the house of my younger sister and her husband and gave birth to five kittens. While the mother was a pure white thoroughbred Chinchila, the kittens were black and white tabbi es of mixed breed. One of these came to our house about two weeks after its birth and was given the name Gonnosuke. A t that time we already had one female Shiba dog and one female brown tabby cat in our house comprising only 13 thu bo. The dog was called Momo and the cat Mii. My wife, who was very much opposed to keeping cats and dogs, instant

16/17

In our house we had a cat with the grandiose name of Gonnosuke. Usuall y with cats and dogs we know who the mother is but not the father. A cat with a large belly wondered into the house of my younger sister and her h usband and gave birth to five kittens. While the mother was a pure white t

24/25

In our house we had a cat with the grandiose na me of Gonnosuke. Usually with cats and dogs we know who the mother is but not the father. A cat

ABCDEFGHIJKLMN
OPQRSTUVWXYZ
abcdefghijklmnopq
rstuvwxyz
1234567890&$¢£¥
fiflæœÆŒÅßÇÌÎÍÏã§
†-———/()''""‹›.,!¡?¿

10/11

In our house we had a cat with the grandiose name of Gonnosuke. Usually with cats and dogs we know who the mother is but not the father. A cat with a large belly wondered into the house of my younger sister and her husband and gave birth to five kittens. While the mother was a pure white thoroughbred Chinchila, the kittens were black and white tabbies of mixed breed. One of these came to our house about two weeks after its birth and was given the name Gonnosuke. At that time we already had one female Shiba dog and one fe male brown tabby cat in our house comprising only 13 thubo. The dog was called Momo and the cat Mii. M

16/17

In our house we had a cat with the grandiose name of Gonnosuke. Usuall y with cats and dogs we know who the mother is but not the father. A cat with a large belly wondered into the house of my younger sister and her husband and gave birth to five kittens. While the mother was a pure whit

24/25

In our house we had a cat with the grandiose na me of Gonnosuke. Usually with cats and dogs we know who the mother is but not the father. A cat

ABCDEFGHIJKLMN
OPQRSTUVWXYZ
abcdefghijklmnopq
rstuvwxyz
1234567890&$¢£¥
fiflœœÅßÇÌÎÍÏã§
†-–—/()""''":;.,!¡?¿

10/11

In our house we had a cat with the grandiose name of Gonnosuke. Usually with cats and dogs we know w
ho the mother is but not the father. A cat with a large belly wondered into the house of my younger sister
and her husband and gave birth to five kittens. While the mother was a pure white thoroughbred Chinch
ila, the kittens were black and white tabbies of mixed breed. One of these came to our house about two w
eeks after its birth and was given the name Gonnosuke. At that time we already had one female Shiba do
g and one female brown tabby cat in our house comprising only 13 thubo. The dog was called Momo and

16/17

In our house we had a cat with the grandiose name of Gonnosuk
e. Usually with cats and dogs we know who the mother is but not
the father. A cat with a large belly wondered into the house of my
younger sister and her husband and gave birth to five kittens. W

24/25

In our house we had a cat with the grandio
se name of Gonnosuke. Usually with cats a
nd dogs we know who the mother is but not

ABCDEFGHIJKLMN
OPQRSTUVWXYZ
abcdefghijklmnopq
rstuvwxyz
1234567890&$¢£¥
fiflæœÆŒÅßÇÌÎÍÏã§
†-–—/()''""":;.,!¡?¿

10/11

In our house we had a cat with the grandiose name of Gonnosuke. Usually with cats and dogs we know who the mother is but not the father. A cat with a large belly wondered into the house of my younger s ister and her husband and gave birth to five kittens. While the mother was a pure white thoroughbred Chinchila, the kittens were black and white tabbies of mixed breed. One of these came to our house ab out two weeks after its birth and was given the name Gonnosuke. At that time we already had one fema le Shiba dog and one female brown tabby cat in our house comprising only 13 thubo. The dog was call

16/17

In our house we had a cat with the grandiose name of Gonnosuk e. Usually with cats and dogs we know who the mother is but no t the father. A cat with a large belly wondered into the house of my younger sister and her husband and gave birth to five kitten

24/25

In our house we had a cat with the grandio se name of Gonnosuke. Usually with cats a nd dogs we know who the mother is but no

ABCDEFGHIJKLM
NOPQRSTUVWXYZ
abcdefghijklmnopq
rstuvwxyz
1234567890&$¢£¥
fiflæœÆŒÅßÇÌÎÍÏã§
†-—––/() '''''':;.,!¡?¿

10/11

In our house we had a cat with the grandiose name of Gonnosuke. Usually with cats and dogs we kno w who the mother is but not the father. A cat with a large belly wondered into the house of my younge r sister and her husband and gave birth to five kittens. While the mother was a pure white thoroughbre d Chinchila, the kittens were black and white tabbies of mixed breed. One of these came to our house about two weeks after its birth and was given the name Gonnosuke. At that time we already had one f emale Shiba dog and one female brown tabby cat in our house comprising only 13 thubo. The dog wa

16/17

In our house we had a cat with the grandiose name of Gonnosu ke. Usually with cats and dogs we know who the mother is but n ot the father. A cat with a large belly wondered into the house o f my younger sister and her husband and gave birth to five kitte

24/25

In our house we had a cat with the grandi ose name of Gonnosuke. Usually with cats and dogs we know who the mother is but n

ABCDEFGHIJKLMNO
PQRSTUVWXYZ
abcdefghijklmnopq
rstuvwxyz
1234567890&$¢£¥
fiflæœÆŒÅßçÌÎÍÏã§†
----——/()''""":;.,!¡?¿

10/11

In our house we had a cat with the grandiose name of Gonnosuke. Usually with cats and dogs we know who the mother is but not the fath er. A cat with a large belly wondered into the house of my younger sister and her husband and gave birth to five kittens. While the mothe r was a pure white thoroughbred Chinchila, the kittens were black and white tabbies of mixed breed. One of these came to our house ab out two weeks after its birth and was given the name Gonnosuke. At that time we already had one female Shiba dog and one female brow n tabby cat in our house comprising only 13 thubo. The dog was called Momo and the cat Mii. My wife, who was very much opposed to ke eping cats and dogs, instantaneously fell for its shaggy appearance and the black tip of its nose and decided on its name, crying this dog

16/17

In our house we had a cat with the grandiose name of Gonnosuke. Usually with cats a nd dogs we know who the mother is but not the father. A cat with a large belly wonde red into the house of my younger sister and her husband and gave birth to five kitten s. While the mother was a pure white thoroughbred Chinchila, the kittens were black

24/25

In our house we had a cat with the grandiose name of Go nnosuke. Usually with cats and dogs we know who the mo ther is but not the father. A cat with a large belly wonder

ABCDEFGHIJKL
MNOPQRSTUVW
XYZabcdefghijkl
mnopqrstuvwxy
z1234567890&
$¢£¥fiflæœÆŒ
ÅßÇÌÎÍÏãą§•
---—/O''""·:;·,!¡?¿

10/11

In our house we had a cat with the grandiose name of Gonnosuke. Usually with ca
ts and dogs we know who the mother is but not the father. A cat with a large belly
wondered into the house of my younger sister and her husband and gave birth to
five kittens. While the mother was a pure white thoroughbred Chinchila, the kitte
ns were black and white tabbies of mixed breed. One of these came to our house
about two weeks after its birth and was given the name Gonnosuke. At that time

16/17

In our house we had a cat with the grandiose name
of Gonnosuke. Usually with cats and dogs we know
who the mother is but not the father. A cat with a l
arge belly wondered into the house of my younger

24/25

In our house we had a cat with th
e grandiose name of Gonnosuke.
Usually with cats and dogs we kn

Poster Bodoni Italic

ABCDEFGHIJK
LMNOPQRSTUV
WXYZabcdefghi
jklmnopqrstuvw
xyz1234567890
&$¢£¥fiflœæ
ÆŒÅßÇÌÎÍÏÏãã§✢
-–——/O''""···,,!¡?¿

10/11

In our house we had a cat with the grandiose name of Gonnosuke. Usually with ca
ts and dogs we know who the mother is but not the father. A cat with a large belly
wondered into the house of my younger sister and her husband and gave birth to
five kittens. While the mother was a pure white thoroughbred Chinchila, the kitte
ns were black and white tabbies of mixed breed. One of these came to our house a
bout two weeks after its birth and was given the name Gonnosuke. At that time we

16/17

In our house we had a cat with the grandiose name
of Gonnosuke. Usually with cats and dogs we know
who the mother is but not the father. A cat with a l
arge belly wondered into the house of my younger

24/25

In our house we had a cat with th
e grandiose name of Gonnosuke.
Usually with cats and dogs we kn

Like **Poster Bodoni Compressed**

ABCDEFGHIJKLMNOP
QRSTUVWXYZ
abcdefghijklmnopq
rstuvwxyz
1234567890&$¢£¥
fiflæœÆŒÅßçÌÎÍÏã§†
-–—/()''""":;.,!¡?¿

10/11

In our house we had a cat with the grandiose name of Gonnosuke. Usually with cats and dogs we know who the mother is but not the father. A cat with a large belly wondered into the house of my younger sister and her husband and gave birth to five kittens. While the mother was a pure white thoroughbred Chinchila, the kittens were black and white tabbies of mixed breed. One of these came to our house about two weeks after its birth and was given the name Gonnosuke. At that time we already had one female Shiba dog and one female brown tabby cat in our house comprising only 13 tubo. The dog was called Momo and the cat Mii. My wife, who was very much opposed to keeping cats and dogs, instantaneously fell for its shaggy appearance and the black tip of its nose and decided on its name, crying this dog's name is Momo. Mii is a stray cat which my daughter picked up.It cried a lot making a sound like mil mil, so we were soon calling it Mii. Of course it was a mixe

16/17

In our house we had a cat with the grandiose name of Gonnosuke. Usually with cats and dogs we know who the mother is but not the father. A cat with a large belly wondered into the house of my younger sister and her husband and gave birth to five kittens. While the mother was a pure white thoroughbred Chinchila, the kittens were black and white tabbies of mixed breed. One of these came to our house a

24/25

In our house we had a cat with the grandiose name of Gonnosuke. Usually with cats and dogs we know who the mother is but not the father. A cat with a large belly wondered into the house of my younger

ABCDEFGHIJKLMN
OPQRSTUVWXYZ
abcdefghijklmno
pqrstuvwxyz
1234567890&$¢£¥
fiflæœÆŒÅßÇÌÎÍÏã§†
-–—/() '' "" :;.,!¡?¿

10/11

In our house we had a cat with the grandiose name of Gonnosuke. Usually with cats and dogs we know who the mother is but not the father. A cat with a la rge belly wondered into the house of my younger sister and her husband and gave birth to five kittens. While the mother was a pure white thoroughbred C hinchila, the kittens were black and white tabbies of mixed breed. One of these came to our house about two weeks after its birth and was given the name Gonnosuke. At that time we already had one female Shiba dog and one female brown tabby cat in our house comprising only 13 tubo. The dog was called Momo and the cat Mii. My wife, who was very much opposed to keeping cats and dogs, instantaneously fell for its shaggy appearance and the black tip of it s nose and decided on its name, crying this dog's name is Momo. Mii is a stray cat which my daughter picked up.It cried a lot making a sound like mil mi

16/17

In our house we had a cat with the grandiose name of Gonnosuke. Usually with cats and dogs we know who the mother is but not the father. A cat with a large belly wondered into the house of m y younger sister and her husband and gave birth to five kittens. While the mother was a pure wh ite thoroughbred Chinchila, the kittens were black and white tabbies of mixed breed. One of thes

24/25

In our house we had a cat with the grandiose name of Gonnosuk e. Usually with cats and dogs we know who the mother is but not the father. A cat with a large belly wondered into the house of m

ABCDEFGHIJKLMN
OPQRSTUVWXYZ
abcdefghijklmnopq
rstuvwxyz
1234567890&$¢£¥
fiflæœÆŒÅßÇÌÎÍÏã§†
-–—/()''""::,,!¡?¿

10/11

In our house we had a cat with the grandiose name of Gonnosuke. Usually with cats and dogs we know who the moth er is but not the father. A cat with a large belly wondered into the house of my younger sister and her husband and gav e birth to five kittens. While the mother was a pure white thoroughbred Chinchila, the kittens were black and white tab bies of mixed breed. One of these came to our house about two weeks after its birth and was given the name Gonnosuk e. At that time we already had one female Shiba dog and one female brown tabby cat in our house comprising only 13 tubo. The dog was called Momo and the cat Mii. My wife, who was very much opposed to keeping cats and dogs, inst

16/17

In our house we had a cat with the grandiose name of Gonnosuke. Usuall y with cats and dogs we know who the mother is but not the father. A cat with a large belly wondered into the house of my younger sister and her h usband and gave birth to five kittens. While the mother was a pure white t

24/25

In our house we had a cat with the grandiose na me of Gonnosuke. Usually with cats and dogs we know who the mother is but not the father. A cat

ABCDEFGHIJKLMN
OPQRSTUVWXYZ
abcdefghijklmnopq
rstuvwxyz
1234567890&$¢£¥
fiflœœÆŒÅßÇÌÎÍÏã§†
———/()''""·;·,!¡?¿

10/11

In our house we had a cat with the grandiose name of Gonnosuke. Usually with cats and dogs we know who the mother is b ut not the father. A cat with a large belly wondered into the house of my younger sister and her husband and gave birth to fi ve kittens. While the mother was a pure white thoroughbred Chinchila, the kittens were black and white tabbies of mixed br eed. One of these came to our house about two weeks after its birth and was given the name Gonnosuke. At that time we alre ady had one female Shiba dog and one female brown tabby cat in our house comprising only 13 tubo. The dog was called M omo and the cat Mii. My wife, who was very much opposed to keeping cats and dogs, instantaneously fell for its shaggy appe

16/17

In our house we had a cat with the grandiose name of Gonnosuke. Usually w ith cats and dogs we know who the mother is but not the father. A cat with a l arge belly wondered into the house of my younger sister and her husband and gave birth to five kittens. While the mother was a pure white thoroughbred C

24/25

In our house we had a cat with the grandiose name of Gonnosuke. Usually with cats and dogs we know who the mother is but not the father. A cat with a la

ABCDEFGHIJKLM
NOPQRSTUVWXYZ
abcdefghijklmnopq
rstuvwxyz
1234567890&$¢£¥
fiflæœÆŒÅßÇÌÎÍÏã§
†-–——/()'''""'.;.,!¡?¿

10/11

In our house we had a cat with the grandiose name of Gonnosuke. Usually with cats and dogs we know who t he mother is but not the father. A cat with a large belly wondered into the house of my younger sister and her husband and gave birth to five kittens. While the mother was a pure white thoroughbred Chinchila, the kitten s were black and white tabbies of mixed breed. One of these came to our house about two weeks after its birt h and was given the name Gonnosuke. At that time we already had one female Shiba dog and one female bro wn tabby cat in our house comprising only 13 tubo. The dog was called Momo and the cat Mii. My wife, who

16/17

In our house we had a cat with the grandiose name of Gonnosuke. U sually with cats and dogs we know who the mother is but not the fat her. A cat with a large belly wondered into the house of my younger sister and her husband and gave birth to five kittens. While the mot

24/25

In our house we had a cat with the grandiose name of Gonnosuke. Usually with cats and do gs we know who the mother is but not the fat

ABCDEFGHIJKLMN
OPQRSTUVWXYZ
abcdefghijklmnopq
rstuvwxyz
1234567890&$¢£¥
fiflæœÆŒÅßÇÌÎÍÏã§†
———/()'"",:;.,!¡?¿

10/11

In our house we had a cat with the grandiose name of Gonnosuke. Usually with cats and dogs we know who th
e mother is but not the father. A cat with a large belly wondered into the house of my younger sister and her hu
sband and gave birth to five kittens. While the mother was a pure white thoroughbred Chinchila, the kittens we
re black and white tabbies of mixed breed. One of these came to our house about two weeks after its birth and
was given the name Gonnosuke. At that time we already had one female Shiba dog and one female brown tabb
y cat in our house comprising only 13 tubo. The dog was called Momo and the cat Mii. My wife, who was very

16/17

In our house we had a cat with the grandiose name of Gonnosuke. Us
ually with cats and dogs we know who the mother is but not the fathe
r. A cat with a large belly wondered into the house of my younger sist
er and her husband and gave birth to five kittens. While the mother

24/25

In our house we had a cat with the grandiose
name of Gonnosuke. Usually with cats and do
gs we know who the mother is but not the fath

ABCDEFGHIJKLM
NOPQRSTUVWXYZ
abcdefghijklmnopq
rstuvwxyz
1234567890&$¢£¥
fiflæœÆŒÅßÇÌÎÍÏã§
†-–—/()''""";,.,!¡?¿

10/11

In our house we had a cat with the grandiose name of Gonnosuke. Usually with cats and dogs we know who the mother is but not the father. A cat with a large belly wondered into the house of my younger sister and her husband and gave birth to five kittens. While the mother was a pure white thoroughbred Chinchila, the kittens were black and white tabbies of mixed breed. One of these came to our house about two weeks after its birth and was given the name Gonnosuke. At that time we already had one female Shiba dog and one female brown tabby cat in our house comprising only 13 tubo. The dog was called Momo and the

16/17

In our house we had a cat with the grandiose name of Gonnosuke. Usually with cats and dogs we know who the mother is but not the father. A cat with a large belly wondered into the house of my younger sister and her husband and gave birth to five kittens. While

24/25

In our house we had a cat with the grandios e name of Gonnosuke. Usually with cats and dogs we know who the mother is but not the

ABCDEFGHIJKLM
NOPQRSTUVWXYZ
abcdefghijklmnopq
rstuvwxyz
1234567890&$¢£¥
fiflæœÆŒÅßÇÌÎÍÏã§
†-–——/()'''""";.,!¡?¿

10/11

In our house we had a cat with the grandiose name of Gonnosuke. Usually with cats and dogs we know who t
he mother is but not the father. A cat with a large belly wondered into the house of my younger sister and her
husband and gave birth to five kittens. While the mother was a pure white thoroughbred Chinchila, the kitte
ns were black and white tabbies of mixed breed. One of these came to our house about two weeks after its bir
th and was given the name Gonnosuke. At that time we already had one female Shiba dog and one female bro
wn tabby cat in our house comprising only 13 tubo. The dog was called Momo and the cat Mii. My wife, who

16/17

In our house we had a cat with the grandiose name of Gonnosuke.
Usually with cats and dogs we know who the mother is but not the f
ather. A cat with a large belly wondered into the house of my young
er sister and her husband and gave birth to five kittens. While the m

24/25

In our house we had a cat with the grandiose
name of Gonnosuke. Usually with cats and d
ogs we know who the mother is but not the fa

ABCDEFGHIJKL
MNOPQRSTU
VWXYZ
abcdefghijklmnopq
rstuvwxyz
1234567890&$¢£¥
fiflæœÆŒÅßÇÌÎÍÏã
§†–——/()''""":;.,!¡?¿

10/11

In our house we had a cat with the grandiose name of Gonnosuke. Usually with cats and dogs we know who the mother is but not the father. A cat with a large belly wondered into the house of my younger sis ter and her husband and gave birth to five kittens. While the mother was a pure white thoroughbred Chi nchila, the kittens were black and white tabbies of mixed breed. One of these came to our house about tw o weeks after its birth and was given the name Gonnosuke. At that time we already had one female Shib a dog and one female brown tabby cat in our house comprising only 13 thubo. The dog was called Momo

16/17

In our house we had a cat with the grandiose name of Gonnosuk e. Usually with cats and dogs we know who the mother is but not the father. A cat with a large belly wondered into the house of my younger sister and her husband and gave birth to five kittens. W

24/25

In our house we had a cat with the grandio se name of Gonnosuke. Usually with cats a nd dogs we know who the mother is but not

ABCDEFGHIJKL
MNOPQRSTU
VWXYZ
abcdefghijklmnopq
rstuvwxyz
1234567890&$¢£¥
fiflæœÆŒÅßÇÌÎÍÏã§
†---—/()''""";.,!¡?¿

10/11

In our house we had a cat with the grandiose name of Gonnosuke. Usually with cats and dogs we know who the mother is but not the father. A cat with a large belly wondered into the house of my younger sis ter and her husband and gave birth to five kittens. While the mother was a pure white thoroughbred Ch inchila, the kittens were black and white tabbies of mixed breed. One of these came to our house about t wo weeks after its birth and was given the name Gonnosuke. At that time we already had one female Sh iba dog and one female brown tabby cat in our house comprising only 13 thubo. The dog was called Mo

16/17

In our house we had a cat with the grandiose name of Gonnosuk e. Usually with cats and dogs we know who the mother is but not the father. A cat with a large belly wondered into the house of m y younger sister and her husband and gave birth to five kittens.

24/25

In our house we had a cat with the grandio se name of Gonnosuke. Usually with cats and dogs we know who the mother is but n

ABCDEFGHIJKL MNOPQRSTU VWXYZ
abcdefghijklmnopq rstuvwxyz
1234567890&$¢£¥ fiflæœÆŒÅßÇÌÎÍÏã §†-–——/()''""'.;.,!¡?¿

10/11

In our house we had a cat with the grandiose name of Gonnosuke. Usually with cats and dogs we know who the mother is but not the father. A cat with a large belly wondered into the house of my younger sister and her husband and gave birth to five kittens. While the mother was a pure white thoroughbred Chinchila, the kittens were black and white tabbies of mixed breed. One of these ca me to our house about two weeks after its birth and was given the name Gonnosuke. At that time we already had one female Shiba dog and one female brown tabby cat in our house comprising onl

16/17

In our house we had a cat with the grandiose name of Gonno suke. Usually with cats and dogs we know who the mother is but not the father. A cat with a large belly wondered into the house of my younger sister and her husband and gave birth to

24/25

In our house we had a cat with the grand iose name of Gonnosuke. Usually with cats and dogs we know who the mother

ABCDEFGHIJKL
MNOPQRSTU
VWXYZ
abcdefghijklmnopqr
stuvwxyz
1234567890&$¢£¥
fiflæœÆŒÅßÇÌÎÍÏã
§†-–——/()''""",;.,!¡?¿

10/11

In our house we had a cat with the grandiose name of Gonnosuke. Usually with cats and dogs we k now who the mother is but not the father. A cat with a large belly wondered into the house of my yo unger sister and her husband and gave birth to five kittens. While the mother was a pure white tho roughbred Chinchila, the kittens were black and white tabbies of mixed breed. One of these came to our house about two weeks after its birth and was given the name Gonnosuke. At that time we al ready had one female Shiba dog and one female brown tabby cat in our house comprising only 13 th

16/17

In our house we had a cat with the grandiose name of Gonnos uke. Usually with cats and dogs we know who the mother is b ut not the father. A cat with a large belly wondered into the ho use of my younger sister and her husband and gave birth to fi

24/25

In our house we had a cat with the gran diose name of Gonnosuke. Usually with c ats and dogs we know who the mother is

ABCDEFGHIJKL MNOPQRSTU VWXYZ
abcdefghijklmnopq rstuvwxyz
1234567890&$¢£¥ fiflæœÆŒÅßÇÌÎÍÏã §†-–——/()''""":;.,!¡?¿

10/11

In our house we had a cat with the grandiose name of Gonnosuke. Usually with cats and dogs we k now who the mother is but not the father. A cat with a large belly wondered into the house of my younger sister and her husband and gave birth to five kittens. While the mother was a pure white thoroughbred Chinchila, the kittens were black and white tabbies of mixed breed. One of these ca me to our house about two weeks after its birth and was given the name Gonnosuke. At that time we already had one female Shiba dog and one female brown tabby cat in our house comprising only

16/17

In our house we had a cat with the grandiose name of Gonnos uke. Usually with cats and dogs we know who the mother is but not the father. A cat with a large belly wondered into the house of my younger sister and her husband and gave birth to

24/25

In our house we had a cat with the grand iose name of Gonnosuke. Usually with ca ts and dogs we know who the mother is b

ABCDEFGHIJKL
MNOPQRSTUVW
XYZabcdefghijkl
mnopqrstuvwxyz
1234567890&$¢£¥
fiflæœÆŒÅßÇÌÎÍÏã
§†-–——/()''""":;.,!¡?¿

10/11

In our house we had a cat with the grandiose name of Gonnosuke. Usually with cats and dogs we k now who the mother is but not the father. A cat with a large belly wondered into the house of my you nger sister and her husband and gave birth to five kittens. While the mother was a pure white thoro ughbred Chinchila, the kittens were black and white tabbies of mixed breed. One of these came to ou r house about two weeks after its birth and was given the name Gonnosuke. At that time we already had one female Shiba dog and one female brown tabby cat in our house comprising only 13 thubo.

16/17

In our house we had a cat with the grandiose name of Gonnos uke. Usually with cats and dogs we know who the mother is b ut not the father. A cat with a large belly wondered into the ho use of my younger sister and her husband and gave birth to fi

24/25

In our house we had a cat with the grand iose name of Gonnosuke. Usually with ca ts and dogs we know who the mother is b

ABCDEFGHIJKL MNOPQRSTU VWXYZ

abcdefghijklmnop qrstuvwxyz

1234567890&$¢£¥ fiflæœÆŒÅßÇÌÎÍÏ ã§†·-–—/()''""":;.,!¡?¿

10/11

In our house we had a cat with the grandiose name of Gonnosuke. Usually with cats an
d dogs we know who the mother is but not the father. A cat with a large belly wondered
into the house of my younger sister and her husband and gave birth to five kittens. Whi
le the mother was a pure white thoroughbred Chinchila, the kittens were black and wh
ite tabbies of mixed breed. One of these came to our house about two weeks after its bi
rth and was given the name Gonnosuke. At that time we already had one female Shiba

16/17

In our house we had a cat with the grandiose name of
Gonnosuke. Usually with cats and dogs we know who t
he mother is but not the father. A cat with a large bell
y wondered into the house of my younger sister and he

24/25

In our house we had a cat with the g
randiose name of Gonnosuke. Usual
ly with cats and dogs we know who t

ABCDEFGHIJKL MNOPQRSTU VWXYZ

abcdefghijklmnop
qrstuvwxyz
1234567890&$¢£¥
fiflæœÆŒÅßÇÌÎÍÏ
ã§†----/()''""";.,!¡?¿

10/11

In our house we had a cat with the grandiose name of Gonnosuke. Usually with cats an d dogs we know who the mother is but not the father. A cat with a large belly wondered into the house of my younger sister and her husband and gave birth to five kittens. Whil e the mother was a pure white thoroughbred Chinchila, the kittens were black and whi te tabbies of mixed breed. One of these came to our house about two weeks after its birth and was given the name Gonnosuke. At that time we already had one female Shiba dog

16/17

In our house we had a cat with the grandiose name of Gonnosuke. Usually with cats and dogs we know who t he mother is but not the father. A cat with a large belly wondered into the house of my younger sister and her

24/25

In our house we had a cat with the g randiose name of Gonnosuke. Usual ly with cats and dogs we know who t

ABCDEFGHIJKLMN
OPQRSTUVWXYZ
abcdefghijklmnopq
rstuvwxyz
1234567890&$¢£¥
fiflæœÆŒÅßÇÌÎÍÏã§†
-–—/()''""":;.,!¡?¿

10/11

In our house we had a cat with the grandiose name of Gonnosuke. Usually with cats and dogs we know who the mother is but not the father. A cat with a large belly wondered into the house of my younger sister and her husband and gave birth to five kittens. While the mother was a pure white thoroughbred Chinchila, the kittens were black and white tabbies of mixed breed. One of these came to our house about two weeks after its birth and was given the name Gonnosuke. At that time we already had one female Shiba dog and one female brown tabby cat in our house comprising only 13 thubo. The dog was called Momo and the cat Mii. My wife, who was very much opposed to keeping cats and dogs, instantaneously fell for its shaggy appearance and the black tip of its nose and decided on its name, crying this dog's

16/17

In our house we had a cat with the grandiose name of Gonnosuke. Usually with cats and dogs we know who the mother is but not the father. A cat with a large belly wondered into the house of my younger sister and her husband and gave birth to five kittens. While the mother was a pure white thoroughbred Chinchila, the kittens were black

24/25

In our house we had a cat with the grandiose name of Gonnosuke. Usually with cats and dogs we know who the mother is but not the father. A cat with a large belly wonder

ABCDEFGHIJKLM
NOPQRSTUVWXYZ
abcdefghijklm
nopqrstuvwxyz
1234567890&$¢£¥fi
flæœÆŒÅßÇÌÎÍÏã§†-
—/()''""":;.,!¡?¿

10/11

In our house we had a cat with the grandiose name of Gonnosuke. Usually wit
h cats and dogs we know who the mother is but not the father. A cat with a
large belly wondered into the house of my younger sister and her husband an
d gave birth to five kittens. While the mother was a pure white thoroughbre
d Chinchila, the kittens were black and white tabbies of mixed breed. One o
f these came to our house about two weeks after its birth and was given the

16/17

In our house we had a cat with the grandiose n
ame of Gonnosuke. Usually with cats and dogs w
e know who the mother is but not the father. A
cat with a large belly wondered into the house

24/25

In our house we had a cat with t
he grandiose name of Gonnosuke.
Usually with cats and dogs we kn

ABCDEFGHIJKLMN
OPQRSTUVWXYZ
abcdefghijklmnopq
rstuvwxyz
1234567890&$¢£¥
fiflæœÆŒÅßÇÌÎÍÏã§
†-——/()''""":;.,!¡?¿

10/11

In our house we had a cat with the grandiose name of Gonnosuke. Usually with cats and dogs we know who the mother is but not the father. A cat with a large belly wondered into the house of my younger sist er and her husband and gave birth to five kittens. While the mother was a pure white thoroughbred Chi nchila, the kittens were black and white tabbies of mixed breed. One of these came to our house about t wo weeks after its birth and was given the name Gonnosuke. At that time we already had one female Shi ba dog and one female brown tabby cat in our house comprising only 13 tubo. The dog was called Momo

16/17

In our house we had a cat with the grandiose name of Gonnosuk e. Usually with cats and dogs we know who the mother is but not the father. A cat with a large belly wondered into the house of my younger sister and her husband and gave birth to five kittens. W

24/25

In our house we had a cat with the grandio se name of Gonnosuke. Usually with cats a nd dogs we know who the mother is but no

ABCDEFGHIJKLMN
OPQRSTUVWXYZ
abcdefghijklmnopqr
stuvwxyz
1234567890&$¢£¥
fiflœœÆŒÅßÇÌÎÍÏã§
†-—–/()'''""".;.,!¡?¿

10/11

In our house we had a cat with the grandiose name of Gonnosuke. Usually with cats and dogs we k now who the mother is but not the father. A cat with a large belly wondered into the house of my yo unger sister and her husband and gave birth to five kittens. While the mother was a pure white tho roughbred Chinchila, the kittens were black and white tabbies of mixed breed. One of these came to our house about two weeks after its birth and was given the name Gonnosuke. At that time we alrea dy had one female Shiba dog and one female brown tabby cat in our house comprising only 13 tub

16/17

In our house we had a cat with the grandiose name of Gonnos uke. Usually with cats and dogs we know who the mother is b ut not the father. A cat with a large belly wondered into the ho use of my younger sister and her husband and gave birth to fi

24/25

In our house we had a cat with the grand iose name of Gonnosuke. Usually with ca ts and dogs we know who the mother is b

ABCDEFGHIJKLMN
OPQRSTUVWXYZ
abcdefghijklmnopq
rstuvwxyz
1234567890&$¢£¥
fiflæœÆŒÅßÇÌÎÍÏã§
†-–—/()''"":;.,!¡?¿

10/11

In our house we had a cat with the grandiose name of Gonnosuke. Usually with cats and dogs we know who the mother is but not the father. A cat with a large belly wondered into the house of my younger si ster and her husband and gave birth to five kittens. While the mother was a pure white thoroughbred C hinchila, the kittens were black and white tabbies of mixed breed. One of these came to our house abo ut two weeks after its birth and was given the name Gonnosuke. At that time we already had one fema le Shiba dog and one female brown tabby cat in our house comprising only 13 tubo. The dog was calle

16/17

In our house we had a cat with the grandiose name of Gonnosuk e. Usually with cats and dogs we know who the mother is but no t the father. A cat with a large belly wondered into the house of my younger sister and her husband and gave birth to five kitten

24/25

In our house we had a cat with the grandio se name of Gonnosuke. Usually with cats a nd dogs we know who the mother is but n

ABCDEFGHIJKLM
NOPQRSTUVWXYZ
abcdefghijklmnopq
rstuvwxyz
1234567890&$¢£¥
fiflœœÆŒÅßÇÌÎÍÏã
§†----——/()' '""".;.,!¡?¿

10/11

In our house we had a cat with the grandiose name of Gonnosuke. Usually with cats and dogs w e know who the mother is but not the father. A cat with a large belly wondered into the house of my younger sister and her husband and gave birth to five kittens. While the mother was a pure white thoroughbred Chinchila, the kittens were black and white tabbies of mixed breed. One of t hese came to our house about two weeks after its birth and was given the name Gonnosuke. At t hat time we already had one female Shiba dog and one female brown tabby cat in our house co

16/17

In our house we had a cat with the grandiose name of Gonn osuke. Usually with cats and dogs we know who the mother is but not the father. A cat with a large belly wondered into t he house of my younger sister and her husband and gave bi

24/25

In our house we had a cat with the gran diose name of Gonnosuke. Usually with cats and dogs we know who the mother

ABCDEFGHIJKL MNOPQRSTUVW XYZabcdefghijklm nopqrstuvwxyz 1234567890&$¢£¥ fiflæœÆŒÅßÇÌÎÍÏ ã§†-–—/()''""":;.,!¡?¿

10/11

In our house we had a cat with the grandiose name of Gonnosuke. Usually with cats and dogs we know who the mother is but not the father. A cat with a large belly wondered into the ho use of my younger sister and her husband and gave birth to five kittens. While the mother w as a pure white thoroughbred Chinchila, the kittens were black and white tabbies of mixed b reed. One of these came to our house about two weeks after its birth and was given the nam e Gonnosuke. At that time we already had one female Shiba dog and one female brown tabby

16/17

In our house we had a cat with the grandiose name of Gon nosuke. Usually with cats and dogs we know who the mot her is but not the father. A cat with a large belly wondere d into the house of my younger sister and her husband an

24/25

In our house we had a cat with the gra ndiose name of Gonnosuke. Usually wi th cats and dogs we know who the mo

ABCDEFGHIJKL MNOPQRSTUVW XYZabcdefghijklm nopqrstuvwxyz 1234567890& $¢£¥fiflœœÆŒ ÅßÇÌÎÍÏã§† ———/O''""":;.,!¡?¿

10/11

In our house we had a cat with the grandiose name of Gonnosuke. Usually with cats and do gs we know who the mother is but not the father. A cat with a large belly wondered into the house of my younger sister and her husband and gave birth to five kittens. While the mothe r was a pure white thoroughbred Chinchila, the kittens were black and white tabbies of mix ed breed. One of these came to our house about two weeks after its birth and was given the name Gonnosuke. At that time we already had one female Shiba dog and one female brown

16/17

In our house we had a cat with the grandiose name of Go nnosuke. Usually with cats and dogs we know who the m other is but not the father. A cat with a large belly wonde red into the house of my younger sister and her husband

24/25

In our house we had a cat with the gr andiose name of Gonnosuke. Usually with cats and dogs we know who the

ABCDEFGHIJKL
MNOPQRSTUVW
XYZabcdefghijk
lmnopqrstuvwx
yz1234567890&
$¢£¥fiflæœÆŒ
ÅßÇÌÂÍÏã§†
--—/()''""·;·,!¡?¿

10/11

In our house we had a cat with the grandiose name of Gonnosuke. Usually with cats and dogs we know who the mother is but not the father. A cat with a large belly wondered into the house of my younger sister and her husband and gave birth to five kittens. While the mother was a pure white thoroughbred Chinchila, the kittens were black and white tabbies of mixed breed. One of these came to our house about two weeks after its birth and was given the name Go

16/17

In our house we had a cat with the grandiose name of Gonnosuke. Usually with cats and dogs we know who the mother is but not the father. A cat with a large belly wondered into the house of my

24/25

In our house we had a cat with the grandiose name of Gonnosuke. Usually with cats and dogs we

ABCDEFGHIJK
LMNOPQRSTUV
WXYZabcdefgh
ijklmnopqrstuv
wxyz12345678
90&$¢£¥fiflæœ
ÆŒÅßÇÌÎÍÏãã§†
––—/()''""•;.,!¡?¿

10/11

In our house we had a cat with the grandiose name of Gonnosuke. Usually with cats and dogs we know who the mother is but not the father. A cat with a large belly wondered into the house of my younger sister and her husban d and gave birth to five kittens. While the mother was a pure white thoroug hbred Chinchila, the kittens were black and white tabbies of mixed breed. O ne of these came to our house about two weeks after its birth and was given

16/17

In our house we had a cat with the grandiose n ame of Gonnosuke. Usually with cats and dogs we know who the mother is but not the father. A cat with a large belly wondered into the hou

24/25

In our house we had a cat with the grandiose name of Gonnos uke. Usually with cats and dog

ABCDEFGHIJKLMNOPQ
RSTUVWXYZ
abcdefghijklmnopq
rstuvwxyz
1234567890&$¢£¥
fiflæœÆŒÅßÇÌÎÍÏã§†
-——/()'’“”:;.,!¡?¿

10/11

In our house we had a cat with the grandiose name of Gonnosuke. Usually with cats and dogs we know who the mother is bu t not the father. A cat with a large belly wondered into the house of my younger sister and her husband and gave birth to five kittens. While the mother was a pure white thoroughbred Chinchila, the kittens were black and white tabbies of mixed bree d. One of these came to our house about two weeks after its birth and was given the name Gonnosuke. At that time we alrea dy had one female Shiba dog and one female brown tabby cat in our house comprising only 13 tubo. The dog was called Mo mo and the cat Mii. My wife, who was very much opposed to keeping cats and dogs, instantaneously fell for its shaggy appear

16/17

In our house we had a cat with the grandiose name of Gonnosuke. Usually wit h cats and dogs we know who the mother is but not the father. A cat with a lar ge belly wondered into the house of my younger sister and her husband and g ave birth to five kittens. While the mother was a pure white thoroughbred Chi

24/25

In our house we had a cat with the grandiose name of Gonnosuke. Usually with cats and dogs we know who the mother is but not the father. A cat with a la

ABCDEFGHIJKLMNOPQ
RSTUVWXYZ
abcdefghijklmnopq
rstuvwxyz
1234567890&$¢£¥
fiflœœÆŒÅßÇÌÎÍÏã§†
-——/()'’"":;.,!¡?¿

10/11

In our house we had a cat with the grandiose name of Gonnosuke. Usually with cats and dogs we know who the mothe r is but not the father. A cat with a large belly wondered into the house of my younger sister and her husband and gav e birth to five kittens. While the mother was a pure white thoroughbred Chinchila, the kittens were black and white tab bies of mixed breed. One of these came to our house about two weeks after its birth and was given the name Gonnosuk e. At that time we already had one female Shiba dog and one female brown tabby cat in our house comprising only 1 3 tubo. The dog was called Momo and the cat Mii. My wife, who was very much opposed to keeping cats and dogs, inst

16/17

In our house we had a cat with the grandiose name of Gonnosuke. Usuall y with cats and dogs we know who the mother is but not the father. A cat with a large belly wondered into the house of my younger sister and her husband and gave birth to five kittens. While the mother was a pure whit

24/25

In our house we had a cat with the grandiose na me of Gonnosuke. Usually with cats and dogs we know who the mother is but not the father. A cat

ABCDEFGHIJKLMNOPQ RSTUVWXYZ
abcdefghijklmnopq rstuvwxyz
1234567890&$¢£¥
fiflæœÆŒÅßÇÌÎÍÏã§†
-——/()''""".;.,!¡?¿

10/11

In our house we had a cat with the grandiose name of Gonnosuke. Usually with cats and dogs we know who the mother i s but not the father. A cat with a large belly wondered into the house of my younger sister and her husband and gave birt h to five kittens. While the mother was a pure white thoroughbred Chinchila, the kittens were black and white tabbies of mixed breed. One of these came to our house about two weeks after its birth and was given the name Gonnosuke. At that time we already had one female Shiba dog and one female brown tabby cat in our house comprising only 13 tubo. The do g was called Momo and the cat Mii. My wife, who was very much opposed to keeping cats and dogs, instantaneously fell

16/17

In our house we had a cat with the grandiose name of Gonnosuke. Usually with cats and dogs we know who the mother is but not the father. A cat wit h a large belly wondered into the house of my younger sister and her husba nd and gave birth to five kittens. While the mother was a pure white thorou

24/25

In our house we had a cat with the grandiose nam e of Gonnosuke. Usually with cats and dogs we kn ow who the mother is but not the father. A cat wit

ABCDEFGHIJKLMNOP
QRSTUVWXYZ
abcdefghijklmnopq
rstuvwxyz
1234567890&$¢£¥
fiflœœÆŒÅßÇÌÎÍÏã§†
-–——/()'‘"",:.,!¡?¿

10/11

In our house we had a cat with the grandiose name of Gonnosuke. Usually with cats and dogs we know who the mot her is but not the father. A cat with a large belly wondered into the house of my younger sister and her husband and gave birth to five kittens. While the mother was a pure white thoroughbred Chinchila, the kittens were black and wh ite tabbies of mixed breed. One of these came to our house about two weeks after its birth and was given the name G onnosuke. At that time we already had one female Shiba dog and one female brown tabby cat in our house comprisi ng only 13 tubo. The dog was called Momo and the cat Mii. My wife, who was very much opposed to keeping cats an

16/17

In our house we had a cat with the grandiose name of Gonnosuke. Usua lly with cats and dogs we know who the mother is but not the father. A c at with a large belly wondered into the house of my younger sister and her husband and gave birth to five kittens. While the mother was a pure

24/25

In our house we had a cat with the grandiose n ame of Gonnosuke. Usually with cats and dogs we know who the mother is but not the father. A

ABCDEFGHIJKLMNO
PQRSTUVWXYZ
abcdefghijklmnopq
rstuvwxyz
1234567890&$¢£¥
fiflæœÆŒÅßÇÌÎÍÏïã§†
——–—/()''""".;.,!¡?¿

10/11

In our house we had a cat with the grandiose name of Gonnosuke. Usually with cats and dogs we know who the mother is but not the father. A cat with a large belly wondered into the house of my younger sister and her husb and and gave birth to five kittens. While the mother was a pure white thoroughbred Chinchila, the kittens were black and white tabbies of mixed breed. One of these came to our house about two weeks after its birth and wa s given the name Gonnosuke. At that time we already had one female Shiba dog and one female brown tabby cat in our house comprising only 13 tubo. The dog was called Momo and the cat Mii. My wife, who was very much op

16/17

In our house we had a cat with the grandiose name of Gonnosuke. Us ually with cats and dogs we know who the mother is but not the fathe r. A cat with a large belly wondered into the house of my younger sist er and her husband and gave birth to five kittens. While the mother w

24/25

In our house we had a cat with the grandiose name of Gonnosuke. Usually with cats and dog s we know who the mother is but not the fathe

ITC Century Bold Condensed Italic

ABCDEFGHIJKLMNOP
QRSTUVWXYZ
abcdefghijklmnopq
rstuvwxyz
1234567890&$¢£¥
fiflœœÆŒÅßÇÌÎÍÏã§†
——/()''""'.;.,!¡?¿

10/11

In our house we had a cat with the grandiose name of Gonnosuke. Usually with cats and dogs we know who t
he mother is but not the father. A cat with a large belly wondered into the house of my younger sister and he
r husband and gave birth to five kittens. While the mother was a pure white thoroughbred Chinchila, the kitt
ens were black and white tabbies of mixed breed. One of these came to our house about two weeks after its b
irth and was given the name Gonnosuke. At that time we already had one female Shiba dog and one female
brown tabby cat in our house comprising only 13 tubo. The dog was called Momo and the cat Mii. My wife, w

16/17

In our house we had a cat with the grandiose name of Gonnosuke.
Usually with cats and dogs we know who the mother is but not the f
ather. A cat with a large belly wondered into the house of my young
er sister and her husband and gave birth to five kittens. While the

24/25

In our house we had a cat with the grandiose
name of Gonnosuke. Usually with cats and d
ogs we know who the mother is but not the fa

ITC Century Ultra Condensed

ABCDEFGHIJKLMN
OPQRSTUVWXYZ
abcdefghijklmnopq
rstuvwxyz
1234567890&$¢£¥
fiflæœÆŒÅßÇÌÎÍÏã
§†-–—/()''""::;.,!¡?¿

10/11

In our house we had a cat with the grandiose name of Gonnosuke. Usually with cats and dogs w e know who the mother is but not the father. A cat with a large belly wondered into the house of my younger sister and her husband and gave birth to five kittens. While the mother was a pure white thoroughbred Chinchila, the kittens were black and white tabbies of mixed breed. One of these came to our house about two weeks after its birth and was given the name Gonnosuke. At that time we already had one female Shiba dog and one female brown tabby cat in our house co

16/17

In our house we had a cat with the grandiose name of Gonn osuke. Usually with cats and dogs we know who the mother is but not the father. A cat with a large belly wondered into the house of my younger sister and her husband and gave b

24/25

In our house we had a cat with the gran diose name of Gonnosuke. Usually with cats and dogs we know who the mother

ABCDEFGHIJKLMN
OPQRSTUVWXYZ
abcdefghijklmnop
qrstuvwxyz
1234567890&$¢£¥
fiflœœÆŒÅßÇÌÎÍÏĩ
§†––——/()'""",:;.,!¡?¿

10/11

In our house we had a cat with the grandiose name of Gonnosuke. Usually with cats and d ogs we know who the mother is but not the father. A cat with a large belly wondered into th e house of my younger sister and her husband and gave birth to five kittens. While the mot her was a pure white thoroughbred Chinchila, the kittens were black and white tabbies of mixed breed. One of these came to our house about two weeks after its birth and was given the name Gonnosuke. At that time we already had one female Shiba dog and one female br

16/17

In our house we had a cat with the grandiose name of Go nnosuke. Usually with cats and dogs we know who the m other is but not the father. A cat with a large belly wonde red into the house of my younger sister and her husban

24/25

In our house we had a cat with the gr andiose name of Gonnosuke. Usually with cats and dogs we know who the

ABCDEFGHIJKLM
NOPQRSTUVWXYZ
abcdefghijklmnopq
rstuvwxyz
1234567890&$¢£¥
fiflæœÆŒÅßÇÌÎÍÏã§†
-–——/()''""":;.,!¡?¿

10/11

In our house we had a cat with the grandiose name of Gonnosuke. Usually with cats and dogs we know who the mother is but not the father. A cat with a large belly wondered into the house of my younger sister and her hus band and gave birth to five kittens. While the mother was a pure white thoroughbred Chinchila, the kittens we re black and white tabbies of mixed breed. One of these came to our house about two weeks after its birth and was given the name Gonnosuke. At that time we already had one female Shiba dog and one female brown tabby cat in our house comprising only 13 thubo. The dog was called Momo and the cat Mii. My wife, who was very

16/17

In our house we had a cat with the grandiose name of Gonnosuke. Us ually with cats and dogs we know who the mother is but not the fathe r. A cat with a large belly wondered into the house of my younger sist er and her husband and gave birth to five kittens. While the mother

24/25

In our house we had a cat with the grandiose name of Gonnosuke. Usually with cats and do gs we know who the mother is but not the fath

ABCDEFGHIJKLMN
OPQRSTUVWXYZ
abcdefghijklmnopq
rstuvwxyz
1234567890&$¢£¥
fiflœœÆŒÅßÇÌÎÍÏã§†
--—––/()''""";.,!¡?¿

10/11

In our house we had a cat with the grandiose name of Gonnosuke. Usually with cats and dogs we know who the mo ther is but not the father. A cat with a large belly wondered into the house of my younger sister and her husband an d gave birth to five kittens. While the mother was a pure white thoroughbred Chinchila, the kittens were black and white tabbies of mixed breed. One of these came to our house about two weeks after its birth and was given the name Gonnosuke. At that time we already had one female Shiba dog and one female brown tabby cat in our house compr ising only 13 thubo. The dog was called Momo and the cat Mii. My wife, who was very much opposed to kee

16/17

In our house we had a cat with the grandiose name of Gonnosuke. Usua lly with cats and dogs we know who the mother is but not the father. A c at with a large belly wondered into the house of my younger sister and her husband and gave birth to five kittens. While the mother was a pure

24/25

In our house we had a cat with the grandiose n ame of Gonnosuke. Usually with cats and dogs we know who the mother is but not the father. A

De Vinne/Text 8-pt. Master, Industrial 731

De Vinne/Text 8-pt.

Bitstream

ABCDEFGHIJKLM
NOPQRSTUVWXYZ
abcdefghijklmnopq
rstuvwxyz
1234567890&$¢£¥
fiflæœÆŒÅßÇÌÎÍÏã§†
-–—/()''""::;.,!¡?¿

10/11

In our house we had a cat with the grandiose name of Gonnosuke. Usually with cats and dogs we know who the mother is but not the father. A cat with a large belly wondered into the house of my younger sister and her hus band and gave birth to five kittens. While the mother was a pure white thoroughbred Chinchila, the kittens wer e black and white tabbies of mixed breed. One of these came to our house about two weeks after its birth and w as given the name Gonnosuke. At that time we already had one female Shiba dog and one female brown tabby cat in our house comprising only 13 thubo. The dog was called Momo and the cat Mii. My wife, who was very m

16/17

In our house we had a cat with the grandiose name of Gonnosuke. Us ually with cats and dogs we know who the mother is but not the fathe r. A cat with a large belly wondered into the house of my younger sist er and her husband and gave birth to five kittens. While the mother

24/25

In our house we had a cat with the grandiose name of Gonnosuke. Usually with cats and do gs we know who the mother is but not the fath

ABCDEFGHIJKLM
NOPQRSTUVWXYZ
abcdefghijklmnopq
rstuvwxyz
1234567890&$¢£¥
fiflœœÆŒÅßÇÌÎÍÏã§†
———/()''""".;.,!¡?¿

10/11

*In our house we had a cat with the grandiose name of Gonnosuke. Usually with cats and dogs we know who the mo
ther is but not the father. A cat with a large belly wondered into the house of my younger sister and her husband an
d gave birth to five kittens. While the mother was a pure white thoroughbred Chinchila, the kittens were black and
white tabbies of mixed breed. One of these came to our house about two weeks after its birth and was given the nam
e Gonnosuke. At that time we already had one female Shiba dog and one female brown tabby cat in our house comp
rising only 13 thubo. The dog was called Momo and the cat Mii. My wife, who was very much opposed to keeping*

16/17

*In our house we had a cat with the grandiose name of Gonnosuke. Usua
lly with cats and dogs we know who the mother is but not the father. A c
at with a large belly wondered into the house of my younger sister and
her husband and gave birth to five kittens. While the mother was a pure*

24/25

*In our house we had a cat with the grandiose n
ame of Gonnosuke. Usually with cats and dogs
we know who the mother is but not the father. A*

ABCDEFGHIJKLMN
OPQRSTUVWXYZ
abcdefghijklmnopq
rstuvwxyz
1234567890&$¢£¥
fiflæœÆŒÅßÇÌÎÍÏã§†
-——/()''""":;.,!¡?¿

10/11

In our house we had a cat with the grandiose name of Gonnosuke. Usually with cats and dogs we know who the mother is but not the father. A cat with a large belly wondered into the house of my younger sister and her husba nd and gave birth to five kittens. While the mother was a pure white thoroughbred Chinchila, the kittens were bla ck and white tabbies of mixed breed. One of these came to our house about two weeks after its birth and was give n the name Gonnosuke. At that time we already had one female Shiba dog and one female brown tabby cat in our house comprising only 13 tubo. The dog was called Momo and the cat Mii. My wife, who was very much opposed

16/17

In our house we had a cat with the grandiose name of Gonnosuke. Usu ally with cats and dogs we know who the mother is but not the father. A cat with a large belly wondered into the house of my younger sister a nd her husband and gave birth to five kittens. While the mother was a

24/25

In our house we had a cat with the grandiose n ame of Gonnosuke. Usually with cats and dogs we know who the mother is but not the father.

401

ABCDEFGHIJKLMN
OPQRSTUVWXYZ
abcdefghijklmnopq
rstuvwxyz
1234567890&$¢£¥
fiflæœÆŒÅßÇÌÎÍÏã§†
-——/()''""".;.,!¡?¿

10/11

In our house we had a cat with the grandiose name of Gonnosuke. Usually with cats and dogs we know who the mother is but not the father. A cat with a large belly wondered into the house of my younger sister and her husband and gave birt h to five kittens. While the mother was a pure white thoroughbred Chinchila, the kittens were black and white tabbies of mixed breed. One of these came to our house about two weeks after its birth and was given the name Gonnosuke. At that time we already had one female Shiba dog and one female brown tabby cat in our house comprising only 13 tubo. The d og was called Momo and the cat Mii. My wife, who was very much opposed to keeping cats and dogs, instantaneously fell

16/17

In our house we had a cat with the grandiose name of Gonnosuke. Usually with cats and dogs we know who the mother is but not the father. A cat wit h a large belly wondered into the house of my younger sister and her husban d and gave birth to five kittens. While the mother was a pure white thoroug

24/25

In our house we had a cat with the grandiose nam e of Gonnosuke. Usually with cats and dogs we kn ow who the mother is but not the father. A cat wit

ABCDEFGHIJKLMNOPQ
RSTUVWXYZ
abcdefghijklmnopq
rstuvwxyz
1234567890&$¢£¥
fiflæœÆŒÅßÇÌÎÍÏã§†
———/()''""":;.,!¡?¿

10/11

In our house we had a cat with the grandiose name of Gonnosuke. Usually with cats and dogs we know who the mother is but not the father. A cat with a large belly wondered into the house of my younger sister and her husband and gave birth to five kittens. While the mother was a pure white thoroughbred Chinchila, the kittens were black and white tabbies of mixed breed. One of these came to our house about two weeks after its birth and was given the name Gonnosuke. At that time we already had one female Shiba dog and one female brown tabby cat in our house comprising only 13 tubo. The dog was called Momo and the cat Mii. My wife, who was very much opposed to keeping cats and dogs, instantaneou

16/17

In our house we had a cat with the grandiose name of Gonnosuke. Usually with cats and dogs we know who the mother is but not the father. A cat with a large belly wondered into the house of my younger sister and her husband and gave birth to five kittens. While the mother was a pure white thor

24/25

In our house we had a cat with the grandiose name of Gonnosuke. Usually with cats and dogs we know who the mother is but not the father. A cat

ABCDEFGHIJKLMNOP
QRSTUVWXYZ
abcdefghijklmnopq
rstuvwxyz
1234567890&$¢£¥
fiflæœÆŒÅßÇÌÎÍÏã§†
———/()''""":;.,!¡?¿

10/11

In our house we had a cat with the grandiose name of Gonnosuke. Usually with cats and dogs we know who the mother is but not the father. A cat with a large belly wondered into the house of my younger sister and her husband and gave birth to five kittens. While the mother was a pure white thoroughbred Chinchila, the kittens were black and white tabbies of mixed breed. One of these came to our house about two weeks after its birth and was given the name Gonnosuke. At that time we already had one female Shiba dog and one female brown tabby cat in our house comprising only 13 tubo. The dog was called Momo and the cat Mii. My wife, who was very much opposed to keeping cats and dogs, in

16/17

In our house we had a cat with the grandiose name of Gonnosuke. Usually with cats and dogs we know who the mother is but not the father. A cat with a large belly wondered into the house of my younger sister and her husband and gave birth to five kittens. While the mother was a pure white

24/25

In our house we had a cat with the grandiose name of Gonnosuke. Usually with cats and dogs we know who the mother is but not the father. A cat

ABCDEFGHIJKLMNOP
QRSTUVWXYZ
abcdefghijklmnopq
rstuvwxyz
1234567890&$¢£¥
fiflæœÆŒÅßÇÌÎÍÏ㧆
-–—/()''""::,.,!¡?¿

10/11

In our house we had a cat with the grandiose name of Gonnosuke. Usually with cats and dogs we know who t he mother is but not the father. A cat with a large belly wondered into the house of my younger sister and he r husband and gave birth to five kittens. While the mother was a pure white thoroughbred Chinchila, the kitt ens were black and white tabbies of mixed breed. One of these came to our house about two weeks after its birth and was given the name Gonnosuke. At that time we already had one female Shiba dog and one female brown tabby cat in our house comprising only 13 tubo. The dog was called Momo and the cat Mii. My wife, w

16/17

In our house we had a cat with the grandiose name of Gonnosuke. U sually with cats and dogs we know who the mother is but not the fa ther. A cat with a large belly wondered into the house of my younge r sister and her husband and gave birth to five kittens. While the m

24/25

In our house we had a cat with the grandiose name of Gonnosuke. Usually with cats and do gs we know who the mother is but not the fat

ABCDEFGHIJKLMNOP
QRSTUVWXYZ
abcdefghijklmnopq
rstuvwxyz
1234567890&$¢£¥
fiflæœÆŒÅßÇÌÎÍÏïã§†
–——/()''""";.,!¡?¿

10/11

In our house we had a cat with the grandiose name of Gonnosuke. Usually with cats and dogs we know who t he mother is but not the father. A cat with a large belly wondered into the house of my younger sister and her husband and gave birth to five kittens. While the mother was a pure white thoroughbred Chinchila, the kitten s were black and white tabbies of mixed breed. One of these came to our house about two weeks after its birt h and was given the name Gonnosuke. At that time we already had one female Shiba dog and one female bro wn tabby cat in our house comprising only 13 tubo. The dog was called Momo and the cat Mii. My wife, who

16/17

In our house we had a cat with the grandiose name of Gonnosuke. U sually with cats and dogs we know who the mother is but not the fat her. A cat with a large belly wondered into the house of my younger sister and her husband and gave birth to five kittens. While the mot

24/25

In our house we had a cat with the grandiose name of Gonnosuke. Usually with cats and do gs we know who the mother is but not the fat

ABCDEFGHIJKLMN
OPQRSTUVWXYZ
abcdefghijklmnopq
rstuvwxyz
1234567890&$¢£¥
fiflæœÆŒÅßÇÌÎÍÏïã§
†-–—/()''""":;.,!¡?¿

10/11

In our house we had a cat with the grandiose name of Gonnosuke. Usually with cats and dogs we k now who the mother is but not the father. A cat with a large belly wondered into the house of my y ounger sister and her husband and gave birth to five kittens. While the mother was a pure white t horoughbred Chinchila, the kittens were black and white tabbies of mixed breed. One of these cam e to our house about two weeks after its birth and was given the name Gonnosuke. At that time we already had one female Shiba dog and one female brown tabby cat in our house comprising only 13

16/17

In our house we had a cat with the grandiose name of Gonnos uke. Usually with cats and dogs we know who the mother is b ut not the father. A cat with a large belly wondered into the h ouse of my younger sister and her husband and gave birth to

24/25

In our house we had a cat with the grand iose name of Gonnosuke. Usually with ca ts and dogs we know who the mother is

ABCDEFGHIJKLMN
OPQRSTUVWXYZ
abcdefghijklmnopq
rstuvwxyz
1234567890&$¢£¥
fiflæœÆŒÅßÇÌÎÍÏã§
†-–—/()''""";:.,!¡?¿

10/11

In our house we had a cat with the grandiose name of Gonnosuke. Usually with cats and dogs w e know who the mother is but not the father. A cat with a large belly wondered into the house o f my younger sister and her husband and gave birth to five kittens. While the mother was a pur e white thoroughbred Chinchila, the kittens were black and white tabbies of mixed breed. One o f these came to our house about two weeks after its birth and was given the name Gonnosuke. A t that time we already had one female Shiba dog and one female brown tabby cat in our house

16/17

In our house we had a cat with the grandiose name of Gonn osuke. Usually with cats and dogs we know who the mother is but not the father. A cat with a large belly wondered into the house of my younger sister and her husband and gave b

24/25

In our house we had a cat with the gra ndiose name of Gonnosuke. Usually wit h cats and dogs we know who the moth

ABCDEFGHIJKLM NOPQRSTUVWX YZabcdefghijklm nopqrstuvwxyz 1234567890& $¢£¥fiflæœÆŒ ÅßçÌÎÍÏÏ㧆 ——/()''""·;.,!¡?¿

10/11

In our house we had a cat with the grandiose name of Gonnosuke. Usually with cats and dogs we know who the mother is but not the father. A cat with a large belly won dered into the house of my younger sister and her husband and gave birth to five kit tens. While the mother was a pure white thoroughbred Chinchila, the kittens were bl ack and white tabbies of mixed breed. One of these came to our house about two we eks after its birth and was given the name Gonnosuke. At that time we already had

16/17

In our house we had a cat with the grandiose name o f Gonnosuke. Usually with cats and dogs we know wh o the mother is but not the father. A cat with a large belly wondered into the house of my younger sister a

24/25

In our house we had a cat with the grandiose name of Gonnosuke. Usu ally with cats and dogs we know w

ABCDEFGHIJKL
MNOPQRSTUVWX
YZabcdefghijklm
nopqrstuvwxyz
1234567890&
$¢£¥fiflæœÆŒ
ÅßÇÌÎÍÏã§†
———/()''""·;.,!¡?¿

10/11

In our house we had a cat with the grandiose name of Gonnosuke. Usually with cats and dogs we know who the mother is but not the father. A cat with a large belly won dered into the house of my younger sister and her husband and gave birth to five kit tens. While the mother was a pure white thoroughbred Chinchila, the kittens were bl ack and white tabbies of mixed breed. One of these came to our house about two we eks after its birth and was given the name Gonnosuke. At that time we already had

16/17

In our house we had a cat with the grandiose name o f Gonnosuke. Usually with cats and dogs we know wh o the mother is but not the father. A cat with a large belly wondered into the house of my younger sister a

24/25

In our house we had a cat with the grandiose name of Gonnosuke. Usu ally with cats and dogs we know w

ABCDEFGHIJKLMNO
PQRSTUVWXYZ
1234567890&$¢£¥
ÆŒÅÇÌÎÍÏ
-——/()''""";,.,¡!?¿

12
QUICK BROWN FOX JUMPS OVER THE LAZY DOG. QUICK BROWN FOX JUMPS OVER THE LAZY DOG. QUICK BROWN FOX JUMPS OVER THE LAZY DOG. QUICK B

18
QUICK BROWN FOX JUMPS OVER THE LAZY DOG. QUICK BROWN FOX JUMPS OVER THE LAZY DOG. QUIC

24
QUICK BROWN FOX JUMPS OVER THE LAZY DOG. QUICK BROWN FOX JUMPS O

36
QUICK BROWN FOX JUMPS OVER THE LAZY DOG. Q

48
QUICK BROWN FOX JUMPS OVER THE

60
QUICK BROWN FOX JU MP S OV

ABCDEFGHIJKLMN
OPQRSTUVWXYZ
abcdefghijklmnopq
rstuvwxyz
1234567890&$¢£¥
fiflæœÆŒÅßÇÌÎÍÏã§
†-–——/()''""":;.,!¡?¿

10/11

In our house we had a cat with the grandiose name of Gonnosuke. Usually with cats and dogs we know who the mother is but not the father. A cat with a large belly wondered into the house of my younger sis ter and her husband and gave birth to five kittens. While the mother was a pure white thoroughbred Ch inchila, the kittens were black and white tabbies of mixed breed. One of these came to our house about two weeks after its birth and was given the name Gonnosuke. At that time we already had one female S hiba dog and one female brown tabby cat in our house comprising only 13 thubo. The dog was called M

16/17

In our house we had a cat with the grandiose name of Gonnosuk e. Usually with cats and dogs we know who the mother is but not the father. A cat with a large belly wondered into the house of m y younger sister and her husband and gave birth to five kittens.

24/25

In our house we had a cat with the grandio se name of Gonnosuke. Usually with cats a nd dogs we know who the mother is but no

ABCDEFGHIJKLMN
OPQRSTUVWXYZ
abcdefghijklmnopq
rstuvwxyz
1234567890&$¢£¥
fiflœœÆŒÅßÇÌÎÍÏã
§†--——/()''""";.,!¡?¿

10/11

In our house we had a cat with the grandiose name of Gonnosuke. Usually with cats and dogs we know who the mother is but not the father. A cat with a large belly wondered into the house of m y younger sister and her husband and gave birth to five kittens. While the mother was a pure wh ite thoroughbred Chinchila, the kittens were black and white tabbies of mixed breed. One of these came to our house about two weeks after its birth and was given the name Gonnosuke. At that ti me we already had one female Shiba dog and one female brown tabby cat in our house comprisi

16/17

In our house we had a cat with the grandiose name of Gonn osuke. Usually with cats and dogs we know who the mother is but not the father. A cat with a large belly wondered into the house of my younger sister and her husband and gave bi

24/25

In our house we had a cat with the gran diose name of Gonnosuke. Usually with cats and dogs we know who the mother

ABCDEFGHIJKLM
NOPQRSTUVWX
YZabcdefghijklmno
pqrstuvwxyz
1234567890&$¢£¥
fiflæœÆŒÅßÇÌÎÍÏã
§†-–—/()''""":;.,!¡?¿

10/11

In our house we had a cat with the grandiose name of Gonnosuke. Usually with cats and dogs w
e know who the mother is but not the father. A cat with a large belly wondered into the house of
my younger sister and her husband and gave birth to five kittens. While the mother was a pure
white thoroughbred Chinchila, the kittens were black and white tabbies of mixed breed. One of
these came to our house about two weeks after its birth and was given the name Gonnosuke. At
that time we already had one female Shiba dog and one female brown tabby cat in our house co

16/17

In our house we had a cat with the grandiose name of Gonno
suke. Usually with cats and dogs we know who the mother
is but not the father. A cat with a large belly wondered into
the house of my younger sister and her husband and gave bi

24/25

In our house we had a cat with the gran
diose name of Gonnosuke. Usually with
cats and dogs we know who the mother

ABCDEFGHIJK
LMNOPQRSTU
VWXYZabcdefg
hijklmnopqrstu
vwxyz12345678
90&$¢£¥fiflæœ
ÆŒÅßÇÌÎÍÏãã§†
–——/()''""•;.,!¡?¿

10/11

In our house we had a cat with the grandiose name of Gonnosuke. Usually wi
th cats and dogs we know who the mother is but not the father. A cat with a
large belly wondered into the house of my younger sister and her husband an
d gave birth to five kittens. While the mother was a pure white thoroughbred
Chinchila, the kittens were black and white tabbies of mixed breed. One of t
hese came to our house about two weeks after its birth and was given the na

16/17

In our house we had a cat with the grandiose na
me of Gonnosuke. Usually with cats and dogs we
know who the mother is but not the father. A ca
t with a large belly wondered into the house of

24/25

In our house we had a cat with t
he grandiose name of Gonnosuk
e. Usually with cats and dogs we

ABCDEFGHIJKLMN
OPQRSTUVWXYZ
abcdefghijklmnopq
rstuvwxyz
1234567890&$¢£¥
fiflæœÆŒÅßÇÌÎÍÏã§
†-–—/()''""":;.,!¡?¿

10/11

In our house we had a cat with the grandiose name of Gonnosuke. Usually with cats and dogs we know who the mother is but not the father. A cat with a large belly wondered into the house of my younger sister and her husband and gave birth to five kittens. While the mother was a pure white thoroughbred Chinchila, the kittens were black and white tabbies of mi xed breed. One of these came to our house about two weeks after its birth and was given the name Gonnosuke. At that tim e we already had one female Shiba dog and one female brown tabby cat in our house comprising only 13 thubo. The dog w as called Momo and the cat Mii. My wife, who was very much opposed to keeping cats and dogs, instantaneously fell for it

16/17

In our house we had a cat with the grandiose name of Gonnosuke. Usually with cats and dogs we know who the mother is but not the father. A cat with a large belly wondered into the house of my younger sister and her husband and gave birth to five kittens. While the mother was a pure white thoroughb

24/25

In our house we had a cat with the grandiose nam e of Gonnosuke. Usually with cats and dogs we kn ow who the mother is but not the father. A cat with

ABCDEFGHIJKLMNO
PQRSTUVWXYZ
abcdefghijklmnopq
rstuvwxyz
1234567890&$¢£¥
fiflæœÆŒÅßçÌÎÍÏã§†
---—/()''""".;,.,!¡?¿

10/11

In our house we had a cat with the grandiose name of Gonnosuke. Usually with cats and dogs we know who t he mother is but not the father. A cat with a large belly wondered into the house of my younger sister and her husband and gave birth to five kittens. While the mother was a pure white thoroughbred Chinchila, the kitte ns were black and white tabbies of mixed breed. One of these came to our house about two weeks after its bi rth and was given the name Gonnosuke. At that time we already had one female Shiba dog and one female br own tabby cat in our house comprising only 13 thubo. The dog was called Momo and the cat Mii. My wife, who

16/17

In our house we had a cat with the grandiose name of Gonnosuke. U sually with cats and dogs we know who the mother is but not the fat her. A cat with a large belly wondered into the house of my younger sister and her husband and gave birth to five kittens. While the mot

24/25

In our house we had a cat with the grandiose name of Gonnosuke. Usually with cats and do gs we know who the mother is but not the fat

ABCDEFGHIJ
KLMNOPQRST
UVWXYZabcdef
ghijklmnopqrstu
vwxyz1234567
890&$¢£¥fifl æ
œÆŒÅßÇÌÎÍÏã§
✠----——/0''""‹›.,!¡?¿

10/11

In our house we had a cat with the grandiose name of Gonnosuke. Usually with
cats and dogs we know who the mother is but not the father. A cat with a large b
elly wondered into the house of my younger sister and her husband and gave bir
th to five kittens. While the mother was a pure white thoroughbred Chinchila, th
e kittens were black and white tabbies of mixed breed. One of these came to our
house about two weeks after its birth and was given the name Gonnosuke. At tha

16/17

In our house we had a cat with the grandiose nam
e of Gonnosuke. Usually with cats and dogs we kn
ow who the mother is but not the father. A cat wit
h a large belly wondered into the house of my you

24/25

In our house we had a cat with t
he grandiose name of Gonnosuke.
Usually with cats and dogs we kn

Normande Italic

ABCDEFGHIJK
LMNOPQRSTU
VWXYZabcdefg
hijklmnopqrstuv
wxyz12345678
90&$¢£¥fiflœœ
ÆŒÅßçÌÎÍÏã§†
––—/()''""";.,!¡?¿

10/11

In our house we had a cat with the grandiose name of Gonnosuke. Usually with c ats and dogs we know who the mother is but not the father. A cat with a large bell y wondered into the house of my younger sister and her husband and gave birth t o five kittens. While the mother was a pure white thoroughbred Chinchila, the kitt ens were black and white tabbies of mixed breed. One of these came to our house about two weeks after its birth and was given the name Gonnosuke. At that time

16/17

In our house we had a cat with the grandiose nam e of Gonnosuke. Usually with cats and dogs we kno w who the mother is but not the father. A cat with a large belly wondered into the house of my younger

24/25

In our house we had a cat with th e grandiose name of Gonnosuke. Usually with cats and dogs we kn

ABCDEFGHIJKLMN
OPQRSTUVWXYZ
abcdefghijklmnopq
rstuvwxyz
1234567890&$¢£¥
fiflæœÆŒÅßÇÌÎÍÏã§
†-–——/()''""":;.,!¡?¿

10/11

In our house we had a cat with the grandiose name of Gonnosuke. Usually with cats and dogs we know who the mother is but not the father. A cat with a large belly wondered into the house of my younger sister and her husband and gave birth to five kittens. While the mother was a pure white thoroughbred Chinchila, the kittens were black and white tabbies of mixed breed. One of these came to our house about two weeks after its birth and was given the name Gonnosuke. At that time we already had one female Shiba dog and one female brown tabby cat in our house comprising only 13 thubo. The dog wa

16/17

In our house we had a cat with the grandiose name of Gonnosu ke. Usually with cats and dogs we know who the mother is but not the father. A cat with a large belly wondered into the house of my younger sister and her husband and gave birth to five kitt

24/25

In our house we had a cat with the grandi ose name of Gonnosuke. Usually with cats and dogs we know who the mother is but

ABCDEFGHIJKLMN
OPQRSTUVWXYZ
abcdefghijklmnopq
rstuvwxyz
1234567890&$¢£¥
fiflæœÆŒÅßÇÌÎÍÏã§†
--——/()''""".;.,!¡?¿

10/11

In our house we had a cat with the grandiose name of Gonnosuke. Usually with cats and dogs we kno
w who the mother is but not the father. A cat with a large belly wondered into the house of my younge
r sister and her husband and gave birth to five kittens. While the mother was a pure white thoroughb
red Chinchila, the kittens were black and white tabbies of mixed breed. One of these came to our hous
e about two weeks after its birth and was given the name Gonnosuke. At that time we already had on
e female Shiba dog and one female brown tabby cat in our house comprising only 13 thubo. The dog

16/17

In our house we had a cat with the grandiose name of Gonnosu
ke. Usually with cats and dogs we know who the mother is but
not the father. A cat with a large belly wondered into the house
of my younger sister and her husband and gave birth to five kit

24/25

In our house we had a cat with the grandi
ose name of Gonnosuke. Usually with cats
and dogs we know who the mother is but

ABCDEFGHIJKL
MNOPQRSTUVW
XYZabcdefghijklm
nopqrstuvwxyz
1234567890&$¢£¥
fiflæœÆŒÅßÇÌÎÍÏã
§†-–—/()''""".;.,!¡?¿

10/11

In our house we had a cat with the grandiose name of Gonnosuke. Usually with cats and dogs we know who the mother is but not the father. A cat with a large belly wondered into the house of m y younger sister and her husband and gave birth to five kittens. While the mother was a pure wh ite thoroughbred Chinchila, the kittens were black and white tabbies of mixed breed. One of thes e came to our house about two weeks after its birth and was given the name Gonnosuke. At that time we already had one female Shiba dog and one female brown tabby cat in our house compris

16/17

In our house we had a cat with the grandiose name of Gonn osuke. Usually with cats and dogs we know who the mother is but not the father. A cat with a large belly wondered into t he house of my younger sister and her husband and gave bir

24/25

In our house we had a cat with the gran diose name of Gonnosuke. Usually with cats and dogs we know who the mother

ABCDEFGHIJKLM
NOPQRSTUVWXYZ
abcdefghijklmnopq
rstuvwxyz
1234567890&$¢£¥
fiflœœÆŒÅßÇÌÎÍÏã
§†-——/()''""‚;.,!¡?¿

10/11

In our house we had a cat with the grandiose name of Gonnosuke. Usually with cats and dogs we kn ow who the mother is but not the father. A cat with a large belly wondered into the house of my youn ger sister and her husband and gave birth to five kittens. While the mother was a pure white thoroug hbred Chinchila, the kittens were black and white tabbies of mixed breed. One of these came to our h ouse about two weeks after its birth and was given the name Gonnosuke. At that time we already ha d one female Shiba dog and one female brown tabby cat in our house comprising only 13 tubo. The d

16/17

In our house we had a cat with the grandiose name of Gonnos uke. Usually with cats and dogs we know who the mother is b ut not the father. A cat with a large belly wondered into the ho use of my younger sister and her husband and gave birth to fiv

24/25

In our house we had a cat with the grandi ose name of Gonnosuke. Usually with cat s and dogs we know who the mother is bu

ABCDEFGHIJKL
MNOPQRSTUVW
XYZabcdefghijklm
nopqrstuvwxyz
1234567890&
$¢£¥fiflæœÆŒ
ÅßçÌÎÍÏã§†
——/()'"""·;.,!¡?¿

10/11

In our house we had a cat with the grandiose name of Gonnosuke. Usually with cats and dogs we know who the mother is but not the father. A cat with a large belly wondered into the house of m y younger sister and her husband and gave birth to five kittens. While the mother was a pure wh ite thoroughbred Chinchila, the kittens were black and white tabbies of mixed breed. One of the se came to our house about two weeks after its birth and was given the name Gonnosuke. At that time we already had one female Shiba dog and one female brown tabby cat in our house comprisi

16/17

In our house we had a cat with the grandiose name of Gonno suke. Usually with cats and dogs we know who the mother is but not the father. A cat with a large belly wondered into the house of my younger sister and her husband and gave birth

24/25

In our house we had a cat with the gran diose name of Gonnosuke. Usually with cats and dogs we know who the mother

ABCDEFGHIJKLMNO
PQRSTUVWXYZ
abcdefghijklmnopq
rstuvwxyz
1234567890&$¢£¥
fiflæœÆŒÅßÇÌÎÍÏã§†
-–—/()''""::;.,!¡?¿

10/11

In our house we had a cat with the grandiose name of Gonnosuke. Usually with cats and dogs we know who the moth er is but not the father. A cat with a large belly wondered into the house of my younger sister and her husband and g ave birth to five kittens. While the mother was a pure white thoroughbred Chinchila, the kittens were black and whit e tabbies of mixed breed. One of these came to our house about two weeks after its birth and was given the name Go nnosuke. At that time we already had one female Shiba dog and one female brown tabby cat in our house comprising only 13 tubo. The dog was called Momo and the cat Mii. My wife, who was very much opposed to keeping cats and do

16/17

In our house we had a cat with the grandiose name of Gonnosuke. Usuall y with cats and dogs we know who the mother is but not the father. A cat with a large belly wondered into the house of my younger sister and her husband and gave birth to five kittens. While the mother was a pure whit

24/25

In our house we had a cat with the grandiose na me of Gonnosuke. Usually with cats and dogs we know who the mother is but not the father. A cat

ABCDEFGHIJKLMNO
PQRSTUVWXYZ
abcdefghijklmnopq
rstuvwxyz
1234567890&$¢£¥
fiflœœÆŒÅßÇÌÎÍÏã§†
———/()''""·,·.,!¡?¿

10/11

In our house we had a cat with the grandiose name of Gonnosuke. Usually with cats and dogs we know who the m other is but not the father. A cat with a large belly wondered into the house of my younger sister and her husband and gave birth to five kittens. While the mother was a pure white thoroughbred Chinchila, the kittens were black and white tabbies of mixed breed. One of these came to our house about two weeks after its birth and was given th e name Gonnosuke. At that time we already had one female Shiba dog and one female brown tabby cat in our hous e comprising only 13 tubo. The dog was called Momo and the cat Mii. My wife, who was very much opposed to kee

16/17

In our house we had a cat with the grandiose name of Gonnosuke. Usu ally with cats and dogs we know who the mother is but not the father. A cat with a large belly wondered into the house of my younger sister an d her husband and gave birth to five kittens. While the mother was a p

24/25

In our house we had a cat with the grandiose n ame of Gonnosuke. Usually with cats and dogs we know who the mother is but not the father. A

ABCDEFGHIJKLMN
OPQRSTUVWXYZ
abcdefghijklmnopq
rstuvwxyz
1234567890&.$¢£¥
fiflæœÆŒÅßÇÌÎÍÏã§
†-–—/()''""":;.,!¡?¿

10/11

In our house we had a cat with the grandiose name of Gonnosuke. Usually with cats and dogs we know who the mother is but not the father. A cat with a large belly wondered into the house of my younger sis ter and her husband and gave birth to five kittens. While the mother was a pure white thoroughbred Ch inchila, the kittens were black and white tabbies of mixed breed. One of these came to our house about two weeks after its birth and was given the name Gonnosuke. At that time we already had one female Sh iba dog and one female brown tabby cat in our house comprising only 13 tubo. The dog was called Mo

16/17

In our house we had a cat with the grandiose name of Gonnosuk e. Usually with cats and dogs we know who the mother is but not the father. A cat with a large belly wondered into the house of my younger sister and her husband and gave birth to five kittens. W

24/25

In our house we had a cat with the grandio se name of Gonnosuke. Usually with cats a nd dogs we know who the mother is but n

ABCDEFGHIJKLMN
OPQRSTUVWXYZ
abcdefghijklmnopq
rstuvwxyz
1234567890&$¢£¥
fiflæœÆŒÅßÇÌÎÍÏã§†
-–——/()''""":;.,!¡?¿

10/11

In our house we had a cat with the grandiose name of Gonnosuke. Usually with cats and dogs we know wh o the mother is but not the father. A cat with a large belly wondered into the house of my younger sister an d her husband and gave birth to five kittens. While the mother was a pure white thoroughbred Chinchila, t he kittens were black and white tabbies of mixed breed. One of these came to our house about two weeks after its birth and was given the name Gonnosuke. At that time we already had one female Shiba dog and o ne female brown tabby cat in our house comprising only 13 tubo. The dog was called Momo and the cat

16/17

In our house we had a cat with the grandiose name of Gonnosuke. Usually with cats and dogs we know who the mother is but not the father. A cat with a large belly wondered into the house of my you nger sister and her husband and gave birth to five kittens. While t

24/25

In our house we had a cat with the grandios e name of Gonnosuke. Usually with cats an d dogs we know who the mother is but not

ABCDEFGHIJKLMN
OPQRSTUVWXYZ
abcdefghijklmnopq
rstuvwxyz
1234567890&$¢£¥
fiflæœÆŒÅßÇÌÎÍÏïã§
†-–—/()''""":;.,!¡?¿

10/11

In our house we had a cat with the grandiose name of Gonnosuke. Usually with cats and dogs we kno
w who the mother is but not the father. A cat with a large belly wondered into the house of my young
er sister and her husband and gave birth to five kittens. While the mother was a pure white thorough
bred Chinchila, the kittens were black and white tabbies of mixed breed. One of these came to ourho
use about two weeks after its birth and was given the name Gonnosuke. At that time we already had o
ne female Shiba dog and one female brown tabby cat in our house comprising only 13 tubo. The dog

16/17

In our house we had a cat with the grandiose name of Gonnos
uke. Usually with cats and dogs we know who the mother is bu
t not the father. A cat with a large belly wondered into the hous
e of my younger sister and her husband and gave birth to five k

24/25

In our house we had a cat with the grandi
ose name of Gonnosuke. Usually with cats
and dogs we know who the mother is but

ABCDEFGHIJKLMN
OPQRSTUVWXYZ
abcdefghijklmnopq
rstuvwxyz
1234567890&$¢£¥
fiflæœÆŒÅßÇÌÎÍÏã§†
---—/()''""':;.,!¡?¿

10/11

In our house we had a cat with the grandiose name of Gonnosuke. Usually with cats and dogs we know who the mother is but not the father. A cat with a large belly wondered into the house of my younger si ster and her husband and gave birth to five kittens. While the mother was a pure white thoroughbred C hinchila, the kittens were black and white tabbies of mixed breed. One of these came to our house abo ut two weeks after its birth and was given the name Gonnosuke. At that time we already had one female Shiba dog and one female brown tabby cat in our house comprising only 13 tubo. The dog was called

16/17

In our house we had a cat with the grandiose name of Gonnosu ke. Usually with cats and dogs we know who the mother is but n ot the father. A cat with a large belly wondered into the house of my younger sister and her husband and gave birth to five kittens

24/25

In our house we had a cat with the grandio se name of Gonnosuke. Usually with cats a nd dogs we know who the mother is but n

ITC Zapf Book Demi

ABCDEFGHIJKLMN
OPQRSTUVWXYZ
abcdefghijklmnopq
rstuvwxyz
1234567890&$¢£¥
fiflæœÆŒÅßÇÌÎÍÏã
§†-–—/()''""";,.,!¡?¿

10/11

In our house we had a cat with the grandiose name of Gonnosuke. Usually with cats and dogs we know who the mother is but not the father. A cat with a large belly wondered into the house of my younger sister and her husband and gave birth to five kittens. While the mother was a pu re white thoroughbred Chinchila, the kittens were black and white tabbies of mixed breed. On e of these came to our house about two weeks after its birth and was given the name Gonnosuk e. At that time we already had one female Shiba dog and one female brown tabby cat in our ho

16/17

In our house we had a cat with the grandiose name of Gon nosuke. Usually with cats and dogs we know who the moth er is but not the father. A cat with a large belly wondered in to the house of my younger sister and her husband and gav

24/25

In our house we had a cat with the gra ndiose name of Gonnosuke. Usually wit h cats and dogs we know who the moth

ABCDEFGHIJKLMN
OPQRSTUVWXYZ
abcdefghijklmnopq
rstuvwxyz
1234567890&$¢£¥
fiflæœÆŒÅßÇÌÎÍÏã§
†-–—/()''""':;.,!¡?¿

10/11

In our house we had a cat with the grandiose name of Gonnosuke. Usually with cats and dogs we know who the mother is but not the father. A cat with a large belly wondered into the house of my younger sister and her husband and gave birth to five kittens. While the mother was a pure white t horoughbred Chinchila, the kittens were black and white tabbies of mixed breed. One of these ca me to our house about two weeks after its birth and was given the name Gonnosuke. At that time we already had one female Shiba dog and one female brown tabby cat in our house comprising o

16/17

In our house we had a cat with the grandiose name of Gonno suke. Usually with cats and dogs we know who the mother is but not the father. A cat with a large belly wondered into the house of my younger sister and her husband and gave birth t

24/25

In our house we had a cat with the gran diose name of Gonnosuke. Usually with cats and dogs we know who the mother

ABCDEFGHIJKLM
NOPQRSTUVWXY
Zabcdefghijklmno
pqrstuvwxyz
1234567890&
$¢£¥fififlæœÆŒ
Åßçìîíïãã§†
———/()''""";;.,!¡?¿

10/11

In our house we had a cat with the grandiose name of Gonnosuke. Usually with cats and do
gs we know who the mother is but not the father. A cat with a large belly wondered into the
house of my younger sister and her husband and gave birth to five kittens. While the mother
was a pure white thoroughbred Chinchila, the kittens were black and white tabbies of mixe
d breed. One of these came to our house about two weeks after its birth and was given the
name Gonnosuke. At that time we already had one female Shiba dog and one female brown

16/17

In our house we had a cat with the grandiose name of Go
nnosuke. Usually with cats and dogs we know who the m
other is but not the father. A cat with a large belly wonde
red into the house of my younger sister and her husband

24/25

In our house we had a cat with the gr
andiose name of Gonnosuke. Usually
with cats and dogs we know who the

ABCDEFGHIJKLM
NOPQRSTUVWXY
Zabcdefghijklmn
opqrstuvwxyz
1234567890&
$¢£¥fiflæœÆŒ
ÅßçÌÎÍÏã§†
——/()''""";.,!¡?¿

10/11

In our house we had a cat with the grandiose name of Gonnosuke. Usually with cats and dog
s we know who the mother is but not the father. A cat with a large belly wondered into the ho
use of my younger sister and her husband and gave birth to five kittens. While the mother wa
s a pure white thoroughbred Chinchila, the kittens were black and white tabbies of mixed br
eed. One of these came to our house about two weeks after its birth and was given the name
Gonnosuke. At that time we already had one female Shiba dog and one female brown tabby

16/17

In our house we had a cat with the grandiose name of Go
nnosuke. Usually with cats and dogs we know who the mo
ther is but not the father. A cat with a large belly wondere
d into the house of my younger sister and her husband an

24/25

In our house we had a cat with the gr
andiose name of Gonnosuke. Usually
with cats and dogs we know who the

ABCDEFGHIJKLM
NOPQRSTUVWXYZ
abcdefghijklmnopq
rstuvwxyz
1234567890&
$¢£¥fiflæœÆŒ
ÅßÇÌÎÍÏã§†
———/()' ' " ":;.,!¡?¿

10/11

In our house we had a cat with the grandiose name of Gonnosuke. Usually with cats and dogs we know who the mother is but not the father. A cat with a large belly wondered into the hous e of my younger sister and her husband and gave birth to five kittens. While the mother was a pure white thoroughbred Chinchila, the kittens were black and white tabbies of mixed breed. O ne of these came to our house about two weeks after its birth and was given the name Gonnos uke. At that time we already had one female Shiba dog and one female brown tabby cat in our

16/17

In our house we had a cat with the grandiose name of Gon nosuke. Usually with cats and dogs we know who the moth er is but not the father. A cat with a large belly wondered i nto the house of my younger sister and her husband and g

24/25

In our house we had a cat with the gra ndiose name of Gonnosuke. Usually wit h cats and dogs we know who the moth

ABCDEFGHIJKLM
NOPQRSTUVWXYZ
abcdefghijklmnopq
rstuvwxyz
1234567890&
$¢£¥fiflæœÆŒ
ÅßÇÌÎÍÏã§†
-–—/()''""::;.,!¡?¿

10/11

In our house we had a cat with the grandiose name of Gonnosuke. Usually with cats and do
gs we know who the mother is but not the father. A cat with a large belly wondered into the
house of my younger sister and her husband and gave birth to five kittens. While the mothe
r was a pure white thoroughbred Chinchila, the kittens were black and white tabbies of mix
ed breed. One of these came to our house about two weeks after its birth and was given the
name Gonnosuke. At that time we already had one female Shiba dog and one female brown

16/17

In our house we had a cat with the grandiose name of Go
nnosuke. Usually with cats and dogs we know who the m
other is but not the father. A cat with a large belly wonde
red into the house of my younger sister and her husband

24/25

In our house we had a cat with the gr
andiose name of Gonnosuke. Usually
with cats and dogs we know who the

ABCDEFGHIJKL
MNOPQRSTUVW
XYZabcdefghijkl
mnopqrstuvwxyz
1234567890&
$¢£¥fiflæœÆŒ
ÅßçÌÎÍÏã§†
——/()''""":;.,!¡?¿

10/11

In our house we had a cat with the grandiose name of Gonnosuke. Usually with cat
s and dogs we know who the mother is but not the father. A cat with a large belly w
ondered into the house of my younger sister and her husband and gave birth to five
kittens. While the mother was a pure white thoroughbred Chinchila, the kittens we
re black and white tabbies of mixed breed. One of these came to our house about tw
o weeks after its birth and was given the name Gonnosuke. At that time we already

16/17

In our house we had a cat with the grandiose name
of Gonnosuke. Usually with cats and dogs we know
who the mother is but not the father. A cat with a l
arge belly wondered into the house of my younger si

24/25

In our house we had a cat with the
grandiose name of Gonnosuke. Usu
ally with cats and dogs we know w

ABCDEFGHIJKLMNO
PQRSTUVWXYZ
abcdefghijklmnopq
rstuvwxyz
1234567890&$¢£¥
fiflæœÆŒÅßÇÌÎÍÏã§†
-–—/()''""":;.,!¡?¿

10/11

In our house we had a cat with the grandiose name of Gonnosuke. Usually with cats and dogs we know who the mother is bu
t not the father. A cat with a large belly wondered into the house of my younger sister and her husband and gave birth to fiv
e kittens. While the mother was a pure white thoroughbred Chinchila, the kittens were black and white tabbies of mixed bre
ed. One of these came to our house about two weeks after its birth and was given the name Gonnosuke. At that time we alre
ady had one female Shiba dog and one female brown tabby cat in our house comprising only 13 tubo. The dog was called Mo
mo and the cat Mii. My wife, who was very much opposed to keeping cats and dogs, instantaneously fell for its shaggy appea

16/17

In our house we had a cat with the grandiose name of Gonnosuke. Usually wit
h cats and dogs we know who the mother is but not the father. A cat with a la
rge belly wondered into the house of my younger sister and her husband and
gave birth to five kittens. While the mother was a pure white thoroughbred C

24/25

In our house we had a cat with the grandiose name
of Gonnosuke. Usually with cats and dogs we know
who the mother is but not the father. A cat with a

ABCDEFGHIJKLMNO
PQRSTUVWXYZ
abcdefghijklmnopq
rstuvwxyz
1234567890&$¢£¥
fiflæœÆŒÅßÇÌÎÍÏã§
†-–—/()''""":;.,!¡?¿

10/11

In our house we had a cat with the grandiose name of Gonnosuke. Usually with cats and dogs we know who the moth er is but not the father. A cat with a large belly wondered into the house of my younger sister and her husband and g ave birth to five kittens. While the mother was a pure white thoroughbred Chinchila, the kittens were black and whit e tabbies of mixed breed. One of these came to our house about two weeks after its birth and was given the name Gon nosuke. At that time we already had one female Shiba dog and one female brown tabby cat in our house comprising only 13 tubo. The dog was called Momo and the cat Mii. My wife, who was very much opposed to keeping cats and dog

16/17

In our house we had a cat with the grandiose name of Gonnosuke. Usuall y with cats and dogs we know who the mother is but not the father. A ca t with a large belly wondered into the house of my younger sister and her husband and gave birth to five kittens. While the mother was a pure whi

24/25

In our house we had a cat with the grandiose na me of Gonnosuke. Usually with cats and dogs we know who the mother is but not the father. A ca

ABCDEFGHIJKLMN
OPQRSTUVWXYZ
abcdefghijklmnopq
rstuvwxyz
1234567890&$¢£¥
fiflæœÆŒÅßçÌÎÍÏã§
†-–—/()''""":;.,!¡?¿

10/11

In our house we had a cat with the grandiose name of Gonnosuke. Usually with cats and dogs we know who the moth er is but not the father. A cat with a large belly wondered into the house of my younger sister and her husband and g ave birth to five kittens. While the mother was a pure white thoroughbred Chinchila, the kittens were black and whi te tabbies of mixed breed. One of these came to our house about two weeks after its birth and was given the name Go nnosuke. At that time we already had one female Shiba dog and one female brown tabby cat in our house comprising only 13 tubo. The dog was called Momo and the cat Mii. My wife, who was very much opposed to keeping cats and do

16/17

In our house we had a cat with the grandiose name of Gonnosuke. Usuall y with cats and dogs we know who the mother is but not the father. A cat with a large belly wondered into the house of my younger sister and her husband and gave birth to five kittens. While the mother was a pure whi

24/25

In our house we had a cat with the grandiose na me of Gonnosuke. Usually with cats and dogs we know who the mother is but not the father. A ca

ABCDEFGHIJKLM
NOPQRSTUVWXYZ
abcdefghijklmnopq
rstuvwxyz
1234567890&$¢£¥
fiflæœÆŒÅßÇÌÎÍÏã
§†-–—/()''""":;.,!¡?¿

10/11

In our house we had a cat with the grandiose name of Gonnosuke. Usually with cats and dogs we kno w who the mother is but not the father. A cat with a large belly wondered into the house of my young er sister and her husband and gave birth to five kittens. While the mother was a pure white thoroug hbred Chinchila, the kittens were black and white tabbies of mixed breed. One of these came to our h ouse about two weeks after its birth and was given the name Gonnosuke. At that time we already ha d one female Shiba dog and one female brown tabby cat in our house comprising only 13 thubo. The

16/17

In our house we had a cat with the grandiose name of Gonnosu ke. Usually with cats and dogs we know who the mother is but not the father. A cat with a large belly wondered into the house of my younger sister and her husband and gave birth to five ki

24/25

In our house we had a cat with the grandi ose name of Gonnosuke. Usually with cats and dogs we know who the mother is but

ABCDEFGHIJKL
MNOPQRSTUVW
XYZabcdefghijklmn
opqrstuvwxyz
1234567890&$¢£¥
fiflæœÆŒÅßÇÌÎÍÏã
§†-–—/()''""·;.,!¡?¿

10/11

In our house we had a cat with the grandiose name of Gonnosuke. Usually with cats and dogs we k now who the mother is but not the father. A cat with a large belly wondered into the house of my yo unger sister and her husband and gave birth to five kittens. While the mother was a pure white thor oughbred Chinchila, the kittens were black and white tabbies of mixed breed. One of these came to our house about two weeks after its birth and was given the name Gonnosuke. At that time we alre ady had one female Shiba dog and one female brown tabby cat in our house comprising only 13 tub

16/17

In our house we had a cat with the grandiose name of Gonnos uke. Usually with cats and dogs we know who the mother is b ut not the father. A cat with a large belly wondered into the ho use of my younger sister and her husband and gave birth to fi

24/25

In our house we had a cat with the grand iose name of Gonnosuke. Usually with ca ts and dogs we know who the mother is b

ABCDEFGHIJKL
MNOPQRSTUVW
XYZabcdefghijklmn
opqrstuvwxyz
1234567890&$¢£¥
fiflæœÆŒÅßÇÌÎÍÏã
§†-–—/()''""·;.,!¡?¿

10/11

In our house we had a cat with the grandiose name of Gonnosuke. Usually with cats and dogs we know who the mother is but not the father. A cat with a large belly wondered into the house of my younger sister and her husband and gave birth to five kittens. While the mother was a pure white thoroughbred Chinchila, the kittens were black and white tabbies of mixed breed. One of these came to our house about two weeks after its birth and was given the name Gonnosuke. At that time we already had one female Shiba dog and one female brown tabby cat in our house comprising o

16/17

In our house we had a cat with the grandiose name of Gonno suke. Usually with cats and dogs we know who the mother is but not the father. A cat with a large belly wondered into the house of my younger sister and her husband and gave birth

24/25

In our house we had a cat with the gran diose name of Gonnosuke. Usually with cats and dogs we know who the mother

ABCDEFGHIJKL
MNOPQRSTUVW
XYZabcdefghijklm
nopqrstuvwxyz
1234567890&$¢£¥
fiflæœÆŒÅßÇÌÎÍÏ
ã§†–——/()''""";.,.,!¡?¿

10/11

In our house we had a cat with the grandiose name of Gonnosuke. Usually with cats and dogs we know who the mother is but not the father. A cat with a large belly wondered into the hous e of my younger sister and her husband and gave birth to five kittens. While the mother was a pure white thoroughbred Chinchila, the kittens were black and white tabbies of mixed breed. One of these came to our house about two weeks after its birth and was given the name Gonn osuke. At that time we already had one female Shiba dog and one female brown tabby cat in o

16/17

In our house we had a cat with the grandiose name of Gon nosuke. Usually with cats and dogs we know who the moth er is but not the father. A cat with a large belly wondered i nto the house of my younger sister and her husband and g

24/25

In our house we had a cat with the gra ndiose name of Gonnosuke. Usually wi th cats and dogs we know who the mot

ABCDEFGHIJKL MNOPQRSTU VWXYZ
abcdefghijklmnopq rstuvwxyz
1234567890&$¢£¥ fiflæœÆŒÅßÇÌÎÍÏã §‡-——/()''""":;.,!¡?¿

10/11

In our house we had a cat with the grandiose name of Gonnosuke. Usually with cats and dogs we know who the mother is but not the father. A cat with a large belly wondered into the house of my younger sister and her husband and gave birth to five kittens. While the mother was a pure white thoroughbred Chinchila, the kittens were black and white tabbies of mixed breed. One of these ca me to our house about two weeks after its birth and was given the name Gonnosuke. At that time we already had one female Shiba dog and one female brown tabby cat in our house comprising o

16/17

In our house we had a cat with the grandiose name of Gonno suke. Usually with cats and dogs we know who the mother is but not the father. A cat with a large belly wondered into the house of my younger sister and her husband and gave birth t

24/25

In our house we had a cat with the gran diose name of Gonnosuke. Usually with cats and dogs we know who the mother i

ABCDEFGHIJKLM NOPQRSTUVWXYZ abcdefghijklmnopq rstuvwxyz 1234567890&$¢£¥ fiflæœÆŒÅßÇÌÎÍÏã §‡-–——/()''""":;.,!¡?¿

10/11

In our house we had a cat with the grandiose name of Gonnosuke. Usually with cats and dogs we know who the mother is but not the father. A cat with a large belly wondered into the house of my y ounger sister and her husband and gave birth to five kittens. While the mother was a pure white th oroughbred Chinchila, the kittens were black and white tabbies of mixed breed. One of these came to our house about two weeks after its birth and was given the name Gonnosuke. At that time we al ready had one female Shiba dog and one female brown tabby cat in our house comprising only 13

16/17

In our house we had a cat with the grandiose name of Gonno suke. Usually with cats and dogs we know who the mother is but not the father. A cat with a large belly wondered into the h ouse of my younger sister and her husband and gave birth to

24/25

In our house we had a cat with the gran diose name of Gonnosuke. Usually with cats and dogs we know who the mother i

ABCDEFGHIJKL
MNOPQRSTU
VWXYZ
abcdefghijklmnopq
rstuvwxyz
1234567890&$¢£¥
fiflæœÆŒÅßÇÌÎÍÏ
ã§‡-–—/()''""":;.,!¡?¿

10/11

In our house we had a cat with the grandiose name of Gonnosuke. Usually with cats and dogs
we know who the mother is but not the father. A cat with a large belly wondered into the house
of my younger sister and her husband and gave birth to five kittens. While the mother was a pu
re white thoroughbred Chinchila, the kittens were black and white tabbies of mixed breed. One
of these came to our house about two weeks after its birth and was given the name Gonnosuke.
At that time we already had one female Shiba dog and one female brown tabby cat in our hous

16/17

In our house we had a cat with the grandiose name of Gon
nosuke. Usually with cats and dogs we know who the moth
er is but not the father. A cat with a large belly wondered i
nto the house of my younger sister and her husband and ga

24/25

In our house we had a cat with the gra
ndiose name of Gonnosuke. Usually wi
th cats and dogs we know who the mot

ABCDEFGHIJKLMN
OPQRSTUVWXYZ
abcdefghijklmnopq
rstuvwxyz
1234567890&$¢£¥
fiflæœÆŒÅßÇÌÎÍÏã§†
——/()''""":;.,!¡?¿

10/11

In our house we had a cat with the grandiose name of Gonnosuke. Usually with cats and dogs we know who the mother is but not the father. A cat with a large belly wondered into the house of my younger sister and her husband and gave birth t o five kittens. While the mother was a pure white thoroughbred Chinchila, the kittens were black and white tabbies of mixe d breed. One of these came to our house about two weeks after its birth and was given the name Gonnosuke. At that time we already had one female Shiba dog and one female brown tabby cat in our house comprising only 13 thubo. The dog w as called Momo and the cat Mii. My wife, who was very much opposed to keeping cats and dogs, instantaneously fell for

16/17

In our house we had a cat with the grandiose name of Gonnosuke. Usually with cats and dogs we know who the mother is but not the father. A cat with a large belly wondered into the house of my younger sister and her husband and gave birth to five kittens. While the mother was a pure white thoroughbr

24/25

In our house we had a cat with the grandiose name of Gonnosuke. Usually with cats and dogs we kno w who the mother is but not the father. A cat with

ABCDEFGHIJKLMN
OPQRSTUVWXYZ
abcdefghijklmnopq
rstuvwxyz
1234567890&$¢£¥
fiflæœÆŒÅßÇÌÎÍÏã§†
——/()''""";.,!¡?¿

10/11

In our house we had a cat with the grandiose name of Gonnosuke. Usually with cats and dogs we know who the mother is but not the father. A cat with a large belly wondered into the house of my younger sister and her husband and gave birth to five kittens. While the mother was a pure white thoroughbred Chinchila, the kittens were black and white tabbies of mixed breed. One of these came to our house about two weeks after its birth and was given the name Gonnosuke. At that time we already had one female Shiba dog and one female brown tabby cat in our house comprising only 13 thubo. The dog was called Momo and the cat Mii. My wife, who was very much opposed to keeping cats and dogs, instantaneously fell for its shaggy

16/17

In our house we had a cat with the grandiose name of Gonnosuke. Usually with cats and dogs we know who the mother is but not the father. A cat with a large belly wondered into the house of my younger sister and her husband and gave birth to five kittens. While the mother was a pure white thoroughbred Ch

24/25

In our house we had a cat with the grandiose name of Gonnosuke. Usually with cats and dogs we know who the mother is but not the father. A cat with

ABCDEFGHIJKLMN
OPQRSTUVWXYZ
abcdefghijklmnopq
rstuvwxyz
1234567890&$¢£¥
fiflæœÆŒÅßÇÌÎÍÏã§
†-–—/()''""".;.,!¡?¿

10/11

In our house we had a cat with the grandiose name of Gonnosuke. Usually with cats and dogs we know who the mother is but not the father. A cat with a large belly wondered into the house of my younger sis ter and her husband and gave birth to five kittens. While the mother was a pure white thoroughbred Ch inchila, the kittens were black and white tabbies of mixed breed. One of these came to our house about two weeks after its birth and was given the name Gonnosuke. At that time we already had one female S hiba dog and one female brown tabby cat in our house comprising only 13 thubo. The dog was called M

16/17

In our house we had a cat with the grandiose name of Gonnosuk e. Usually with cats and dogs we know who the mother is but not the father. A cat with a large belly wondered into the house of m y younger sister and her husband and gave birth to five kittens.

24/25

In our house we had a cat with the grandio se name of Gonnosuke. Usually with cats a nd dogs we know who the mother is but no

ABCDEFGHIJKLMN
OPQRSTUVWXYZ
abcdefghijklmnopq
rstuvwxyz
1234567890&$¢£¥
fiflœœÆŒÅßÇÌÎÍÏã§
†-–—/()'""";.,!¡?¿

10/11

In our house we had a cat with the grandiose name of Gonnosuke. Usually with cats and dogs we know who the mother is but not the father. A cat with a large belly wondered into the house of my younger sist er and her husband and gave birth to five kittens. While the mother was a pure white thoroughbred Chin chila, the kittens were black and white tabbies of mixed breed. One of these came to our house about tw o weeks after its birth and was given the name Gonnosuke. At that time we already had one female Shib a dog and one female brown tabby cat in our house comprising only 13 thubo. The dog was called Momo

16/17

In our house we had a cat with the grandiose name of Gonnosuk e. Usually with cats and dogs we know who the mother is but not the father. A cat with a large belly wondered into the house of m y younger sister and her husband and gave birth to five kittens.

24/25

In our house we had a cat with the grandio se name of Gonnosuke. Usually with cats a nd dogs we know who the mother is but no

ABCDEFGHIJKL MNOPQRSTU VWXYZ

abcdefghijklmnopq rstuvwxyz

1234567890&$¢£¥

fiflæœÆŒÅßÇÌÎÍÏã§

†-–—/()''""":;.,!¡?¿

10/11

In our house we had a cat with the grandiose name of Gonnosuke. Usually with cats and dogs we know who the mother is but not the father. A cat with a large belly wondered into the house of my younger si ster and her husband and gave birth to five kittens. While the mother was a pure white thoroughbred Chinchila, the kittens were black and white tabbies of mixed breed. One of these came to our house ab out two weeks after its birth and was given the name Gonnosuke. At that time we already had one fem ale Shiba dog and one female brown tabby cat in our house comprising only 13 thubo. The dog was cal

16/17

In our house we had a cat with the grandiose name of Gonnosuk e. Usually with cats and dogs we know who the mother is but no t the father. A cat with a large belly wondered into the house of my younger sister and her husband and gave birth to five kitten

24/25

In our house we had a cat with the grandio se name of Gonnosuke. Usually with cats a nd dogs we know who the mother is but no

Cheltenham Bold Italic

ABCDEFGHIJKL
MNOPQRSTU
VWXYZ
abcdefghijklmnopq
rstuvwxyz
1234567890&$¢£¥
fiflæœÆŒÅßÇÌÎÍÏã
§†--——/()''""·;.,!¡?¿

10/11

In our house we had a cat with the grandiose name of Gonnosuke. Usually with cats and dogs we know who the mother is but not the father. A cat with a large belly wondered into the house of my younger si ster and her husband and gave birth to five kittens. While the mother was a pure white thoroughbred C hinchila, the kittens were black and white tabbies of mixed breed. One of these came to our house abo ut two weeks after its birth and was given the name Gonnosuke. At that time we already had one fema le Shiba dog and one female brown tabby cat in our house comprising only 13 thubo. The dog was calle

16/17

In our house we had a cat with the grandiose name of Gonnosuk e. Usually with cats and dogs we know who the mother is but no t the father. A cat with a large belly wondered into the house of my younger sister and her husband and gave birth to five kittens.

24/25

In our house we had a cat with the grandio se name of Gonnosuke. Usually with cats and dogs we know who the mother is but

ABCDEFGHIJKLMN
OPQRSTUVWXYZ
abcdefghijklmn
opqrstuvwxyz
1234567890&$¢£¥
fiflæœÆŒÅßÇÌÎÍÏã§†
-–—/()''""::;.,!¡?¿

10/11

In our house we had a cat with the grandiose name of Gonnosuke. Usually with cats and dogs we know who the mother is but not the fathe r. A cat with a large belly wondered into the house of my younger sister and her husband and gave birth to five kittens. While the mother w as a pure white thoroughbred Chinchila, the kittens were black and white tabbies of mixed breed. One of these came to our house about two weeks after its birth and was given the name Gonnosuke. At that time we already had one female Shiba dog and one female brown tabby ca t in our house comprising only 13 thubo. The dog was called Momo and the cat Mii. My wife, who was very much opposed to keeping cats a nd dogs, instantaneously fell for its shaggy appearance and the black tip of its nose and decided on its name, crying this dog's name is Mom

16/17

In our house we had a cat with the grandiose name of Gonnosuke. Usually with cats an d dogs we know who the mother is but not the father. A cat with a large belly wondered into the house of my younger sister and her husband and gave birth to five kittens. Whi le the mother was a pure white thoroughbred Chinchila, the kittens were black and whi

24/25

In our house we had a cat with the grandiose name of Gon nosuke. Usually with cats and dogs we know who the mot her is but not the father. A cat with a large belly wondere

Cheltenham Bold Condensed Italic

*ABCDEFGHIJKLMN
OPQRSTUVWXYZ
abcdefghijklmnopq
rstuvwxyz
1234567890&$¢£¥
fiflæœÆŒÅßÇÌÎÍÏã§†
-–—/()''""".;.,!¡?¿*

10/11

In our house we had a cat with the grandiose name of Gonnosuke. Usually with cats and dogs we know who the mother is but not the father. A cat with a large belly wondered into the house of my younger sister and her husband and gave birth to five kittens. While the mother was a pure white thoroughbred Chinchila, the kittens were black and white tabbies of mixed breed. One of these came to our house about two weeks after its birth and was given the name Gonnosuke. At that time we already had one female Shiba dog and one female brown tabby cat in our house comprising only 13 thubo. The dog was called Momo and the cat Mii. My wife, who was very much opposed to keeping cats and dogs, instantaneously fell for its shaggy appearance and the black tip of its nose and decided on its name, crying this dog's name is Mo

16/17

In our house we had a cat with the grandiose name of Gonnosuke. Usually with cats and dogs we know who the mother is but not the father. A cat with a large belly wondered into the house of my younger sister and her husband and gave birth to five kittens. While the mother was a pure white thoroughbred Chinchila, the kittens were black and

24/25

In our house we had a cat with the grandiose name of Gonnosuke. Usually with cats and dogs we know who the mother is but not the father. A cat with a large belly wonder

ABCDEFGHIJKLMNOP
QRSTUVWXYZ
abcdefghijklmnop
qrstuvwxyz
1234567890&$¢£¥
fiflæœÆŒÅßÇÌÎÍÏïã§†
-–—/()'''""''":;.,!¡?¿

10/11

In our house we had a cat with the grandiose name of Gonnosuke. Usually with cats and dogs we know who the mother is but not the father. A cat with a large belly wondered into the house of my younger sister and her husband and gave birth to five kittens. While the mother was a pure white thoroug hbred Chinchila, the kittens were black and white tabbies of mixed breed. One of these came to our house about two weeks after its birth and was give n the name Gonnosuke. At that time we already had one female Shiba dog and one female brown tabby cat in our house comprising only 13 thubo. The dog was called Momo and the cat Mii. My wife, who was very much opposed to keeping cats and dogs, instantaneously fell for its shaggy appearance and the black tip of its nose and decided on its name, crying this dog's name is Momo. Mii is a stray cat which my daughter picked up. It cried a lot

16/17

In our house we had a cat with the grandiose name of Gonnosuke. Usually with cats and dogs we know who the mother is but not the father. A cat with a large belly wondered into the hous e of my younger sister and her husband and gave birth to five kittens. While the mother was a pure white thoroughbred Chinchila, the kittens were black and white tabbies of mixed breed.

24/25

In our house we had a cat with the grandiose name of Gonnos uke. Usually with cats and dogs we know who the mother is bu t not the father. A cat with a large belly wondered into the hou

ABCDEFGHIJKLMNO
PQRSTUVWXYZ
abcdefghijklmnopq
rstuvwxyz
1234567890&$¢£¥
fiflæœÆŒÅßÇÌÎÍÏã§†
——/()'’“”:;.,!¡?¿

10/11

In our house we had a cat with the grandiose name of Gonnosuke. Usually with cats and dogs we know wh
o the mother is but not the father. A cat with a large belly wondered into the house of my younger sister and
her husband and gave birth to five kittens. While the mother was a pure white thoroughbred Chinchila, the k
ittens were black and white tabbies of mixed breed. One of these came to our house about two weeks after i
ts birth and was given the name Gonnosuke. At that time we already had one female Shiba dog and one fem
ale brown tabby cat in our house comprising only 13 tubo. The dog was called Momo and the cat Mii. My wi

16/17

In our house we had a cat with the grandiose name of Gonnosuke.
Usually with cats and dogs we know who the mother is but not the
father. A cat with a large belly wondered into the house of my youn
ger sister and her husband and gave birth to five kittens. While the

24/25

In our house we had a cat with the grandiose
name of Gonnosuke. Usually with cats and d
ogs we know who the mother is but not the

ABCDEFGHIJKLMNO
PQRSTUVWXYZ
abcdefghijklmnopq
rstuvwxyz
1234567890&$¢£¥
fiflœœÆŒÅßÇÌÎÍÏïã§†
———/()'’“”:;.,!¡?¿

10/11

In our house we had a cat with the grandiose name of Gonnosuke. Usually with cats and dogs we know w ho the mother is but not the father. A cat with a large belly wondered into the house of my younger sister a nd her husband and gave birth to five kittens. While the mother was a pure white thoroughbred Chinchila, the kittens were black and white tabbies of mixed breed. One of these came to our house about two week s after its birth and was given the name Gonnosuke. At that time we already had one female Shiba dog an d one female brown tabby cat in our house comprising only 13 tubo. The dog was called Momo and the ca

16/17

In our house we had a cat with the grandiose name of Gonnosuk e. Usually with cats and dogs we know who the mother is but not the father. A cat with a large belly wondered into the house of my younger sister and her husband and gave birth to five kittens. Whil

24/25

In our house we had a cat with the grandios e name of Gonnosuke. Usually with cats an d dogs we know who the mother is but not

ABCDEFGHIJKLMNO
PQRSTUVWXYZ
abcdefghijklmnopq
rstuvwxyz
1234567890&$¢£¥
fiflæœÆŒÅßÇÌÎÍÏã§
†-––—/()''""".;.,!¡?¿

10/11

In our house we had a cat with the grandiose name of Gonnosuke. Usually with cats and dogs we kn ow who the mother is but not the father. A cat with a large belly wondered into the house of my you nger sister and her husband and gave birth to five kittens. While the mother was a pure white thorou ghbred Chinchila, the kittens were black and white tabbies of mixed breed. One of these came to ou r house about two weeks after its birth and was given the name Gonnosuke. At that time we already had one female Shiba dog and one female brown tabby cat in our house comprising only 13 tubo. T

16/17

In our house we had a cat with the grandiose name of Gonnos uke. Usually with cats and dogs we know who the mother is b ut not the father. A cat with a large belly wondered into the ho use of my younger sister and her husband and gave birth to fiv

24/25

In our house we had a cat with the grandi ose name of Gonnosuke. Usually with cat s and dogs we know who the mother is b

ABCDEFGHIJKLMNO

PQRSTUVWXYZ

abcdefghijklmnopq

rstuvwxyz

1234567890&$¢£¥

fiflœœÆŒÅßÇÌÎÍÏã§

†-––—/()''""":;.,!¡?¿

10/11

In our house we had a cat with the grandiose name of Gonnosuke. Usually with cats and dogs we k now who the mother is but not the father. A cat with a large belly wondered into the house of my yo unger sister and her husband and gave birth to five kittens. While the mother was a pure white thoro ughbred Chinchila, the kittens were black and white tabbies of mixed breed. One of these came to o ur house about two weeks after its birth and was given the name Gonnosuke. At that time we alrea dy had one female Shiba dog and one female brown tabby cat in our house comprising only 13 tubo.

16/17

In our house we had a cat with the grandiose name of Gonnos uke. Usually with cats and dogs we know who the mother is b ut not the father. A cat with a large belly wondered into the ho use of my younger sister and her husband and gave birth to fiv

24/25

In our house we had a cat with the grand iose name of Gonnosuke. Usually with ca ts and dogs we know who the mother is

ABCDEFGHIJKLMN
OPQRSTUVWXYZ
abcdefghijklmnopq
rstuvwxyz
1234567890&$¢£¥
fiflæœÆŒÅßÇÌÎÍÏã
§†-–——/O''""";:.,!¡?¿

10/11

In our house we had a cat with the grandiose name of Gonnosuke. Usually with cats and dogs we know who the mother is but not the father. A cat with a large belly wondered into the house of my younger sister and her husband and gave birth to five kittens. While the mother was a p ure white thoroughbred Chinchila, the kittens were black and white tabbies of mixed breed. O ne of these came to our house about two weeks after its birth and was given the name Gonnos uke. At that time we already had one female Shiba dog and one female brown tabby cat in our

16/17

In our house we had a cat with the grandiose name of Gon nosuke. Usually with cats and dogs we know who the moth er is but not the father. A cat with a large belly wondered in to the house of my younger sister and her husband and ga

24/25

In our house we had a cat with the gra ndiose name of Gonnosuke. Usually wit h cats and dogs we know who the moth

ABCDEFGHIJKLMN
OPQRSTUVWXYZ
abcdefghijklmnopq
rstuvwxyz
1234567890&$¢£¥
fiflæœÆŒÅßÇÌÎÍÏã§
†–——/Q''""":;.,!¡?¿

10/11

In our house we had a cat with the grandiose name of Gonnosuke. Usually with cats and dogs we know who the mother is but not the father. A cat with a large belly wondered into the hous e of my younger sister and her husband and gave birth to five kittens. While the mother was a pure white thoroughbred Chinchila, the kittens were black and white tabbies of mixed breed. One of these came to our house about two weeks after its birth and was given the name Gonn osuke. At that time we already had one female Shiba dog and one female brown tabby cat in

16/17

In our house we had a cat with the grandiose name of Gon nosuke. Usually with cats and dogs we know who the moth er is but not the father. A cat with a large belly wondered i nto the house of my younger sister and her husband and g

24/25

In our house we had a cat with the gra ndiose name of Gonnosuke. Usually wi th cats and dogs we know who the mot

ABCDEFGHIJKLM
NOPQRSTUVWXY
Zabcdefghijklmn
opqrstuvwxyz
1234567890&
$¢£¥fiflæœÆŒ
ÅßÇÌÎÍÏã§†
‐–—/()''""":;.,!¡?¿

10/11

In our house we had a cat with the grandiose name of Gonnosuke. Usually with cat
s and dogs we know who the mother is but not the father. A cat with a large belly w
ondered into the house of my younger sister and her husband and gave birth to fiv
e kittens. While the mother was a pure white thoroughbred Chinchila, the kittens
were black and white tabbies of mixed breed. One of these came to our house abo
ut two weeks after its birth and was given the name Gonnosuke. At that time we al

16/17

In our house we had a cat with the grandiose name
of Gonnosuke. Usually with cats and dogs we know
who the mother is but not the father. A cat with a la
rge belly wondered into the house of my younger si

24/25

In our house we had a cat with the
grandiose name of Gonnosuke. Us
ually with cats and dogs we know

ABCDEFGHIJKL
MNOPQRSTUVW
XYZabcdefghijkl
mnopqrstuvwxyz
1234567890&
$¢£¥fiflæœÆŒ
ÅßÇÌÎÍÏãã§†
———/()''"".,;.,!¡?¿

10/11

In our house we had a cat with the grandiose name of Gonnosuke. Usually with cat
s and dogs we know who the mother is but not the father. A cat with a large belly
wondered into the house of my younger sister and her husband and gave birth to fi
ve kittens. While the mother was a pure white thoroughbred Chinchila, the kittens
were black and white tabbies of mixed breed. One of these came to our house abou
t two weeks after its birth and was given the name Gonnosuke. At that time we alre

16/17

In our house we had a cat with the grandiose name
of Gonnosuke. Usually with cats and dogs we know
who the mother is but not the father. A cat with a la
rge belly wondered into the house of my younger sis

24/25

In our house we had a cat with th
e grandiose name of Gonnosuke. U
sually with cats and dogs we kno

ABCDEFGHIJKLMNOPQ RSTUVWXYZ

abcdefghijklmnopq rstuvwxyz

1234567890&$¢£¥ fiflæœÆŒÅßÇÌÎÍÏã§† ———/()ˋˆˊ""":;.,!¡?¿

10/11

In our house we had a cat with the grandiose name of Gonnosuke. Usually with cats and dogs we know who the mother is but not the father. A cat with a large belly wondered into the house of my younger sister and her husband and gave birth to five ki ttens. While the mother was a pure white thoroughbred Chinchila, the kittens were black and white tabbies of mixed breed. On e of these came to our house about two weeks after its birth and was given the name Gonnosuke. At that time we already had one female Shiba dog and one female brown tabby cat in our house comprising only 13 tubo. The dog was called Momo and t he cat Mii. My wife, who was very much opposed to keeping cats and dogs, instantaneously fell for its shaggy appearance an

16/17

In our house we had a cat with the grandiose name of Gonnosuke. Usually wit h cats and dogs we know who the mother is but not the father. A cat with a lar ge belly wondered into the house of my younger sister and her husband and g ave birth to five kittens. While the mother was a pure white thoroughbred Chin

24/25

In our house we had a cat with the grandiose name of Gonnosuke. Usually with cats and dogs we know who the mother is but not the father. A cat with a lar

ABCDEFGHIJKLMNOPQ RSTUVWXYZ

abcdefghijklmnopq rstuvwxyz

1234567890&$¢£¥

fiflæœÆŒÅßÇÌÎÏĨã§†

————/()ˋˆˊˇ˝""·;·,!¡?¿

10/11

In our house we had a cat with the grandiose name of Gonnosuke. Usually with cats and dogs we know who the mother is but not the father. A cat with a large belly wondered into the house of my younger sister and her husband and gave bir th to five kittens. While the mother was a pure white thoroughbred Chinchila, the kittens were black and white tabbies of mixed breed. One of these came to our house about two weeks after its birth and was given the name Gonnosuke. At that time we already had one female Shiba dog and one female brown tabby cat in our house comprising only 13 tubo. The do g was called Momo and the cat Mii. My wife, who was very much opposed to keeping cats and dogs, instantaneously fell

16/17

In our house we had a cat with the grandiose name of Gonnosuke. Usually with cats and dogs we know who the mother is but not the father. A cat wit h a large belly wondered into the house of my younger sister and her husba nd and gave birth to five kittens. While the mother was a pure white thorou

24/25

In our house we had a cat with the grandiose nam e of Gonnosuke. Usually with cats and dogs we kn ow who the mother is but not the father. A cat wit

ABCDEFGHIJKLMNO
PQRSTUVWXYZ
abcdefghijklmnopq
rstuvwxyz
1234567890&$¢£¥
fiflæœÆŒÅßÇÏÌÍÏã§†
———/()ˋˊˆˇ˜¨;,,!¡?¿

10/11

In our house we had a cat with the grandiose name of Gonnosuke. Usually with cats and dogs we know who the mother is but not the father. A cat with a large belly wondered into the house of my younger sister and h er husband and gave birth to five kittens. While the mother was a pure white thoroughbred Chinchila, the k ittens were black and white tabbies of mixed breed. One of these came to our house about two weeks after it s birth and was given the name Gonnosuke. At that time we already had one female Shiba dog and one femal e brown tabby cat in our house comprising only 13 tubo. The dog was called Momo and the cat Mii. My wife

16/17

In our house we had a cat with the grandiose name of Gonnosuke. U sually with cats and dogs we know who the mother is but not the fa ther. A cat with a large belly wondered into the house of my younge r sister and her husband and gave birth to five kittens. While the

24/25

In our house we had a cat with the grandiose name of Gonnosuke. Usually with cats and do gs we know who the mother is but not the fat

ABCDEFGHIJKL
MNOPQRSTUVW
XYZabcdefghijklm
nopqrstuvwxyz
1234567890&
$¢£¥fiflæœ
ÆŒÅßÇÌÎÍÏã§†
——–—/()"'""·;.,!¡?¿

10/11

In our house we had a cat with the grandiose name of Gonnosuke. Usually with cats and dogs we know who the mother is but not the father. A cat with a large belly wondered into the house of my younger sister and her husband and gave birth to five kittens. While the mother was a pure white thoroughbred Chinchila, the kittens were black and white tabbies of mixed breed. One of these came to our house about two weeks after its birth and was given the name Gonnosuke. At that time we already had one female Shiba dog and one female bro

16/17

In our house we had a cat with the grandiose name of Go nnosuke. Usually with cats and dogs we know who the m other is but not the father. A cat with a large belly wonde red into the house of my younger sister and her husband

24/25

In our house we had a cat with the gr andiose name of Gonnosuke. Usually with cats and dogs we know who the

ABCDEFGHIJKL
MNOPQRSTUVW
XYZabcdefghijklm
nopqrstuvwxyz
1234567890&
$¢£¥fiflæœ
ÆŒÅßÇÌÎÍÏã§†
-----/()"'""'.;.,!¡?¿

10/11

In our house we had a cat with the grandiose name of Gonnosuke. Usually with cats and d
ogs we know who the mother is but not the father. A cat with a large belly wondered into
the house of my younger sister and her husband and gave birth to five kittens. While the
mother was a pure white thoroughbred Chinchila, the kittens were black and white tabbie
s of mixed breed. One of these came to our house about two weeks after its birth and was
given the name Gonnosuke. At that time we already had one female Shiba dog and one fe

16/17

In our house we had a cat with the grandiose name of G
onnosuke. Usually with cats and dogs we know who the
mother is but not the father. A cat with a large belly wo
ndered into the house of my younger sister and her hus

24/25

In our house we had a cat with the gr
andiose name of Gonnosuke. Usually
with cats and dogs we know who the

ABCDEFGHIJKL
MNOPQRSTUVW
XYZabcdefghijklm
nopqrstuvwxyz
1234567890&
$¢£¥fiflæœ
ÆŒÅßÇÌÎÍÏã§†
——/()""""·;.,!¡?¿

10/11

In our house we had a cat with the grandiose name of Gonnosuke. Usually with cats and dogs we know who the mother is but not the father. A cat with a large belly wondered in to the house of my younger sister and her husband and gave birth to five kittens. While the mother was a pure white thoroughbred Chinchila, the kittens were black and white tabbies of mixed breed. One of these came to our house about two weeks after its birth and was given the name Gonnosuke. At that time we already had one female Shiba dog

16/17

In our house we had a cat with the grandiose name of Gonnosuke. Usually with cats and dogs we know who t he mother is but not the father. A cat with a large belly wondered into the house of my younger sister and her

24/25

In our house we had a cat with the g randiose name of Gonnosuke. Usuall y with cats and dogs we know who t

ABCDEFGHIJKL
MNOPQRSTUVW
XYZabcdefghijkl
mnopqrstuvwxyz
1234567890&
$¢£¥fiflæœ
ÆŒÅßÇÌÎÍÏã§†
-––—/()""""·;.,!¡?¿

10/11

In our house we had a cat with the grandiose name of Gonnosuke. Usually with cats an
d dogs we know who the mother is but not the father. A cat with a large belly wondere
d into the house of my younger sister and her husband and gave birth to five kittens.
While the mother was a pure white thoroughbred Chinchila, the kittens were black an
d white tabbies of mixed breed. One of these came to our house about two weeks after
its birth and was given the name Gonnosuke. At that time we already had one female

16/17

In our house we had a cat with the grandiose name of
Gonnosuke. Usually with cats and dogs we know who
the mother is but not the father. A cat with a large be
lly wondered into the house of my younger sister and

24/25

In our house we had a cat with the
grandiose name of Gonnosuke. Usua
lly with cats and dogs we know who

Clarendon Black

ABCDEFGHIJKL
MNOPQRSTUVW
XYZabcdefghijkl
mnopqrstuvwxyz
1234567890&
$¢£¥fiflæœ
ÆŒÅßÇÌÎÍÏã§†
———/0""""·;.,!¡?¿

10/11

In our house we had a cat with the grandiose name of Gonnosuke. Usually with cats and dogs we know who the mother is but not the father. A cat with a large belly won dered into the house of my younger sister and her husband and gave birth to five kit tens. While the mother was a pure white thoroughbred Chinchila, the kittens were bl ack and white tabbies of mixed breed. One of these came to our house about two wee ks after its birth and was given the name Gonnosuke. At that time we already had o

16/17

In our house we had a cat with the grandiose name o f Gonnosuke. Usually with cats and dogs we know w ho the mother is but not the father. A cat with a larg e belly wondered into the house of my younger sister

24/25

In our house we had a cat with the grandiose name of Gonnosuke. Usu ally with cats and dogs we know w

ABCDEFGHIJKLMNO
PQRSTUVWXYZ
abcdefghijklmnopq
rstuvwxyz
1234567890&$¢£¥
fiflæœÆŒÅßçÌÎÍÏãã§†
-——/()''""":;.,!¡?¿

10/11

In our house we had a cat with the grandiose name of Gonnosuke. Usually with cats and dogs we know who the mother is but n ot the father. A cat with a large belly wondered into the house of my younger sister and her husband and gave birth to five kitten s. While the mother was a pure white thoroughbred Chinchila, the kittens were black and white tabbies of mixed breed. One of these came to our house about two weeks after its birth and was given the name Gonnosuke. At that time we already had one fe male Shiba dog and one female brown tabby cat in our house comprising only 13 thubo. The dog was called Momo and the cat Mii. My wife, who was very much opposed to keeping cats and dogs, instantaneously fell for its shaggy appearance and the blac

16/17

In our house we had a cat with the grandiose name of Gonnosuke. Usually with cats and dogs we know who the mother is but not the father. A cat with a large belly wondered into the house of my younger sister and her husband and gave b irth to five kittens. While the mother was a pure white thoroughbred Chinchila,

24/25

In our house we had a cat with the grandiose name o f Gonnosuke. Usually with cats and dogs we know wh o the mother is but not the father. A cat with a large

ABCDEFGHIJKLMN
OPQRSTUVWXYZ
abcdefghijklmnopq
rstuvwxyz
1234567890&$¢£¥
fiflæœÆŒÅßÇÌÎÍÏã§†
-–—/()''""":;.,!¡?¿

10/11

In our house we had a cat with the grandiose name of Gonnosuke. Usually with cats and dogs we know who the moth
er is but not the father. A cat with a large belly wondered into the house of my younger sister and her husband and ga
ve birth to five kittens. While the mother was a pure white thoroughbred Chinchila, the kittens were black and white
tabbies of mixed breed. One of these came to our house about two weeks after its birth and was given the name Gonn
osuke. At that time we already had one female Shiba dog and one female brown tabby cat in our house comprising on
ly 13 thubo. The dog was called Momo and the cat Mii. My wife, who was very much opposed to keeping cats and dog

16/17

In our house we had a cat with the grandiose name of Gonnosuke. Usuall
y with cats and dogs we know who the mother is but not the father. A cat
with a large belly wondered into the house of my younger sister and her h
usband and gave birth to five kittens. While the mother was a pure white

24/25

In our house we had a cat with the grandiose na
me of Gonnosuke. Usually with cats and dogs we
know who the mother is but not the father. A cat

ABCDEFGHIJKL
MNOPQRSTUVW
XYZabcdefghijkl
mnopqrstuvwxyz
1234567890&
$¢£¥fiflæœÆŒ
ÅßÇÌÎÍÏã§†
——/()'"""·:;.,!¡?¿

10/11

In our house we had a cat with the grandiose name of Gonnosuke. Usually with cats and d
ogs we know who the mother is but not the father. A cat with a large belly wondered into t
he house of my younger sister and her husband and gave birth to five kittens. While the m
other was a pure white thoroughbred Chinchila, the kittens were black and white tabbies
of mixed breed. One of these came to our house about two weeks after its birth and was gi
ven the name Gonnosuke. At that time we already had one female Shiba dog and one fema

16/17

In our house we had a cat with the grandiose name of G
onnosuke. Usually with cats and dogs we know who the
mother is but not the father. A cat with a large belly won
dered into the house of my younger sister and her husba

24/25

In our house we had a cat with the gr
andiose name of Gonnosuke. Usually
with cats and dogs we know who the

ABCDEFGHIJKL
MNOPQRSTUVW
XYZabcdefghijklm
nopqrstuvwxyz
1234567890&
$¢£¥fiflæœÆŒ
ÅßÇÌÎÍÏã§†
——/()''""'.,.,!¡?¿

10/11

In our house we had a cat with the grandiose name of Gonnosuke. Usually with cats and dog
s we know who the mother is but not the father. A cat with a large belly wondered into the hou
se of my younger sister and her husband and gave birth to five kittens. While the mother was
a pure white thoroughbred Chinchila, the kittens were black and white tabbies of mixed bree
d. One of these came to our house about two weeks after its birth and was given the name Go
nnosuke. At that time we already had one female Shiba dog and one female brown tabby cat

16/17

In our house we had a cat with the grandiose name of Go
nnosuke. Usually with cats and dogs we know who the mo
ther is but not the father. A cat with a large belly wondere
d into the house of my younger sister and her husband an

24/25

In our house we had a cat with the gra
ndiose name of Gonnosuke. Usually w
ith cats and dogs we know who the mo

Like **Corona Bold**

ABCDEFGHIJKL MNOPQRSTUVW XYZabcdefghijkl mnopqrstuvwxyz 1234567890& $¢£¥fiflæœÆŒ ÅßÇÌÎÍÏã§† ––——/()''""".;.,!¡?¿

10/11

In our house we had a cat with the grandiose name of Gonnosuke. Usually with cats and d ogs we know who the mother is but not the father. A cat with a large belly wondered into t he house of my younger sister and her husband and gave birth to five kittens. While the m other was a pure white thoroughbred Chinchila, the kittens were black and white tabbies of mixed breed. One of these came to our house about two weeks after its birth and was giv en the name Gonnosuke. At that time we already had one female Shiba dog and one female

16/17

In our house we had a cat with the grandiose name of G onnosuke. Usually with cats and dogs we know who the mother is but not the father. A cat with a large belly wo ndered into the house of my younger sister and her husb

24/25

In our house we had a cat with the gr andiose name of Gonnosuke. Usually with cats and dogs we know who the

Like **Corona Bold Italic**

ABCDEFGHIJKL
MNOPQRSTUVW
XYZabcdefghijklm
nopqrstuvwxyz
1234567890&
$¢£¥fiflæœÆŒ
ÅßÇÌÎÍÏã§†
——/()''""·,·,!¡?¿

10/11

In our house we had a cat with the grandiose name of Gonnosuke. Usually with cats and dog s we know who the mother is but not the father. A cat with a large belly wondered into the ho use of my younger sister and her husband and gave birth to five kittens. While the mother w as a pure white thoroughbred Chinchila, the kittens were black and white tabbies of mixed br eed. One of these came to our house about two weeks after its birth and was given the name Gonnosuke. At that time we already had one female Shiba dog and one female brown tabby c

16/17

In our house we had a cat with the grandiose name of Go nnosuke. Usually with cats and dogs we know who the m other is but not the father. A cat with a large belly wonder ed into the house of my younger sister and her husband a

24/25

In our house we had a cat with the gra ndiose name of Gonnosuke. Usually w ith cats and dogs we know who the mo

ABCDEFGHIJKLMN
OPQRSTUVWXYZ
abcdefghijklmn
opqrstuvwxyz
1234567890&
$¢£¥fiflæœÆŒÅßÇ
ÌÎÍÏã§†--/()
''""•;,.,!¡?¿

10/11

In our house we had a cat with the grandiose name of Gonnosuke. Usually wit
h cats and dogs we know who the mother is but not the father. A cat with a
large belly wondered into the house of my younger sister and her husband an
d gave birth to five kittens. While the mother was a pure white thoroughbre
d Chinchila, the kittens were black and white tabbies of mixed breed. One o
f these came to our house about two weeks after its birth and was given the

16/17

In our house we had a cat with the grandiose n
ame of Gonnosuke. Usually with cats and dogs w
e know who the mother is but not the father. A
cat with a large belly wondered into the house

24/25

In our house we had a cat with t
he grandiose name of Gonnosuke.
Usually with cats and dogs we kn

ABCDEFGHIJKLMN

OPQRSTUVWXYZ

abcdefghijklmn

opqrstuvwxyz

1234567890&

$¢£¥fiflæœÆŒÅßÇ

ÌÎÍÏ ã§†——/( )

' ' " " : ; • , ! ¡ ? ¿

10/11

In our house we had a cat with the grandiose name of Gonnosuke. Usually wit
h cats and dogs we know who the mother is but not the father. A cat with a
large belly wondered into the house of my younger sister and her husband an
d gave birth to five kittens. While the mother was a pure white thoroughbre
d Chinchila, the kittens were black and white tabbies of mixed breed. One o
f these came to our house about two weeks after its birth and was given the

16/17

In our house we had a cat with the grandiose
name of Gonnosuke. Usually with cats and dogs
we know who the mother is but not the father.
A cat with a large belly wondered into the ho

24/25

In our house we had a cat with t
he grandiose name of Gonnosuke.
Usually with cats and dogs we kn

ABCDEFGHIJKLMN
OPQRSTUVWXYZ
abcdefghijklmn
opqrstuvwxyz
1234567890&
$¢£¥fiflæœÆŒÅßÇ
ÌÎÍÏã§†--/()
´'""⁚;.,!¡?¿

10/11

In our house we had a cat with the grandiose name of Gonnosuke. Usually wit
h cats and dogs we know who the mother is but not the father. A cat with a
large belly wondered into the house of my younger sister and her husband an
d gave birth to five kittens. While the mother was a pure white thoroughbre
d Chinchila, the kittens were black and white tabbies of mixed breed. One o
f these came to our house about two weeks after its birth and was given the

16/17

In our house we had a cat with the grandiose n
ame of Gonnosuke. Usually with cats and dogs w
e know who the mother is but not the father. A
cat with a large belly wondered into the house

24/25

In our house we had a cat with t
he grandiose name of Gonnosuke.
Usually with cats and dogs we kn

ABCDEFGHIJKLMN
OPQRSTUVWXYZ
abcdefghijklmn
opqrstuvwxyz
1234567890&
$¢£¥fiflæœÆŒÅßÇ
ÌÎÍÏã§†--/()
''""：；．，！¡？¿

10/11

In our house we had a cat with the grandiose name of Gonnosuke. Usually wit
h cats and dogs we know who the mother is but not the father. A cat with a
large belly wondered into the house of my younger sister and her husband an
d gave birth to five kittens. While the mother was a pure white thoroughbre
d Chinchila, the kittens were black and white tabbies of mixed breed. One o
f these came to our house about two weeks after its birth and was given the

16/17

In our house we had a cat with the grandiose
name of Gonnosuke. Usually with cats and dogs
we know who the mother is but not the father.
A cat with a large belly wondered into the ho

24/25

In our house we had a cat with t
he grandiose name of Gonnosuke.
Usually with cats and dogs we kn

ABCDEFGHIJKLMNO
PQRSTUVWXYZ
abcdefghijklmnopq
rstuvwxyz
1234567890&$¢£¥
fiflæœÆŒÅßÇÌÎÍÏã§†
——/()`´""":;.,!¡?¿

10/11

In our house we had a cat with the grandiose name of Gonnosuke. Usually with cats and dogs we know who the mother is but not the father. A cat with a large belly wondered into the house of my younger sis ter and her husband and gave birth to five kittens. While the mother was a pure white thoroughbred Chi nchila, the kittens were black and white tabbies of mixed breed. One of these came to our house about t wo weeks after its birth and was given the name Gonnosuke. At that time we already had one female Sh iba dog and one female brown tabby cat in our house comprising only 13 thubo. The dog was called Mo

16/17

In our house we had a cat with the grandiose name of Gonnosuk e. Usually with cats and dogs we know who the mother is but not the father. A cat with a large belly wondered into the house of m y younger sister and her husband and gave birth to five kittens.

24/25

In our house we had a cat with the grandio se name of Gonnosuke. Usually with cats a nd dogs we know who the mother is but no

ABCDEFGHIJKLMNO
PQRSTUVWXYZ
abcdefghijklmnopqrs
tuvwxyz
1234567890G$¢£¥
fiflæœÆŒÅßÇÌÎÍÏã§†
-–——/()`´˜""":;.,!¡?¿

10/11

In our house we had a cat with the grandiose name of Gonnosuke. Usually with cats and dogs we know who the mother is but not the father. A cat with a large belly wondered into the house of my younger si ster and her husband and gave birth to five kittens. While the mother was a pure white thoroughbred C hinchila, the kittens were black and white tabbies of mixed breed. One of these came to our house abou t two weeks after its birth and was given the name Gonnosuke. At that time we already had one female Shiba dog and one female brown tabby cat in our house comprising only 13 thubo. The dog was called

16/17

In our house we had a cat with the grandiose name of Gonnosuk e. Usually with cats and dogs we know who the mother is but no t the father. A cat with a large belly wondered into the house of my younger sister and her husband and gave birth to five kitten

24/25

In our house we had a cat with the grandio se name of Gonnosuke. Usually with cats a nd dogs we know who the mother is but n

Egyptian 505 Medium

ABCDEFGHIJKLMN
OPQRSTUVWXYZ
abcdefghijklmnopq
rstuvwxyz
1234567890G$¢£¥
fiflæœÆŒÅßÇÌÎÍÏã§†
-–—/()ˋˊˆˇ""":;.,!¡?¿

10/11

In our house we had a cat with the grandiose name of Gonnosuke. Usually with cats and dogs we kno
w who the mother is but not the father. A cat with a large belly wondered into the house of my young
er sister and her husband and gave birth to five kittens. While the mother was a pure white thoroughb
red Chinchila, the kittens were black and white tabbies of mixed breed. One of these came to our hous
e about two weeks after its birth and was given the name Gonnosuke. At that time we already had one
female Shiba dog and one female brown tabby cat in our house comprising only 13 thubo. The dog was

16/17

In our house we had a cat with the grandiose name of Gonnosu
ke. Usually with cats and dogs we know who the mother is but
not the father. A cat with a large belly wondered into the house
of my younger sister and her husband and gave birth to five kitt

24/25

In our house we had a cat with the grandi
ose name of Gonnosuke. Usually with cats
and dogs we know who the mother is but

ABCDEFGHIJKLMN
OPQRSTUVWXYZ
abcdefghijklmnopq
rstuvwxyz
1234567890G$¢£¥
fiflæœÆŒÅßÇÌÎÍÏã§
†-–——/()ˇ´""":;.,!¡?¿

10/11

In our house we had a cat with the grandiose name of Gonnosuke. Usually with cats and dogs we kno w who the mother is but not the father. A cat with a large belly wondered into the house of my young er sister and her husband and gave birth to five kittens. While the mother was a pure white thorough bred Chinchila, the kittens were black and white tabbies of mixed breed. One of these came to our ho use about two weeks after its birth and was given the name Gonnosuke. At that time we already had one female Shiba dog and one female brown tabby cat in our house comprising only 13 thubo. The do

16/17

In our house we had a cat with the grandiose name of Gonnosuk e. Usually with cats and dogs we know who the mother is but no t the father. A cat with a large belly wondered into the house of my younger sister and her husband and gave birth to five kitten

24/25

In our house we had a cat with the grandio se name of Gonnosuke. Usually with cats a nd dogs we know who the mother is but n

ABCDEFGHIJKLM
NOPQRSTUVWXYZ
abcdefghijklmnopq
rstuvwxyz
1234567890&$¢£¥
fiflæœÆŒÅßÇÌÎÍÏÏã§
†-–——/()''""":;.,!¡?¿

10/11

In our house we had a cat with the grandiose name of Gonnosuke. Usually with cats and dogs we know who the mother is but not the father. A cat with a large belly wondered into the house of m y younger sister and her husband and gave birth to five kittens. While the mother was a pure whi te thoroughbred Chinchila, the kittens were black and white tabbies of mixed breed. One of these came to our house about two weeks after its birth and was given the name Gonnosuke. At that ti me we already had one female Shiba dog and one female brown tabby cat in our house comprising

16/17

In our house we had a cat with the grandiose name of Gonno suke. Usually with cats and dogs we know who the mother is but not the father. A cat with a large belly wondered into the house of my younger sister and her husband and gave birth t

24/25

In our house we had a cat with the gran diose name of Gonnosuke. Usually with cats and dogs we know who the mother

ABCDEFGHIJKLMN
OPQRSTUVWXYZ
abcdefghijklmnopq
rstuvwxyz
1234567890&$¢£¥
fiflæœÆŒÅßÇÌÎÍÏã§
†-–—/()''""":;.,!¡?¿

10/11

In our house we had a cat with the grandiose name of Gonnosuke. Usually with cats and dogs we know who the mother is but not the father. A cat with a large belly wondered into the house of my younger sister and h er husband and gave birth to five kittens. While the mother was a pure white thoroughbred Chinchila, the kit tens were black and white tabbies of mixed breed. One of these came to our house about two weeks after its birth and was given the name Gonnosuke. At that time we already had one female Shiba dog and one femal e brown tabby cat in our house comprising only 13 tubo. The dog was called Momo and the cat Mii. My wife,

16/17

In our house we had a cat with the grandiose name of Gonn osuke. Usually with cats and dogs we know who the mother is but not the father. A cat with a large belly wondered into t he house of my younger sister and her husband and gave bir

24/25

In our house we had a cat with the gran diose name of Gonnosuke. Usually with cats and dogs we know who the mother

ABCDEFGHIJKLM
NOPQRSTUVWXYZ
abcdefghijklmnop
qrstuvwxyz
1234567890&$¢£¥
fiflæœÆŒÅßÇÌÎÍÏã
§†-–——/()''""":;.,!¡?¿

10/11

In our house we had a cat with the grandiose name of Gonnosuke. Usually with cats and d
ogs we know who the mother is but not the father. A cat with a large belly wondered into
the house of my younger sister and her husband and gave birth to five kittens. While the
mother was a pure white thoroughbred Chinchila, the kittens were black and white tabbi
es of mixed breed. One of these came to our house about two weeks after its birth and was
given the name Gonnosuke. At that time we already had one female Shiba dog and one fem

16/17

In our house we had a cat with the grandiose name of G
onnosuke. Usually with cats and dogs we know who the
mother is but not the father. A cat with a large belly wo
ndered into the house of my younger sister and her husb

24/25

In our house we had a cat with the gr
andiose name of Gonnosuke. Usually
with cats and dogs we know who the

ABCDEFGHIJKL MNOPQRSTUV WXYZ

abcdefghijklmnop qrstuvwxyz

1234567890&$¢£¥ fiflæœÆŒÅßçÌÎÍÏ ã§†-–—/()''''""",.,!¡?¿

10/11

In our house we had a cat with the grandiose name of Gonnosuke. Usually with cats an
d dogs we know who the mother is but not the father. A cat with a large belly wondered
into the house of my younger sister and her husband and gave birth to five kittens. Whi
le the mother was a pure white thoroughbred Chinchila, the kittens were black and wh
ite tabbies of mixed breed. One of these came to our house about two weeks after its bi
rth and was given the name Gonnosuke. At that time we already had one female Shiba

16/17

In our house we had a cat with the grandiose name of
Gonnosuke. Usually with cats and dogs we know who
the mother is but not the father. A cat with a large bell
y wondered into the house of my younger sister and he

24/25

In our house we had a cat with the g
randiose name of Gonnosuke. Usuall
y with cats and dogs we know who t

ABCDEFGHIJKL
MNOPQRSTUVW
XYZabcdefghijkl
mnopqrstuvwxyz
1234567890&
$¢£¥fiflæœÆŒ
ÅßÇÌÎÍÏã§†
——/()''""":;.,!¡?¿

10/11

In our house we had a cat with the grandiose name of Gonnosuke. Usually with cats and do
gs we know who the mother is but not the father. A cat with a large belly wondered into the
house of my younger sister and her husband and gave birth to five kittens. While the mothe
r was a pure white thoroughbred Chinchila, the kittens were black and white tabbies of mix
ed breed. One of these came to our house about two weeks after its birth and was given the
name Gonnosuke. At that time we already had one female Shiba dog and one female brown

16/17

In our house we had a cat with the grandiose name of Go
nnosuke. Usually with cats and dogs we know who the m
other is but not the father. A cat with a large belly wonder
ed into the house of my younger sister and her husband a

24/25

In our house we had a cat with the gra
ndiose name of Gonnosuke. Usually w
ith cats and dogs we know who the m

ABCDEFGHIJKL
MNOPQRSTUVW
XYZabcdefghijklm
nopqrstuvwxyz
1234567890&
$¢£¥fiflœœÆŒ
ÅßÇÌÎÍÏã§†
-——/()''""";.,!¡?¿

10/11

In our house we had a cat with the grandiose name of Gonnosuke. Usually with cats and dog
s we know who the mother is but not the father. A cat with a large belly wondered into the ho
use of my younger sister and her husband and gave birth to five kittens. While the mother wa
s a pure white thoroughbred Chinchila, the kittens were black and white tabbies of mixed bre
ed. One of these came to our house about two weeks after its birth and was given the name G
onnosuke. At that time we already had one female Shiba dog and one female brown tabby ca

16/17

In our house we had a cat with the grandiose name of Go
nnosuke. Usually with cats and dogs we know who the mo
ther is but not the father. A cat with a large belly wondere
d into the house of my younger sister and her husband an

24/25

In our house we had a cat with the gra
ndiose name of Gonnosuke. Usually w
ith cats and dogs we know who the mo

Like **Excelsior Bold**

ABCDEFGHIJKL
MNOPQRSTUVW
XYZabcdefghijkl
mnopqrstuvwxyz
1234567890&
$¢£¥fiflæœÆŒ
ÅßÇÌÎÍÏãã§†
———/()""''".;.,!¡?¿

10/11

In our house we had a cat with the grandiose name of Gonnosuke. Usually with cats and dogs we know who the mother is but not the father. A cat with a large belly wondered int o the house of my younger sister and her husband and gave birth to five kittens. While th e mother was a pure white thoroughbred Chinchila, the kittens were black and white tab bies of mixed breed. One of these came to our house about two weeks after its birth and was given the name Gonnosuke. At that time we already had one female Shiba dog and o

16/17

In our house we had a cat with the grandiose name of G onnosuke. Usually with cats and dogs we know who the mother is but not the father. A cat with a large belly wo ndered into the house of my younger sister and her hus

24/25

In our house we had a cat with the g randiose name of Gonnosuke. Usuall y with cats and dogs we know who th

ABCDEFGHIJKL
MNOPQRSTUVW
XYZabcdefghijkl
mnopqrstuvwxyz
1234567890&
$¢£¥fiflœœÆŒ
ÅßÇÌÎÍÏã§†
——/()''""·,.,!¡?¿

10/11

In our house we had a cat with the grandiose name of Gonnosuke. Usually with cats an
d dogs we know who the mother is but not the father. A cat with a large belly wondered
into the house of my younger sister and her husband and gave birth to five kittens. Wh
ile the mother was a pure white thoroughbred Chinchila, the kittens were black and w
hite tabbies of mixed breed. One of these came to our house about two weeks after its bi
rth and was given the name Gonnosuke. At that time we already had one female Shiba

16/17

In our house we had a cat with the grandiose name of
Gonnosuke. Usually with cats and dogs we know who
the mother is but not the father. A cat with a large bell
y wondered into the house of my younger sister and h

24/25

In our house we had a cat with the g
randiose name of Gonnosuke. Usua
lly with cats and dogs we know who

ABCDEFGHIJKL MNOPQRSTUV WXYZabcdefghijk lmnopqrstuvwxyz 1234567890& $¢£¥fiflæœÆŒ ÅßÇÌÎÍÏã§† -–—/()''""".:;.,!¡?¿

10/11

In our house we had a cat with the grandiose name of Gonnosuke. Usually with cats and dogs we know who the mother is but not the father. A cat with a large belly wondered int o the house of my younger sister and her husband and gave birth to five kittens. While th e mother was a pure white thoroughbred Chinchila, the kittens were black and white tab bies of mixed breed. One of these came to our house about two weeks after its birth and was given the name Gonnosuke. At that time we already had one female Shiba dog and

16/17

In our house we had a cat with the grandiose name of Gonnosuke. Usually with cats and dogs we know who t he mother is but not the father. A cat with a large belly wondered into the house of my younger sister and her

24/25

In our house we had a cat with the g randiose name of Gonnosuke. Usuall y with cats and dogs we know who t

ABCDEFGHIJKL
MNOPQRSTUVW
XYZabcdefghijkl
mnopqrstuvwxyz
1234567890&
$¢£¥fiflœœÆŒ
ÅßÇÌÎÍÏã§†
––——/() ''""".;.,!¡?¿

10/11

In our house we had a cat with the grandiose name of Gonnosuke. Usually with cats and dogs we know who the mother is but not the father. A cat with a large belly wondered into the house of my younger sister and her husband and gave birth to five kittens. While the mother was a pure white thoroughbred Chinchila, the kittens were black and white tabbies of mixed breed. One of these came to our house about two weeks after its birth and was given the name Gonnosuke. At that time we already had one female Shiba dog and

16/17

In our house we had a cat with the grandiose name of Gonnosuke. Usually with cats and dogs we know who the mother is but not the father. A cat with a large belly wondered into the house of my younger sister and her h

24/25

In our house we had a cat with the grandiose name of Gonnosuke. Usually with cats and dogs we know who t

ABCDEFGHIJKL
MNOPQRSTUVW
XYZabcdefghijkl
mnopqrstuvwxyz
1234567890&
$¢£¥fiflæœÆŒ
ÅßÇÌÎÍÏãã§†
——/()'""",.;.,!¡?¿

10/11

In our house we had a cat with the grandiose name of Gonnosuke. Usually with cats and
dogs we know who the mother is but not the father. A cat with a large belly wondered in
to the house of my younger sister and her husband and gave birth to five kittens. While
the mother was a pure white thoroughbred Chinchila, the kittens were black and white
tabbies of mixed breed. One of these came to our house about two weeks after its birth
and was given the name Gonnosuke. At that time we already had one female Shiba dog

16/17

In our house we had a cat with the grandiose name of
Gonnosuke. Usually with cats and dogs we know who t
he mother is but not the father. A cat with a large belly
wondered into the house of my younger sister and her

24/25

In our house we had a cat with the g
randiose name of Gonnosuke. Usual
ly with cats and dogs we know who t

ABCDEFGHIJKLMNO
PQRSTUVWXYZ
abcdefghijklmnopq
rstuvwxyz
1234567890&$¢£¥
fiflæœÆŒÅßÇÌÎÍÏã§†
-–—/()''""":;.,!¡?¿

10/11

In our house we had a cat with the grandiose name of Gonnosuke. Usually with cats and dogs we know who the mother is but not the father. A cat with a large belly wondered into the house of my younger sis ter and her husband and gave birth to five kittens. While the mother was a pure white thoroughbred Chi nchila, the kittens were black and white tabbies of mixed breed. One of these came to our house about t wo weeks after its birth and was given the name Gonnosuke. At that time we already had one female Sh iba dog and one female brown tabby cat in our house comprising only 13 tubo. The dog was called Mo

16/17

In our house we had a cat with the grandiose name of Gonnosuk e. Usually with cats and dogs we know who the mother is but no t the father. A cat with a large belly wondered into the house of my younger sister and her husband and gave birth to five kittens.

24/25

In our house we had a cat with the grandio se name of Gonnosuke. Usually with cats a nd dogs we know who the mother is but n

ABCDEFGHIJKLMNO
PQRSTUVWXYZ
abcdefghijklmnopq
rstuvwxyz
1234567890&$¢£¥
fiflæœÆŒÅßÇÌÎÍÏãß
†-–—/()''""":;.,!¡?¿

10/11

In our house we had a cat with the grandiose name of Gonnosuke. Usually with cats and dogs we kno w who the mother is but not the father. A cat with a large belly wondered into the house of my younge r sister and her husband and gave birth to five kittens. While the mother was a pure white thoroughbre d Chinchila, the kittens were black and white tabbies of mixed breed. One of these came to our house about two weeks after its birth and was given the name Gonnosuke. At that time we already had one f emale Shiba dog and one female brown tabby cat in our house comprising only 13 tubo. The dog was

16/17

In our house we had a cat with the grandiose name of Gonnosu ke. Usually with cats and dogs we know who the mother is but not the father. A cat with a large belly wondered into the house of my younger sister and her husband and gave birth to five kitt

24/25

In our house we had a cat with the grandi ose name of Gonnosuke. Usually with cats and dogs we know who the mother is but

ABCDEFGHIJKLMN
OPQRSTUVWXYZ
abcdefghijklmnopq
rstuvwxyz
1234567890&$¢£¥
fiflæœÆŒÅßÇÌÎÍÏã§
†-–—/()''""";.,!¡?¿

10/11

In our house we had a cat with the grandiose name of Gonnosuke. Usually with cats and dogs we kn
ow who the mother is but not the father. A cat with a large belly wondered into the house of my you
nger sister and her husband and gave birth to five kittens. While the mother was a pure white thoro
ughbred Chinchila, the kittens were black and white tabbies of mixed breed. One of these came to o
ur house about two weeks after its birth and was given the name Gonnosuke. At that time we alread
y had one female Shiba dog and one female brown tabby cat in our house comprising only 13 tubo.

16/17

In our house we had a cat with the grandiose name of Gonnos
uke. Usually with cats and dogs we know who the mother is b
ut not the father. A cat with a large belly wondered into the ho
use of my younger sister and her husband and gave birth to fi

24/25

In our house we had a cat with the grandi
ose name of Gonnosuke. Usually with cat
s and dogs we know who the mother is b

ITC Lubalin Graph Extra Light, Geometric Slabserif 761
ITC Lubalin Graph Extra Light

ABCDEFGHIJKLMN
OPQRSTUVWXYZ
abcdefghijklmnop
qrstuvwxyz
1234567890&$¢£¥
fiflœœœÆŒÅßÇÌÎÍÏ
ã§†-–—/()````'"'":;.,!¡?¿

10/11

In our house we had a cat with the grandiose name of Gonnosuke. Usually with cats and dogs we know who the mother is but not the father. A cat with a large belly wondered into the house of my younger sister and her husband and gave birth to five kittens. While the mother was a pure white thoroughbred Chinchila, the kittens were black and white tabbies of mixed breed. One of these came to our house about two weeks after its birth and was given the name Gonnosuke. At that time we already had one female Shiba dog and one

16/17

In our house we had a cat with the grandiose name of Gonnosuke. Usually with cats and dogs we know who the mother is but not the father. A cat with a large belly wondered into the house of my younger sister and her hu

24/25

In our house we had a cat with the g randiose name of Gonnosuke. Usuall y with cats and dogs we know who th

ABCDEFGHIJKLMN
OPQRSTUVWXYZ
abcdefghijklmnop
qrstuvwxyz
1234567890&$¢£¥
fiflœœœÆŒÅßÇÌÎÍÏ
ã§†-–—/()ˇ`"":;.,!¡?¿

10/11

In our house we had a cat with the grandiose name of Gonnosuke. Usually with cats and dogs we know who the mother is but not the father. A cat with a large belly wondered into the house of my younger sister and her husband and gave birth to five kittens. While the mother was a pure white thoroughbred Chinchila, the kittens were black and white tabbi es of mixed breed. One of these came to our house about two weeks after its birth and was given the name Gonnosuke. At that time we already had one female Shiba dog and one

16/17

In our house we had a cat with the grandiose name of Gonnosuke. Usually with cats and dogs we know who .th e mother is but not the father. A cat with a large belly w ondered into the house of my younger sister and her hu

24/25

In our house we had a cat with the g randiose name of Gonnosuke. Usuall y with cats and dogs we know who t

ABCDEFGHIJKLMN
OPQRSTUVWXYZ
abcdefghijklmno
pqrstuvwxyz
1234567890&$¢£¥
fiflœœ ÆŒÅßÇÌÎÍÏ
ã§†-–—/()ˮˮ˝˶:;.,!¡?¿

10/11

In our house we had a cat with the grandiose name of Gonnosuke. Usually with cats and dogs we know who the mother is but not the father. A cat with a large belly wondered int o the house of my younger sister and her husband and gave birth to five kittens. While th e mother was a pure white thoroughbred Chinchila, the kittens were black and white ta bbies of mixed breed. One of these came to our house about two weeks after its birth and was given the name Gonnosuke. At that time we already had one female Shiba dog and

16/17

In our house we had a cat with the grandiose name of Gonnosuke. Usually with cats and dogs we know who t he mother is but not the father. A cat with a large belly wondered into the house of my younger sister and her

24/25

In our house we had a cat with the g randiose name of Gonnosuke. Usuall y with cats and dogs we know who t

ABCDEFGHIJKLM
NOPQRSTUVWXYZ
abcdefghijklmno
pqrstuvwxyz
1234567890&$¢£¥
fiflœoeÆŒÅßÇÌÎÍÏ
ã§†-–—/()ˇˊ""";,.,!¡?¿

10/11

In our house we had a cat with the grandiose name of Gonnosuke. Usually with cats and
dogs we know who the mother is but not the father. A cat with a large belly wondered into
the house of my younger sister and her husband and gave birth to five kittens. While the
mother was a pure white thoroughbred Chinchila, the kittens were black and white tabbi
es of mixed breed. One of these came to our house about two weeks after its birth and wa
s given the name Gonnosuke. At that time we already had one female Shiba dog and on

16/17

In our house we had a cat with the grandiose name of
Gonnosuke. Usually with cats and dogs we know who th
e mother is but not the father. A cat with a large belly w
ondered into the house of my younger sister and her hu

24/25

In our house we had a cat with the g
randiose name of Gonnosuke. Usuall
y with cats and dogs we know who t

ABCDEFGHIJKLMN
OPQRSTUVWXYZ
abcdefghijklmno
pqrstuvwxyz
1234567890&$¢£¥
fiflœœÆŒÅßÇÌÎÍÏ
ã§†-–—/()""'"":;.,!i?¿

10/11

In our house we had a cat with the grandiose name of Gonnosuke. Usually with cats an
d dogs we know who the mother is but not the father. A cat with a large belly wondered
into the house of my younger sister and her husband and gave birth to five kittens. Whil
e the mother was a pure white thoroughbred Chinchila, the kittens were black and whit
e tabbies of mixed breed. One of these came to our house about two weeks after its birt
h and was given the name Gonnosuke. At that time we already had one female Shiba

16/17

In our house we had a cat with the grandiose name of
Gonnosuke. Usually with cats and dogs we know who
the mother is but not the father. A cat with a large belly
wondered into the house of my younger sister and her

24/25

In our house we had a cat with the
grandiose name of Gonnosuke. Usu
ally with cats and dogs we know wh

ABCDEFGHIJKLM
NOPQRSTUVWXYZ
abcdefghijklmno
pqrstuvwxyz
1234567890&$¢£¥
fiflœœ ÆŒÅßÇÌÎÍÏ
ã§†-–—/()''""":;.,!¡?¿

10/11

In our house we had a cat with the grandiose name of Gonnosuke. Usually with cats an
d dogs we know who the mother is but not the father. A cat with a large belly wondered
into the house of my younger sister and her husband and gave birth to five kittens. Whil
e the mother was a pure white thoroughbred Chinchila, the kittens were black and whit
e tabbies of mixed breed. One of these came to our house about two weeks after its birt
h and was given the name Gonnosuke. At that time we already had one female Shiba

16/17

In our house we had a cat with the grandiose name of
Gonnosuke. Usually with cats and dogs we know who t
he mother is but not the father. A cat with a large belly
wondered into the house of my younger sister and her

24/25

In our house we had a cat with the
grandiose name of Gonnosuke. Usu
ally with cats and dogs we know wh

ABCDEFGHIJKLM
NOPQRSTUVWXYZ
abcdefghijklmno
pqrstuvwxyz
1234567890&$¢£¥
fiflœœÆŒÅßÇÌÎÍÏ
ã§†-–—/()''""":;.,!¡?¿

10/11

In our house we had a cat with the grandiose name of Gonnosuke. Usually with cats a
nd dogs we know who the mother is but not the father. A cat with a large belly wonder
ed into the house of my younger sister and her husband and gave birth to five kittens.
While the mother was a pure white thoroughbred Chinchila, the kittens were black an
d white tabbies of mixed breed. One of these came to our house about two weeks after
its birth and was given the name Gonnosuke. At that time we already had one female

16/17

In our house we had a cat with the grandiose name o
f Gonnosuke. Usually with cats and dogs we know wh
o the mother is but not the father. A cat with a large b
elly wondered into the house of my younger sister an

24/25

In our house we had a cat with the
grandiose name of Gonnosuke. Usu
ally with cats and dogs we know w

ABCDEFGHIJKLM

NOPQRSTUVWXYZ

abcdefghijklmno

pqrstuvwxyz

1234567890&$¢£¥

fiflœœÆŒÅßÇÌÎÍÍ

ã§†–-——/()""""":;.,!¡?¿

10/11

In our house we had a cat with the grandiose name of Gonnosuke. Usually with cats a nd dogs we know who the mother is but not the father. A cat with a large belly wonder ed into the house of my younger sister and her husband and gave birth to five kittens. While the mother was a pure white thoroughbred Chinchila, the kittens were black an d white tabbies of mixed breed. One of these came to our house about two weeks after its birth and was given the name Gonnosuke. At that time we already had one female

16/17

In our house we had a cat with the grandiose name o f Gonnosuke. Usually with cats and dogs we know wh o the mother is but not the father. A cat with a large b elly wondered into the house of my younger sister an

24/25

In our house we had a cat with the grandiose name of Gonnosuke. Usu ally with cats and dogs we know w

ABCDEFGHIJKLM
NOPQRSTUVWXYZ
abcdefghijklmno
pqrstuvwxyz
1234567890&$¢£¥
fiflœœÆŒÅßÇÌÎÍÏ
ãß†----——/()''""";.,!¡?¿

10/11

In our house we had a cat with the grandiose name of Gonnosuke. Usually with cats and dogs we know who the mother is but not the father. A cat with a large belly won dered into the house of my younger sister and her husband and gave birth to five kitt ens. While the mother was a pure white thoroughbred Chinchila, the kittens were bla ck and white tabbies of mixed breed. One of these came to our house about two wee ks after its birth and was given the name Gonnosuke. At that time we already had on

16/17

In our house we had a cat with the grandiose name of Gonnosuke. Usually with cats and dogs we know who the mother is but not the father. A cat with a larg e belly wondered into the house of my younger sister

24/25

In our house we had a cat with the grandiose name of Gonnosuke. Usu ally with cats and dogs we know w

ABCDEFGHIJKL
MNOPQRSTUVW
XYZabcdefghijkl
mnopqrstuvwxyz
1234567890&
$¢£¥fiflœœÆŒ
ÅßçÌÎÍÏã§†
-–—/()''""":;.,!i?¿

10/11

In our house we had a cat with the grandiose name of Gonnosuke. Usually with cats and dogs we know who the mother is but not the father. A cat with a large belly won dered into the house of my younger sister and her husband and gave birth to five kit tens. While the mother was a pure white thoroughbred Chinchila, the kittens were bl ack and white tabbies of mixed breed. One of these came to our house about two we eks after its birth and was given the name Gonnosuke. At that time we already had

16/17

In our house we had a cat with the grandiose name of Gonnosuke. Usually with cats and dogs we know who the mother is but not the father. A cat with a lar ge belly wondered into the house of my younger sist

24/25

In our house we had a cat with the grandiose name of Gonnosuke. Us ually with cats and dogs we know

ABCDEFGHIJKLMN
OPQRSTUVWXYZ
abcdefghijklmnopq
rstuvwxyz
1234567890&$¢£¥
fiflæœÆŒÅßÇÌÎÍÏã
§†-–——/()''""":;.,!¡?¿

10/11

In our house we had a cat with the grandiose name of Gonnosuke. Usually with cats and dogs we k now who the mother is but not the father. A cat with a large belly wondered into the house of my yo unger sister and her husband and gave birth to five kittens. While the mother was a pure white thor oughbred Chinchila, the kittens were black and white tabbies of mixed breed. One of these came to our house about two weeks after its birth and was given the name Gonnosuke. At that time we alrea dy had one female Shiba dog and one female brown tabby cat in our house comprising only 13 tub

16/17

In our house we had a cat with the grandiose name of Gonnos uke. Usually with cats and dogs we know who the mother is b ut not the father. A cat with a large belly wondered into the ho use of my younger sister and her husband and gave birth to fi

24/25

In our house we had a cat with the grand iose name of Gonnosuke. Usually with ca ts and dogs we know who the mother is

ABCDEFGHIJKLMN
OPQRSTUVWXYZ
abcdefghijklmnopq
rstuvwxyz
1234567890&$¢£¥
fiflæœÆŒÅßÇÌÎÍÏã§
†-–——/()''""":;.,!¡?¿

10/11

In our house we had a cat with the grandiose name of Gonnosuke. Usually with cats and dogs we kno w who the mother is but not the father. A cat with a large belly wondered into the house of my younge r sister and her husband and gave birth to five kittens. While the mother was a pure white thoroughbr ed Chinchila, the kittens were black and white tabbies of mixed breed. One of these came to our hous e about two weeks after its birth and was given the name Gonnosuke. At that time we already had one female Shiba dog and one female brown tabby cat in our house comprising only 13 tubo. The dog was

16/17

In our house we had a cat with the grandiose name of Gonnosu ke. Usually with cats and dogs we know who the mother is but not the father. A cat with a large belly wondered into the house of my younger sister and her husband and gave birth to five kitt

24/25

In our house we had a cat with the grandi ose name of Gonnosuke. Usually with cats and dogs we know who the mother is but

ABCDEFGHIJKLMN
OPQRSTUVWXYZ
abcdefghijklmnopq
rstuvwxyz
1234567890&$¢£¥
fiflæœÆŒÅßÇÌÎÍÏã
§†-‑–—/()''"""";.,!¡?¿

10/11

In our house we had a cat with the grandiose name of Gonnosuke. Usually with cats and dogs we know who the mother is but not the father. A cat with a large belly wondered into the house of my younger sister and her husband and gave birth to five kittens. While the mother was a pure white thoroughbred Chinchila, the kittens were black and white tabbies of mixed breed. One of these ca me to our house about two weeks after its birth and was given the name Gonnosuke. At that time we already had one female Shiba dog and one female brown tabby cat in our house comprising o

16/17

In our house we had a cat with the grandiose name of Gonno suke. Usually with cats and dogs we know who the mother is but not the father. A cat with a large belly wondered into the house of my younger sister and her husband and gave birth t

24/25

In our house we had a cat with the gran diose name of Gonnosuke. Usually with cats and dogs we know who the mother

Like **Melior Bold Italic**

ABCDEFGHIJKL MNOPQRSTUVW XYZ

abcdefghijklmnopq rstuvwxyz

1234567890&$¢£¥

fiflæœÆŒÅßÇÌÎÍÏã

§†-–——/()""""·;.,!¡?¿

10/11

In our house we had a cat with the grandiose name of Gonnosuke. Usually with cats and dogs
we know who the mother is but not the father. A cat with a large belly wondered into the house
of my younger sister and her husband and gave birth to five kittens. While the mother was a pu
re white thoroughbred Chinchila, the kittens were black and white tabbies of mixed breed. On
e of these came to our house about two weeks after its birth and was given the name Gonnosuk
e. At that time we already had one female Shiba dog and one female brown tabby cat in our ho

16/17

In our house we had a cat with the grandiose name of Gonn
osuke. Usually with cats and dogs we know who the mother
is but not the father. A cat with a large belly wondered into
the house of my younger sister and her husband and gave b

24/25

In our house we had a cat with the gra
ndiose name of Gonnosuke. Usually wit
h cats and dogs we know who the moth

ABCDEFGHIJKLMN
OPQRSTUVWXYZ
abcdefghijklmnopq
rstuvwxyz
1234567890&$¢£¥
fiflæœÆŒÅßÇÌÎÍÏã
§†-——/()''""":;.,!¡?¿

10/11

In our house we had a cat with the grandiose name of Gonnosuke. Usually with cats and dogs we k
now who the mother is but not the father. A cat with a large belly wondered into the house of my you
nger sister and her husband and gave birth to five kittens. While the mother was a pure white thorou
ghbred Chinchila, the kittens were black and white tabbies of mixed breed. One of these came to ou
r house about two weeks after its birth and was given the name Gonnosuke. At that time we already
had one female Shiba dog and one female brown tabby cat in our house comprising only 13 tubo. T

16/17

In our house we had a cat with the grandiose name of Gonnos
uke. Usually with cats and dogs we know who the mother is bu
t not the father. A cat with a large belly wondered into the hous
e of my younger sister and her husband and gave birth to five

24/25

In our house we had a cat with the grandi
ose name of Gonnosuke. Usually with cat
s and dogs we know who the mother is b

ABCDEFGHIJKLMN
OPQRSTUVWXYZ
abcdefghijklmnopq
rstuvwxyz
1234567890&$¢£¥
fiflæœÆŒÅßÇÌÍÎÏï ã
§†-–—/()''""":;.,!¡?¿

10/11

In our house we had a cat with the grandiose name of Gonnosuke. Usually with cats and dogs we k now who the mother is but not the father. A cat with a large belly wondered into the house of my yo unger sister and her husband and gave birth to five kittens. While the mother was a pure white thor oughbred Chinchila, the kittens were black and white tabbies of mixed breed. One of these came to our house about two weeks after its birth and was given the name Gonnosuke. At that time we alre ady had one female Shiba dog and one female brown tabby cat in our house comprising only 13 tu

16/17

In our house we had a cat with the grandiose name of Gonnos uke. Usually with cats and dogs we know who the mother is b ut not the father. A cat with a large belly wondered into the ho use of my younger sister and her husband and gave birth to fi

24/25

In our house we had a cat with the grand iose name of Gonnosuke. Usually with ca ts and dogs we know who the mother is b

ABCDEFGHIJKLMN
OPQRSTUVWXYZ
abcdefghijklmnopq
rstuvwxyz
1234567890&$¢£¥
fiflæœÆŒÅßÇÌÎÍÏã
§†-—––/()"""''':;.,!¡?¿

10/11

In our house we had a cat with the grandiose name of Gonnosuke. Usually with cats and dogs we know who the mother is but not the father. A cat with a large belly wondered into the house of my y ounger sister and her husband and gave birth to five kittens. While the mother was a pure white th oroughbred Chinchila, the kittens were black and white tabbies of mixed breed. One of these came to our house about two weeks after its birth and was given the name Gonnosuke. At that time we al ready had one female Shiba dog and one female brown tabby cat in our house comprising only 13

16/17

In our house we had a cat with the grandiose name of Gonno suke. Usually with cats and dogs we know who the mother is but not the father. A cat with a large belly wondered into the h ouse of my younger sister and her husband and gave birth to

24/25

In our house we had a cat with the grand iose name of Gonnosuke. Usually with ca ts and dogs we know who the mother is b

Like **Memphis Medium Italic**

ABCDEFGHIJKLMN
OPQRSTUVWXYZ
abcdefghijklmnopq
rstuvwxyz
1234567890&$¢£¥
fiflæœÆŒÅßÇÌÎÍÏã
§†-——/()''"":;.,!¡?¿

10/11

In our house we had a cat with the grandiose name of Gonnosuke. Usually with cats and dogs we know who the mother is but not the father. A cat with a large belly wondered into the house of my y ounger sister and her husband and gave birth to five kittens. While the mother was a pure white tho roughbred Chinchila, the kittens were black and white tabbies of mixed breed. One of these came to our house about two weeks after its birth and was given the name Gonnosuke. At that time we al ready had one female Shiba dog and one female brown tabby cat in our house comprising only 13

16/17

In our house we had a cat with the grandiose name of Gonno suke. Usually with cats and dogs we know who the mother is but not the father. A cat with a large belly wondered into the h ouse of my younger sister and her husband and gave birth to

24/25

In our house we had a cat with the gran diose name of Gonnosuke. Usually with cats and dogs we know who the mother i

Like **Memphis Bold**

ABCDEFGHIJKLMN
OPQRSTUVWXYZ
abcdefghijklmnopq
rstuvwxyz
1234567890&$¢£¥
fiflæœÆŒÅßÇÌÎÍÏã
§†-–—/()""""'':;.,!¡?¿

10/11

In our house we had a cat with the grandiose name of Gonnosuke. Usually with cats and dogs
we know who the mother is but not the father. A cat with a large belly wondered into the house
of my younger sister and her husband and gave birth to five kittens. While the mother was a pu
re white thoroughbred Chinchila, the kittens were black and white tabbies of mixed breed. One
of these came to our house about two weeks after its birth and was given the name Gonnosuke.
At that time we already had one female Shiba dog and one female brown tabby cat in our hous

16/17

In our house we had a cat with the grandiose name of Gon
nosuke. Usually with cats and dogs we know who the moth
er is but not the father. A cat with a large belly wondered in
to the house of my younger sister and her husband and gav

24/25

In our house we had a cat with the gran
diose name of Gonnosuke. Usually with
cats and dogs we know who the mother

Like **Memphis Bold Italic**

ABCDEFGHIJKLMN
OPQRSTUVWXYZ
abcdefghijklmnopq
rstuvwxyz
1234567890&$¢£¥
fiflæœÆŒÅßÇÌÎÍÏã
§†-–—/()""''''':;.,!¡?¿

10/11

In our house we had a cat with the grandiose name of Gonnosuke. Usually with cats and dogs w
e know who the mother is but not the father. A cat with a large belly wondered into the house of
my younger sister and her husband and gave birth to five kittens. While the mother was a pure w
hite thoroughbred Chinchila, the kittens were black and white tabbies of mixed breed. One of th
ese came to our house about two weeks after its birth and was given the name Gonnosuke. At th
at time we already had one female Shiba dog and one female brown tabby cat in our house com

16/17

In our house we had a cat with the grandiose name of Gonn
osuke. Usually with cats and dogs we know who the mother
is but not the father. A cat with a large belly wondered into t
he house of my younger sister and her husband and gave bi

24/25

In our house we had a cat with the gran
diose name of Gonnosuke. Usually with
cats and dogs we know who the mother

Like **Memphis Extra Bold**

ABCDEFGHIJKLM
NOPQRSTUVWX
YZabcdefghijklmn
opqrstuvwxyz
1234567890&
$¢£¥fiflæœÆŒÅ
ßÇÌÎÍÏã§†
——/()"""''.,;.,!¡?¿

10/11

In our house we had a cat with the grandiose name of Gonnosuke. Usually with cats and do
gs we know who the mother is but not the father. A cat with a large belly wondered into the
house of my younger sister and her husband and gave birth to five kittens. While the mothe
r was a pure white thoroughbred Chinchila, the kittens were black and white tabbies of mix
ed breed. One of these came to our house about two weeks after its birth and was given the
name Gonnosuke. At that time we already had one female Shiba dog and one female brown

16/17

In our house we had a cat with the grandiose name of Go
nnosuke. Usually with cats and dogs we know who the m
other is but not the father. A cat with a large belly wonde
red into the house of my younger sister and her husband

24/25

In our house we had a cat with the gr
andiose name of Gonnosuke. Usually
with cats and dogs we know who the

ABCDEFGHIJKLM
NOPQRSTUVWX
YZabcdefghijklmn
opqrstuvwxyz
1234567890&$¢£¥
fiflæœÆŒÅßÇÌÍÎÏ
ã§†-–—/()""''"":;.,!¡?¿

10/11

In our house we had a cat with the grandiose name of Gonnosuke. Usually with cats and dog
s we know who the mother is but not the father. A cat with a large belly wondered into the h
ouse of my younger sister and her husband and gave birth to five kittens. While the mother
was a pure white thoroughbred Chinchila, the kittens were black and white tabbies of mixe
d breed. One of these came to our house about two weeks after its birth and was given the n
ame Gonnosuke. At that time we already had one female Shiba dog and one female brown ta

16/17

In our house we had a cat with the grandiose name of Go
nnosuke. Usually with cats and dogs we know who the mo
ther is but not the father. A cat with a large belly wonder
ed into the house of my younger sister and her husband a

24/25

In our house we had a cat with the gra
ndiose name of Gonnosuke. Usually w
ith cats and dogs we know who the mo

ABCDEFGHIJKLMNOPQ
RSTUVWXYZ
abcdefghijklmnopq
rstuvwxyz
1234567890&$¢£¥
fiflæœÆŒÅßÇÌÎÍÏã§†
——/()""''''.;.,!¡?¿

10/11

In our house we had a cat with the grandiose name of Gonnosuke. Usually with cats and dogs we know who the mother is but not the father. A cat with a large belly wondered into the house of my younger sister and her husband and gave birth to five kittens. While the mother was a pure white thoroughbred Chinchila, the kittens were black and white tabbies of mixed breed. One of these came to our house about two we eks after its birth and was given the name Gonnosuke. At that time we already had one female Shiba dog and one female brown tabby cat in our house comprising only 13 tubo. The dog was called Momo and the cat Mii. My wife, who was very much opposed to keeping cats and do gs, instantaneously fell for its shaggy appearance and the black tip of its nose and decided on its name, crying this dog's name is Momo. Mii

16/17

In our house we had a cat with the grandiose name of Gonnosuke. Usually with cats an d dogs we know who the mother is but not the father. A cat with a large belly wondered into the house of my younger sister and her husband and gave birth to five kittens. Whi le the mother was a pure white thoroughbred Chinchila, the kittens were black and whi

24/25

In our house we had a cat with the grandiose name of Gon nosuke. Usually with cats and dogs we know who the mot her is but not the father. A cat with a large belly wondered

ABCDEFGHIJKLMNOPQ
RSTUVWXYZ

abcdefghijklmnopq
rstuvwxyz

1234567890&$¢£¥

fiflæœÆŒÅßÇÌÎÍÏã§†

-–——/()""""'':;.,!¡?¿

10/11

In our house we had a cat with the grandiose name of Gonnosuke. Usually with cats and dogs we know who the mother is but not the fath er. A cat with a large belly wondered into the house of my younger sister and her husband and gave birth to five kittens. While the mother was a pure white thoroughbred Chinchila, the kittens were black and white tabbies of mixed breed. One of these came to our house about t wo weeks after its birth and was given the name Gonnosuke. At that time we already had one female Shiba dog and one female brown tab by cat in our house comprising only 13 tubo. The dog was called Momo and the cat Mii. My wife, who was very much opposed to keeping cats and dogs, instantaneously fell for its shaggy appearance and the black tip of its nose and decided on its name, crying this dog's name

16/17

In our house we had a cat with the grandiose name of Gonnosuke. Usually with cats a nd dogs we know who the mother is but not the father. A cat with a large belly wonder ed into the house of my younger sister and her husband and gave birth to five kittens. While the mother was a pure white thoroughbred Chinchila, the kittens were black an

24/25

In our house we had a cat with the grandiose name of Go nnosuke. Usually with cats and dogs we know who the m other is but not the father. A cat with a large belly wonde

Geometric Slabserif 703 Extra Bold Condensed

Like **Memphis Extra Bold Condensed**

Bitstream

ABCDEFGHIJKLMNOPQ RSTUVWXYZ

abcdefghijklmnopq rstuvwxyz

1234567890&$¢£¥ fiflæœÆŒÅßÇÌÎÍÏã§† ———/()""""":;.,!¡?¿

10/11

In our house we had a cat with the grandiose name of Gonnosuke. Usually with cats and dogs we know who the mother is but not the fa ther. A cat with a large belly wondered into the house of my younger sister and her husband and gave birth to five kittens. While the m other was a pure white thoroughbred Chinchila, the kittens were black and white tabbies of mixed breed. One of these came to our hou se about two weeks after its birth and was given the name Gonnosuke. At that time we already had one female Shiba dog and one fema le brown tabby cat in our house comprising only 13 tubo. The dog was called Momo and the cat Mii. My wife, who was very much oppo sed to keeping cats and dogs, instantaneously fell for its shaggy appearance and the black tip of its nose and decided on its name, cryin

16/17

In our house we had a cat with the grandiose name of Gonnosuke. Usually with cats and dogs we know who the mother is but not the father. A cat with a large belly won dered into the house of my younger sister and her husband and gave birth to five kit tens. While the mother was a pure white thoroughbred Chinchila, the kittens were b

24/25

In our house we had a cat with the grandiose name of G onnosuke. Usually with cats and dogs we know who the mother is but not the father. A cat with a large belly wo

Pica 10 Pitch

ABCDEFGHIJKLMNOP
QRSTUVWXYZabcdef
ghijklmnopqrstuv
wxyz1234567890&
$¢£¥fiflæœÆŒ
ÅßÇÌÎÍÏã§†-——/( )
' ' '' '' : ; . , ! ¡ ? ¿

10/11

In our house we had a cat with the grandiose name of Gonnosuke. Usually wit
h cats and dogs we know who the mother is but not the father. A cat with a
large belly wondered into the house of my younger sister and her husband an
d gave birth to five kittens. While the mother was a pure white thoroughbre
d Chinchila, the kittens were black and white tabbies of mixed breed. One o
f these came to our house about two weeks after its birth and was given the

16/17

In our house we had a cat with the grandiose n
ame of Gonnosuke. Usually with cats and dogs w
e know who the mother is but not the father. A
cat with a large belly wondered into the house

24/25

In our house we had a cat with t
he grandiose name of Gonnosuke.
Usually with cats and dogs we kn

Playbill

ABCDEFGHIJKLMNOPQ
RSTUVWXYZ
abcdefghijklmnopq
rstuvwxyz
1234567890&$¢£¥
fiflæœÆŒÅßÇÌÎÏÍÃ§†
-——/()''""":;.,!¡?¿

10/11

In our house we had a cat with the grandiose name of Gonnosuke. Usually with cats and dogs we know who the mother is but not the father. A cat with a large belly wondered in to the house of my younger sister and her husband and gave birth to five kittens. While the mother was a pure white thoroughbred Chinchila, the kittens were black and white ta bbies of mixed breed. One of these came to our house about two weeks after its birth and was given the name Gonnosuke. At that time we already had one female Shiba dog and one female brown tabby cat in our house comprising only 13 tubo. The dog was called Momo and the cat Mii. My wife, who was very much opposed to keeping cats and dogs, ins tantaneously fell for its shaggy appearance and the black tip of its nose and decided on its name, crying this dog's name is Momo. Mii is a stray cat which my daughter picked u p.It cried a lot making a sound like mil mil, so we were soon calling it Mii. Of course it was a mixed breed and had all the characteristics of a Japanese cat. In our house we ha

16/17

In our house we had a cat with the grandiose name of Gonnosuke. Usually with cats and dogs we know who th e mother is but not the father. A cat with a large belly wondered into the house of my younger sister and her h usband and gave birth to five kittens. While the mother was a pure white thoroughbred Chinchila, the kittens were black and white tabbies of mixed breed. One of these came to our house about two weeks after its birth

24/25

In our house we had a cat with the grandiose name of Gonnosuke. Usually with cats and dogs we know who the mother is but not the father. A cat with a large belly wondered into the house of my younger sister and her h

ABCDEFGHIJKLM
NOPQRSTUVWXYZ
abcdefghijklm
nopqrstuvwxyz
1234567890&$¢
£¥fiflæœÆŒÅßÇ
ÌÎÍÏ㧆-——/()
' ' " " : ; . , ! ¡ ? ¿

10/11

In our house we had a cat with the grandiose name of Gonnosuke. Usually wit
h cats and dogs we know who the mother is but not the father. A cat with a
large belly wondered into the house of my younger sister and her husband an
d gave birth to five kittens. While the mother was a pure white thoroughbre
d Chinchila, the kittens were black and white tabbies of mixed breed. One o
f these came to our house about two weeks after its birth and was given the

16/17

In our house we had a cat with the grandiose n
ame of Gonnosuke. Usually with cats and dogs w
e know who the mother is but not the father. A
cat with a large belly wondered into the house

24/25

In our house we had a cat with t
he grandiose name of Gonnosuke.
Usually with cats and dogs we kn

ABCDEFGHIJKLM
NOPQRSTUVWXYZ
abcdefghijklm
nopqrstuvwxyz
1234567890&$¢
£¥fiflæœÆŒÅßÇ
ÌÎÍÏã§†---—/( )
' ' " " : ; . , ! ¡ ? ¿

10/11

In our house we had a cat with the grandiose name of Gonnosuke. Usually wit h cats and dogs we know who the mother is but not the father. A cat with a large belly wondered into the house of my younger sister and her husband an d gave birth to five kittens. While the mother was a pure white thoroughbre d Chinchila, the kittens were black and white tabbies of mixed breed. One o f these came to our house about two weeks after its birth and was given the

16/17

In our house we had a cat with the grandiose name of Gonnosuke. Usually with cats and dogs we know who the mother is but not the father. A cat with a large belly wondered into the ho

24/25

In our house we had a cat with t he grandiose name of Gonnosuke. Usually with cats and dogs we kn

529

ABCDEFGHIJKLM
NOPQRSTUVWXYZ
abcdefghijklm
nopqrstuvwxyz
1234567890&$¢
£¥fiflæœÆŒÅßÇ
ÌÎÍÏã§†---/()
''""::;.,!¡?¿

10/11

In our house we had a cat with the grandiose name of Gonnosuke. Usually wit
h cats and dogs we know who the mother is but not the father. A cat with a
large belly wondered into the house of my younger sister and her husband an
d gave birth to five kittens. While the mother was a pure white thoroughbre
d Chinchila, the kittens were black and white tabbies of mixed breed. One o
f these came to our house about two weeks after its birth and was given the

16/17

In our house we had a cat with the grandiose n
ame of Gonnosuke. Usually with cats and dogs w
e know who the mother is but not the father. A
cat with a large belly wondered into the house

24/25

In our house we had a cat with t
he grandiose name of Gonnosuke.
Usually with cats and dogs we kn

ABCDEFGHIJKLM
NOPQRSTUVWXYZ
abcdefghijklm
nopqrstuvwxyz
1234567890&$¢
£¥fiflæœÆŒÅßÇ
ÌÎÍÏã§†---/()
' ' " " : ; . , ! ¡ ? ¿

10/11

In our house we had a cat with the grandiose name of Gonnosuke. Usually wit
h cats and dogs we know who the mother is but not the father. A cat with a
large belly wondered into the house of my younger sister and her husband an
d gave birth to five kittens. While the mother was a pure white thoroughbre
d Chinchila, the kittens were black and white tabbies of mixed breed. One o
f these came to our house about two weeks after its birth and was given the

16/17

In our house we had a cat with the grandiose
name of Gonnosuke. Usually with cats and dogs
we know who the mother is but not the father.
A cat with a large belly wondered into the ho

24/25

In our house we had a cat with t
he grandiose name of Gonnosuke.
Usually with cats and dogs we kn

ABCDEFGHIJKLMNO
PQRSTUVWXYZ
abcdefghijklmnopq
rstuvwxyz
1234567890&$¢£¥
fiflæœÆŒÅßÇÌÎÍÏã§†
-–——/()''""":;.,!¡?¿

In our house we had a cat with the grandiose name of Gonnosuke. Usually with cats and dogs we know who the mother is but not the father. A cat with a large belly wondered into the house of my younger sister and her husband and gave birth to five kittens. While the mother was a pure white thoroughbred Chinchila, the kittens were black and white tabbies of mixed breed. One of the se came to our house about two weeks after its birth and was given the name Gonnosuke. At that time we already had one female Shiba dog and one female brown tabby cat in our house comprising only 13 tubo. The dog was called Momo and the cat Mii. My wi fe, who was very much opposed to keeping cats and dogs, instantaneously fell for its shaggy appearance and the black tip of its

In our house we had a cat with the grandiose name of Gonnosuke. Usually with c ats and dogs we know who the mother is but not the father. A cat with a large b elly wondered into the house of my younger sister and her husband and gave bir th to five kittens. While the mother was a pure white thoroughbred Chinchila, t

In our house we had a cat with the grandiose name of Gonnosuke. Usually with cats and dogs we know who the mother is but not the father. A cat with a large b

ABCDEFGHIJKLMN
OPQRSTUVWXYZ
abcdefghijklmnopq
rstuvwxyz
1234567890&$¢£¥
fiflæœÆŒÅßÇÌÎÍÏã§†
——/()''""":;.,!¡?¿

10/11

In our house we had a cat with the grandiose name of Gonnosuke. Usually with cats and dogs we know who the mother is but not the father. A cat with a large belly wondered into the house of my younger sister and her husband and gave birth to five kittens. While the mother was a pure white thoroughbred Chinchila, the kitten s were black and white tabbies of mixed breed. One of these came to our house about two weeks after its bi rth and was given the name Gonnosuke. At that time we already had one female Shiba dog and one female brown tabby cat in our house comprising only 13 tubo. The dog was called Momo and the cat Mii. My wife,

16/17

In our house we had a cat with the grandiose name of Gonnosuke. Usually with cats and dogs we know who the mother is but not the f ather. A cat with a large belly wondered into the house of my young er sister and her husband and gave birth to five kittens. While the m

24/25

In our house we had a cat with the grandiose name of Gonnosuke. Usually with cats and d ogs we know who the mother is but not the fa

ABCDEFGHIJKLMN
OPQRSTUVWXYZ
abcdefghijklmnopq
rstuvwxyz
1234567890&$¢£¥
fiflæœÆŒÅßÇÌÎÍÏã§
†-–—/()''""";.,!¡?¿

10/11

In our house we had a cat with the grandiose name of Gonnosuke. Usually with cats and dogs we know wh o the mother is but not the father. A cat with a large belly wondered into the house of my younger sister an d her husband and gave birth to five kittens. While the mother was a pure white thoroughbred Chinchila, t he kittens were black and white tabbies of mixed breed. One of these came to our house about two weeks after its birth and was given the name Gonnosuke. At that time we already had one female Shiba dog and one female brown tabby cat in our house comprising only 13 tubo. The dog was called Momo and the cat

16/17

In our house we had a cat with the grandiose name of Gonnosuke. Usually with cats and dogs we know who the mother is but not the father. A cat with a large belly wondered into the house of my youn ger sister and her husband and gave birth to five kittens. While the

24/25

In our house we had a cat with the grandios e name of Gonnosuke. Usually with cats and dogs we know who the mother is but not the

ABCDEFGHIJKLMN
OPQRSTUVWXYZ
abcdefghijklmnopq
rstuvwxyz
1234567890&$¢£¥
fiflæœÆŒÅßÇÌÎÍÏã§
†-–—/()'’“”:;.,!¡?¿

10/11

In our house we had a cat with the grandiose name of Gonnosuke. Usually with cats and dogs we know who the mother is but not the father. A cat with a large belly wondered into the house of my younger sist er and her husband and gave birth to five kittens. While the mother was a pure white thoroughbred Chi nchila, the kittens were black and white tabbies of mixed breed. One of these came to our house about two weeks after its birth and was given the name Gonnosuke. At that time we already had one female S hiba dog and one female brown tabby cat in our house comprising only 13 tubo. The dog was called M

16/17

In our house we had a cat with the grandiose name of Gonnosuk e. Usually with cats and dogs we know who the mother is but not the father. A cat with a large belly wondered into the house of m y younger sister and her husband and gave birth to five kittens.

24/25

In our house we had a cat with the grandio se name of Gonnosuke. Usually with cats a nd dogs we know who the mother is but no

Like **Rockwell Medium Italic**

ABCDEFGHIJKLMN
OPQRSTUVWXYZ
abcdefghijklmnopq
rstuvwxyz
1234567890&$¢£¥
fiflæœÆŒÅßÇÌÎÍÏã§
†-——/()''""":;.,!¡?¿

10/11

In our house we had a cat with the grandiose name of Gonnosuke. Usually with cats and dogs we kno w who the mother is but not the father. A cat with a large belly wondered into the house of my young er sister and her husband and gave birth to five kittens. While the mother was a pure white thorough bred Chinchila, the kittens were black and white tabbies of mixed breed. One of these came to our h ouse about two weeks after its birth and was given the name Gonnosuke. At that time we already ha d one female Shiba dog and one female brown tabby cat in our house comprising only 13 tubo. The d

16/17

In our house we had a cat with the grandiose name of Gonnosu ke. Usually with cats and dogs we know who the mother is but not the father. A cat with a large belly wondered into the house of my younger sister and her husband and gave birth to five kit

24/25

In our house we had a cat with the grandi ose name of Gonnosuke. Usually with cats and dogs we know who the mother is but

Like **Rockwell Bold**

ABCDEFGHIJKLM
NOPQRSTUVWXY
Zabcdefghijklmnop
qrstuvwxyz
1234567890&$¢£¥
fiflæœÆŒÅßÇÌÎÍÏã
§†-–—/()'"'"":;.,!¡?¿

10/11

In our house we had a cat with the grandiose name of Gonnosuke. Usually with cats and dogs we know who the mother is but not the father. A cat with a large belly wondered into the house of m y younger sister and her husband and gave birth to five kittens. While the mother was a pure wh ite thoroughbred Chinchila, the kittens were black and white tabbies of mixed breed. One of the se came to our house about two weeks after its birth and was given the name Gonnosuke. At that time we already had one female Shiba dog and one female brown tabby cat in our house compri

16/17

In our house we had a cat with the grandiose name of Gonn osuke. Usually with cats and dogs we know who the mother is but not the father. A cat with a large belly wondered into t he house of my younger sister and her husband and gave bi

24/25

In our house we had a cat with the gran diose name of Gonnosuke. Usually with cats and dogs we know who the mother

Like **Rockwell Extra Bold**

ABCDEFGHIJKL
MNOPQRSTUVW
XYZabcdefghij
klmnopqrstuvw
xyz1234567890&
$¢£¥fiflæœÆŒ
ÅßÇÌÎÍÏïã§†
––—/()''""·;.,!¡?¿

10/11

In our house we had a cat with the grandiose name of Gonnosuke. Usually with c
ats and dogs we know who the mother is but not the father. A cat with a large bel
ly wondered into the house of my younger sister and her husband and gave birth
to five kittens. While the mother was a pure white thoroughbred Chinchila, the ki
ttens were black and white tabbies of mixed breed. One of these came to our hou
se about two weeks after its birth and was given the name Gonnosuke. At that tim

16/17

In our house we had a cat with the grandiose nam
e of Gonnosuke. Usually with cats and dogs we kn
ow who the mother is but not the father. A cat with
a large belly wondered into the house of my youn

24/25

In our house we had a cat with th
e grandiose name of Gonnosuke.
Usually with cats and dogs we kn

ABCDEFGHIJKLMNO
PQRSTUVWXYZ
abcdefghijklmnopq
rstuvwxyz
1234567890&$¢£¥
fiflæœÆŒÅßÇÌÎÍÏã§†
———/()''""":;.,!¡?¿

10/11

In our house we had a cat with the grandiose name of Gonnosuke. Usually with cats and dogs we know who the mother is but not the father. A cat with a large belly wondered into the house of my younger sister and her husband and gave birth to five kittens. While the mother was a pure white thoroughbred Chinchila, the kittens were black and white tabbies of mixed breed. One of these came to our house about two weeks after its birth and was given the name Gonnosuke. At that time we already had one female Shiba dog and one female brown tabby cat in our house comprising only 13 tubo. The dog was called Momo and the cat

16/17

In our house we had a cat with the grandiose name of Gonnosuke. Usually with cats and dogs we know who the mother is but not the father. A cat with a large belly wondered into the house of my younger sister and her husband and gave birth to five kittens. While

24/25

In our house we had a cat with the grandiose name of Gonnosuke. Usually with cats and dogs we know who the mother is but not th

ABCDEFGHIJKLMNO
PQRSTUVWXYZ
abcdefghijklmnopq
rstuvwxyz
1234567890&$¢£¥
fiflæœÆŒÅßÇÌÎÍÏã§†
–—–––/()''""":;.,!¡?¿

10/11

In our house we had a cat with the grandiose name of Gonnosuke. Usually with cats and dogs we know who the mother is but not the father. A cat with a large belly wondered into the house of my younger sister and her husband and gave birth to five kittens. While the mother was a pure white thoroughbred Chinchila, the kittens were black and white tabbies of mixed breed. One of these came to our house about two weeks after its birth and was given the name Gonnosuke. At that time we already had one female Shiba dog and one female brown tabby cat in our house comprising only 13 tubo. The dog was called Momo and the cat Mii.

16/17

In our house we had a cat with the grandiose name of Gonnosuke. Usually with cats and dogs we know who the mother is but not the father. A cat with a large belly wondered into the house of my younger sister and her husband and gave birth to five kittens. While the

24/25

In our house we had a cat with the grandiose name of Gonnosuke. Usually with cats and dogs we know who the mother is but not th

ABCDEFGHIJKLMN
OPQRSTUVWXYZ
abcdefghijklmnopq
rstuvwxyz
1234567890&$¢£¥
fiflæœÆŒÅßÇÌÎÍÏã§
†-——/()''""":;.,!¡?¿

10/11

In our house we had a cat with the grandiose name of Gonnosuke. Usually with cats and dogs we know who the mother is but not the father. A cat with a large belly wondered into the house of my younger siste r and her husband and gave birth to five kittens. While the mother was a pure white thoroughbred Chinch ila, the kittens were black and white tabbies of mixed breed. One of these came to our house about two w eeks after its birth and was given the name Gonnosuke. At that time we already had one female Shiba do g and one female brown tabby cat in our house comprising only 13 tubo. The dog was called Momo and t

16/17

In our house we had a cat with the grandiose name of Gonnosuk e. Usually with cats and dogs we know who the mother is but not the father. A cat with a large belly wondered into the house of my younger sister and her husband and gave birth to five kittens. Whi

24/25

In our house we had a cat with the grandios e name of Gonnosuke. Usually with cats an d dogs we know who the mother is but not

ABCDEFGHIJKLMN

OPQRSTUVWXYZ

abcdefghijklmnopq

rstuvwxyz

1234567890&$¢£¥

fiflæœÆŒÅßÇÌÎÍÏĩ㧧

†-–—/()''""":;.,!¡?¿

10/11

*In our house we had a cat with the grandiose name of Gonnosuke. Usually with cats and dogs we know w
ho the mother is but not the father. A cat with a large belly wondered into the house of my younger sister
and her husband and gave birth to five kittens. While the mother was a pure white thoroughbred Chinchi
la, the kittens were black and white tabbies of mixed breed. One of these came to our house about two w
eeks after its birth and was given the name Gonnosuke. At that time we already had one female Shiba do
g and one female brown tabby cat in our house comprising only 13 tubo. The dog was called Momo and t*

16/17

*In our house we had a cat with the grandiose name of Gonnosuke.
Usually with cats and dogs we know who the mother is but not th
e father. A cat with a large belly wondered into the house of my yo
unger sister and her husband and gave birth to five kittens. While*

24/25

*In our house we had a cat with the grandios
e name of Gonnosuke. Usually with cats an
d dogs we know who the mother is but not*

ABCDEFGHIJKLMN
OPQRSTUVWXYZ
abcdefghijklmnopq
rstuvwxyz
1234567890&$¢£¥
fiflæœÆŒÅßÇÌÎÍÏã§
†-–—/()''""":;.,!¡?¿

10/11

In our house we had a cat with the grandiose name of Gonnosuke. Usually with cats and dogs we know who the mother is but not the father. A cat with a large belly wondered into the house of my younger sister and her husband and gave birth to five kittens. While the mother was a pure white t horoughbred Chinchila, the kittens were black and white tabbies of mixed breed. One of these cam e to our house about two weeks after its birth and was given the name Gonnosuke. At that time w e already had one female Shiba dog and one female brown tabby cat in our house comprising only

16/17

In our house we had a cat with the grandiose name of Gonno suke. Usually with cats and dogs we know who the mother is but not the father. A cat with a large belly wondered into the house of my younger sister and her husband and gave birth t

24/25

In our house we had a cat with the grand iose name of Gonnosuke. Usually with ca ts and dogs we know who the mother is

ABCDEFGHIJKLMN
OPQRSTUVWXYZ
abcdefghijklmnopq
rstuvwxyz
1234567890&$¢£¥
fiflæœÆŒÅßÇÌÎÍÏã
§†-–—/()""""":;.,!¡?¿

10/11

In our house we had a cat with the grandiose name of Gonnosuke. Usually with cats and dogs we k
now who the mother is but not the father. A cat with a large belly wondered into the house of my yo
unger sister and her husband and gave birth to five kittens. While the mother was a pure white thor
oughbred Chinchila, the kittens were black and white tabbies of mixed breed. One of these came to
our house about two weeks after its birth and was given the name Gonnosuke. At that time we alre
ady had one female Shiba dog and one female brown tabby cat in our house comprising only 13 tub

16/17

In our house we had a cat with the grandiose name of Gonnos
uke. Usually with cats and dogs we know who the mother is b
ut not the father. A cat with a large belly wondered into the h
ouse of my younger sister and her husband and gave birth to f

24/25

In our house we had a cat with the grand
iose name of Gonnosuke. Usually with ca
ts and dogs we know who the mother is

ABCDEFGHIJKLM
NOPQRSTUVWXYZ
abcdefghijklmnopq
rstuvwxyz
1234567890&$¢£¥
fiflæœÆŒÅßÇÌÎÍÏã§
†-–—/()''""'':;.,!¡?¿

10/11

In our house we had a cat with the grandiose name of Gonnosuke. Usually with cats and dogs we know who the mother is but not the father. A cat with a large belly wondered into the hous e of my younger sister and her husband and gave birth to five kittens. While the mother was a pure white thoroughbred Chinchila, the kittens were black and white tabbies of mixed breed. One of these came to our house about two weeks after its birth and was given the name Gonno suke. At that time we already had one female Shiba dog and one female brown tabby cat in our

16/17

In our house we had a cat with the grandiose name of Gon nosuke. Usually with cats and dogs we know who the moth er is but not the father. A cat with a large belly wondered i nto the house of my younger sister and her husband and ga

24/25

In our house we had a cat with the gra ndiose name of Gonnosuke. Usually wi th cats and dogs we know who the mot

ABCDEFGHIJKLM NOPQRSTUVWX YZabcdefghijklm nopqrstuvwxyz 1234567890&$¢£¥ fiflæœÆŒÅßÇÌÎÍÏã §†-–—/()''""":;.,!¡?¿

10/11

In our house we had a cat with the grandiose name of Gonnosuke. Usually with cats and dogs we know who the mother is but not the father. A cat with a large belly wondered i nto the house of my younger sister and her husband and gave birth to five kittens. Whil e the mother was a pure white thoroughbred Chinchila, the kittens were black and whi te tabbies of mixed breed. One of these came to our house about two weeks after its birt h and was given the name Gonnosuke. At that time we already had one female Shiba do

16/17

In our house we had a cat with the grandiose name of Gonnosuke. Usually with cats and dogs we know who t he mother is but not the father. A cat with a large bell y wondered into the house of my younger sister and he

24/25

In our house we had a cat with the g randiose name of Gonnosuke. Usuall y with cats and dogs we know who t

ABCDEFGHIJKLMNO
PQRSTUVWXYZ
abcdefghijklmnopq
rstuvwxyz
1234567890&$¢£¥
fiflæœÆŒÅßçÌÎÍÏョ†
-—––/()''""":;.,!¡?¿

10/11

In our house we had a cat with the grandiose name of Gonnosuke. Usually with cats and dogs we know who the mothe r is but not the father. A cat with a large belly wondered into the house of my younger sister and her husband and gave birth to five kittens. While the mother was a pure white thoroughbred Chinchila, the kittens were black and white tabb ies of mixed breed. One of these came to our house about two weeks after its birth and was given the name Gonnosuke. At that time we already had one female Shiba dog and one female brown tabby cat in our house comprising only 13 tub o. The dog was called Momo and the cat Mii. My wife, who was very much opposed to keeping cats and dogs, instanta

16/17

In our house we had a cat with the grandiose name of Gonnosuke. Usually with cats and dogs we know who the mother is but not the father. A cat w ith a large belly wondered into the house of my younger sister and her hus band and gave birth to five kittens. While the mother was a pure white th

24/25

In our house we had a cat with the grandiose na me of Gonnosuke. Usually with cats and dogs we know who the mother is but not the father. A cat

ABCDEFGHIJKLMNO
PQRSTUVWXYZ
abcdefghijklmnopq
rstuvwxyz
1234567890&$¢£¥
fiflæœÆŒÅßÇÌÎÍÏã§†
——/()'''"":;.,!¡?¿

10/11

In our house we had a cat with the grandiose name of Gonnosuke. Usually with cats and dogs we know who the mother is but not the father. A cat with a large belly wondered into the house of my younger sist er and her husband and gave birth to five kittens. While the mother was a pure white thoroughbred Chi nchila, the kittens were black and white tabbies of mixed breed. One of these came to our house about two weeks after its birth and was given the name Gonnosuke. At that time we already had one female Sh iba dog and one female brown tabby cat in our house comprising only 13 tubo. The dog was called Mo

16/17

In our house we had a cat with the grandiose name of Gonnosuk e. Usually with cats and dogs we know who the mother is but not the father. A cat with a large belly wondered into the house of my younger sister and her husband and gave birth to five kittens. Wh

24/25

In our house we had a cat with the grandi ose name of Gonnosuke. Usually with cats and dogs we know who the mother is but n

ABCDEFGHIJKLMN

OPQRSTUVWXYZ

abcdefghijklmnopq

rstuvwxyz

1234567890&$¢£¥

fiflœœÆŒÅßÇÌÎÍÏã§

†-–——/()"""":;.,!¡?¿*

10/11

In our house we had a cat with the grandiose name of Gonnosuke. Usually with cats and dogs we know who the mother is but not the father. A cat with a large belly wondered into the house of my younger sist er and her husband and gave birth to five kittens. While the mother was a pure white thoroughbred Chi nchila, the kittens were black and white tabbies of mixed breed. One of these came to our house about t wo weeks after its birth and was given the name Gonnosuke. At that time we already had one female Sh iba dog and one female brown tabby cat in our house comprising only 13 tubo. The dog was called Mo

16/17

In our house we had a cat with the grandiose name of Gonnosuk e. Usually with cats and dogs we know who the mother is but not the father. A cat with a large belly wondered into the house of my younger sister and her husband and gave birth to five kittens. W

24/25

In our house we had a cat with the grandio se name of Gonnosuke. Usually with cats a nd dogs we know who the mother is but not

ABCDEFGHIJKLMN
OPQRSTUVWXYZ
abcdefghijklmnopq
rstuvwxyz
1234567890&$¢£¥
fiflæœÆŒÅßÇÌÎÍÏã§
†-–—/()""''":;.,!¡?¿

10/11

In our house we had a cat with the grandiose name of Gonnosuke. Usually with cats and dogs we know who the mother is but not the father. A cat with a large belly wondered into the house of m y younger sister and her husband and gave birth to five kittens. While the mother was a pure whi te thoroughbred Chinchila, the kittens were black and white tabbies of mixed breed. One of thes e came to our house about two weeks after its birth and was given the name Gonnosuke. At that t ime we already had one female Shiba dog and one female brown tabby cat in our house comprisi

16/17

In our house we had a cat with the grandiose name of Gonn osuke. Usually with cats and dogs we know who the mother is but not the father. A cat with a large belly wondered into t he house of my younger sister and her husband and gave bi

24/25

In our house we had a cat with the gran diose name of Gonnosuke. Usually with cats and dogs we know who the mother

ABCDEFGHIJKLMN

OPQRSTUVWXYZ

abcdefghijklmnopq

rstuvwxyz

1234567890&$¢£¥

fiflœœÆŒÅßÇÌÎÍÏã§

†-——/()""""':;.,!¡?¿

10/11

In our house we had a cat with the grandiose name of Gonnosuke. Usually with cats and dogs we k now who the mother is but not the father. A cat with a large belly wondered into the house of my yo unger sister and her husband and gave birth to five kittens. While the mother was a pure white thor oughbred Chinchila, the kittens were black and white tabbies of mixed breed. One of these came t o our house about two weeks after its birth and was given the name Gonnosuke. At that time we alr eady had one female Shiba dog and one female brown tabby cat in our house comprising only 13

16/17

In our house we had a cat with the grandiose name of Gonno suke. Usually with cats and dogs we know who the mother is but not the father. A cat with a large belly wondered into the h ouse of my younger sister and her husband and gave birth to

24/25

In our house we had a cat with the grand iose name of Gonnosuke. Usually with c ats and dogs we know who the mother is

ABCDEFGHIJKLMN
OPQRSTUVWXYZ
abcdefghijklmnopq
rstuvwxyz
1234567890&$¢£¥
fiflæœÆŒÅßÇÌÎÍÏã
§†-–—/()''""":;.,!¡?¿

10/11

In our house we had a cat with the grandiose name of Gonnosuke. Usually with cats and dogs w
e know who the mother is but not the father. A cat with a large belly wondered into the house of
my younger sister and her husband and gave birth to five kittens. While the mother was a pure w
hite thoroughbred Chinchila, the kittens were black and white tabbies of mixed breed. One of th
ese came to our house about two weeks after its birth and was given the name Gonnosuke. At th
at time we already had one female Shiba dog and one female brown tabby cat in our house com

16/17

In our house we had a cat with the grandiose name of Gonn
osuke. Usually with cats and dogs we know who the mother
is but not the father. A cat with a large belly wondered into t
he house of my younger sister and her husband and gave bi

24/25

In our house we had a cat with the gran
diose name of Gonnosuke. Usually with
cats and dogs we know who the mother

ABCDEFGHIJKLMN
OPQRSTUVWXYZ
abcdefghijklmnopq
rstuvwxyz
1234567890&$¢£¥
fiflœœÆŒÅßÇÌÎÍÏã
§†-–—/()''""":;.,!¡?¿

10/11

In our house we had a cat with the grandiose name of Gonnosuke. Usually with cats and dogs w
e know who the mother is but not the father. A cat with a large belly wondered into the house of
my younger sister and her husband and gave birth to five kittens. While the mother was a pure
white thoroughbred Chinchila, the kittens were black and white tabbies of mixed breed. One of
these came to our house about two weeks after its birth and was given the name Gonnosuke. At
that time we already had one female Shiba dog and one female brown tabby cat in our house c

16/17

In our house we had a cat with the grandiose name of Gonn
osuke. Usually with cats and dogs we know who the mother
is but not the father. A cat with a large belly wondered into t
he house of my younger sister and her husband and gave b

24/25

In our house we had a cat with the gran
diose name of Gonnosuke. Usually with
cats and dogs we know who the mother

ABCDEFGHIJKLMN
OPQRSTUVWXYZ
abcdefghijklmnopq
rstuvwxyz
1234567890&
$¢£¥fiflæœÆŒ
ÅßÇÌÎÍÏã§†
-—/()''""":;.,!¡?¿

10/11

In our house we had a cat with the grandiose name of Gonnosuke. Usually with cats and dogs we know who the mother is but not the father. A cat with a large belly wondered into the house of m y younger sister and her husband and gave birth to five kittens. While the mother was a pure whi te thoroughbred Chinchila, the kittens were black and white tabbies of mixed breed. One of thes e came to our house about two weeks after its birth and was given the name Gonnosuke. At that t ime we already had one female Shiba dog and one female brown tabby cat in our house compris

16/17

In our house we had a cat with the grandiose name of Gonn osuke. Usually with cats and dogs we know who the mother i s but not the father. A cat with a large belly wondered into t he house of my younger sister and her husband and gave bir

24/25

In our house we had a cat with the gran diose name of Gonnosuke. Usually with cats and dogs we know who the mother

ABCDEFGHIJKLMNOPQ
RSTUVWXYZ
abcdefghijklmnopq
rstuvwxyz
1234567890&$¢£¥
fiflœœÆŒÅßÇÌÎÍÏïã§†
-–—/()''""":;.,!i?¿

10/11

In our house we had a cat with the grandiose name of Gonnosuke. Usually with cats and dogs we know who the mothe
r is but not the father. A cat with a large belly wondered into the house of my younger sister and her husband and gav
e birth to five kittens. While the mother was a pure white thoroughbred Chinchila, the kittens were black and white ta
bbies of mixed breed. One of these came to our house about two weeks after its birth and was given the name Gonnosu
ke. At that time we already had one female Shiba dog and one female brown tabby cat in our house comprising only 1
3 tubo. The dog was called Momo and the cat Mii. My wife, who was very much opposed to keeping cats and dogs, inst

16/17

In our house we had a cat with the grandiose name of Gonnosuke. Usually
with cats and dogs we know who the mother is but not the father. A cat w
ith a large belly wondered into the house of my younger sister and her hu
sband and gave birth to five kittens. While the mother was a pure white t

24/25

In our house we had a cat with the grandiose na
me of Gonnosuke. Usually with cats and dogs we
know who the mother is but not the father. A cat

ABCDEFGHIJKL
MNOPQRSTU
VWXYZ
abcdefghijklmnopq
rstuvwxyz
1234567890&$¢£¥
fiflæœÆŒÅßÇÌÎÍÏã
§†-–—/()''""".;.,!¡?¿

10/11

In our house we had a cat with the grandiose name of Gonnosuke. Usually with cats and dogs we know who the mother is but not the father. A cat with a large belly wondered into the house of m y younger sister and her husband and gave birth to five kittens. While the mother was a pure whi te thoroughbred Chinchila, the kittens were black and white tabbies of mixed breed. One of these came to our house about two weeks after its birth and was given the name Gonnosuke. At that ti me we already had one female Shiba dog and one female brown tabby cat in our house comprisin

16/17

In our house we had a cat with the grandiose name of Gonno suke. Usually with cats and dogs we know who the mother is but not the father. A cat with a large belly wondered into the house of my younger sister and her husband and gave birth

24/25

In our house we had a cat with the gran diose name of Gonnosuke. Usually with cats and dogs we know who the mother

ABCDEFGHIJKL MNOPQRSTU VWXYZ abcdefghijklmnopq rstuvwxyz 1234567890&$¢£¥ fiflœœÆŒÅßÇÌÎÍÏã §†--——/()''""".;.,!¡?¿

10/11

In our house we had a cat with the grandiose name of Gonnosuke. Usually with cats and dogs we kn ow who the mother is but not the father. A cat with a large belly wondered into the house of my young er sister and her husband and gave birth to five kittens. While the mother was a pure white thorough bred Chinchila, the kittens were black and white tabbies of mixed breed. One of these came to our ho use about two weeks after its birth and was given the name Gonnosuke. At that time we already had one female Shiba dog and one female brown tabby cat in our house comprising only 13 thubo. The do

16/17

In our house we had a cat with the grandiose name of Gonnos uke. Usually with cats and dogs we know who the mother is bu t not the father. A cat with a large belly wondered into the hous e of my younger sister and her husband and gave birth to five

24/25

In our house we had a cat with the grandi ose name of Gonnosuke. Usually with cat s and dogs we know who the mother is but

Like **Textype Bold**

ABCDEFGHIJKL
MNOPQRSTUVW
XYZabcdefghijklm
nopqrstuvwxyz
1234567890&
$¢£¥fiflæœ
ÆŒÅßÇÌÎÍÏã§†
——/()''""".,;.,!¡?¿

10/11

In our house we had a cat with the grandiose name of Gonnosuke. Usually with cats and dogs
we know who the mother is but not the father. A cat with a large belly wondered into the hous
e of my younger sister and her husband and gave birth to five kittens. While the mother was a
pure white thoroughbred Chinchila, the kittens were black and white tabbies of mixed breed.
One of these came to our house about two weeks after its birth and was given the name Gonn
osuke. At that time we already had one female Shiba dog and one female brown tabby cat in

16/17

In our house we had a cat with the grandiose name of Gon
nosuke. Usually with cats and dogs we know who the moth
er is but not the father. A cat with a large belly wondered
into the house of my younger sister and her husband and g

24/25

In our house we had a cat with the gra
ndiose name of Gonnosuke. Usually wi
th cats and dogs we know who the mot

Like **Textype Bold Italic**

ABCDEFGHIJKL MNOPQRSTU VWXYZ

abcdefghijklmnopq
rstuvwxyz
1234567890&$¢£¥
fiflœœÆŒÅßÇÌÎÍÏ
ã§†----——/()''""";.,!¡?¿

10/11

In our house we had a cat with the grandiose name of Gonnosuke. Usually with cats and dogs we know who the mother is but not the father. A cat with a large belly wondered into the hous e of my younger sister and her husband and gave birth to five kittens. While the mother was a pure white thoroughbred Chinchila, the kittens were black and white tabbies of mixed breed. One of these came to our house about two weeks after its birth and was given the name Gonno suke. At that time we already had one female Shiba dog and one female brown tabby cat in ou

16/17

In our house we had a cat with the grandiose name of Gon nosuke. Usually with cats and dogs we know who the moth er is but not the father. A cat with a large belly wondered into the house of my younger sister and her husband and

24/25

In our house we had a cat with the gra ndiose name of Gonnosuke. Usually wi th cats and dogs we know who the mot

ABCDEFGHIJKL
MNOPQRSTUVW
XYZabcdefghijklm
nopqrstuvwxyz
1234567890&$¢£¥
fiflæœÆŒÅßÇÌÎÍÏã
§†-–—/()"""":;.,!¡?¿

10/11

In our house we had a cat with the grandiose name of Gonnosuke. Usually with cats and dogs we know who the mother is but not the father. A cat with a large belly wondered into the house of m y younger sister and her husband and gave birth to five kittens. While the mother was a pure whi te thoroughbred Chinchila, the kittens were black and white tabbies of mixed breed. One of these came to our house about two weeks after its birth and was given the name Gonnosuke. At that ti me we already had one female Shiba dog and one female brown tabby cat in our house comprisi

16/17

In our house we had a cat with the grandiose name of Gonn osuke. Usually with cats and dogs we know who the mother is but not the father. A cat with a large belly wondered into t he house of my younger sister and her husband and gave bir

24/25

In our house we had a cat with the gran diose name of Gonnosuke. Usually with cats and dogs we know who the mother

ABCDEFGHIJKLM
NOPQRSTUVWXYZ
abcdefghijklmnopq
rstuvwxyz
1234567890&$¢£¥
fiflæœÆŒÅßÇÌÎÍÏã
§†-–—/()''""·;·,!¡?¿

10/11

In our house we had a cat with the grandiose name of Gonnosuke. Usually with cats and dogs we k now who the mother is but not the father. A cat with a large belly wondered into the house of my yo unger sister and her husband and gave birth to five kittens. While the mother was a pure white thoro ughbred Chinchila, the kittens were black and white tabbies of mixed breed. One of these came to ou r house about two weeks after its birth and was given the name Gonnosuke. At that time we already had one female Shiba dog and one female brown tabby cat in our house comprising only 13 tsubo.

16/17

In our house we had a cat with the grandiose name of Gonnos uke. Usually with cats and dogs we know who the mother is b ut not the father. A cat with a large belly wondered into the ho use of my younger sister and her husband and gave birth to fiv

24/25

In our house we had a cat with the grand iose name of Gonnosuke. Usually with ca ts and dogs we know who the mother is b

ABCDEFGHIJKL
MNOPQRSTUVW
XYZabcdefghijklm
nopqrstuvwxyz
1234567890&$¢£¥
fiflæœÆŒÅßÇÌÎÍÏã
§†--——/()'"""·:;.,·!¡?¿

10/11

In our house we had a cat with the grandiose name of Gonnosuke. Usually with cats and dogs we know who the mother is but not the father. A cat with a large belly wondered into the hous e of my younger sister and her husband and gave birth to five kittens. While the mother was a pure white thoroughbred Chinchila, the kittens were black and white tabbies of mixed breed. One of these came to our house about two weeks after its birth and was given the name Gonn osuke. At that time we already had one female Shiba dog and one female brown tabby cat in

16/17

In our house we had a cat with the grandiose name of Gon nosuke. Usually with cats and dogs we know who the mot her is but not the father. A cat with a large belly wondered into the house of my younger sister and her husband and g

24/25

In our house we had a cat with the gra ndiose name of Gonnosuke. Usually wi th cats and dogs we know who the mot

ABCDEFGHIJKL
MNOPQRSTUVW
XYZabcdefghijklm
nopqrstuvwxyz
1234567890&$¢£¥
fiflæœÆŒÅßÇÌÎÍÏã
§†-–—/()'’“”:;.,!¡?¿

10/11

In our house we had a cat with the grandiose name of Gonnosuke. Usually with cats and dogs we know who the mother is but not the father. A cat with a large belly wondered into the house o f my younger sister and her husband and gave birth to five kittens. While the mother was a pure white thoroughbred Chinchila, the kittens were black and white tabbies of mixed breed. One of t hese came to our house about two weeks after its birth and was given the name Gonnosuke. At t hat time we already had one female Shiba dog and one female brown tabby cat in our house co

16/17

In our house we had a cat with the grandiose name of Gon nosuke. Usually with cats and dogs we know who the moth er is but not the father. A cat with a large belly wondered in to the house of my younger sister and her husband and gave

24/25

In our house we had a cat with the gra ndiose name of Gonnosuke. Usually wi th cats and dogs we know who the mot

ABCDEFGHIJKL
MNOPQRSTUVW
XYZabcdefghijklm
nopqrstuvwxyz
1234567890&$¢£¥
fiflæœÆŒÅßÇÌÎÍÏ
ã§†-–—/()"'"":;.,!¡?¿

10/11

In our house we had a cat with the grandiose name of Gonnosuke. Usually with cats and d
ogs we know who the mother is but not the father. A cat with a large belly wondered into t
he house of my younger sister and her husband and gave birth to five kittens. While the m
other was a pure white thoroughbred Chinchila, the kittens were black and white tabbies
of mixed breed. One of these came to our house about two weeks after its birth and was gi
ven the name Gonnosuke. At that time we already had one female Shiba dog and one fema

16/17

In our house we had a cat with the grandiose name of G
onnosuke. Usually with cats and dogs we know who the
mother is but not the father. A cat with a large belly won
dered into the house of my younger sister and her husba

24/25

In our house we had a cat with the gr
andiose name of Gonnosuke. Usually
with cats and dogs we know who the

ABCDEFGHIJKL
MNOPQRSTUVW
XYZabcdefghijklm
nopqrstuvwxyz
1234567890&$¢£¥
fiflæœÆŒÅßÇÌÎÍÏã
§†-–—/()''""",;..,!¡?¿

10/11

In our house we had a cat with the grandiose name of Gonnosuke. Usually with cats and do gs we know who the mother is but not the father. A cat with a large belly wondered into the h ouse of my younger sister and her husband and gave birth to five kittens. While the mother w as a pure white thoroughbred Chinchila, the kittens were black and white tabbies of mixed b reed. One of these came to our house about two weeks after its birth and was given the name Gonnosuke. At that time we already had one female Shiba dog and one female brown tabby

16/17

In our house we had a cat with the grandiose name of Go nnosuke. Usually with cats and dogs we know who the m other is but not the father. A cat with a large belly wonder ed into the house of my younger sister and her husband a

24/25

In our house we had a cat with the gr andiose name of Gonnosuke. Usually with cats and dogs we know who the

ABCDEFGHIJKL
MNOPQRSTUVW
XYZabcdefghijkl
mnopqrstuvwxyz
1234567890&
$¢£¥fiflæœÆŒ
ÅßÇÌÎÍÏãã§†
-——/()''""".,,.!¡?¿

10/11

In our house we had a cat with the grandiose name of Gonnosuke. Usually with cats a
nd dogs we know who the mother is but not the father. A cat with a large belly wonder
ed into the house of my younger sister and her husband and gave birth to five kittens.
While the mother was a pure white thoroughbred Chinchila, the kittens were black an
d white tabbies of mixed breed. One of these came to our house about two weeks after
its birth and was given the name Gonnosuke. At that time we already had one female

16/17

In our house we had a cat with the grandiose name of
Gonnosuke. Usually with cats and dogs we know who
the mother is but not the father. A cat with a large bel
ly wondered into the house of my younger sister and

24/25

In our house we had a cat with the
grandiose name of Gonnosuke. Usu
ally with cats and dogs we know wh

ABCDEFGHIJKL MNOPQRSTUVW XYZabcdefghijkl mnopqrstuvwxyz 1234567890& $¢£¥fiflæœÆŒ ÅßÇÌÎÍÏãã§† -——/()''""";;.,!¡?¿

10/11

In our house we had a cat with the grandiose name of Gonnosuke. Usually with cats an d dogs we know who the mother is but not the father. A cat with a large belly wondered into the house of my younger sister and her husband and gave birth to five kittens. Whil e the mother was a pure white thoroughbred Chinchila, the kittens were black and whit e tabbies of mixed breed. One of these came to our house about two weeks after its birth and was given the name Gonnosuke. At that time we already had one female Shiba dog

16/17

In our house we had a cat with the grandiose name of Gonnosuke. Usually with cats and dogs we know who t he mother is but not the father. A cat with a large belly wondered into the house of my younger sister and her

24/25

In our house we had a cat with the g randiose name of Gonnosuke. Usual ly with cats and dogs we know who t

567

ABCDEFGHIJKLMNO
PQRSTUVWXYZ
abcdefghijklmnopq
rstuvwxyz
1234567890&$¢£¥
fiflæœÆŒÅßÇÌÎÍÏã§†
-–——/()''""":;.,!¡?¿

10/11

In our house we had a cat with the grandiose name of Gonnosuke. Usually with cats and dogs we know who the mother is but not the father. A cat with a large belly wondered into the house of my younger sister and her husband and gave birth to five kittens. While the mother was a pure white thoroughbred Chinchila, the kittens were black and white tabbies of mixed breed. One of these came to our house about two weeks after its birth and was given the name Gonnosuke. At that time we already had one female Shiba dog and one female brown tabby cat in our house comprising only 13 tsubo. The dog was called Momo and the cat Mii. My wife,

16/17

In our house we had a cat with the grandiose name of Gonnosuke. Usually with cats and dogs we know who the mother is but not the father. A cat with a large belly wondered into the house of my younger sister and her husband and gave birth to five kittens. While the mother w

24/25

In our house we had a cat with the grandiose name of Gonnosuke. Usually with cats and dogs we know who the mother is but not the fat

ABCDEFGHIJKLMNOP
QRSTUVWXYZ
abcdefghijklmnopq
rstuvwxyz
1234567890&$¢£¥
fiflæœÆŒÅßÇÌÎÍÏã§†
––——/()'’“”.:;.,!¡?¿

10/11

In our house we had a cat with the grandiose name of Gonnosuke. Usually with cats and dogs we know who the mother is but not the father. A cat with a large belly wondered into the house of my younger sister and her husband and gave birth t o five kittens. While the mother was a pure white thoroughbred Chinchila, the kittens were black and white tabbies of mix ed breed. One of these came to our house about two weeks after its birth and was given the name Gonnosuke. At that time we already had one female Shiba dog and one female brown tabby cat in our house comprising only 13 tsubo. The dog wa s called Momo and the cat Mii. My wife, who was very much opposed to keeping cats and dogs, instantaneously fell for its

16/17

In our house we had a cat with the grandiose name of Gonnosuke. Usually with cats and dogs we know who the mother is but not the father. A cat with a large belly wondered into the house of my younger sister and her husband and gave birth to five kittens. While the mother was a pure white thoroughb

24/25

In our house we had a cat with the grandiose nam e of Gonnosuke. Usually with cats and dogs we kn ow who the mother is but not the father. A cat wit

ABCDEFGHIJKLMN
OPQRSTUVWXYZ
abcdefghijklmnopq
rstuvwxyz
1234567890&$¢£¥
fiflæœÆŒÅßÇÌÎÍÏã§†
––——/()''""".;.,!¡?¿

10/11

In our house we had a cat with the grandiose name of Gonnosuke. Usually with cats and dogs we know who the mother is but not the father. A cat with a large belly wondered into the house of my younger sister and h er husband and gave birth to five kittens. While the mother was a pure white thoroughbred Chinchila, the ki ttens were black and white tabbies of mixed breed. One of these came to our house about two weeks after its birth and was given the name Gonnosuke. At that time we already had one female Shiba dog and one female brown tabby cat in our house comprising only 13 tsubo. The dog was called Momo and the cat Mii. My wife,

16/17

In our house we had a cat with the grandiose name of Gonnosuke. Usually with cats and dogs we know who the mother is but not the father. A cat with a large belly wondered into the house of my youn ger sister and her husband and gave birth to five kittens. While the

24/25

In our house we had a cat with the grandiose name of Gonnosuke. Usually with cats and d ogs we know who the mother is but not the f

ABCDEFGHIJKLMNO
PQRSTUVWXYZ
abcdefghijklmnopq
rstuvwxyz
1234567890&$¢£¥
fiflœœÆŒÅßÇÌÎÍÏã§†
———/()''""":;.,!¡?¿

10/11

In our house we had a cat with the grandiose name of Gonnosuke. Usually with cats and dogs we know who the m other is but not the father. A cat with a large belly wondered into the house of my younger sister and her husband and gave birth to five kittens. While the mother was a pure white thoroughbred Chinchila, the kittens were black a nd white tabbies of mixed breed. One of these came to our house about two weeks after its birth and was given the name Gonnosuke. At that time we already had one female Shiba dog and one female brown tabby cat in our house comprising only 13 tsubo. The dog was called Momo and the cat Mii. My wife, who was very much opposed to kee

16/17

In our house we had a cat with the grandiose name of Gonnosuke. Usu ally with cats and dogs we know who the mother is but not the father. A cat with a large belly wondered into the house of my younger sister and her husband and gave birth to five kittens. While the mother was a pur

24/25

In our house we had a cat with the grandiose n ame of Gonnosuke. Usually with cats and dogs we know who the mother is but not the father. A

ABCDEFGHIJKLMN
OPQRSTUVWXYZ
abcdefghijklmnopq
rstuvwxyz
1234567890&$¢£¥
fiflæœÆŒÅßÇÌÎÍÏã§†
-–——/()''""":;.,!¡?¿

10/11

In our house we had a cat with the grandiose name of Gonnosuke. Usually with cats and dogs we know w
ho the mother is but not the father. A cat with a large belly wondered into the house of my younger sister
and her husband and gave birth to five kittens. While the mother was a pure white thoroughbred Chinchi
la, the kittens were black and white tabbies of mixed breed. One of these came to our house about two w
eeks after its birth and was given the name Gonnosuke. At that time we already had one female Shiba do
g and one female brown tabby cat in our house comprising only 13 tsubo. The dog was called Momo and

16/17

In our house we had a cat with the grandiose name of Gonnosuk
e. Usually with cats and dogs we know who the mother is but not
the father. A cat with a large belly wondered into the house of my
younger sister and her husband and gave birth to five kittens. Wh

24/25

In our house we had a cat with the grandios
e name of Gonnosuke. Usually with cats an
d dogs we know who the mother is but not

ABCDEFGHIJKLMN
OPQRSTUVWXYZ
abcdefghijklmnopq
rstuvwxyz
1234567890&$¢£¥
fiflæœÆŒÅßÇÌÎÍÏã§†
––—/()''""·;·,!¡?¿

10/11

In our house we had a cat with the grandiose name of Gonnosuke. Usually with cats and dogs we know who t he mother is but not the father. A cat with a large belly wondered into the house of my younger sister and her husband and gave birth to five kittens. While the mother was a pure white thoroughbred Chinchila, the kitten s were black and white tabbies of mixed breed. One of these came to our house about two weeks after its birth and was given the name Gonnosuke. At that time we already had one female Shiba dog and one female brown tabby cat in our house comprising only 13 tsubo. The dog was called Momo and the cat Mii. My wife, who was

16/17

In our house we had a cat with the grandiose name of Gonnosuke. U sually with cats and dogs we know who the mother is but not the fat her. A cat with a large belly wondered into the house of my younger sister and her husband and gave birth to five kittens. While the mot

24/25

In our house we had a cat with the grandiose name of Gonnosuke. Usually with cats and do gs we know who the mother is but not the fat

573

ABCDEFGHIJKLMN
OPQRSTUVWXYZ
abcdefghijklmnopq
rstuvwxyz
1234567890&$¢£¥
fiflæœÆŒÅßÇÌÎÍÏã§
†-––—/()''""".:;.,!¡?¿

10/11

In our house we had a cat with the grandiose name of Gonnosuke. Usually with cats and dogs we kno w who the mother is but not the father. A cat with a large belly wondered into the house of my younge r sister and her husband and gave birth to five kittens. While the mother was a pure white thoroughbr ed Chinchila, the kittens were black and white tabbies of mixed breed. One of these came to our hous e about two weeks after its birth and was given the name Gonnosuke. At that time we already had on e female Shiba dog and one female brown tabby cat in our house comprising only 13 tsubo. The dog

16/17

In our house we had a cat with the grandiose name of Gonnosu ke. Usually with cats and dogs we know who the mother is but not the father. A cat with a large belly wondered into the house of my younger sister and her husband and gave birth to five kitt

24/25

In our house we had a cat with the grandi ose name of Gonnosuke. Usually with cats and dogs we know who the mother is but

ABCDEFGHIJKLMN
OPQRSTUVWXYZ
abcdefghijklmnopq
rstuvwxyz
1234567890&$¢£¥
fiflæœÆŒÅßÇÌÎÍÏã§
†-–——/()'"''".;.,!¡?¿

10/11

In our house we had a cat with the grandiose name of Gonnosuke. Usually with cats and dogs we know who the mother is but not the father. A cat with a large belly wondered into the house of my younger sister and h er husband and gave birth to five kittens. While the mother was a pure white thoroughbred Chinchila, the k ittens were black and white tabbies of mixed breed. One of these came to our house about two weeks after it s birth and was given the name Gonnosuke. At that time we already had one female Shiba dog and one fem ale brown tabby cat in our house comprising only 13 tsubo. The dog was called Momo and the cat Mii. My

16/17

In our house we had a cat with the grandiose name of Gonnosuke. Usually with cats and dogs we know who the mother is but not the father. A cat with a large belly wondered into the house of my youn ger sister and her husband and gave birth to five kittens. While the

24/25

In our house we had a cat with the grandios e name of Gonnosuke. Usually with cats and dogs we know who the mother is but not the

ABCDEFGHIJKL
MNOPQRSTUVW
XYZ
abcdefghijklmnopq
rstuvwxyz
1234567890&$¢£¥
fiflæœÆŒÅßÇÌÎÍÏã
§†-–—/()''""".;.,!¡?¿

10/11

In our house we had a cat with the grandiose name of Gonnosuke. Usually with cats and dogs we know w
ho the mother is but not the father. A cat with a large belly wondered into the house of my younger sister
and her husband and gave birth to five kittens. While the mother was a pure white thoroughbred Chinchi
la, the kittens were black and white tabbies of mixed breed. One of these came to our house about two w
eeks after its birth and was given the name Gonnosuke. At that time we already had one female Shiba dog
and one female brown tabby cat in our house comprising only 13 tsubo. The dog was called Momo and t

16/17

In our house we had a cat with the grandiose name of Gonnosuk
e. Usually with cats and dogs we know who the mother is but not
the father. A cat with a large belly wondered into the house of my
younger sister and her husband and gave birth to five kittens. Whi

24/25

In our house we had a cat with the grandios
e name of Gonnosuke. Usually with cats an
d dogs we know who the mother is but not

ABCDEFGHIJKL
MNOPQRSTUVW
XYZ

abcdefghijklmnopqrst
uvwxyz
1234567890&$¢£¥
fiflæœÆŒÅßÇÌÎÍÏã
§†-——/() ''"".:;.,!¡?¿

10/11

In our house we had a cat with the grandiose name of Gonnosuke. Usually with cats and dogs we know who the mother is but not the father. A cat with a large belly wondered into the house of my younger sister and her husb and and gave birth to five kittens. While the mother was a pure white thoroughbred Chinchila, the kittens wer e black and white tabbies of mixed breed. One of these came to our house about two weeks after its birth and w as given the name Gonnosuke. At that time we already had one female Shiba dog and one female brown tabby cat in our house comprising only 13 tsubo. The dog was called Momo and the cat Mii. My wife, who was very

16/17

In our house we had a cat with the grandiose name of Gonnosuke. U sually with cats and dogs we know who the mother is but not the fathe r. A cat with a large belly wondered into the house of my younger siste r and her husband and gave birth to five kittens. While the mother

24/25

In our house we had a cat with the grandiose name of Gonnosuke. Usually with cats and do gs we know who the mother is but not the fath

ABCDEFGHIJKL
MNOPQRSTUVW
XYZ
abcdefghijklmnopq
rstuvwxyz
1234567890&$¢£¥
fiflæœÆŒÅßÇÌÎÍÏã
§†----——/()''""".,;.,!¡?¿

10/11

In our house we had a cat with the grandiose name of Gonnosuke. Usually with cats and dogs we know who the mother is but not the father. A cat with a large belly wondered into the house of my younger sister and her husband and gave birth to five kittens. While the mother was a pure white t horoughbred Chinchila, the kittens were black and white tabbies of mixed breed. One of these cam e to our house about two weeks after its birth and was given the name Gonnosuke. At that time w e already had one female Shiba dog and one female brown tabby cat in our house comprising only

16/17

In our house we had a cat with the grandiose name of Gonno suke. Usually with cats and dogs we know who the mother is but not the father. A cat with a large belly wondered into the house of my younger sister and her husband and gave birth t

24/25

In our house we had a cat with the gran diose name of Gonnosuke. Usually with cats and dogs we know who the mother i

ABCDEFGHIJKL
MNOPQRSTUVW
XYZ

abcdefghijklmnopq
rstuvwxyz
1234567890&$¢£¥
fiflæœÆŒÅßÇÌÎÍÏã
§†--——/() ‘’“«»”.;.,!¡?¿

10/11

In our house we had a cat with the grandiose name of Gonnosuke. Usually with cats and dogs we know w
ho the mother is but not the father. A cat with a large belly wondered into the house of my younger sister
a nd her husband and gave birth to five kittens. While the mother was a pure white thoroughbred
Chinchil a, the kittens were black and white tabbies of mixed breed. One of these came to our house
about two weeks after its birth and was given the name Gonnosuke. At that time we already had one
female Shiba dog an d one female brown tabby cat in our house comprising only 13 tsubo. The dog was

16/17

In our house we had a cat with the grandiose name of Gonnosuke.
Usually with cats and dogs we know who the mother is but not the
father. A cat with a large belly wondered into the house of my you
nger sister and her husband and gave birth to five kittens. While

24/25

In our house we had a cat with the grandios
e name of Gonnosuke. Usually with cats an
d dogs we know who the mother is but not th

ABCDEFGHIJKLMN
OPQRSTUVWXYZ
abcdefghijklmnopq
rstuvwxyz
1234567890&$¢£¥
fiflæœÆŒÅßÇÌÎÍÏā§†
———/()''""":;.,!¡?¿

10/11

In our house we had a cat with the grandiose name of Gonnosuke. Usually with cats and dogs we know who the mot her is but not the father. A cat with a large belly wondered into the house of my younger sister and her husband and gave birth to five kittens. While the mother was a pure white thoroughbred Chinchila, the kittens were black and wh ite tabbies of mixed breed. One of these came to our house about two weeks after its birth and was given the name G onnosuke. At that time we already had one female Shiba dog and one female brown tabby cat in our house comprisi ng only 13 tsubo. The dog was called Momo and the cat Mii. My wife, who was very much opposed to keeping cats

16/17

In our house we had a cat with the grandiose name of Gonnosuke. Usual ly with cats and dogs we know who the mother is but not the father. A c at with a large belly wondered into the house of my younger sister and h er husband and gave birth to five kittens. While the mother was a pure w

24/25

In our house we had a cat with the grandiose na me of Gonnosuke. Usually with cats and dogs w e know who the mother is but not the father. A

ABCDEFGHIJKLMN
OPQRSTUVWXYZ
abcdefghijklmnopq
rstuvwxyz
1234567890&$¢£¥
fiflæœÆŒÅßÇÌÎÍÏã§†
——/()'‘'"",.;..,'¡?¿

10/11

In our house we had a cat with the grandiose name of Gonnosuke. Usually with cats and dogs we know who the mother is b ut not the father. A cat with a large belly wondered into the house of my younger sister and her husband and gave birth to f ive kittens. While the mother was a pure white thoroughbred Chinchila, the kittens were black and white tabbies of mixed breed. One of these came to our house about two weeks after its birth and was given the name Gonnosuke. At that time we already had one female Shiba dog and one female brown tabby cat in our house comprising only 13 tsubo. The dog was cal led Momo and the cat Mii. My wife, who was very much opposed to keeping cats and dogs, instantaneously fell for its shagg

16/17

In our house we had a cat with the grandiose name of Gonnosuke. Usually w ith cats and dogs we know who the mother is but not the father. A cat with a large belly wondered into the house of my younger sister and her husband an d gave birth to five kittens. While the mother was a pure white thoroughbred

24/25

In our house we had a cat with the grandiose name of Gonnosuke. Usually with cats and dogs we know who the mother is but not the father. A cat with a

ABCDEFGHIJKLMN
OPQRSTUVWXYZ
abcdefghijklmnopq
rstuvwxyz
1234567890&$¢£¥
fiflæœÆŒÅßÇÌÎÍÏā§†
-—––/()''""";,.,!¡?¿

10/11

In our house we had a cat with the grandiose name of Gonnosuke. Usually with cats and dogs we know who the mother is but not the father. A cat with a large belly wondered into the house of my younger sister and her husba nd and gave birth to five kittens. While the mother was a pure white thoroughbred Chinchila, the kittens were bla ck and white tabbies of mixed breed. One of these came to our house about two weeks after its birth and was give n the name Gonnosuke. At that time we already had one female Shiba dog and one female brown tabby cat in our house comprising only 13 tsubo. The dog was called Momo and the cat Mii. My wife, who was very much oppose

16/17

In our house we had a cat with the grandiose name of Gonnosuke. Usu ally with cats and dogs we know who the mother is but not the father. A cat with a large belly wondered into the house of my younger sister a nd her husband and gave birth to five kittens. While the mother was a

24/25

In our house we had a cat with the grandiose n ame of Gonnosuke. Usually with cats and dogs we know who the mother is but not the father.

ABCDEFGHIJKLMN
OPQRSTUVWXYZ

abcdefghijklmnopq
rstuvwxyz
1234567890&$¢£¥
fiflæœÆŒÅßÇÌÎÍÏã§†
———/()''""";;.,!¡?¿

10/11

In our house we had a cat with the grandiose name of Gonnosuke. Usually with cats and dogs we know who the moth er is but not the father. A cat with a large belly wondered into the house of my younger sister and her husband and ga ve birth to five kittens. While the mother was a pure white thoroughbred Chinchila, the kittens were black and white tabbies of mixed breed. One of these came to our house about two weeks after its birth and was given the name Gonn osuke. At that time we already had one female Shiba dog and one female brown tabby cat in our house comprising o nly 13 tsubo. The dog was called Momo and the cat Mii. My wife, who was very much opposed to keeping cats and d

16/17

In our house we had a cat with the grandiose name of Gonnosuke. Usual ly with cats and dogs we know who the mother is but not the father. A ca t with a large belly wondered into the house of my younger sister and her husband and gave birth to five kittens. While the mother was a pure whi

24/25

In our house we had a cat with the grandiose na me of Gonnosuke. Usually with cats and dogs we know who the mother is but not the father. A cat

ABCDEFGHIJKLMN
OPQRSTUVWXYZ
abcdefghijklmnopq
rstuvwxyz
1234567890&$¢£¥
fiflæœÆŒÅßÇÌÎÍÏã
§†-——/()'"""::;.,!¡?¿

10/11

In our house we had a cat with the grandiose name of Gonnosuke. Usually with cats and dogs we know who t he mother is but not the father. A cat with a large belly wondered into the house of my younger sister and her husband and gave birth to five kittens. While the mother was a pure white thoroughbred Chinchila, the kitten s were black and white tabbies of mixed breed. One of these came to our house about two weeks after its birth and was given the name Gonnosuke. At that time we already had one female Shiba dog and one female brown tabby cat in our house comprising only 13 tsubo. The dog was called Momo and the cat Mii. My wife, who w

16/17

In our house we had a cat with the grandiose name of Gonnosuke. U sually with cats and dogs we know who the mother is but not the fat her. A cat with a large belly wondered into the house of my younger sister and her husband and gave birth to five kittens. While the mot

24/25

In our house we had a cat with the grandiose name of Gonnosuke. Usually with cats and d ogs we know who the mother is but not the fa

ABCDEFGHIJKLMN OPQRSTUVWXYZ abcdefghijklmnopq rstuvwxyz 1234567890&$¢£¥ fiflæœÆŒÅßÇÌÎÍÏã §†-–—/()''""‚;.,!¡?¿

10/11

In our house we had a cat with the grandiose name of Gonnosuke. Usually with cats and dogs we know who the mother is but not the father. A cat with a large belly wondered into the house of my younger sister and her husb and and gave birth to five kittens. While the mother was a pure white thoroughbred Chinchila, the kittens were black and white tabbies of mixed breed. One of these came to our house about two weeks after its birth and was given the name Gonnosuke. At that time we already had one female Shiba dog and one female brown tabby cat in our house comprising only 13 tsubo. The dog was called Momo and the cat Mii. My wife, who was very muc

16/17

In our house we had a cat with the grandiose name of Gonnosuke. Us ually with cats and dogs we know who the mother is but not the fathe r. A cat with a large belly wondered into the house of my younger siste r and her husband and gave birth to five kittens. While the mother w

24/25

In our house we had a cat with the grandiose name of Gonnosuke. Usually with cats and do gs we know who the mother is but not the fath

ABCDEFGHIJKL
MNOPQRSTUVW
XYZabcdefghijklmno
pqrstuvwxyz
1234567890&$¢£¥
fiflæœÆŒÅßÇÌÎÍÏã
§†–——/()''""",;.,!¡?¿

10/11

In our house we had a cat with the grandiose name of Gonnosuke. Usually with cats and dogs we know w
ho the mother is but not the father. A cat with a large belly wondered into the house of my younger sister
and her husband and gave birth to five kittens. While the mother was a pure white thoroughbred Chinchil
a, the kittens were black and white tabbies of mixed breed. One of these came to our house about two wee
ks after its birth and was given the name Gonnosuke. At that time we already had one female Shiba dog an
d one female brown tabby cat in our house comprising only 13 tsubo. The dog was called Momo and the c

16/17

In our house we had a cat with the grandiose name of Gonnosuke.
Usually with cats and dogs we know who the mother is but not th
e father. A cat with a large belly wondered into the house of my y
ounger sister and her husband and gave birth to five kittens. While

24/25

In our house we had a cat with the grandios
e name of Gonnosuke. Usually with cats an
d dogs we know who the mother is but not

ABCDEFGHIJKL
MNOPQRSTUVW
XYZabcdefghijklmno
pqrstuvwxyz
1234567890&$¢£¥
fiflæœÆŒÅßÇÌÎÍÏã
§†----——/()''""·:,.,!¡?¿

10/11

In our house we had a cat with the grandiose name of Gonnosuke. Usually with cats and dogs we know w ho the mother is but not the father. A cat with a large belly wondered into the house of my younger sister a nd her husband and gave birth to five kittens. While the mother was a pure white thoroughbred Chinchil a, the kittens were black and white tabbies of mixed breed. One of these came to our house about two wee ks after its birth and was given the name Gonnosuke. At that time we already had one female Shiba dog a nd one female brown tabby cat in our house comprising only 13 tsubo. The dog was called Momo and the c

16/17

In our house we had a cat with the grandiose name of Gonnosuke. Usually with cats and dogs we know who the mother is but not the father. A cat with a large belly wondered into the house of my you nger sister and her husband and gave birth to five kittens. While t

24/25

In our house we had a cat with the grandios e name of Gonnosuke. Usually with cats an d dogs we know who the mother is but not t

ABCDEFGHIJKL
MNOPQRSTUVW
XYZabcdefghijklmn
opqrstuvwxyz
1234567890&$¢£¥
fiflæœÆŒÅßÇÌÎÍÏã
§†–——/()''""";,.,!¡?¿

10/11

In our house we had a cat with the grandiose name of Gonnosuke. Usually with cats and dogs we kn ow who the mother is but not the father. A cat with a large belly wondered into the house of my you nger sister and her husband and gave birth to five kittens. While the mother was a pure white thorou ghbred Chinchila, the kittens were black and white tabbies of mixed breed. One of these came to our house about two weeks after its birth and was given the name Gonnosuke. At that time we already h ad one female Shiba dog and one female brown tabby cat in our house comprising only 13 tsubo. The

16/17

In our house we had a cat with the grandiose name of Gonnos uke. Usually with cats and dogs we know who the mother is bu t not the father. A cat with a large belly wondered into the hou se of my younger sister and her husband and gave birth to five

24/25

In our house we had a cat with the grandi ose name of Gonnosuke. Usually with cat s and dogs we know who the mother is bu

ABCDEFGHIJKL
MNOPQRSTUVW
XYZabcdefghijklmn
opqrstuvwxyz
1234567890&$¢£¥
fiflæœÆŒÅßÇÌÎÍÏã
§†-–——/()''""·;.,!¡?¿

10/11

In our house we had a cat with the grandiose name of Gonnosuke. Usually with cats and dogs we know w ho the mother is but not the father. A cat with a large belly wondered into the house of my younger sister and her husband and gave birth to five kittens. While the mother was a pure white thoroughbred Chinch ila, the kittens were black and white tabbies of mixed breed. One of these came to our house about two w eeks after its birth and was given the name Gonnosuke. At that time we already had one female Shiba do g and one female brown tabby cat in our house comprising only 13 tsubo. The dog was called Momo and t

16/17

In our house we had a cat with the grandiose name of Gonnosuke. Usually with cats and dogs we know who the mother is but not th e father. A cat with a large belly wondered into the house of my y ounger sister and her husband and gave birth to five kittens. Whil

24/25

In our house we had a cat with the grandios e name of Gonnosuke. Usually with cats an d dogs we know who the mother is but not t

ABCDEFGHIJKLMN
OPQRSTUVWXYZ
abcdefghijklmnopq
rstuvwxyz
1234567890&$¢£¥
fiflæœÆŒÅßÇÌÎÍÏã§†
———/()''"":;.,!¡?¿

10/11

In our house we had a cat with the grandiose name of Gonnosuke. Usually with cats and dogs we know who the moth er is but not the father. A cat with a large belly wondered into the house of my younger sister and her husband and ga ve birth to five kittens. While the mother was a pure white thoroughbred Chinchila, the kittens were black and whit e tabbies of mixed breed. One of these came to our house about two weeks after its birth and was given the name Gon nosuke. At that time we already had one female Shiba dog and one female brown tabby cat in our house comprising o nly 13 tsubo. The dog was called Momo and the cat Mii. My wife, who was very much opposed to keeping cats and d

16/17

In our house we had a cat with the grandiose name of Gonnosuke. Usuall y with cats and dogs we know who the mother is but not the father. A ca t with a large belly wondered into the house of my younger sister and her husband and gave birth to five kittens. While the mother was a pure whi

24/25

In our house we had a cat with the grandiose na me of Gonnosuke. Usually with cats and dogs w e know who the mother is but not the father. A c

ABCDEFGHIJKLMN
OPQRSTUVWXYZ
abcdefghijklmnopq
rstuvwxyz
1234567890&$¢£¥
fiflæœÆŒÅßÇÌÎÍÏã§†
———/()''""":;.,!¡?¿

10/11

In our house we had a cat with the grandiose name of Gonnosuke. Usually with cats and dogs we know who the mother is but not t
he father. A cat with a large belly wondered into the house of my younger sister and her husband and gave birth to five kittens. Wh
ile the mother was a pure white thoroughbred Chinchila, the kittens were black and white tabbies of mixed breed. One of these came
to our house about two weeks after its birth and was given the name Gonnosuke. At that time we already had one female Shiba dog
and one female brown tabby cat in our house comprising only 13 tsubo. The dog was called Momo and the cat Mii. My wife, who
was very much opposed to keeping cats and dogs, instantaneously fell for its shaggy appearance and the black tip of its nose and deci

16/17

In our house we had a cat with the grandiose name of Gonnosuke. Usually with c
ats and dogs we know who the mother is but not the father. A cat with a large bel
ly wondered into the house of my younger sister and her husband and gave birth to
five kittens. While the mother was a pure white thoroughbred Chinchila, the kitte

24/25

In our house we had a cat with the grandiose name of
Gonnosuke. Usually with cats and dogs we know who
the mother is but not the father. A cat with a large bel

ABCDEFGHIJKLMN
OPQRSTUVWXYZ
abcdefghijklmnopq
rstuvwxyz
1234567890&$¢£¥
fiflæœÆŒÅßÇÌÎÍÏã§†
——/()''""·;·,!¡?¿

10/11

In our house we had a cat with the grandiose name of Gonnosuke. Usually with cats and dogs we know wh o the mother is but not the father. A cat with a large belly wondered into the house of my younger sister an d her husband and gave birth to five kittens. While the mother was a pure white thoroughbred Chinchila, t he kittens were black and white tabbies of mixed breed. One of these came to our house about two weeks a fter its birth and was given the name Gonnosuke. At that time we already had one female Shiba dog and on e female brown tabby cat in our house comprising only 13 tsubo. The dog was called Momo and the cat Mii.

16/17

In our house we had a cat with the grandiose name of Gonnosuke. Usually with cats and dogs we know who the mother is but not the father. A cat with a large belly wondered into the house of my youn ger sister and her husband and gave birth to five kittens. While the

24/25

In our house we had a cat with the grandios e name of Gonnosuke. Usually with cats and dogs we know who the mother is but not th

ABCDEFGHIJKLMN
OPQRSTUVWXYZ
abcdefghijklmnopq
rstuvwxyz
1234567890&$¢£¥
fiflæœÆŒÅßÇÌÎÍÏã§†
——/()""""·;.,!¡?¿

10/11

In our house we had a cat with the grandiose name of Gonnosuke. Usually with cats and dogs we know who the mother is but not the father. A cat with a large belly wondered into the house of my younger sister and her husba nd and gave birth to five kittens. While the mother was a pure white thoroughbred Chinchila, the kittens were b lack and white tabbies of mixed breed. One of these came to our house about two weeks after its birth and was gi ven the name Gonnosuke. At that time we already had one female Shiba dog and one female brown tabby cat in our house comprising only 13 tsubo. The dog was called Momo and the cat Mii. My wife, who was very much oppo

16/17

In our house we had a cat with the grandiose name of Gonnosuke. Us ually with cats and dogs we know who the mother is but not the fathe r. A cat with a large belly wondered into the house of my younger siste r and her husband and gave birth to five kittens. While the mother w

24/25

In our house we had a cat with the grandiose n ame of Gonnosuke. Usually with cats and dogs we know who the mother is but not the father.

ABCDEFGHIJKLMNO
PQRSTUVWXYZ
abcdefghijklmnopq
rstuvwxyz
1234567890&$¢£¥
fiflæœÆŒÅßÇÌÎÍÏã§†
——/()''""·;·,!¡?¿

10/11

In our house we had a cat with the grandiose name of Gonnosuke. Usually with cats and dogs we kno w who the mother is but not the father. A cat with a large belly wondered into the house of my younge r sister and her husband and gave birth to five kittens. While the mother was a pure white thoroughbre d Chinchila, the kittens were black and white tabbies of mixed breed. One of these came to our house about two weeks after its birth and was given the name Gonnosuke. At that time we already had one fe male Shiba dog and one female brown tabby cat in our house comprising only 13 tsubo. The dog was c

16/17

In our house we had a cat with the grandiose name of Gonnosu ke. Usually with cats and dogs we know who the mother is but not the father. A cat with a large belly wondered into the house of my younger sister and her husband and gave birth to five kitt

24/25

In our house we had a cat with the grandi ose name of Gonnosuke. Usually with cats and dogs we know who the mother is but

ABCDEFGHIJKLMNO
PQRSTUVWXYZ
abcdefghijklmnopq
rstuvwxyz
1234567890&$¢£¥
fiflæœÆŒÅßçÌÎÍÏã§†
———/()''""";.,!¡?¿

10/11

In our house we had a cat with the grandiose name of Gonnosuke. Usually with cats and dogs we know who the mother is but not the father. A cat with a large belly wondered into the house of my younger siste r and her husband and gave birth to five kittens. While the mother was a pure white thoroughbred Chinc hila, the kittens were black and white tabbies of mixed breed. One of these came to our house about two weeks after its birth and was given the name Gonnosuke. At that time we already had one female Shiba dog and one female brown tabby cat in our house comprising only 13 tsubo. The dog was called Momo a

16/17

In our house we had a cat with the grandiose name of Gonnosuk e. Usually with cats and dogs we know who the mother is but not the father. A cat with a large belly wondered into the house of my younger sister and her husband and gave birth to five kittens. Wh

24/25

In our house we had a cat with the grandio se name of Gonnosuke. Usually with cats a nd dogs we know who the mother is but not

ABCDEFGHIJKLMN
OPQRSTUVWXYZ
abcdefghijklmnopq
rstuvwxyz
1234567890&$¢£¥
fiflæœÆŒÅßÇÌÎÍÏĩ
§†-–—/()''""":;.,!¡?¿

10/11

In our house we had a cat with the grandiose name of Gonnosuke. Usually with cats and dogs we know who the mother is but not the father. A cat with a large belly wondered into the hous e of my younger sister and her husband and gave birth to five kittens. While the mother was a pure white thoroughbred Chinchila, the kittens were black and white tabbies of mixed breed. One of these came to our house about two weeks after its birth and was given the name Gonno suke. At that time we already had one female Shiba dog and one female brown tabby cat in our

16/17

In our house we had a cat with the grandiose name of Gon nosuke. Usually with cats and dogs we know who the moth er is but not the father. A cat with a large belly wondered i nto the house of my younger sister and her husband and g

24/25

In our house we had a cat with the gra ndiose name of Gonnosuke. Usually wi th cats and dogs we know who the mot

ABCDEFGHIJKLMN
OPQRSTUVWXYZ
abcdefghijklmnopq
rstuvwxyz
1234567890&$¢£¥
fiflæœÆŒÅßÇÌÎÍÏ
ãſ†-–—/O'"""¡.;.,!¡?¿

10/11

In our house we had a cat with the grandiose name of Gonnosuke. Usually with cats and dogs we know who the mother is but not the father. A cat with a large belly wondered into the hous e of my younger sister and her husband and gave birth to five kittens. While the mother was a pure white thoroughbred Chinchila, the kittens were black and white tabbies of mixed breed. One of these came to our house about two weeks after its birth and was given the name Gonn osuke. At that time we already had one female Shiba dog and one female brown tabby cat in o

16/17

In our house we had a cat with the grandiose name of Go nnosuke. Usually with cats and dogs we know who the mo ther is but not the father. A cat with a large belly wondere d into the house of my younger sister and her husband an

24/25

In our house we had a cat with the gr andiose name of Gonnosuke. Usually with cats and dogs we know who the

ABCDEFGHIJKLMN
OPQRSTUVWXYZ
abcdefghijklmnopq
rstuvwxyz
1234567890&$¢£¥
fiflæœÆŒÅßÇÌÎÍÏã§†
-——/()''""";:.,!¡?¿

10/11

In our house we had a cat with the grandiose name of Gonnosuke. Usually with cats and dogs we know who the mother is but not the father. A cat with a large belly wondered into the house of my younger sister and her husb and and gave birth to five kittens. While the mother was a pure white thoroughbred Chinchila, the kittens wer e black and white tabbies of mixed breed. One of these came to our house about two weeks after its birth and w as given the name Gonnosuke. At that time we already had one female Shiba dog and one female brown tabby cat in our house comprising only 13 tsubo. The dog was called Momo and the cat Mii. My wife,

16/17

In our house we had a cat with the grandiose name of Gonnosuke. Us ually with cats and dogs we know who the mother is but not the fathe r. A cat with a large belly wondered into the house of my younger sist er and her husband and gave birth to five kittens. While the mother

24/25

In our house we had a cat with the grandiose name of Gonnosuke. Usually with cats and do gs we know who the mother is but not the fat

ABCDEFGHIJKLMN
OPQRSTUVWXYZ
abcdefghijklmnopq
rstuvwxyz
1234567890&$¢£¥
fiflæœÆŒÅßÇÌÎÍÏã§†
-——/() '' "" :;.,!¡?¿

10/11

In our house we had a cat with the grandiose name of Gonnosuke. Usually with cats and dogs we know who the mother is but not the father. A cat with a large belly wondered into the house of my younger sister and her husband and gave birt h to five kittens. While the mother was a pure white thoroughbred Chinchila, the kittens were black and white tabbies of mixed breed. One of these came to our house about two weeks after its birth and was given the name Gonnosuke. At th at time we already had one female Shiba dog and one female brown tabby cat in our house comprising only 13 tsubo. Th e dog was called Momo and the cat Mii. My wife, who was very much opposed to keeping cats and dogs, instantaneousl

16/17

In our house we had a cat with the grandiose name of Gonnosuke. Usually with cats and dogs we know who the mother is but not the father. A cat wit h a large belly wondered into the house of my younger sister and her husba nd and gave birth to five kittens. While the mother was a pure white thorou

24/25

In our house we had a cat with the grandiose nam e of Gonnosuke. Usually with cats and dogs we k now who the mother is but not the father. A cat w

599

ABCDEFGHIJKL MNOPQRSTUVW XYZabcdefghijklmnop qrstuvwxyz 1234567890&$¢£¥ fiflæœÆŒÅßÇÌÎÍÏĩã§ †-–—/()''""";:.,!¡?¿

10/11

In our house we had a cat with the grandiose name of Gonnosuke. Usually with cats and dogs we know wh o the mother is but not the father. A cat with a large belly wondered into the house of my younger sister an d her husband and gave birth to five kittens. While the mother was a pure white thoroughbred Chinchila, t he kittens were black and white tabbies of mixed breed. One of these came to our house about two weeks af ter its birth and was given the name Gonnosuke. At that time we already had one female Shiba dog and one female brown tabby cat in our house comprising only 13 tsubo. The dog was called Momo and the cat Mii.

16/17

In our house we had a cat with the grandiose name of Gonnosuke. Usually with cats and dogs we know who the mother is but not the father. A cat with a large belly wondered into the house of my you nger sister and her husband and gave birth to five kittens. While th

24/25

In our house we had a cat with the grandios e name of Gonnosuke. Usually with cats an d dogs we know who the mother is but not t

ABCDEFGHIJKL MNOPQRSTUVW XYZabcdefghijklmnop qrstuvwxyz 1234567890&$¢£¥ fiflæœÆŒÅßÇÌÎÍÏã§ †-——/()'’“”:;.,!¡?¿

10/11

In our house we had a cat with the grandiose name of Gonnosuke. Usually with cats and dogs we know wh o the mother is but not the father. A cat with a large belly wondered into the house of my younger sister an d her husband and gave birth to five kittens. While the mother was a pure white thoroughbred Chinchila, t he kittens were black and white tabbies of mixed breed. One of these came to our house about two weeks aft er its birth and was given the name Gonnosuke. At that time we already had one female Shiba dog and one female brown tabby cat in our house comprising only 13 tsubo. The dog was called Momo and the cat Mii.

16/17

In our house we had a cat with the grandiose name of Gonnosuke. Usually with cats and dogs we know who the mother is but not the father. A cat with a large belly wondered into the house of my youn ger sister and her husband and gave birth to five kittens. While the

24/25

In our house we had a cat with the grandios e name of Gonnosuke. Usually with cats an d dogs we know who the mother is but not th

ABCDEFGHIJKL MNOPQRSTUVW XYZabcdefghijklmn opqrstuvwxyz 1234567890&$¢£¥ fiflæœÆŒÅßÇÌÎÍÏã §†·-–—/()''""'.;.,!¡?¿

10/11

In our house we had a cat with the grandiose name of Gonnosuke. Usually with cats and dogs we k
now who the mother is but not the father. A cat with a large belly wondered into the house of my y
ounger sister and her husband and gave birth to five kittens. While the mother was a pure white tho
roughbred Chinchila, the kittens were black and white tabbies of mixed breed. One of these came to
our house about two weeks after its birth and was given the name Gonnosuke. At that time we alrea
dy had one female Shiba dog and one female brown tabby cat in our house comprising only 13 tsub

16/17

In our house we had a cat with the grandiose name of Gonnos
uke. Usually with cats and dogs we know who the mother is b
ut not the father. A cat with a large belly wondered into the ho
use of my younger sister and her husband and gave birth to fiv

24/25

In our house we had a cat with the grand
iose name of Gonnosuke. Usually with ca
ts and dogs we know who the mother is b

ABCDEFGHIJKL
MNOPQRSTUVW
XYZabcdefghijkl
mnopqrstuvwxyz
1234567890&
$¢£¥fiflæœÆŒ
Åßçìîíïïã§†
·-——/()""""";:.,!¡?¿

10/11

In our house we had a cat with the grandiose name of Gonnosuke. Usually with cats and dogs we know who the mother is but not the father. A cat with a large belly wo ndered into the house of my younger sister and her husband and gave birth to five k ittens. While the mother was a pure white thoroughbred Chinchila, the kittens were black and white tabbies of mixed breed. One of these came to our house about two w eeks after its birth and was given the name Gonnosuke. At that time we already had

16/17

In our house we had a cat with the grandiose name of Gonnosuke. Usually with cats and dogs we know who the mother is but not the father. A cat with a la rge belly wondered into the house of my younger sis

24/25

In our house we had a cat with the grandiose name of Gonnosuke. Usu ally with cats and dogs we know w

ABCDEFGHIJKL
MNOPQRSTUVW
XYZabcdefghijkl
mnopqrstuvwxyz
1234567890&
$¢£¥fifl œœÆŒ
ÅßÇÌÎÍÏã§†
ˈ——/()''""";.,·!¡?¿

10/11

In our house we had a cat with the grandiose name of Gonnosuke. Usually with ca
ts and dogs we know who the mother is but not the father. A cat with a large belly
wondered into the house of my younger sister and her husband and gave birth to fi
ve kittens. While the mother was a pure white thoroughbred Chinchila, the kittens
were black and white tabbies of mixed breed. One of these came to our house about
two weeks after its birth and was given the name Gonnosuke. At that time we alre

16/17

In our house we had a cat with the grandiose name
of Gonnosuke. Usually with cats and dogs we know
who the mother is but not the father. A cat with a l
arge belly wondered into the house of my younger si

24/25

In our house we had a cat with th
e grandiose name of Gonnosuke. U
sually with cats and dogs we kno

ABCDEFGHIJKLMN
OPQRSTUVWXYZ
abcdefghijklmnopq
rstuvwxyz
1234567890&$¢£¥
fiflæœÆŒÅßÇÌÎÍÏã§
†----——/()''""":.;.,!¡?¿

10/11

In our house we had a cat with the grandiose name of Gonnosuke. Usually with cats and dogs we kn ow who the mother is but not the father. A cat with a large belly wondered into the house of my youn ger sister and her husband and gave birth to five kittens. While the mother was a pure white thoroug hbred Chinchila, the kittens were black and white tabbies of mixed breed. One of these came to our house about two weeks after its birth and was given the name Gonnosuke. At that time we already h ad one female Shiba dog and one female brown tabby cat in our house comprising only 13 tsubo. Th

16/17

In our house we had a cat with the grandiose name of Gonnos uke. Usually with cats and dogs we know who the mother is bu t not the father. A cat with a large belly wondered into the hous e of my younger sister and her husband and gave birth to five k

24/25

In our house we had a cat with the grandi ose name of Gonnosuke. Usually with ca ts and dogs we know who the mother is b

ABCDEFGHIJKLMN
OPQRSTUVWXYZ
abcdefghijklmnopq
rstuvwxyz
1234567890&$¢£¥
fiflœœÆŒÅßÇÌÎÍÏã§
†----——/()''"",,.,.,!¡?¿

10/11

In our house we had a cat with the grandiose name of Gonnosuke. Usually with cats and dogs we know who the mother is but not the father. A cat with a large belly wondered into the house of my younger sist er and her husband and gave birth to five kittens. While the mother was a pure white thoroughbred Chi nchila, the kittens were black and white tabbies of mixed breed. One of these came to our house about t wo weeks after its birth and was given the name Gonnosuke. At that time we already had one female Shi ba dog and one female brown tabby cat in our house comprising only 13 tsubo. The dog was called Mo

16/17

In our house we had a cat with the grandiose name of Gonnosuk e. Usually with cats and dogs we know who the mother is but no t the father. A cat with a large belly wondered into the house of m y younger sister and her husband and gave birth to five kittens.

24/25

In our house we had a cat with the grandio se name of Gonnosuke. Usually with cats a nd dogs we know who the mother is but no

ABCDEFGHIJKL
MNOPQRSTUVW
XYZabcdefghijklmn
opqrstuvwxyz
1234567890&$¢£¥
fiflæœÆŒÅßÇÌÎÍÏã
§†-–—/()''""":;.,!¡?¿

10/11

In our house we had a cat with the grandiose name of Gonnosuke. Usually with cats and dogs w
e know who the mother is but not the father. A cat with a large belly wondered into the house of
my younger sister and her husband and gave birth to five kittens. While the mother was a pure
white thoroughbred Chinchila, the kittens were black and white tabbies of mixed breed. One of t
hese came to our house about two weeks after its birth and was given the name Gonnosuke. At t
hat time we already had one female Shiba dog and one female brown tabby cat in our house co

16/17

In our house we had a cat with the grandiose name of Gonn
osuke. Usually with cats and dogs we know who the mother
is but not the father. A cat with a large belly wondered into t
he house of my younger sister and her husband and gave bir

24/25

In our house we had a cat with the gran
diose name of Gonnosuke. Usually with
cats and dogs we know who the mother

ABCDEFGHIJKL MNOPQRSTUVW XYZabcdefghijklmn opqrstuvwxyz 1234567890&$¢£¥ fiflœœÆŒÅßÇÌÎÍÏã §†-–—/()''""";:.,!¡?¿

10/11

In our house we had a cat with the grandiose name of Gonnosuke. Usually with cats and dogs we know who the mother is but not the father. A cat with a large belly wondered into the house of my y ounger sister and her husband and gave birth to five kittens. While the mother was a pure white th oroughbred Chinchila, the kittens were black and white tabbies of mixed breed. One of these came t o our house about two weeks after its birth and was given the name Gonnosuke. At that time we al ready had one female Shiba dog and one female brown tabby cat in our house comprising only 13 t

16/17

In our house we had a cat with the grandiose name of Gonnos uke. Usually with cats and dogs we know who the mother is b ut not the father. A cat with a large belly wondered into the h ouse of my younger sister and her husband and gave birth to

24/25

In our house we had a cat with the gran diose name of Gonnosuke. Usually with c ats and dogs we know who the mother is

ABCDEFGHIJKL
MNOPQRSTUVW
XYZabcdefghijklm
nopqrstuvwxyz123
4567890&$¢£¥fifl
æœÆŒÅßÇÌÎÍÏã§
†-–——/()''""::;.,!¡?¿

10/11

In our house we had a cat with the grandiose name of Gonnosuke. Usually with cats and do
gs we know who the mother is but not the father. A cat with a large belly wondered into the
house of my younger sister and her husband and gave birth to five kittens. While the mothe
r was a pure white thoroughbred Chinchila, the kittens were black and white tabbies of mix
ed breed. One of these came to our house about two weeks after its birth and was given the
name Gonnosuke. At that time we already had one female Shiba dog and one female brown

16/17

In our house we had a cat with the grandiose name of Go
nnosuke. Usually with cats and dogs we know who the m
other is but not the father. A cat with a large belly wonde
red into the house of my younger sister and her husband

24/25

In our house we had a cat with the gr
andiose name of Gonnosuke. Usually
with cats and dogs we know who the

ABCDEFGHIJKLM
NOPQRSTUVWX
YZabcdefghijklmn
opqrstuvwxyz123
4567890&$¢£¥
fiflœœÆŒÅßÇÌÎÍÏã
§†-–—/()''""":;.,!¡?¿

10/11

In our house we had a cat with the grandiose name of Gonnosuke. Usually with cats and do
gs we know who the mother is but not the father. A cat with a large belly wondered into the
house of my younger sister and her husband and gave birth to five kittens. While the mother
was a pure white thoroughbred Chinchila, the kittens were black and white tabbies of mixed
breed. One of these came to our house about two weeks after its birth and was given the nam
e Gonnosuke. At that time we already had one female Shiba dog and one female brown tabb

16/17

In our house we had a cat with the grandiose name of Go
nnosuke. Usually with cats and dogs we know who the m
other is but not the father. A cat with a large belly wonde
red into the house of my younger sister and her husband

24/25

In our house we had a cat with the gr
andiose name of Gonnosuke. Usually
with cats and dogs we know who the

ABCDEFGHIJKL
MNOPQRSTUVW
XYZabcdefghijkl
mnopqrstuvwxyz
1234567890&$¢
£¥fiflæœÆŒ
ÅßçÌÎÍÏã§†
———/()''""",.;.,!¡?¿

10/11

In our house we had a cat with the grandiose name of Gonnosuke. Usually with cats a
nd dogs we know who the mother is but not the father. A cat with a large belly wonde
red into the house of my younger sister and her husband and gave birth to five kitten
s. While the mother was a pure white thoroughbred Chinchila, the kittens were black
and white tabbies of mixed breed. One of these came to our house about two weeks af
ter its birth and was given the name Gonnosuke. At that time we already had one fem

16/17

In our house we had a cat with the grandiose name of
Gonnosuke. Usually with cats and dogs we know who
the mother is but not the father. A cat with a large bel
ly wondered into the house of my younger sister and

24/25

In our house we had a cat with the
grandiose name of Gonnosuke. Usu
ally with cats and dogs we know w

ABCDEFGHIJKL
MNOPQRSTUV
WXYZabcdefghij
klmnopqrstuvwx
yz1234567890&
$¢£¥fiflæœÆŒ
ÅßÇÌÎÍÏã§†
–‒—/()''""":;.,!¡?¿

10/11

In our house we had a cat with the grandiose name of Gonnosuke. Usually with cats a nd dogs we know who the mother is but not the father. A cat with a large belly wonder ed into the house of my younger sister and her husband and gave birth to five kittens. While the mother was a pure white thoroughbred Chinchila, the kittens were black an d white tabbies of mixed breed. One of these came to our house about two weeks after i ts birth and was given the name Gonnosuke. At that time we already had one female S

16/17

In our house we had a cat with the grandiose name of Gonnosuke. Usually with cats and dogs we know who the mother is but not the father. A cat with a large bel ly wondered into the house of my younger sister and h

24/25

In our house we had a cat with the grandiose name of Gonnosuke. Usu ally with cats and dogs we know w

ABCDEFGHIJKLM
NOPQRSTUVWXYZ
abcdefghijklmnopq
rstuvwxyz
1234567890&$¢£¥
fiflæœÆŒÅßÇÌÎÍÏã§
†-–—/()""''''.,;..,!¡?¿

10/11

In our house we had a cat with the grandiose name of Gonnosuke. Usually with cats and dogs we kno w who the mother is but not the father. A cat with a large belly wondered into the house of my young er sister and her husband and gave birth to five kittens. While the mother was a pure white thorough bred Chinchila, the kittens were black and white tabbies of mixed breed. One of these came to our hou se about two weeks after its birth and was given the name Gonnosuke. At that time we already had o ne female Shiba dog and one female brown tabby cat in our house comprising only 13 tsubo. The dog

16/17

In our house we had a cat with the grandiose name of Gonnosu ke. Usually with cats and dogs we know who the mother is but not the father. A cat with a large belly wondered into the house of my younger sister and her husband and gave birth to five kit

24/25

In our house we had a cat with the grandi ose name of Gonnosuke. Usually with cats and dogs we know who the mother is but

ABCDEFGHIJKLMN
OPQRSTUVWXYZ
abcdefghijklmnopq
rstuvwxyz
1234567890&$¢£¥
fiflæœÆŒÅßÇÌÎÍÏã§†
———/()""""",;.,!¡?¿

10/11

In our house we had a cat with the grandiose name of Gonnosuke. Usually with cats and dogs we know who the mother is but not the father. A cat with a large belly wondered into the house of my younger sister and her husb and and gave birth to five kittens. While the mother was a pure white thoroughbred Chinchila, the kittens were b lack and white tabbies of mixed breed. One of these came to our house about two weeks after its birth and was gi ven the name Gonnosuke. At that time we already had one female Shiba dog and one female brown tabby cat in o ur house comprising only 13 tsubo. The dog was called Momo and the cat Mii. My wife, who was very much op

16/17

In our house we had a cat with the grandiose name of Gonnosuke. Us ually with cats and dogs we know who the mother is but not the fathe r. A cat with a large belly wondered into the house of my younger sist er and her husband and gave birth to five kittens. While the mother w

24/25

In our house we had a cat with the grandiose name of Gonnosuke. Usually with cats and do gs we know who the mother is but not the fath

ABCDEFGHIJKL MNOPQRSTUVW XYZabcdefghijklmn opqrstuvwxyz 1234567890&$¢£¥ fiflæœÆŒÅßÇÌÎÍÏã §†-–—/()""''""·;.,!¡?¿

10/11

In our house we had a cat with the grandiose name of Gonnosuke. Usually with cats and dogs we k now who the mother is but not the father. A cat with a large belly wondered into the house of my y ounger sister and her husband and gave birth to five kittens. While the mother was a pure white th oroughbred Chinchila, the kittens were black and white tabbies of mixed breed. One of these came to our house about two weeks after its birth and was given the name Gonnosuke. At that time we a lready had one female Shiba dog and one female brown tabby cat in our house comprising only 13

16/17

In our house we had a cat with the grandiose name of Gonnos uke. Usually with cats and dogs we know who the mother is but not the father. A cat with a large belly wondered into the house of my younger sister and her husband and gave birth t

24/25

In our house we had a cat with the grand iose name of Gonnosuke. Usually with c ats and dogs we know who the mother is

ABCDEFGHIJKLM
NOPQRSTUVWX
YZabcdefghijklmnop
qrstuvwxyz
1234567890&$¢£¥
fiflæœÆŒÅßÇÌÎÍÏã§
+-——/()''""";,.,!¡?¿

10/11

In our house we had a cat with the grandiose name of Gonnosuke. Usually with cats and dogs we kn ow who the mother is but not the father. A cat with a large belly wondered into the house of my youn ger sister and her husband and gave birth to five kittens. While the mother was a pure white thoroug hbred Chinchila, the kittens were black and white tabbies of mixed breed. One of these came to our ho use about two weeks after its birth and was given the name Gonnosuke. At that time we already had one female Shiba dog and one female brown tabby cat in our house comprising only 13 tsubo. The dog

16/17

In our house we had a cat with the grandiose name of Gonnosu ke. Usually with cats and dogs we know who the mother is but not the father. A cat with a large belly wondered into the house of my younger sister and her husband and gave birth to five kit

24/25

In our house we had a cat with the grandi ose name of Gonnosuke. Usually with cat s and dogs we know who the mother is bu

ABCDEFGHIJKL
MNOPQRSTUVWX
YZabcdefghijklmnop
qrstuvwxyz
1234567890&$¢£¥
fiflæœÆŒÅßÇÌÎÍÏĩ
§†-–—/()''""":;.,!¡?¿

10/11

In our house we had a cat with the grandiose name of Gonnosuke. Usually with cats and dogs we know who the mother is but not the father. A cat with a large belly wondered into the house of my younger sis ter and her husband and gave birth to five kittens. While the mother was a pure white thoroughbred Chi nchila, the kittens were black and white tabbies of mixed breed. One of these came to our house about t wo weeks after its birth and was given the name Gonnosuke. At that time we already had one female Sh iba dog and one female brown tabby cat in our house comprising only 13 tsubo. The dog was called Mo

16/17

In our house we had a cat with the grandiose name of Gonnosuk e. Usually with cats and dogs we know who the mother is but no t the father. A cat with a large belly wondered into the house of my younger sister and her husband and gave birth to five kittens.

24/25

In our house we had a cat with the grandio se name of Gonnosuke. Usually with cats a nd dogs we know who the mother is but n

ABCDEFGHIJKL
MNOPQRSTUVW
XYZabcdefghijklmn
opqrstuvwxyz
1234567890&$¢£¥
fiflæœÆŒÅßÇÌÎÍÏã
§†--——/()''""";:.,!¡?¿

10/11

In our house we had a cat with the grandiose name of Gonnosuke. Usually with cats and dogs we know who the mother is but not the father. A cat with a large belly wondered into the house of my younger sis ter and her husband and gave birth to five kittens. While the mother was a pure white thoroughbred Ch inchila, the kittens were black and white tabbies of mixed breed. One of these came to our house about two weeks after its birth and was given the name Gonnosuke. At that time we already had one female S hiba dog and one female brown tabby cat in our house comprising only 13 tsubo. The dog was called

16/17

In our house we had a cat with the grandiose name of Gonnosu ke. Usually with cats and dogs we know who the mother is but n ot the father. A cat with a large belly wondered into the house of my younger sister and her husband and gave birth to five kittens.

24/25

In our house we had a cat with the grandio se name of Gonnosuke. Usually with cats a nd dogs we know who the mother is but n

ABCDEFGHIJKL
MNOPQRSTUVW
XYZabcdefghijklmn
opqrstuvwxyz
1234567890&$¢£¥
fiflæœÆŒÅßÇÌÎÍÏã
§†----—/()''""'.:;.,!¡?¿

10/11

In our house we had a cat with the grandiose name of Gonnosuke. Usually with cats and dogs we know who the mother is but not the father. A cat with a large belly wondered into the house of my younger sis ter and her husband and gave birth to five kittens. While the mother was a pure white thoroughbred Chi nchila, the kittens were black and white tabbies of mixed breed. One of these came to our house about t wo weeks after its birth and was given the name Gonnosuke. At that time we already had one female Sh iba dog and one female brown tabby cat in our house comprising only 13 tsubo. The dog was called Mo

16/17

In our house we had a cat with the grandiose name of Gonnosuk e. Usually with cats and dogs we know who the mother is but no t the father. A cat with a large belly wondered into the house of my younger sister and her husband and gave birth to five kittens.

24/25

In our house we had a cat with the grandio se name of Gonnosuke. Usually with cats a nd dogs we know who the mother is but n

ABCDEFGHIJKL
MNOPQRSTUVW
XYZabcdefghijklmn
opqrstuvwxyz
1234567890&$¢£¥
fiflæœÆŒÅßÇÌÎÍÏã
§†------/()''""".:;.,!¡?¿

10/11

In our house we had a cat with the grandiose name of Gonnosuke. Usually with cats and dogs we kno w who the mother is but not the father. A cat with a large belly wondered into the house of my younge r sister and her husband and gave birth to five kittens. While the mother was a pure white thoroughbre d Chinchila, the kittens were black and white tabbies of mixed breed. One of these came to our house about two weeks after its birth and was given the name Gonnosuke. At that time we already had one f emale Shiba dog and one female brown tabby cat in our house comprising only 13 tsubo. The dog was

16/17

In our house we had a cat with the grandiose name of Gonnosu ke. Usually with cats and dogs we know who the mother is but not the father. A cat with a large belly wondered into the house of my younger sister and her husband and gave birth to five kitt

24/25

In our house we had a cat with the grandi ose name of Gonnosuke. Usually with cats and dogs we know who the mother is but

ABCDEFGHIJKL
MNOPQRSTUVW
XYZabcdefghijklmn
opqrstuvwxyz
1234567890&$¢£¥
fiflæœÆŒÅßÇÌÎÍÏã
§†-–——/()''""";.,!¡?¿

10/11

In our house we had a cat with the grandiose name of Gonnosuke. Usually with cats and dogs we know who the mother is but not the father. A cat with a large belly wondered into the house of my younger sister and her husband and gave birth to five kittens. While the mother was a pure w hite thoroughbred Chinchila, the kittens were black and white tabbies of mixed breed. One of the se came to our house about two weeks after its birth and was given the name Gonnosuke. At that time we already had one female Shiba dog and one female brown tabby cat in our house comprisi

16/17

In our house we had a cat with the grandiose name of Gonno suke. Usually with cats and dogs we know who the mother i s but not the father. A cat with a large belly wondered into t he house of my younger sister and her husband and gave birt

24/25

In our house we had a cat with the gran diose name of Gonnosuke. Usually with cats and dogs we know who the mother

ABCDEFGHIJKL
MNOPQRSTUVW
XYZabcdefghijklm
nopqrstuvwxyz
1234567890&$¢£¥
fiflæœÆŒÅßÇÌÎÍÏã
§†-–——/()''""".;.,!¡?¿

10/11

In our house we had a cat with the grandiose name of Gonnosuke. Usually with cats and dogs we know who the mother is but not the father. A cat with a large belly wondered into the house of my younger sister and her husband and gave birth to five kittens. While the mother was a pur e white thoroughbred Chinchila, the kittens were black and white tabbies of mixed breed. One of these came to our house about two weeks after its birth and was given the name Gonnosuke. At that time we already had one female Shiba dog and one female brown tabby cat in our house

16/17

In our house we had a cat with the grandiose name of Gonn osuke. Usually with cats and dogs we know who the mothe r is but not the father. A cat with a large belly wondered int o the house of my younger sister and her husband and gave

24/25

In our house we had a cat with the gran diose name of Gonnosuke. Usually wit h cats and dogs we know who the moth

ABCDEFGHIJKL
MNOPQRSTUVW
XYZabcdefghijklm
nopqrstuvwxyz
1234567890&$¢£¥
fiflæœÆŒÅßÇÌÎÍÏã
§†-–—/()''""·;.,!¡?¿

10/11

In our house we had a cat with the grandiose name of Gonnosuke. Usually with cats and dogs we know who the mother is but not the father. A cat with a large belly wondered into the house of my younger sister and her husband and gave birth to five kittens. While the mother was a pure w hite thoroughbred Chinchila, the kittens were black and white tabbies of mixed breed. One of the se came to our house about two weeks after its birth and was given the name Gonnosuke. At that time we already had one female Shiba dog and one female brown tabby cat in our house comprisi

16/17

In our house we had a cat with the grandiose name of Gonno suke. Usually with cats and dogs we know who the mother i s but not the father. A cat with a large belly wondered into t he house of my younger sister and her husband and gave birt

24/25

In our house we had a cat with the gran diose name of Gonnosuke. Usually with cats and dogs we know who the mother

ABCDEFGHIJKL
MNOPQRSTUVW
XYZabcdefghijklm
nopqrstuvwxyz
1234567890&$¢£¥
fiflæœÆŒÅßÇÌÎÍÏã
§†-–——/()''""";.,!¡?¿

10/11

In our house we had a cat with the grandiose name of Gonnosuke. Usually with cats and dogs we know who the mother is but not the father. A cat with a large belly wondered into the hous e of my younger sister and her husband and gave birth to five kittens. While the mother was a pure white thoroughbred Chinchila, the kittens were black and white tabbies of mixed breed. One of these came to our house about two weeks after its birth and was given the name Gonno suke. At that time we already had one female Shiba dog and one female brown tabby cat in our

16/17

In our house we had a cat with the grandiose name of Gon nosuke. Usually with cats and dogs we know who the mot her is but not the father. A cat with a large belly wondered into the house of my younger sister and her husband and g

24/25

In our house we had a cat with the gra ndiose name of Gonnosuke. Usually wi th cats and dogs we know who the mot

ABCDEFGHIJKLMN
OPQRSTUVWXYZ
abcdefghijklmnopq
rstuvwxyz
1234567890&$¢£¥
fiflæœÆŒÅßÇÌÎÍÏã§†
-——/()"""":;.,!¡?¿

10/11

In our house we had a cat with the grandiose name of Gonnosuke. Usually with cats and dogs we know who the mother is but not the father. A cat with a large belly wondered into the house of my younger sister and her husb and and gave birth to five kittens. While the mother was a pure white thoroughbred Chinchila, the kittens were black and white tabbies of mixed breed. One of these came to our house about two weeks after its birth and was given the name Gonnosuke. At that time we already had one female Shiba dog and one female brown tabby cat in our house comprising only 13 tsubo. The dog was called Momo and the cat Mii. My wife, who was very much

16/17

In our house we had a cat with the grandiose name of Gonnosuke. Us ually with cats and dogs we know who the mother is but not the fathe r. A cat with a large belly wondered into the house of my younger sist er and her husband and gave birth to five kittens. While the mother w

24/25

In our house we had a cat with the grandiose n ame of Gonnosuke. Usually with cats and dogs we know who the mother is but not the father.

ABCDEFGHIJKLMNO
PQRSTUVWXYZ
abcdefghijklmnopq
rstuvwxyz
1234567890&$¢£¥
fiflæœÆŒÅßÇÌÎÍÏã§†
———/()"""",:;.,!¡?¿

10/11

In our house we had a cat with the grandiose name of Gonnosuke. Usually with cats and dogs we know who the mother is but not the fa
ther. A cat with a large belly wondered into the house of my younger sister and her husband and gave birth to five kittens. While the mot
her was a pure white thoroughbred Chinchila, the kittens were black and white tabbies of mixed breed. One of these came to our house ab
out two weeks after its birth and was given the name Gonnosuke. At that time we already had one female Shiba dog and one female brow
n tabby cat in our house comprising only 13 tsubo. The dog was called Momo and the cat Mii. My wife, who was very much opposed
to keeping cats and dogs, instantaneously fell for its shaggy appearance and the black tip of its nose and decided on its name, crying this

16/17

In our house we had a cat with the grandiose name of Gonnosuke. Usually with cats
and dogs we know who the mother is but not the father. A cat with a large belly won
dered into the house of my younger sister and her husband and gave birth to five kitte
ns. While the mother was a pure white thoroughbred Chinchila, the kittens were blac

24/25

In our house we had a cat with the grandiose name of G
onnosuke. Usually with cats and dogs we know who the
mother is but not the father. A cat with a large belly won

ABCDEFGHIJKLMN
OPQRSTUVWXYZ
abcdefghijklmnopq
rstuvwxyz
1234567890&$¢£¥
fiflæœÆŒÅßÇÌÎÍÏã§†
————/()""""":;.,!¡?¿

10/11

In our house we had a cat with the grandiose name of Gonnosuke. Usually with cats and dogs we know who the mother is but not the father. A cat with a large belly wondered into the house of my younger sister and h er husband and gave birth to five kittens. While the mother was a pure white thoroughbred Chinchila, the ki ttens were black and white tabbies of mixed breed. One of these came to our house about two weeks after it s birth and was given the name Gonnosuke. At that time we already had one female Shiba dog and one femal e brown tabby cat in our house comprising only 13 tsubo. The dog was called Momo and the cat Mii. My wi

16/17

In our house we had a cat with the grandiose name of Gonnosuke. Usually with cats and dogs we know who the mother is but not the father. A cat with a large belly wondered into the house of my youn ger sister and her husband and gave birth to five kittens. While the

24/25

In our house we had a cat with the grandiose name of Gonnosuke. Usually with cats and d ogs we know who the mother is but not the f

ABCDEFGHIJKLMN
OPQRSTUVWXYZ
abcdefghijklmnopq
rstuvwxyz
1234567890&$¢£¥
fiflæœÆŒÅßÇÌÎÍÏã
§†-–——/()"""":;·.,!¡?¿

10/11

In our house we had a cat with the grandiose name of Gonnosuke. Usually with cats and dogs we know who the mother is but not the father. A cat with a large belly wondered into the house of my younger si ster and her husband and gave birth to five kittens. While the mother was a pure white thoroughbred C hinchila, the kittens were black and white tabbies of mixed breed. One of these came to our house abo ut two weeks after its birth and was given the name Gonnosuke. At that time we already had one femal e Shiba dog and one female brown tabby cat in our house comprising only 13 tsubo. The dog was calle

16/17

In our house we had a cat with the grandiose name of Gonnosuk e. Usually with cats and dogs we know who the mother is but no t the father. A cat with a large belly wondered into the house of my younger sister and her husband and gave birth to five kittens

24/25

In our house we had a cat with the grandio se name of Gonnosuke. Usually with cats a nd dogs we know who the mother is but n

ABCDEFGHIJKLM
NOPQRSTUVWX
YZabcdefghijklmn
opqrstuvwxyz
1234567890&
$¢£¥fiflæœÆŒ
ÅßÇÌÎÍÏã§†
-–—/()"""":;.,!¡?¿

10/11

In our house we had a cat with the grandiose name of Gonnosuke. Usually with cats an
d dogs we know who the mother is but not the father. A cat with a large belly wondered
into the house of my younger sister and her husband and gave birth to five kittens. Whil
e the mother was a pure white thoroughbred Chinchila, the kittens were black and white
tabbies of mixed breed. One of these came to our house about two weeks after its birth
and was given the name Gonnosuke. At that time we already had one female Shiba dog

16/17

In our house we had a cat with the grandiose name of
Gonnosuke. Usually with cats and dogs we know who
the mother is but not the father. A cat with a large belly
wondered into the house of my younger sister and her

24/25

In our house we had a cat with the g
randiose name of Gonnosuke. Usual
ly with cats and dogs we know who

ABCDEFGHIJKLM
NOPQRSTUVWX
YZabcdefghijklmn
opqrstuvwxyz
1234567890&
$¢£¥fiflœœÆŒ
ÅßÇÌÎÍÏãã§†
-–—/()""""":;.,!¡?¿

10/11

In our house we had a cat with the grandiose name of Gonnosuke. Usually with cats and
dogs we know who the mother is but not the father. A cat with a large belly wondered in
to the house of my younger sister and her husband and gave birth to five kittens. While th
e mother was a pure white thoroughbred Chinchila, the kittens were black and white tabb
ies of mixed breed. One of these came to our house about two weeks after its birth and w
as given the name Gonnosuke. At that time we already had one female Shiba dog and o

16/17

In our house we had a cat with the grandiose name of
Gonnosuke. Usually with cats and dogs we know who
the mother is but not the father. A cat with a large belly
wondered into the house of my younger sister and her

24/25

In our house we had a cat with the g
randiose name of Gonnosuke. Usuall
y with cats and dogs we know who

ABCDEFGHIJKLM
NOPQRSTUVWX
YZabcdefghijklmn
opqrstuvwxyz
1234567890&
$¢£¥fiflæœÆŒ
ÅßçÌÎÍÏã§†
----——/()""""::;..,!¡?¿

10/11

In our house we had a cat with the grandiose name of Gonnosuke. Usually with cats an
d dogs we know who the mother is but not the father. A cat with a large belly wondere
d into the house of my younger sister and her husband and gave birth to five kittens. W
hile the mother was a pure white thoroughbred Chinchila, the kittens were black and w
hite tabbies of mixed breed. One of these came to our house about two weeks after its
birth and was given the name Gonnosuke. At that time we already had one female Shib

16/17

In our house we had a cat with the grandiose name of
Gonnosuke. Usually with cats and dogs we know who
the mother is but not the father. A cat with a large bell
y wondered into the house of my younger sister and h

24/25

In our house we had a cat with the
grandiose name of Gonnosuke. Usu
ally with cats and dogs we know w

ABCDEFGHIJKL MNOPQRSTUVW XYZabcdefghijkl mnopqrstuvwxyz 1234567890& $¢£¥fiflæœÆŒ ÅßÇÌÎÍÏÃ§† -–—/()''""":;.,!¡?¿

10/11

In our house we had a cat with the grandiose name of Gonnosuke. Usually with cats and dogs we know who the mother is but not the father. A cat with a large belly won dered into the house of my younger sister and her husband and gave birth to five kitt ens. While the mother was a pure white thoroughbred Chinchila, the kittens were bla ck and white tabbies of mixed breed. One of these came to our house about two wee ks after its birth and was given the name Gonnosuke. At that time we already had on

16/17

In our house we had a cat with the grandiose name o f Gonnosuke. Usually with cats and dogs we know w ho the mother is but not the father. A cat with a large belly wondered into the house of my younger sister

24/25

In our house we had a cat with the grandiose name of Gonnosuke. Usu ally with cats and dogs we know w

ABCDEFGHIJKLMN
OPQRSTUVWXYZ
abcdefghijklmnopq
rstuvwxyz
1234567890&$¢£¥
fiflæœÆŒÅßÇÌÎÍÏã
§†----——/() '' "" :;.,! ¡?¿

10/11

In our house we had a cat with the grandiose name of Gonnosuke. Usually with cats and dogs we know who the mother is but not the father. A cat with a large belly wondered into the house of my younger sis ter and her husband and gave birth to five kittens. While the mother was a pure white thoroughbred Ch inchila, the kittens were black and white tabbies of mixed breed. One of these came to our house about two weeks after its birth and was given the name Gonnosuke. At that time we already had one female Sh iba dog and one female brown tabby cat in our house comprising only 13 tsubo. The dog was called Mo

16/17

In our house we had a cat with the grandiose name of Gonnosuk e. Usually with cats and dogs we know who the mother is but not the father. A cat with a large belly wondered into the house of m y younger sister and her husband and gave birth to five kittens.

24/25

In our house we had a cat with the grandio se name of Gonnosuke. Usually with cats a nd dogs we know who the mother is but no

ABCDEFGHIJKLMN
OPQRSTUVWXYZ
abcdefghijklmnopq
rstuvwxyz
1234567890&$¢£¥
fiflæœÆŒÅßÇÌÎÍÏã§†
-——/() '’“”:;.,!¡?¿

10/11

In our house we had a cat with the grandiose name of Gonnosuke. Usually with cats and dogs we know who the mo ther is but not the father. A cat with a large belly wondered into the house of my younger sister and her husband and gave birth to five kittens. While the mother was a pure white thoroughbred Chinchila, the kittens were black and whit e tabbies of mixed breed. One of these came to our house about two weeks after its birth and was given the name Gonn osuke. At that time we already had one female Shiba dog and one female brown tabby cat in our house comprising on ly 13 tsubo. The dog was called Momo and the cat Mii. My wife, who was very much opposed to keeping cats and do

16/17

In our house we had a cat with the grandiose name of Gonnosuke. Usua lly with cats and dogs we know who the mother is but not the father. A ca t with a large belly wondered into the house of my younger sister and her husband and gave birth to five kittens. While the mother was a pure whi

24/25

In our house we had a cat with the grandiose na me of Gonnosuke. Usually with cats and dogs w e know who the mother is but not the father. A ca

ABCDEFGHIJKLMN
OPQRSTUVWXYZ
abcdefghijklmnopq
rstuvwxyz
1234567890&$¢£¥
fiflæœÆŒÅßÇÌÎÍÏã
§†-–—/()'"""`:;.,!¡?¿

10/11

In our house we had a cat with the grandiose name of Gonnosuke. Usually with cats and dogs we know who the mother is but not the father. A cat with a large belly wondered into the house of my younger sis ter and her husband and gave birth to five kittens. While the mother was a pure white thoroughbred Chi nchila, the kittens were black and white tabbies of mixed breed. One of these came to our house about two weeks after its birth and was given the name Gonnosuke. At that time we already had one female Sh iba dog and one female brown tabby cat in our house comprising only 13 tsubo. The dog was called Mo

16/17

In our house we had a cat with the grandiose name of Gonnosuk e. Usually with cats and dogs we know who the mother is but not the father. A cat with a large belly wondered into the house of m y younger sister and her husband and gave birth to five kittens.

24/25

In our house we had a cat with the grandio se name of Gonnosuke. Usually with cats a nd dogs we know who the mother is but no

ABCDEFGHIJKLMN OPQRSTUVWXYZ abcdefghijklmnopq rstuvwxyz 1234567890&$¢£¥ fiflæœÆŒÅßÇÌÎÍÏã§† ———/()''""·:;·.,·!¡?¿

10/11

In our house we had a cat with the grandiose name of Gonnosuke. Usually with cats and dogs we know who the mother is but not the father. A cat with a large belly wondered into the house of my younger sister and her husban d and gave birth to five kittens. While the mother was a pure white thoroughbred Chinchila, the kittens were blac k and white tabbies of mixed breed. One of these came to our house about two weeks after its birth and was given the name Gonnosuke. At that time we already had one female Shiba dog and one female brown tabby cat in our h ouse comprising only 13 tsubo. The dog was called Momo and the cat Mii. My wife, who was very much opposed

16/17

In our house we had a cat with the grandiose name of Gonnosuke. Usu ally with cats and dogs we know who the mother is but not the father. A cat with a large belly wondered into the house of my younger sister and her husband and gave birth to five kittens. While the mother was a pu

24/25

In our house we had a cat with the grandiose n ame of Gonnosuke. Usually with cats and dogs we know who the mother is but not the father.

ABCDEFGHIJKL MNOPQRSTUVW XYZabcdefghijklm nopqrstuvwxyz 1234567890&

$¢£¥fiflæœÆŒ ÅßÇÌÎÍÏãã§† ———/0""""·;.,!¡?¿

10/11

In our house we had a cat with the grandiose name of Gonnosuke. Usually with cats and dogs we know who the mother is but not the father. A cat with a large belly wondered into the house of my younger sister and her husband and gave birth to five kittens. While the mother was a pure white thoroughbred Chinchila, the kittens were black and white tabbies of mixed breed. One of these came to our house about two weeks after its birth and was given the name Gonnosuke. At that time we already had one female Shiba dog and one female brown

16/17

In our house we had a cat with the grandiose name of Gonnosuke. Usually with cats and dogs we know who the mother is but not the father. A cat with a large belly wondered into the house of my younger sister and her husband

24/25

In our house we had a cat with the grandiose name of Gonnosuke. Usually with cats and dogs we know who the

ABCDEFGHIJKL
MNOPQRSTUVWX
YZabcdefghijklmno
pqrstuvwxyz
1234567890&
$¢£¥fiflæœÆŒ
ÅßÇÌÎÍÏã§†
———/0""""":;.,!¡?¿

10/11

In our house we had a cat with the grandiose name of Gonnosuke. Usually with cats and dog
s we know who the mother is but not the father. A cat with a large belly wondered into the ho
use of my younger sister and her husband and gave birth to five kittens. While the mother wa
s a pure white thoroughbred Chinchila, the kittens were black and white tabbies of mixed bre
ed. One of these came to our house about two weeks after its birth and was given the name G
onnosuke. At that time we already had one female Shiba dog and one female brown tabby ca

16/17

In our house we had a cat with the grandiose name of Gon
nosuke. Usually with cats and dogs we know who the mot
her is but not the father. A cat with a large belly wondered
into the house of my younger sister and her husband and

24/25

In our house we had a cat with the gra
ndiose name of Gonnosuke. Usually w
ith cats and dogs we know who the m

ABCDEFGHIJKL
MNOPQRSTUVW
XYZabcdefghijkl
mnopqrstuvwxyz
1234567890&
$¢£¥fiflæœÆŒ
ÅßÇÌÎÍÏãã§†
——/()''""":;.,!¡?¿

10/11

In our house we had a cat with the grandiose name of Gonnosuke. Usually with cats a
nd dogs we know who the mother is but not the father. A cat with a large belly wonder
ed into the house of my younger sister and her husband and gave birth to five kittens.
While the mother was a pure white thoroughbred Chinchila, the kittens were black an
d white tabbies of mixed breed. One of these came to our house about two weeks after
its birth and was given the name Gonnosuke. At that time we already had one female

16/17

In our house we had a cat with the grandiose name of
Gonnosuke. Usually with cats and dogs we know who
the mother is but not the father. A cat with a large be
lly wondered into the house of my younger sister and

24/25

In our house we had a cat with the
grandiose name of Gonnosuke. Usu
ally with cats and dogs we know wh

ABCDEFGHIJKL
MNOPQRSTUVW
XYZabcdefghijkl
mnopqrstuvwxyz
1234567890&
$¢£¥fiflæœÆŒ
ÅßÇÌÎÍÏã§†
——/()''""":;.,!¡?¿

10/11

In our house we had a cat with the grandiose name of Gonnosuke. Usually with cats and dogs we know who the mother is but not the father. A cat with a large belly won dered into the house of my younger sister and her husband and gave birth to five kit tens. While the mother was a pure white thoroughbred Chinchila, the kittens were b lack and white tabbies of mixed breed. One of these came to our house about two we eks after its birth and was given the name Gonnosuke. At that time we already had

16/17

In our house we had a cat with the grandiose name of Gonnosuke. Usually with cats and dogs we know who the mother is but not the father. A cat with a la rge belly wondered into the house of my younger sist

24/25

In our house we had a cat with the grandiose name of Gonnosuke. Usu ally with cats and dogs we know w

ABCDEFGHIJKL
MNOPQRSTUV
WXYZ
abcdefghijklmnopq
rstuvwxyz
1234567890&$¢£¥
fiflæœÆŒÅßÇÌÎÍÏã
§†-–—/()''""";:.,!¡?¿

10/11

In our house we had a cat with the grandiose name of Gonnosuke. Usually with cats and dogs we know who the mother is but not the father. A cat with a large belly wondered into the house of m y younger sister and her husband and gave birth to five kittens. While the mother was a pure whit e thoroughbred Chinchila, the kittens were black and white tabbies of mixed breed. One of these c ame to our house about two weeks after its birth and was given the name Gonnosuke. At that tim e we already had one female Shiba dog and one female brown tabby cat in our house comprising

16/17

In our house we had a cat with the grandiose name of Gonn osuke. Usually with cats and dogs we know who the mother is but not the father. A cat with a large belly wondered into t he house of my younger sister and her husband and gave birt

24/25

In our house we had a cat with the gran diose name of Gonnosuke. Usually with cats and dogs we know who the mother

ABCDEFGHIJKL MNOPQRSTUVW XYZ
abcdefghijklmnopq rstuvwxyz
1234567890&$¢£¥ fiflæœÆŒÅßÇÌÎÍÏã §†-–——/()''""";:.,!¡?¿

10/11

In our house we had a cat with the grandiose name of Gonnosuke. Usually with cats and dogs we know w ho the mother is but not the father. A cat with a large belly wondered into the house of my younger sister a nd her husband and gave birth to five kittens. While the mother was a pure white thoroughbred Chinchil a, the kittens were black and white tabbies of mixed breed. One of these came to our house about two wee ks after its birth and was given the name Gonnosuke. At that time we already had one female Shiba dog and one female brown tabby cat in our house comprising only 13 tsubo. The dog was called Momo and the

16/17

In our house we had a cat with the grandiose name of Gonnosuke. Usually with cats and dogs we know who the mother is but not th e father. A cat with a large belly wondered into the house of my yo unger sister and her husband and gave birth to five kittens. Whil

24/25

In our house we had a cat with the grandio se name of Gonnosuke. Usually with cats a nd dogs we know who the mother is but not

ABCDEFGHIJKL MNOPQRSTUVW XYZ
abcdefghijklmnopq rstuvwxyz
1234567890&$¢£¥ fiflæœÆŒÅßÇÌÎÍÏã §†-——/()''""":.;.,!¡?¿

10/11

In our house we had a cat with the grandiose name of Gonnosuke. Usually with cats and dogs we know wh o the mother is but not the father. A cat with a large belly wondered into the house of my younger sister an d her husband and gave birth to five kittens. While the mother was a pure white thoroughbred Chinchila, t he kittens were black and white tabbies of mixed breed. One of these came to our house about two weeks after its birth and was given the name Gonnosuke. At that time we already had one female Shiba dog and one female brown tabby cat in our house comprising only 13 tsubo. The dog was called Momo and the cat

16/17

In our house we had a cat with the grandiose name of Gonnosuke. Usually with cats and dogs we know who the mother is but not the father. A cat with a large belly wondered into the house of my you nger sister and her husband and gave birth to five kittens. While t

24/25

In our house we had a cat with the grandios e name of Gonnosuke. Usually with cats an d dogs we know who the mother is but not t

ABCDEFGHIJKLMN
OPQRSTUVWXYZ
abcdefghijklmnopq
rstuvwxyz
1234567890&$¢£¥
fiflæœÆŒÅßÇÌÎÍÏã§†
———/()''""·;·.,!¡?¿

10/11

In our house we had a cat with the grandiose name of Gonnosuke. Usually with cats and dogs we know who the mother
is but not the father. A cat with a large belly wondered into the house of my younger sister and her husband and gave bi
rth to five kittens. While the mother was a pure white thoroughbred Chinchila, the kittens were black and white tabbies
of mixed breed. One of these came to our house about two weeks after its birth and was given the name Gonnosuke. At t
hat time we already had one female Shiba dog and one female brown tabby cat in our house comprising only 13 tsubo.
The dog was called Momo and the cat Mii. My wife, who was very much opposed to keeping cats and dogs, instantaneo

16/17

In our house we had a cat with the grandiose name of Gonnosuke. Usuall
y with cats and dogs we know who the mother is but not the father. A cat w
ith a large belly wondered into the house of my younger sister and her husb
and and gave birth to five kittens. While the mother was a pure white thor

24/25

In our house we had a cat with the grandiose na
me of Gonnosuke. Usually with cats and dogs we
know who the mother is but not the father. A cat

ABCDEFGHIJKL
MNOPQRSTUVW
XYZ

abcdefghijklmnopq
rstuvwxyz
1234567890&$¢£¥
fiflæœÆŒÅßÇÌÎÍÏã§
†—————/()⁶⁹⁶⁶⁹⁹ .. :; ., ,. .° !¡?¿

10/11

In our house we had a cat with the grandiose name of Gonnosuke. Usually with cats and dogs we know who the m
other is but not the father. A cat with a large belly wondered into the house of my younger sister and her husband
and gave birth to five kittens. While the mother was a pure white thoroughbred Chinchila, the kittens were black
and white tabbies of mixed breed. One of these came to our house about two weeks after its birth and was given th
e name Gonnosuke. At that time we already had one female Shiba dog and one female brown tabby cat in our hou
se comprising only 13 tsubo. The dog was called Momo and the cat Mii. My wife, who was very much opposed to

16/17

In our house we had a cat with the grandiose name of Gonnosuke. Usu
ally with cats and dogs we know who the mother is but not the father.
A cat with a large belly wondered into the house of my younger sister a
nd her husband and gave birth to five kittens. While the mother was a

24/25

In our house we had a cat with the grandiose na
me of Gonnosuke. Usually with cats and dogs
we know who the mother is but not the father.

ABCDEFGHIJKLMN
OPQRSTUVWXYZ
abcdefghijklmnopq
rstuvwxyz
1234567890&$¢£¥
fiflæœÆŒÅßÇÌÎÍÏ ã §
†-–—/()''""":;.,!¡?¿

10/11

In our house we had a cat with the grandiose name of Gonnosuke. Usually with cats and dogs we know w
ho the mother is but not the father. A cat with a large belly wondered into the house of my younger sister
and her husband and gave birth to five kittens. While the mother was a pure white thoroughbred Chinch
ila, the kittens were black and white tabbies of mixed breed. One of these came to our house about two
weeks after its birth and was given the name Gonnosuke. At that time we already had one female Shiba d
og and one female brown tabby cat in our house comprising only 13 tsubo. The dog was called Momo an

16/17

In our house we had a cat with the grandiose name of Gonnosuk
e. Usually with cats and dogs we know who the mother is but not
the father. A cat with a large belly wondered into the house of my
younger sister and her husband and gave birth to five kittens. W

24/25

In our house we had a cat with the grandio
se name of Gonnosuke. Usually with cats a
nd dogs we know who the mother is but no

ABCDEFGHIJKLMN
OPQRSTUVWXYZ
abcdefghijklmnopq
rstuvwxyz
1234567890&$¢£¥
fiflœœÆŒÅßÇÌÎÍÏã
§†--——/() ""“”.;.,.!¡?¿

10/11

In our house we had a cat with the grandiose name of Gonnosuke. Usually with cats and dogs we know who the mother is but not the father. A cat with a large belly wondered into the house of my younger sister and her husband and gave birth to five kittens. While the mother was a pure white thoroughbred Chinchila, the kitte ns were black and white tabbies of mixed breed. One of these came to our house about two weeks after its birt h and was given the name Gonnosuke. At that time we already had one female Shiba dog and one female br own tabby cat in our house comprising only 13 tsubo. The dog was called Momo and the cat Mii. My wife, w

16/17

In our house we had a cat with the grandiose name of Gonnosuke. Usually with cats and dogs we know who the mother is but not the f ather. A cat with a large belly wondered into the house of my younge r sister and her husband and gave birth to five kittens. While the m

24/25

In our house we had a cat with the grandiose name of Gonnosuke. Usually with cats and d ogs we know who the mother is but not the fa

ABCDEFGHIJKL
MNOPQRSTUVW
XYZabcdefghijklm
nopqrstuvwxyz
1234567890&
$¢£¥fiflæœÆŒ
ÅßçÌÎÍÏã§†
———/()'""":;.,!¡?¿

10/11

In our house we had a cat with the grandiose name of Gonnosuke. Usually with cats and dogs we know who the mother is but not the father. A cat with a large belly wondered into the hous e of my younger sister and her husband and gave birth to five kittens. While the mother was a pure white thoroughbred Chinchila, the kittens were black and white tabbies of mixed breed. One of these came to our house about two weeks after its birth and was given the name Gonn osuke. At that time we already had one female Shiba dog and one female brown tabby cat in o

16/17

In our house we had a cat with the grandiose name of Gon nosuke. Usually with cats and dogs we know who the moth er is but not the father. A cat with a large belly wondered i nto the house of my younger sister and her husband and g

24/25

In our house we had a cat with the gra ndiose name of Gonnosuke. Usually wi th cats and dogs we know who the mot

ABCDEFGHIJKLMNO
PQRSTUVWXYZ
abcdefghijklmnopq
rstuvwxyz
1234567890&$¢£¥
fiflæœÆŒÅßÇÌÎÍÏïã§†
——/()''""":;.,!¡?¿

10/11

In our house we had a cat with the grandiose name of Gonnosuke. Usually with cats and dogs we know who t he mother is but not the father. A cat with a large belly wondered into the house of my younger sister and her husband and gave birth to five kittens. While the mother was a pure white thoroughbred Chinchila, the kitten s were black and white tabbies of mixed breed. One of these came to our house about two weeks after its birth and was given the name Gonnosuke. At that time we already had one female Shiba dog and one female brown tabby cat in our house comprising only 13 tsubo. The dog was called Momo and the cat Mii. My wife, who was

16/17

In our house we had a cat with the grandiose name of Gonnosuke. U sually with cats and dogs we know who the mother is but not the fat her. A cat with a large belly wondered into the house of my younger sister and her husband and gave birth to five kittens. While the mot

24/25

In our house we had a cat with the grandiose name of Gonnosuke. Usually with cats and do gs we know who the mother is but not the fat

ABCDEFGHIJKLMNO
PQRSTUVWXYZ
abcdefghijklmnopq
rstuvwxyz
1234567890&$¢£¥
fiflœœÆŒÅßÇÌÎÍÏã§†
———/()''""".;.,!¡?¿

10/11

In our house we had a cat with the grandiose name of Gonnosuke. Usually with cats and dogs we know who the mother is but not the father. A cat with a large belly wondered into the house of my younger sister and h er husband and gave birth to five kittens. While the mother was a pure white thoroughbred Chinchila, the ki ttens were black and white tabbies of mixed breed. One of these came to our house about two weeks after its birth and was given the name Gonnosuke. At that time we already had one female Shiba dog and one female brown tabby cat in our house comprising only 13 tsubo. The dog was called Momo and the cat Mii. My wife,

16/17

In our house we had a cat with the grandiose name of Gonnosuke. Usually with cats and dogs we know who the mother is but not the f ather. A cat with a large belly wondered into the house of my young er sister and her husband and gave birth to five kittens. While the

24/25

In our house we had a cat with the grandiose name of Gonnosuke. Usually with cats and d ogs we know who the mother is but not the f

ABCDEFGHIJKLMNO
PQRSTUVWXYZ
abcdefghijklmnopq
rstuvwxyz
1234567890&$¢£¥
fiflæœÆŒÅßÇÌÎÍÏã§†
-–—/()'""":;.,!¡?¿

10/11

In our house we had a cat with the grandiose name of Gonnosuke. Usually with cats and dogs we know who t he mother is but not the father. A cat with a large belly wondered into the house of my younger sister and her husband and gave birth to five kittens. While the mother was a pure white thoroughbred Chinchila, the kitten s were black and white tabbies of mixed breed. One of these came to our house about two weeks after its birth and was given the name Gonnosuke. At that time we already had one female Shiba dog and one female brown tabby cat in our house comprising only 13 tsubo. The dog was called Momo and the cat Mii. My wife, who was

16/17

In our house we had a cat with the grandiose name of Gonnosuke. U sually with cats and dogs we know who the mother is but not the fat her. A cat with a large belly wondered into the house of my younger sister and her husband and gave birth to five kittens. While the mot

24/25

In our house we had a cat with the grandiose name of Gonnosuke. Usually with cats and do gs we know who the mother is but not the fat

ABCDEFGHIJKLMNO
PQRSTUVWXYZ
abcdefghijklmnopq
rstuvwxyz
1234567890&$¢£¥
fiflæœÆŒÅßÇÌÎÍÏã§†
-—––/()''""";.,!¡?¿

10/11

In our house we had a cat with the grandiose name of Gonnosuke. Usually with cats and dogs we know who the mother is but not the father. A cat with a large belly wondered into the house of my younger sister and h er husband and gave birth to five kittens. While the mother was a pure white thoroughbred Chinchila, the kit tens were black and white tabbies of mixed breed. One of these came to our house about two weeks after its birth and was given the name Gonnosuke. At that time we already had one female Shiba dog and one female brown tabby cat in our house comprising only 13 tsubo. The dog was called Momo and the cat Mii. My wife,

16/17

In our house we had a cat with the grandiose name of Gonnosuke. Usually with cats and dogs we know who the mother is but not the f ather. A cat with a large belly wondered into the house of my young er sister and her husband and gave birth to five kittens.

24/25

In our house we had a cat with the grandiose name of Gonnosuke. Usually with cats and d ogs we know who the mother is but not the f

ABCDEFGHIJKLMN
OPQRSTUVWXYZ
abcdefghijklmnopq
rstuvwxyz
1234567890&$¢£¥
fiflæœÆŒÅßÇÌÎÍÏã
§†-–—/()''""";;.,!¡?¿

10/11

In our house we had a cat with the grandiose name of Gonnosuke. Usually with cats and dogs we know wh o the mother is but not the father. A cat with a large belly wondered into the house of my younger sister an d her husband and gave birth to five kittens. While the mother was a pure white thoroughbred Chinchila, t he kittens were black and white tabbies of mixed breed. One of these came to our house about two weeks af ter its birth and was given the name Gonnosuke. At that time we already had one female Shiba dog and one female brown tabby cat in our house comprising only 13 tsubo. The dog was called Momo and the cat Mii.

16/17

In our house we had a cat with the grandiose name of Gonnosuke. Usually with cats and dogs we know who the mother is but not the father. A cat with a large belly wondered into the house of my youn ger sister and her husband and gave birth to five kittens. While the

24/25

In our house we had a cat with the grandios e name of Gonnosuke. Usually with cats and dogs we know who the mother is but not the

ABCDEFGHIJKLMN
OPQRSTUVWXYZ
abcdefghijklmnopq
rstuvwxyz
1234567890&$¢£¥
fiflæœÆŒÅßÇÌÎÍÏã
§†-–——/()''""";.,!¡?¿

10/11

In our house we had a cat with the grandiose name of Gonnosuke. Usually with cats and dogs we know who the mother is but not the father. A cat with a large belly wondered into the house of my younger sist er and her husband and gave birth to five kittens. While the mother was a pure white thoroughbred Chin chila, the kittens were black and white tabbies of mixed breed. One of these came to our house about two weeks after its birth and was given the name Gonnosuke. At that time we already had one female Shiba d og and one female brown tabby cat in our house comprising only 13 tsubo. The dog was called Momo an

16/17

In our house we had a cat with the grandiose name of Gonnosuk e. Usually with cats and dogs we know who the mother is but not the father. A cat with a large belly wondered into the house of my younger sister and her husband and gave birth to five kittens. Wh

24/25

In our house we had a cat with the grandio se name of Gonnosuke. Usually with cats a nd dogs we know who the mother is but not

ABCDEFGHIJKLMN
OPQRSTUVWXYZ
abcdefghijklmnopq
rstuvwxyz
1234567890&$¢£¥
fiflæœÆŒÅßÇÌÎÍÏã
§†‡-–——/()''""".;.,!¡?¿

10/11

In our house we had a cat with the grandiose name of Gonnosuke. Usually with cats and dogs w
e know who the mother is but not the father. A cat with a large belly wondered into the house of
my younger sister and her husband and gave birth to five kittens. While the mother was a pure
white thoroughbred Chinchila, the kittens were black and white tabbies of mixed breed. One of t
hese came to our house about two weeks after its birth and was given the name Gonnosuke. At t
hat time we already had one female Shiba dog and one female brown tabby cat in our house co

16/17

In our house we had a cat with the grandiose name of Gonn
osuke. Usually with cats and dogs we know who the mother
is but not the father. A cat with a large belly wondered into
the house of my younger sister and her husband and gave bi

24/25

In our house we had a cat with the gran
diose name of Gonnosuke. Usually with
cats and dogs we know who the mother

ABCDEFGHIJKLM
NOPQRSTUVWXYZ
abcdefghijklmnopq
rstuvwxyz
1234567890&
$¢£¥fiflæœÆŒ
ÅßÇÌÎÍÏã§†
-—/()''""·;.,·!¡?¿

10/11

In our house we had a cat with the grandiose name of Gonnosuke. Usually with cats and dogs w
e know who the mother is but not the father. A cat with a large belly wondered into the house o
f my younger sister and her husband and gave birth to five kittens. While the mother was a pur
e white thoroughbred Chinchila, the kittens were black and white tabbies of mixed breed. One o
f these came to our house about two weeks after its birth and was given the name Gonnosuke. A
t that time we already had one female Shiba dog and one female brown tabby cat in our house

16/17

In our house we had a cat with the grandiose name of Gonn
osuke. Usually with cats and dogs we know who the mother
is but not the father. A cat with a large belly wondered into
the house of my younger sister and her husband and gave b

24/25

In our house we had a cat with the gra
ndiose name of Gonnosuke. Usually wit
h cats and dogs we know who the moth

ABCDEFGHIJKL
MNOPQRSTUVW
XYZabcdefghijklmno
pqrstuvwxyz
1234567890&$¢£¥
fiflæœÆŒÅßÇÌÎÍÏã§
†-–—/()'’“”:;.,!¡?¿

10/11

In our house we had a cat with the grandiose name of Gonnosuke. Usually with cats and dogs we know who the mother is but not the father. A cat with a large belly wondered into the house of my younger sister and her husband and gave birth to five kittens. While the mother was a pure white thoroughbred Chinchila, the kittens were black and white tabbies of mixed breed. One of these came to our house about two weeks after its birth and was given the name Gonnosuke. At that time we already had one female Shiba dog and one female brown tabby cat in our house comprising only 13 tsubo. The dog was called Momo and the cat Mii. My wife,

16/17

In our house we had a cat with the grandiose name of Gonnosuke. Usually with cats and dogs we know who the mother is but not the father. A cat with a large belly wondered into the house of my younger sister and her husband and gave birth to five kittens. While the m

24/25

In our house we had a cat with the grandiose name of Gonnosuke. Usually with cats and dogs we know who the mother is but not the f

ABCDEFGHIJKLMN
OPQRSTUVWXYZ
abcdefghijklmnopq
rstuvwxyz
1234567890&$¢£¥
fiflæœÆŒÅßÇÌÎÍÏã§†
---—/()·'""";..,!¡?¿

10/11

In our house we had a cat with the grandiose name of Gonnosuke. Usually with cats and dogs we know who the mother is but not the father. A cat with a large belly wondered into the house of my younger sister and her husband and gave birth to five ki ttens. While the mother was a pure white thoroughbred Chinchila, the kittens were black and white tabbies of mixed breed. O ne of these came to our house about two weeks after its birth and was given the name Gonnosuke. At that time we already ha d one female Shiba dog and one female brown tabby cat in our house comprising only 13 tsubo. The dog was called Momo an d the cat Mü. My wife, who was very much opposed to keeping cats and dogs, instantaneously fell for its shaggy appearance

16/17

In our house we had a cat with the grandiose name of Gonnosuke. Usually wi th cats and dogs we know who the mother is but not the father. A cat with a la rge belly wondered into the house of my younger sister and her husband and g ave birth to five kittens. While the mother was a pure white thoroughbred Chi

24/25

In our house we had a cat with the grandiose name of Gonnosuke. Usually with cats and dogs we know who the mother is but not the father. A cat with a la

ABCDEFGHIJKL
MNOPQRSTUVW
XYZabcdefghijklmn
opqrstuvwxyz
1234567890&$¢£¥
fiflæœÆŒÅßÇÌÎÍÏã
§†‡-–—/()'"""':;.,!¡?¿

10/11

In our house we had a cat with the grandiose name of Gonnosuke. Usually with cats and dogs we know
who the mother is but not the father. A cat with a large belly wondered into the house of my younger sis
ter and her husband and gave birth to five kittens. While the mother was a pure white thoroughbred Chi
nchila, the kittens were black and white tabbies of mixed breed. One of these came to our house about t
wo weeks after its birth and was given the name Gonnosuke. At that time we already had one female Shi
ba dog and one female brown tabby cat in our house comprising only 13 tsubo. The dog was called Mom

16/17

In our house we had a cat with the grandiose name of Gonnosuk
e. Usually with cats and dogs we know who the mother is but not
the father. A cat with a large belly wondered into the house of m
y younger sister and her husband and gave birth to five kittens.

24/25

In our house we had a cat with the grandio
se name of Gonnosuke. Usually with cats a
nd dogs we know who the mother is but no

ABCDEFGHIJKLM
NOPQRSTUVWXYZ
abcdefghijklmnopq
rstuvwxyz
1234567890&$¢£¥
fiflæœÆŒÅßÇÌÎÍÏã
§†----/()""""";,.,!¡?¿

10/11

In our house we had a cat with the grandiose name of Gonnosuke. Usually with cats and dogs we know who the mother is but not the father. A cat with a large belly wondered into the house of my younger sister and her husba nd and gave birth to five kittens. While the mother was a pure white thoroughbred Chinchila, the kittens were bl ack and white tabbies of mixed breed. One of these came to our house about two weeks after its birth and was giv en the name Gonnosuke. At that time we already had one female Shiba dog and one female brown tabby cat in o ur house comprising only 13 tsubo. The dog was called Momo and the cat Mii. My wife, who was very much oppos

16/17

In our house we had a cat with the grandiose name of Gonnosuke. Us ually with cats and dogs we know who the mother is but not the father. A cat with a large belly wondered into the house of my younger sister and her husband and gave birth to five kittens. While the mother was

24/25

In our house we had a cat with the grandiose n ame of Gonnosuke. Usually with cats and dog s we know who the mother is but not the father.

ABCDEFGHIJKL MNOPQRSTUVW XYZabcdefghijklmn opqrstuvwxyz 1234567890&$¢£¥ fiflæœÆŒÅßÇÌÎÍÏã §†-–—/()''""",;.,!¡?¿

10/11

In our house we had a cat with the grandiose name of Gonnosuke. Usually with cats and dogs we know who the mother is but not the father. A cat with a large belly wondered into the house of my younger sister and her husband and gave birth to five kittens. While the mother was a pure white t horoughbred Chinchila, the kittens were black and white tabbies of mixed breed. One of these ca me to our house about two weeks after its birth and was given the name Gonnosuke. At that time we already had one female Shiba dog and one female brown tabby cat in our house comprising onl

16/17

In our house we had a cat with the grandiose name of Gonno suke. Usually with cats and dogs we know who the mother is but not the father. A cat with a large belly wondered into the house of my younger sister and her husband and gave birth to

24/25

In our house we had a cat with the grand iose name of Gonnosuke. Usually with c ats and dogs we know who the mother is

*ABCDEFGHIJKL
MNOPQRSTUVW
XYZabcdefghijklm
nopqrstuvwxyz
1234567890&$¢£¥
fiflæœÆŒÅßÇÌÎÍÏ
ã§†-–—/()'''""".,,.,!¡?¿*

10/11

*In our house we had a cat with the grandiose name of Gonnosuke. Usually with cats and dogs
we know who the mother is but not the father. A cat with a large belly wondered into the house
of my younger sister and her husband and gave birth to five kittens. While the mother was a pu
re white thoroughbred Chinchila, the kittens were black and white tabbies of mixed breed. One
of these came to our house about two weeks after its birth and was given the name Gonnosuke.
At that time we already had one female Shiba dog and one female brown tabby cat in our hous*

16/17

*In our house we had a cat with the grandiose name of Gon
nosuke. Usually with cats and dogs we know who the moth
er is but not the father. A cat with a large belly wondered in
to the house of my younger sister and her husband and gav*

24/25

*In our house we had a cat with the gra
ndiose name of Gonnosuke. Usually w
ith cats and dogs we know who the mo*

ABCDEFGHIJKL
MNOPQRSTUVW
XYZabcdefghijklm
nopqrstuvwxyz
1234567890&$¢£¥
fiflæœÆŒÅßÇÌÎÍÏ
ã§†-–——/()''""";:,.,!¡?¿

10/11

In our house we had a cat with the grandiose name of Gonnosuke. Usually with cats and dogs we know who the mother is but not the father. A cat with a large belly wondered into the house of my younger sister and her husband and gave birth to five kittens. While the mother was a pu re white thoroughbred Chinchila, the kittens were black and white tabbies of mixed breed. One of these came to our house about two weeks after its birth and was given the name Gonnosuke. At that time we already had one female Shiba dog and one female brown tabby cat in our hous

16/17

In our house we had a cat with the grandiose name of Gon nosuke. Usually with cats and dogs we know who the moth er is but not the father. A cat with a large belly wondered in to the house of my younger sister and her husband and gav

24/25

In our house we had a cat with the gran diose name of Gonnosuke. Usually wit h cats and dogs we know who the moth

ABCDEFGHIJKLM
NOPQRSTUVWX
YZabcdefghijklmn
opqrstuvwxyz12345
67890&$¢£¥fiflæœ
ÆŒÅßÇÌÎÍÏã§†
———/()''""·,·.,!¡?¿

10/11

In our house we had a cat with the grandiose name of Gonnosuke. Usually with cats and dogs we know who the mother is but not the father. A cat with a large belly wondered into the house of my younger sister and her husband and gave birth to five kittens. While the mother was a pu re white thoroughbred Chinchila, the kittens were black and white tabbies of mixed breed. One of these came to our house about two weeks after its birth and was given the name Gonnosuke. At that time we already had one female Shiba dog and one female brown tabby cat in our hous

16/17

In our house we had a cat with the grandiose name of Gon nosuke. Usually with cats and dogs we know who the moth er is but not the father. A cat with a large belly wondered i nto the house of my younger sister and her husband and ga

24/25

In our house we had a cat with the gra ndiose name of Gonnosuke. Usually wi th cats and dogs we know who the mot

ABCDEFGHIJKL
MNOPQRSTUVW
XYZabcdefghijklmno
pqrstuvwxyz
1234567890&$¢£¥
fiflæœÆŒÅßÇÌÎÍÏã§
†-–——/()''""";.,,!¡?¿

10/11

In our house we had a cat with the grandiose name of Gonnosuke. Usually with cats and dogs we know wh o the mother is but not the father. A cat with a large belly wondered into the house of my younger sister an d her husband and gave birth to five kittens. While the mother was a pure white thoroughbred Chinchila, t he kittens were black and white tabbies of mixed breed. One of these came to our house about two weeks a fter its birth and was given the name Gonnosuke. At that time we already had one female Shiba dog and on e female brown tabby cat in our house comprising only 13 tsubo. The dog was called Momo and the cat M

16/17

In our house we had a cat with the grandiose name of Gonnosuke. Usually with cats and dogs we know who the mother is but not the father. A cat with a large belly wondered into the house of my you nger sister and her husband and gave birth to five kittens. While t

24/25

In our house we had a cat with the grandios e name of Gonnosuke. Usually with cats and dogs we know who the mother is but not th

ABCDEFGHIJKLM
NOPQRSTUVWXYZ
abcdefghijklmnopq
rstuvwxyz
1234567890&$¢£¥
fiflæœÆŒÅßÇÌÎÍÏã§†
———/()'''""'·;·,·,·!¡?¿

10/11

In our house we had a cat with the grandiose name of Gonnosuke. Usually with cats and dogs we know who the moth er is but not the father. A cat with a large belly wondered into the house of my younger sister and her husband and ga ve birth to five kittens. While the mother was a pure white thoroughbred Chinchila, the kittens were black and white tabbies of mixed breed. One of these came to our house about two weeks after its birth and was given the name Gonno suke. At that time we already had one female Shiba dog and one female brown tabby cat in our house comprising onl y 13 tsubo. The dog was called Momo and the cat Mii. My wife, who was very much opposed to keeping cats and dogs,

16/17

In our house we had a cat with the grandiose name of Gonnosuke. Usual ly with cats and dogs we know who the mother is but not the father. A ca t with a large belly wondered into the house of my younger sister and her husband and gave birth to five kittens. While the mother was a pure wh

24/25

In our house we had a cat with the grandiose na me of Gonnosuke. Usually with cats and dogs we know who the mother is but not the father. A cat

ABCDEFGHIJKL
MNOPQRSTUVW
XYZabcdefghijklmn
opqrstuvwxyz
1234567890&$¢£¥
fiflæœÆŒÅßÇÌÎÍÏã
§†-–—/()''""":;.,!¡?¿

10/11

In our house we had a cat with the grandiose name of Gonnosuke. Usually with cats and dogs we k
now who the mother is but not the father. A cat with a large belly wondered into the house of my y
ounger sister and her husband and gave birth to five kittens. While the mother was a pure white th
oroughbred Chinchila, the kittens were black and white tabbies of mixed breed. One of these cam
e to our house about two weeks after its birth and was given the name Gonnosuke. At that time we
already had one female Shiba dog and one female brown tabby cat in our house comprising only 13

16/17

In our house we had a cat with the grandiose name of Gonno
suke. Usually with cats and dogs we know who the mother is
but not the father. A cat with a large belly wondered into the
house of my younger sister and her husband and gave birth to

24/25

In our house we had a cat with the grand
iose name of Gonnosuke. Usually with c
ats and dogs we know who the mother is

ABCDEFGHIJKL MNOPQRSTUVW XYZabcdefghijklmno pqrstuvwxyz 1234567890&$¢£¥ fiflæœÆŒÅßÇÌÎÍÏã §†-–—/()''""".;.,!¡?¿

10/11

In our house we had a cat with the grandiose name of Gonnosuke. Usually with cats and dogs we know w
ho the mother is but not the father. A cat with a large belly wondered into the house of my younger sister
and her husband and gave birth to five kittens. While the mother was a pure white thoroughbred Chinch
ila, the kittens were black and white tabbies of mixed breed. One of these came to our house about two we
eks after its birth and was given the name Gonnosuke. At that time we already had one female Shiba do
g and one female brown tabby cat in our house comprising only 13 tsubo. The dog was called Momo and

16/17

In our house we had a cat with the grandiose name of Gonnosuk
e. Usually with cats and dogs we know who the mother is but not
the father. A cat with a large belly wondered into the house of my
younger sister and her husband and gave birth to five kittens. W

24/25

In our house we had a cat with the grandios
e name of Gonnosuke. Usually with cats an
d dogs we know who the mother is but not t

ABCDEFGHIJKLMN
OPQRSTUVWXYZ
abcdefghijklmnopq
rstuvwxyz
1234567890&$¢£¥
fiflæœÆŒÅßÇÌÎÍÏã
§†-–——/()''""":;.,!¡?¿

10/11

In our house we had a cat with the grandiose name of Gonnosuke. Usually with cats and dogs we know who the mother is but not the father. A cat with a large belly wondered into the house of my younger sis ter and her husband and gave birth to five kittens. While the mother was a pure white thoroughbred Chi nchila, the kittens were black and white tabbies of mixed breed. One of these came to our house about t wo weeks after its birth and was given the name Gonnosuke. At that time we already had one female Sh iba dog and one female brown tabby cat in our house comprising only 13 tsubo. The dog was called Mo

16/17

In our house we had a cat with the grandiose name of Gonnosuk e. Usually with cats and dogs we know who the mother is but no t the father. A cat with a large belly wondered into the house of my younger sister and her husband and gave birth to five kittens.

24/25

In our house we had a cat with the grandio se name of Gonnosuke. Usually with cats a nd dogs we know who the mother is but no

ABCDEFGHIJKLMN
OPQRSTUVWXYZ
abcdefghijklmnopq
rstuvwxyz
1234567890&$¢£¥
fiflæœÆŒÅßÇÌÎÍÏã
§†-—––/()''""":;.,!¡?¿

10/11

In our house we had a cat with the grandiose name of Gonnosuke. Usually with cats and dogs we know who the mother is but not the father. A cat with a large belly wondered into the house of my younger sis ter and her husband and gave birth to five kittens. While the mother was a pure white thoroughbred Ch inchila, the kittens were black and white tabbies of mixed breed. One of these came to our house about two weeks after its birth and was given the name Gonnosuke. At that time we already had one female S hiba dog and one female brown tabby cat in our house comprising only 13 tsubo. The dog was called M

16/17

In our house we had a cat with the grandiose name of Gonnosu ke. Usually with cats and dogs we know who the mother is but n ot the father. A cat with a large belly wondered into the house of my younger sister and her husband and gave birth to five kittens.

24/25

In our house we had a cat with the grandio se name of Gonnosuke. Usually with cats and dogs we know who the mother is but n

ABCDEFGHIJKL MNOPQRSTUVW XYZabcdefghijklmn opqrstuvwxyz 1234567890&$¢£¥ fiflæœÆŒÅßÇÌÎÍÏã§ †-–—/()''""·;.,!¡?¿

10/11

In our house we had a cat with the grandiose name of Gonnosuke. Usually with cats and dogs we kno w who the mother is but not the father. A cat with a large belly wondered into the house of my younge r sister and her husband and gave birth to five kittens. While the mother was a pure white thoroughbr ed Chinchila, the kittens were black and white tabbies of mixed breed. One of these came to our hous e about two weeks after its birth and was given the name Gonnosuke. At that time we already had one female Shiba dog and one female brown tabby cat in our house comprising only 13 tsubo. The dog wa

16/17

In our house we had a cat with the grandiose name of Gonnosu ke. Usually with cats and dogs we know who the mother is but not the father. A cat with a large belly wondered into the house of my younger sister and her husband and gave birth to five kitt

24/25

In our house we had a cat with the grandi ose name of Gonnosuke. Usually with cats and dogs we know who the mother is but

ABCDEFGHIJKLMN
OPQRSTUVWXYZ
abcdefghijklmnopq
rstuvwxyz
1234567890&$¢£¥
fiflæœÆŒÅßÇÌÎÍÏã§
†-–——/()''""":;.,!¡?¿

10/11

In our house we had a cat with the grandiose name of Gonnosuke. Usually with cats and dogs we kn
ow who the mother is but not the father. A cat with a large belly wondered into the house of my you
nger sister and her husband and gave birth to five kittens. While the mother was a pure white thorou
ghbred Chinchila, the kittens were black and white tabbies of mixed breed. One of these came to our
house about two weeks after its birth and was given the name Gonnosuke. At that time we already h
ad one female Shiba dog and one female brown tabby cat in our house comprising only 13 tsubo. Th

16/17

In our house we had a cat with the grandiose name of Gonnos
uke. Usually with cats and dogs we know who the mother is b
ut not the father. A cat with a large belly wondered into the ho
use of my younger sister and her husband and gave birth to fiv

24/25

In our house we had a cat with the grandi
ose name of Gonnosuke. Usually with cat
s and dogs we know who the mother is b

ABCDEFGHIJKLMNO
PQRSTUVWXYZ
abcdefghijklmnopq
rstuvwxyz
1234567890&$¢£¥
fiflæœÆŒÅßÇÌÎÍÏã§†
-——/()''""":;.,!¡?¿

10/11

In our house we had a cat with the grandiose name of Gonnosuke. Usually with cats and dogs we know who the mother is but not the father. A cat with a large belly wondered into the house of my younger sister and her husba nd and gave birth to five kittens. While the mother was a pure white thoroughbred Chinchila, the kittens were bl ack and white tabbies of mixed breed. One of these came to our house about two weeks after its birth and was giv en the name Gonnosuke. At that time we already had one female Shiba dog and one female brown tabby cat in o ur house comprising only 13 tsubo. The dog was called Momo and the cat Mii. My wife, who was very much oppo

16/17

In our house we had a cat with the grandiose name of Gonnosuke. Us ually with cats and dogs we know who the mother is but not the fathe r. A cat with a large belly wondered into the house of my younger siste r and her husband and gave birth to five kittens. While the mother wa

24/25

In our house we had a cat with the grandiose name of Gonnosuke. Usually with cats and do gs we know who the mother is but not the fath

ABCDEFGHIJKL
MNOPQRSTUVW
XYZabcdefghijklmn
opqrstuvwxyz
1234567890&$¢£¥
fiflæœÆŒÅßÇÌÎÍÏã
§†--——/()''""";,.,!¡?¿

10/11

In our house we had a cat with the grandiose name of Gonnosuke. Usually with cats and dogs we know who the mother is but not the father. A cat with a large belly wondered into the house of m y younger sister and her husband and gave birth to five kittens. While the mother was a pure whi te thoroughbred Chinchila, the kittens were black and white tabbies of mixed breed. One of these came to our house about two weeks after its birth and was given the name Gonnosuke. At that ti me we already had one female Shiba dog and one female brown tabby cat in our house comprisin

16/17

In our house we had a cat with the grandiose name of Gonno suke. Usually with cats and dogs we know who the mother i s but not the father. A cat with a large belly wondered into th e house of my younger sister and her husband and gave birth

24/25

In our house we had a cat with the gran diose name of Gonnosuke. Usually with cats and dogs we know who the mother

ABCDEFGHIJKLMNO
PQRSTUVWXYZ
abcdefghijklmnopq
rstuvwxyz
1234567890&$¢£¥
fiflæœÆŒÅßÇÌÎÍÏã§†
-----/()''""":;.,!¡?¿

10/11

In our house we had a cat with the grandiose name of Gonnosuke. Usually with cats and dogs we know who the mother is but not the father. A cat with a large belly wondered into the house of my younger sister and her husba nd and gave birth to five kittens. While the mother was a pure white thoroughbred Chinchila, the kittens were bl ack and white tabbies of mixed breed. One of these came to our house about two weeks after its birth and was giv en the name Gonnosuke. At that time we already had one female Shiba dog and one female brown tabby cat in o ur house comprising only 13 tsubo. The dog was called Momo and the cat Mii. My wife, who was very much oppo

16/17

In our house we had a cat with the grandiose name of Gonnosuke. Us ually with cats and dogs we know who the mother is but not the fathe r. A cat with a large belly wondered into the house of my younger siste r and her husband and gave birth to five kittens. While the mother wa

24/25

In our house we had a cat with the grandiose name of Gonnosuke. Usually with cats and do gs we know who the mother is but not the fath

ABCDEFGHIJKL
MNOPQRSTUVW
XYZabcdefghijklm
nopqrstuvwxyz
1234567890&
$¢£¥fiflæœÆŒ
ÅßçÌÎÍÏã§†
-–—/()""""·;·,!¡?¿

10/11

In our house we had a cat with the grandiose name of Gonnosuke. Usually with cats and d ogs we know who the mother is but not the father. A cat with a large belly wondered into the house of my younger sister and her husband and gave birth to five kittens. While the mother was a pure white thoroughbred Chinchila, the kittens were black and white tabbi es of mixed breed. One of these came to our house about two weeks after its birth and was given the name Gonnosuke. At that time we already had one female Shiba dog and one fe

16/17

In our house we had a cat with the grandiose name of G onnosuke. Usually with cats and dogs we know who the mother is but not the father. A cat with a large belly wo ndered into the house of my younger sister and her hus

24/25

In our house we had a cat with the gr andiose name of Gonnosuke. Usually with cats and dogs we know who the

ABCDEFGHIJKLM
NOPQRSTUVWXYZ
abcdefghijklmnopq
rstuvwxyz
1234567890&$¢£¥
fiflæœÆŒÅßÇÌÎÍÏã§
†-——/()''""",.,!¡?¿

10/11

In our house we had a cat with the grandiose name of Gonnosuke. Usually with cats and dogs we kn ow who the mother is but not the father. A cat with a large belly wondered into the house of my youn ger sister and her husband and gave birth to five kittens. While the mother was a pure white thoroug hbred Chinchila, the kittens were black and white tabbies of mixed breed. One of these came to our h ouse about two weeks after its birth and was given the name Gonnosuke. At that time we already ha d one female Shiba dog and one female brown tabby cat in our house comprising only 13 tsubo. The

16/17

In our house we had a cat with the grandiose name of Gonnos uke. Usually with cats and dogs we know who the mother is bu t not the father. A cat with a large belly wondered into the hous e of my younger sister and her husband and gave birth to five

24/25

In our house we had a cat with the grand iose name of Gonnosuke. Usually with cat s and dogs we know who the mother is bu

ABCDEFGHIJKLMN
OPQRSTUVWXYZ
abcdefghijklmnopq
rstuvwxyz
1234567890&$¢£¥
fiflæœÆŒÅßÇÌÎÍÏã
§†-–——/()''""";,.,!¡?¿

10/11

In our house we had a cat with the grandiose name of Gonnosuke. Usually with cats and dogs w
e know who the mother is but not the father. A cat with a large belly wondered into the house o
f my younger sister and her husband and gave birth to five kittens. While the mother was a pure
white thoroughbred Chinchila, the kittens were black and white tabbies of mixed breed. One of
these came to our house about two weeks after its birth and was given the name Gonnosuke. At
that time we already had one female Shiba dog and one female brown tabby cat in our house co

16/17

In our house we had a cat with the grandiose name of Gonn
osuke. Usually with cats and dogs we know who the mother
is but not the father. A cat with a large belly wondered into
the house of my younger sister and her husband and gave bi

24/25

In our house we had a cat with the gran
diose name of Gonnosuke. Usually with
cats and dogs we know who the mother

ABCDEFGHIJKLMN
OPQRSTUVWXYZ
abcdefghijklmnopq
rstuvwxyz
1234567890&$¢£¥
fiflœœÆŒÅßÇÌÎÍÏã
§†-–——/()''""":;.,!¡?¿

10/11

In our house we had a cat with the grandiose name of Gonnosuke. Usually with cats and dogs we know who the mother is but not the father. A cat with a large belly wondered into the house of my younger sist er and her husband and gave birth to five kittens. While the mother was a pure white thoroughbred Chi nchila, the kittens were black and white tabbies of mixed breed. One of these came to our house about t wo weeks after its birth and was given the name Gonnosuke. At that time we already had one female Sh iba dog and one female brown tabby cat in our house comprising only 13 tsubo. The dog was called Mo

16/17

In our house we had a cat with the grandiose name of Gonnosuk e. Usually with cats and dogs we know who the mother is but not the father. A cat with a large belly wondered into the house of m y younger sister and her husband and gave birth to five kittens.

24/25

In our house we had a cat with the grandio se name of Gonnosuke. Usually with cats a nd dogs we know who the mother is but no

ABCDEFGHIJKL MNOPQRSTUVW XYZabcdefghijklm nopqrstuvwxyz 1234567890&

$¢£¥fiflæœÆŒ ÅßÇÌÎÍÏã§†
——/()''""·:;.,!¡?¿

10/11

In our house we had a cat with the grandiose name of Gonnosuke. Usually with cats and d ogs we know who the mother is but not the father. A cat with a large belly wondered into t he house of my younger sister and her husband and gave birth to five kittens. While the m other was a pure white thoroughbred Chinchila, the kittens were black and white tabbies o f mixed breed. One of these came to our house about two weeks after its birth and was give n the name Gonnosuke. At that time we already had one female Shiba dog and one female

16/17

In our house we had a cat with the grandiose name of G onnosuke. Usually with cats and dogs we know who the mother is but not the father. A cat with a large belly won dered into the house of my younger sister and her husba

24/25

In our house we had a cat with the gr andiose name of Gonnosuke. Usually with cats and dogs we know who the

ABCDEFGHIJKL
MNOPQRSTUVW
XYZabcdefghijklm
nopqrstuvwxyz
1234567890&
$¢£¥fiflæœÆŒ
ÅßÇÌÎÍÏã§†
———/()''""";.,!¡?¿

10/11

In our house we had a cat with the grandiose name of Gonnosuke. Usually with cats and dogs we know who the mother is but not the father. A cat with a large belly wondered into the house of my younger sister and her husband and gave birth to five kittens. While the mother was a pure white thoroughbred Chinchila, the kittens were black and white tabbies of mixed breed. One of these came to our house about two weeks after its birth and was given the name Gonnosuke. At that time we already had one female Shiba dog and one female brown tabby cat in

16/17

In our house we had a cat with the grandiose name of Gon nosuke. Usually with cats and dogs we know who the mot her is but not the father. A cat with a large belly wondered into the house of my younger sister and her husband and g

24/25

In our house we had a cat with the gra ndiose name of Gonnosuke. Usually wi th cats and dogs we know who the mot

ABCDEFGHIJKL
MNOPQRSTUVW
XYZabcdefghijk
lmnopqrstuvwx
yz1234567890&
$¢£¥fiflæœÆŒ
ÅßçÌÎÍÏã§†
——/()''""·;.,!¡?¿

10/11

In our house we had a cat with the grandiose name of Gonnosuke. Usually with ca ts and dogs we know who the mother is but not the father. A cat with a large belly wondered into the house of my younger sister and her husband and gave birth to f ive kittens. While the mother was a pure white thoroughbred Chinchila, the kitte ns were black and white tabbies of mixed breed. One of these came to our house a bout two weeks after its birth and was given the name Gonnosuke. At that time w

16/17

In our house we had a cat with the grandiose name of Gonnosuke. Usually with cats and dogs we know who the mother is but not the father. A cat with a l arge belly wondered into the house of my younger

24/25

In our house we had a cat with th e grandiose name of Gonnosuke. U sually with cats and dogs we kno

ABCDEFGHIJKL
MNOPQRSTUVW
XYZabcdefghijkl
mnopqrstuvwxyz
1234567890&
$¢£¥fiflæœÆŒ
ÅßçÌÎÍÏã§†
——/()''''''"":;.,!¡?¿

10/11

In our house we had a cat with the grandiose name of Gonnosuke. Usually with cats and dogs we know who the mother is but not the father. A cat with a large belly won dered into the house of my younger sister and her husband and gave birth to five kitt ens. While the mother was a pure white thoroughbred Chinchila, the kittens were bla ck and white tabbies of mixed breed. One of these came to our house about two weeks after its birth and was given the name Gonnosuke. At that time we already had one

16/17

In our house we had a cat with the grandiose name of Gonnosuke. Usually with cats and dogs we know w ho the mother is but not the father. A cat with a larg e belly wondered into the house of my younger sister

24/25

In our house we had a cat with the grandiose name of Gonnosuke. Usu ally with cats and dogs we know w

ABCDEFGHIJKL
MNOPQRSTUVW
XYZabcdefghijklm
nopqrstuvwxyz
1234567890&
$¢£¥fiflæœÆŒ
ÅßÇÌÎÍÏã§†
-–—/O''""·,;.,!¡?¿

10/11

In our house we had a cat with the grandiose name of Gonnosuke. Usually with cats and dog s we know who the mother is but not the father. A cat with a large belly wondered into the h ouse of my younger sister and her husband and gave birth to five kittens. While the mother was a pure white thoroughbred Chinchila, the kittens were black and white tabbies of mixe d breed. One of these came to our house about two weeks after its birth and was given the n ame Gonnosuke. At that time we already had one female Shiba dog and one female brown ta

16/17

In our house we had a cat with the grandiose name of Go nnosuke. Usually with cats and dogs we know who the mo ther is but not the father. A cat with a large belly wonder ed into the house of my younger sister and her husband a

24/25

In our house we had a cat with the gra ndiose name of Gonnosuke. Usually wi th cats and dogs we know who the mo

ABCDEFGHIJKL
MNOPQRSTUVW
XYZabcdefghijklm
nopqrstuvwxyz
1234567890&
$¢£¥fiflæœÆŒ
ÅßÇÌÎÍÏã§†
–––—/O ''""·,.,!¡?¿

10/11

In our house we had a cat with the grandiose name of Gonnosuke. Usually with cats and dogs we know who the mother is but not the father. A cat with a large belly wondered into the house of my younger sister and her husband and gave birth to five kittens. While the mother was a p ure white thoroughbred Chinchila, the kittens were black and white tabbies of mixed breed. On e of these came to our house about two weeks after its birth and was given the name Gonnosuk e. At that time we already had one female Shiba dog and one female brown tabby cat in our ho

16/17

In our house we had a cat with the grandiose name of Gon nosuke. Usually with cats and dogs we know who the moth er is but not the father. A cat with a large belly wondered i nto the house of my younger sister and her husband and ga

24/25

In our house we had a cat with the gra ndiose name of Gonnosuke. Usually wi th cats and dogs we know who the mot

ABCDEFGHIJKL
MNOPQRSTUVW
XYZabcdefghijkl
mnopqrstuvwxyz
1234567890&
$¢£₤¥fiflæœÆŒ
ÅßÇÌÎÍÏã§†
––——/O''""";:.,!¡?¿

10/11

In our house we had a cat with the grandiose name of Gonnosuke. Usually with cats and dog
s we know who the mother is but not the father. A cat with a large belly wondered into the h
ouse of my younger sister and her husband and gave birth to five kittens. While the mother
was a pure white thoroughbred Chinchila, the kittens were black and white tabbies of mixed
breed. One of these came to our house about two weeks after its birth and was given the na
me Gonnosuke. At that time we already had one female Shiba dog and one female brown tab

16/17

In our house we had a cat with the grandiose name of Go
nnosuke. Usually with cats and dogs we know who the mo
ther is but not the father. A cat with a large belly wondere
d into the house of my younger sister and her husband an

24/25

In our house we had a cat with the gra
ndiose name of Gonnosuke. Usually w
ith cats and dogs we know who the mo

ABCDEFGHIJKL
MNOPQRSTUVW
XYZabcdefghijklm
nopqrstuvwxyz
1234567890&
$¢£¥fiflæœÆŒ
ÅßÇÌÎÍÏã§†
-----——/()''""·:;·.,!¡?¿

10/11

In our house we had a cat with the grandiose name of Gonnosuke. Usually with cats and do gs we know who the mother is but not the father. A cat with a large belly wondered into the house of my younger sister and her husband and gave birth to five kittens. While the mother was a pure white thoroughbred Chinchila, the kittens were black and white tabbies of mixed breed. One of these came to our house about two weeks after its birth and was given the nam e Gonnosuke. At that time we already had one female Shiba dog and one female brown tabb

16/17

In our house we had a cat with the grandiose name of Go nnosuke. Usually with cats and dogs we know who the m other is but not the father. A cat with a large belly wonde red into the house of my younger sister and her husband

24/25

In our house we had a cat with the gr andiose name of Gonnosuke. Usually with cats and dogs we know who the

ABCDEFGHIJK
LMNOPQRSTU
VWXYZabcdefg
hijklmnopqrstu
vwxyz12345678
90&$¢£¥fiflæœ
ÆŒÅßÇÌÎÍÏĩã§†
———/O''""¡;.,°•?¿

10/11

In our house we had a cat with the grandiose name of Gonnosuke. Usually wit
h cats and dogs we know who the mother is but not the father. A cat with a lar
ge belly wondered into the house of my younger sister and her husband and g
ave birth to five kittens. While the mother was a pure white thoroughbred Chi
nchila, the kittens were black and white tabbies of mixed breed. One of these
came to our house about two weeks after its birth and was given the name Go

16/17

In our house we had a cat with the grandiose na
me of Gonnosuke. Usually with cats and dogs we
know who the mother is but not the father. A cat
with a large belly wondered into the house of my

24/25

In our house we had a cat with t
he grandiose name of Gonnosuk
e. Usually with cats and dogs we

ABCDEFGHIJK
LMNOPQRSTU
VWXYZabcdefg
hijklmnopqrstu
vwxyz12345678
90&$¢£¥ſififlæœ
ÆŒÅßÇÌÍÎÏÏãã§†
———/O ''66'' :;.,•;!;?¿

10/11

In our house we had a cat with the grandiose name of Gonnosuke. Usually with cats and dogs we know who the mother is but not the father. A cat with a large belly wondered into the house of my younger sister and her husban d and gave birth to five kittens. While the mother was a pure white thoroug hbred Chinchila, the kittens were black and white tabbies of mixed breed. O ne of these came to our house about two weeks after its birth and was given

16/17

In our house we had a cat with the grandiose n ame of Gonnosuke. Usually with cats and dogs we know who the mother is but not the father. A cat with a large belly wondered into the hous

24/25

In our house we had a cat with the grandiose name of Gonnosu ke. Usually with cats and dogs

ABCDEFGHIJKL MNOPQRSTUVW XYZabcdefghijklmn opqrstuvwxyz 1234567890&$¢£¥ fiflæœÆŒÅßÇÌÎÍÏã §†-–—/()''""":;.,!¡?¿

10/11

In our house we had a cat with the grandiose name of Gonnosuke. Usually with cats and dogs we know who the mother is but not the father. A cat with a large belly wondered into the house of my younger sis ter and her husband and gave birth to five kittens. While the mother was a pure white thoroughbred Chi nchila, the kittens were black and white tabbies of mixed breed. One of these came to our house about t wo weeks after its birth and was given the name Gonnosuke. At that time we already had one female Sh iba dog and one female brown tabby cat in our house comprising only 13 tsubo. The dog was called Mo

16/17

In our house we had a cat with the grandiose name of Gonnosuk e. Usually with cats and dogs we know who the mother is but not the father. A cat with a large belly wondered into the house of m y younger sister and her husband and gave birth to five kittens.

24/25

In our house we had a cat with the grandio se name of Gonnosuke. Usually with cats a nd dogs we know who the mother is but no

ABCDEFGHIJKL
MNOPQRSTUVW
XYZabcdefghijklmn
opqrstuvwxyz
1234567890&$¢£¥
fiflæœÆŒÅßÇÌÎÍÏã
§†-–—/()''""·;·,!¡?¿

10/11

In our house we had a cat with the grandiose name of Gonnosuke. Usually with cats and dogs we know w ho the mother is but not the father. A cat with a large belly wondered into the house of my younger sister a nd her husband and gave birth to five kittens. While the mother was a pure white thoroughbred Chinchila, the kittens were black and white tabbies of mixed breed. One of these came to our house about two weeks after its birth and was given the name Gonnosuke. At that time we already had one female Shiba dog and one female brown tabby cat in our house comprising only 13 tsubo. The dog was called Momo and the cat

16/17

In our house we had a cat with the grandiose name of Gonnosuke. Usually with cats and dogs we know who the mother is but not the father. A cat with a large belly wondered into the house of my you nger sister and her husband and gave birth to five kittens. While th

24/25

In our house we had a cat with the grandios e name of Gonnosuke. Usually with cats an d dogs we know who the mother is but not t

ABCDEFGHIJKL
MNOPQRSTUVW
XYZabcdefghijklmn
opqrstuvwxyz
1234567890&$¢£¥
fiflæœÆŒÅßÇÌÎÍÏĩ
§†-–—/()''""''.;,.!¡?¿

10/11

In our house we had a cat with the grandiose name of Gonnosuke. Usually with cats and dogs we know who the mother is but not the father. A cat with a large belly wondered into the house of my younger sis ter and her husband and gave birth to five kittens. While the mother was a pure white thoroughbred Chi nchila, the kittens were black and white tabbies of mixed breed. One of these came to our house about t wo weeks after its birth and was given the name Gonnosuke. At that time we already had one female Sh iba dog and one female brown tabby cat in our house comprising only 13 tsubo. The dog was called Mo

16/17

In our house we had a cat with the grandiose name of Gonnosuk e. Usually with cats and dogs we know who the mother is but not the father. A cat with a large belly wondered into the house of m y younger sister and her husband and gave birth to five kittens.

24/25

In our house we had a cat with the grandio se name of Gonnosuke. Usually with cats a nd dogs we know who the mother is but no

ABCDEFGHIJKL
MNOPQRSTUVW
XYZabcdefghijklmn
opqrstuvwxyz
1234567890&$¢£¥
fiflæœÆŒÅßÇÌÎÍÏã
§†----——/()''""",;.,!¡?¿

10/11

In our house we had a cat with the grandiose name of Gonnosuke. Usually with cats and dogs we kno w who the mother is but not the father. A cat with a large belly wondered into the house of my younge r sister and her husband and gave birth to five kittens. While the mother was a pure white thoroughbre d Chinchila, the kittens were black and white tabbies of mixed breed. One of these came to our house about two weeks after its birth and was given the name Gonnosuke. At that time we already had one f emale Shiba dog and one female brown tabby cat in our house comprising only 13 tsubo. The dog was

16/17

In our house we had a cat with the grandiose name of Gonnosu ke. Usually with cats and dogs we know who the mother is but not the father. A cat with a large belly wondered into the house of my younger sister and her husband and gave birth to five kitt

24/25

In our house we had a cat with the grandi ose name of Gonnosuke. Usually with cats and dogs we know who the mother is but n

ABCDEFGHIJKLMN
OPQRSTUVWXYZ
abcdefghijklmnopq
rstuvwxyz
1234567890&$¢£¥
fiflæœÆŒÅßÇÌÎÍÏã
§†-–—/()''""·:;.,!¡?¿

10/11

In our house we had a cat with the grandiose name of Gonnosuke. Usually with cats and dogs we know w
ho the mother is but not the father. A cat with a large belly wondered into the house of my younger sister
and her husband and gave birth to five kittens. While the mother was a pure white thoroughbred Chinchi
la, the kittens were black and white tabbies of mixed breed. One of these came to our house about two we
eks after its birth and was given the name Gonnosuke. At that time we already had one female Shiba dog
and one female brown tabby cat in our house comprising only 13 tsubo. The dog was called Momo and t

16/17

In our house we had a cat with the grandiose name of Gonnosuk
e. Usually with cats and dogs we know who the mother is but not
the father. A cat with a large belly wondered into the house of my
younger sister and her husband and gave birth to five kittens. Wh

24/25

In our house we had a cat with the grandios
e name of Gonnosuke. Usually with cats an
d dogs we know who the mother is but not t

ABCDEFGHIJKLMN
OPQRSTUVWXYZ
abcdefghijklmnopq
rstuvwxyz
1234567890&$¢£¥
fiflœœ ÆŒÅßÇÌÎÍÏ ã§†
——/() ' ' " " :;.,!¡?¿

10/11

In our house we had a cat with the grandiose name of Gonnosuke. Usually with cats and dogs we know who the mother is but not the father. A cat with a large belly wondered into the house of my younger sist er and her husband and gave birth to five kittens. While the mother was a pure white thoroughbred Chin chila, the kittens were black and white tabbies of mixed breed. One of these came to our house about two weeks after its birth and was given the name Gonnosuke. At that time we already had one female Shiba dog and one female brown tabby cat in our house comprising only 13 tsubo. The dog was called Momo a

16/17

In our house we had a cat with the grandiose name of Gonnosuk e. Usually with cats and dogs we know who the mother is but not the father. A cat with a large belly wondered into the house of my younger sister and her husband and gave birth to five kittens. Wh

24/25

In our house we had a cat with the grandio se name of Gonnosuke. Usually with cats a nd dogs we know who the mother is but not

ABCDEFGHIJKLM
NOPQRSTUVWXYZ
abcdefghijklmnopq
rstuvwxyz
1234567890&$¢£¥
fiflæœÆŒÅßÇÌÎÍÏã
§✝-–—/()''""".;.,!¡?¿

10/11

In our house we had a cat with the grandiose name of Gonnosuke. Usually with cats and dogs we know who the mother is but not the father. A cat with a large belly wondered into the house of m y younger sister and her husband and gave birth to five kittens. While the mother was a pure whi te thoroughbred Chinchila, the kittens were black and white tabbies of mixed breed. One of thes e came to our house about two weeks after its birth and was given the name Gonnosuke. At that t ime we already had one female Shiba dog and one female brown tabby cat in our house comprisi

16/17

In our house we had a cat with the grandiose name of Gonn osuke. Usually with cats and dogs we know who the mother is but not the father. A cat with a large belly wondered into t he house of my younger sister and her husband and gave bir

24/25

In our house we had a cat with the gran diose name of Gonnosuke. Usually with cats and dogs we know who the mother

ABCDEFGHIJKLM
NOPQRSTUVWXYZ
abcdefghijklmnopq
rstuvwxyz
1234567890&$¢£¥
fiflœœÆŒÅßÇÌÎÍÏã
§†-–——/()''""·;.,!¡?¿

10/11

In our house we had a cat with the grandiose name of Gonnosuke. Usually with cats and dogs we kno w who the mother is but not the father. A cat with a large belly wondered into the house of my younge r sister and her husband and gave birth to five kittens. While the mother was a pure white thoroughb red Chinchila, the kittens were black and white tabbies of mixed breed. One of these came to our hous e about two weeks after its birth and was given the name Gonnosuke. At that time we already had on e female Shiba dog and one female brown tabby cat in our house comprising only 13 tsubo. The dog

16/17

In our house we had a cat with the grandiose name of Gonnosu ke. Usually with cats and dogs we know who the mother is but not the father. A cat with a large belly wondered into the house of my younger sister and her husband and gave birth to five kit

24/25

In our house we had a cat with the grandi ose name of Gonnosuke. Usually with cats and dogs we know who the mother is but

ABCDEFGHIJKLMN
OPQRSTUVWXYZ
abcdefghijklmnopq
rstuvwxyz
1234567890&$¢£¥
fiflæœÆŒÅßÇÌÎÍÏã§
†———/()''""·:;·.,!¡?¿

10/11

In our house we had a cat with the grandiose name of Gonnosuke. Usually with cats and dogs we know wh
o the mother is but not the father. A cat with a large belly wondered into the house of my younger sister an
d her husband and gave birth to five kittens. While the mother was a pure white thoroughbred Chinchila,
the kittens were black and white tabbies of mixed breed. One of these came to our house about two weeks
after its birth and was given the name Gonnosuke. At that time we already had one female Shiba dog and
one female brown tabby cat in our house comprising only 13 tsubo. The dog was called Momo and the cat

16/17

In our house we had a cat with the grandiose name of Gonnosuke.
Usually with cats and dogs we know who the mother is but not the
father. A cat with a large belly wondered into the house of my you
nger sister and her husband and gave birth to five kittens. While t

24/25

In our house we had a cat with the grandios
e name of Gonnosuke. Usually with cats and
dogs we know who the mother is but not the

ABCDEFGHIJKLMN
OPQRSTUVWXYZ
abcdefghijklmnopq
rstuvwxyz
1234567890&$¢£¥
fiflœœÆŒÅßÇÌÎÍÏã
§†–——/()‘’‘‘’’:;.,!¡?¿

10/11

In our house we had a cat with the grandiose name of Gonnosuke. Usually with cats and dogs we know who the mother is but not the father. A cat with a large belly wondered into the house of my younger siste r and her husband and gave birth to five kittens. While the mother was a pure white thoroughbred Chinc hila, the kittens were black and white tabbies of mixed breed. One of these came to our house about two weeks after its birth and was given the name Gonnosuke. At that time we already had one female Shiba d og and one female brown tabby cat in our house comprising only 13 tsubo. The dog was called Momo and

16/17

In our house we had a cat with the grandiose name of Gonnosuk e. Usually with cats and dogs we know who the mother is but not the father. A cat with a large belly wondered into the house of my younger sister and her husband and gave birth to five kittens. Wh

24/25

In our house we had a cat with the grandio se name of Gonnosuke. Usually with cats a nd dogs we know who the mother is but not

ABCDEFGHIJKLM
NOPQRSTUVWXYZ
abcdefghijklmnopq
rstuvwxyz
1234567890&$¢£¥
fiflæœÆŒÅßÇÌÎÍÏã
§†----——/()''""::;.,!¡?¿

10/11

In our house we had a cat with the grandiose name of Gonnosuke. Usually with cats and dogs we kno
w who the mother is but not the father. A cat with a large belly wondered into the house of my young
er sister and her husband and gave birth to five kittens. While the mother was a pure white thorough
bred Chinchila, the kittens were black and white tabbies of mixed breed. One of these came to our h
ouse about two weeks after its birth and was given the name Gonnosuke. At that time we already had
one female Shiba dog and one female brown tabby cat in our house comprising only 13 tsubo. The d

16/17

In our house we had a cat with the grandiose name of Gonnosu
ke. Usually with cats and dogs we know who the mother is but
not the father. A cat with a large belly wondered into the house
of my younger sister and her husband and gave birth to five kit

24/25

In our house we had a cat with the grandi
ose name of Gonnosuke. Usually with cats
and dogs we know who the mother is but

ABCDEFGHIJKLM
NOPQRSTUVWXYZ
abcdefghijklmnopq
rstuvwxyz
1234567890&$¢£
¥fiflœœÆŒÅßÇÌÎÍÏ
ã§†–——/()''""·;.,!¡?¿

10/11

In our house we had a cat with the grandiose name of Gonnosuke. Usually with cats and dogs we kno
w who the mother is but not the father. A cat with a large belly wondered into the house of my young
er sister and her husband and gave birth to five kittens. While the mother was a pure white thoroughb
red Chinchila, the kittens were black and white tabbies of mixed breed. One of these came to our ho
use about two weeks after its birth and was given the name Gonnosuke. At that time we already had o
ne female Shiba dog and one female brown tabby cat in our house comprising only 13 tsubo. The do

16/17

In our house we had a cat with the grandiose name of Gonnos
uke. Usually with cats and dogs we know who the mother is but
not the father. A cat with a large belly wondered into the house
of my younger sister and her husband and gave birth to five kit

24/25

In our house we had a cat with the grandi
ose name of Gonnosuke. Usually with cats
and dogs we know who the mother is but

ABCDEFGHIJKL
MNOPQRSTUVW
XYZabcdefghijk
lmnopqrstuvwx
yz1234567890&
$¢£¥fifl æœÆŒ
ÅßçÌÎÍÏã§❦
———/()'"''•••.,:;'!¡?¿

10/11

In our house we had a cat with the grandiose name of Gonnosuke. Usually with c
ats and dogs we know who the mother is but not the father. A cat with a large be
lly wondered into the house of my younger sister and her husband and gave birt
h to five kittens. While the mother was a pure white thoroughbred Chinchila, the
kittens were black and white tabbies of mixed breed. One of these came to our ho
use about two weeks after its birth and was given the name Gonnosuke. At that t

16/17

In our house we had a cat with the grandiose nam
e of Gonnosuke. Usually with cats and dogs we kno
w who the mother is but not the father. A cat with
a large belly wondered into the house of my youn

24/25

In our house we had a cat with t
he grandiose name of Gonnosuke.
Usually with cats and dogs we kn

ABCDEFGHIJKLM
NOPQRSTUVWXYZ
abcdefghijklmnopq
rstuvwxyz
1234567890&$¢£¥
fiflæœÆŒÅßÇÌÎÍÏã§†
———/()''"":;.,!¡?¿

10/11

In our house we had a cat with the grandiose name of Gonnosuke. Usually with cats and dogs we know who t he mother is but not the father. A cat with a large belly wondered into the house of my younger sister and her husband and gave birth to five kittens. While the mother was a pure white thoroughbred Chinchila, the kitten s were black and white tabbies of mixed breed. One of these came to our house about two weeks after its birt h and was given the name Gonnosuke. At that time we already had one female Shiba dog and one female bro wn tabby cat in our house comprising only 13 tsubo. The dog was called Momo and the cat Mii. My wife, who

16/17

In our house we had a cat with the grandiose name of Gonnosuke. Usually with cats and dogs we know who the mother is but not the f ather. A cat with a large belly wondered into the house of my young er sister and her husband and gave birth to five kittens. While the m

24/25

In our house we had a cat with the grandiose name of Gonnosuke. Usually with cats and d ogs we know who the mother is but not the fa

ABCDEFGHIJKLMN
OPQRSTUVWXYZ
abcdefghijklmnopq
rstuvwxyz
1234567890&$¢£¥
fiflæœÆŒÅßçÌÎÍÏã§
†-——/()‘’“‘’”.:;.,!¡?¿

10/11

*In our house we had a cat with the grandiose name of Gonnosuke. Usually with cats and dogs we know who t
he mother is but not the father. A cat with a large belly wondered into the house of my younger sister and her
husband and gave birth to five kittens. While the mother was a pure white thoroughbred Chinchila, the kitten
s were black and white tabbies of mixed breed. One of these came to our house about two weeks after its birth
and was given the name Gonnosuke. At that time we already had one female Shiba dog and one female brown
tabby cat in our house comprising only 13 tsubo. The dog was called Momo and the cat Mii. My wife, who wa*

16/17

*In our house we had a cat with the grandiose name of Gonnosuke. U
sually with cats and dogs we know who the mother is but not the fat
her. A cat with a large belly wondered into the house of my younger
sister and her husband and gave birth to five kittens. While the mot*

24/25

*In our house we had a cat with the grandiose
name of Gonnosuke. Usually with cats and d
ogs we know who the mother is but not the fa*

ABCDEFGHIJKLM NOPQRSTUVWXYZ abcdefghijklmnopq rstuvwxyz 1234567890&$¢£¥ fiflæœÆŒÅßÇÌÎÍÏ ã §†-–—/()''""·;.,!¡?¿

10/11

In our house we had a cat with the grandiose name of Gonnosuke. Usually with cats and dogs we know w ho the mother is but not the father. A cat with a large belly wondered into the house of my younger sister and her husband and gave birth to five kittens. While the mother was a pure white thoroughbred Chinchi la, the kittens were black and white tabbies of mixed breed. One of these came to our house about two w eeks after its birth and was given the name Gonnosuke. At that time we already had one female Shiba do g and one female brown tabby cat in our house comprising only 13 tsubo. The dog was called Momo and

16/17

In our house we had a cat with the grandiose name of Gonnosuk e. Usually with cats and dogs we know who the mother is but not the father. A cat with a large belly wondered into the house of my younger sister and her husband and gave birth to five kittens. Wh

24/25

In our house we had a cat with the grandios e name of Gonnosuke. Usually with cats an d dogs we know who the mother is but not

ABCDEFGHIJKLM
NOPQRSTUVWXYZ
abcdefghijklmnopq
rstuvwxyz
1234567890&$¢£¥
fiflæœÆŒÅßÇÌÎÍÏã§
†-–——/()'''‹›'''.,;.,!¡?¿

10/11

In our house we had a cat with the grandiose name of Gonnosuke. Usually with cats and dogs we know w
ho the mother is but not the father. A cat with a large belly wondered into the house of my younger sister
and her husband and gave birth to five kittens. While the mother was a pure white thoroughbred Chinchi
la, the kittens were black and white tabbies of mixed breed. One of these came to our house about two we
eks after its birth and was given the name Gonnosuke. At that time we already had one female Shiba dog
and one female brown tabby cat in our house comprising only 13 tsubo. The dog was called Momo and th

16/17

In our house we had a cat with the grandiose name of Gonnosuke.
Usually with cats and dogs we know who the mother is but not th
e father. A cat with a large belly wondered into the house of my y
ounger sister and her husband and gave birth to five kittens. Whil

24/25

In our house we had a cat with the grandios
e name of Gonnosuke. Usually with cats an
d dogs we know who the mother is but not t

ABCDEFGHIJKLM
NOPQRSTUVWXYZ
abcdefghijklmnopq
rstuvwxyz
1234567890&$¢£¥
fiflæœÆŒÅßÇÌÎÍÏã
§†–-——/()''""·;·.,!¡?¿

10/11

In our house we had a cat with the grandiose name of Gonnosuke. Usually with cats and dogs we k
now who the mother is but not the father. A cat with a large belly wondered into the house of my y
ounger sister and her husband and gave birth to five kittens. While the mother was a pure white t
horoughbred Chinchila, the kittens were black and white tabbies of mixed breed. One of these ca
me to our house about two weeks after its birth and was given the name Gonnosuke. At that time
we already had one female Shiba dog and one female brown tabby cat in our house comprising on

16/17

In our house we had a cat with the grandiose name of Gonno
suke. Usually with cats and dogs we know who the mother is
but not the father. A cat with a large belly wondered into the
house of my younger sister and her husband and gave birth t

24/25

In our house we had a cat with the gran
diose name of Gonnosuke. Usually with c
ats and dogs we know who the mother is

ABCDEFGHIJKLM NOPQRSTUVWXYZ abcdefghijklmnopq rstuvwxyz 1234567890&$¢£¥ fiflæœÆŒÅßÇÌÎÍÏã §†-–—/()''""‚;.,!¡?¿

10/11

In our house we had a cat with the grandiose name of Gonnosuke. Usually with cats and dogs we kn ow who the mother is but not the father. A cat with a large belly wondered into the house of my you nger sister and her husband and gave birth to five kittens. While the mother was a pure white thoro ughbred Chinchila, the kittens were black and white tabbies of mixed breed. One of these came to o ur house about two weeks after its birth and was given the name Gonnosuke. At that time we alread y had one female Shiba dog and one female brown tabby cat in our house comprising only 13 tsubo.

16/17

In our house we had a cat with the grandiose name of Gonnos uke. Usually with cats and dogs we know who the mother is b ut not the father. A cat with a large belly wondered into the h ouse of my younger sister and her husband and gave birth to f

24/25

In our house we had a cat with the grand iose name of Gonnosuke. Usually with ca ts and dogs we know who the mother is b

ABCDEFGHIJKL
MNOPQRSTUVW
XYZabcdefghijklm
nopqrstuvwxyz
1234567890&$¢£¥
fiflæœÆŒÅßÇÌÎÍÏ
ã§†--——/()''""‚;.‚'¡?¿

10/11

In our house we had a cat with the grandiose name of Gonnosuke. Usually with cats and do
gs we know who the mother is but not the father. A cat with a large belly wondered into th
e house of my younger sister and her husband and gave birth to five kittens. While the mot
her was a pure white thoroughbred Chinchila, the kittens were black and white tabbies of
mixed breed. One of these came to our house about two weeks after its birth and was given
the name Gonnosuke. At that time we already had one female Shiba dog and one female b

16/17

In our house we had a cat with the grandiose name of G
onnosuke. Usually with cats and dogs we know who the
mother is but not the father. A cat with a large belly won
dered into the house of my younger sister and her husba

24/25

In our house we had a cat with the gr
andiose name of Gonnosuke. Usually
with cats and dogs we know who the

ABCDEFGHIJKL
MNOPQRSTUVW
XYZabcdefghijklm
nopqrstuvwxyz
1234567890&
$¢£¥fiflæœÆŒ
ÅßçÌÎÍÏã§†
——/()''""::.,!¡?¿

10/11

In our house we had a cat with the grandiose name of Gonnosuke. Usually with cats and dogs we know who the mother is but not the father. A cat with a large belly wondered into the house of my younger sister and her husband and gave birth to five kittens. While the mother was a pure white thoroughbred Chinchila, the kittens were black and white tabbies of mixed breed. One of these came to our house about two weeks after its birth and was given the name Gonnosuke. At that time we already had one female Shiba dog and one female brown

16/17

In our house we had a cat with the grandiose name of Gonnosuke. Usually with cats and dogs we know who the mother is but not the father. A cat with a large belly wondered into the house of my younger sister and her husban

24/25

In our house we had a cat with the grandiose name of Gonnosuke. Usually with cats and dogs we know who the

ABCDEFGHIJKLMN
OPQRSTUVWXYZ
abcdefghijklmnopq
rstuvwxyz
1234567890&$¢£¥
fiflæœÆŒÅßÇÌÎÍÏã§
†----——/()''""::;.,!¡?¿

10/11

In our house we had a cat with the grandiose name of Gonnosuke. Usually with cats and dogs w
e know who the mother is but not the father. A cat with a large belly wondered into the house of
my younger sister and her husband and gave birth to five kittens. While the mother was a pure
white thoroughbred Chinchila, the kittens were black and white tabbies of mixed breed. One of t
hese came to our house about two weeks after its birth and was given the name Gonnosuke. At t
hat time we already had one female Shiba dog and one female brown tabby cat in our house co

16/17

In our house we had a cat with the grandiose name of Gonn
osuke. Usually with cats and dogs we know who the mother
is but not the father. A cat with a large belly wondered into t
he house of my younger sister and her husband and gave bi

24/25

In our house we had a cat with the gran
diose name of Gonnosuke. Usually with
cats and dogs we know who the mother

ABCDEFGHIJKLMN
OPQRSTUVWXYZ
abcdefghijklmnopq
rstuvwxyz
1234567890&$¢£¥
fiflœœÆŒÅßÇÌÎÍÏãß
†-–—/()''""",;.,!¡?¿

10/11

In our house we had a cat with the grandiose name of Gonnosuke. Usually with cats and dogs w e know who the mother is but not the father. A cat with a large belly wondered into the house of my younger sister and her husband and gave birth to five kittens. While the mother was a pure white thoroughbred Chinchila, the kittens were black and white tabbies of mixed breed. One of t hese came to our house about two weeks after its birth and was given the name Gonnosuke. At t hat time we already had one female Shiba dog and one female brown tabby cat in our house co

16/17

In our house we had a cat with the grandiose name of Gonn osuke. Usually with cats and dogs we know who the mother is but not the father. A cat with a large belly wondered into the house of my younger sister and her husband and gave b

24/25

In our house we had a cat with the gran diose name of Gonnosuke. Usually with cats and dogs we know who the mother

ABCDEFGHIJKLMN
OPQRSTUVWXYZ
abcdefghijklmnopq
rstuvwxyz
1234567890&$¢£¥
fiflæœÆŒÅßÇÌÎÍÏã
§†-–—/0''""":;.,!¡?¿

10/11

In our house we had a cat with the grandiose name of Gonnosuke. Usually with cats and dogs we know who the mother is but not the father. A cat with a large belly wondered into the house of my younger sister and her husband and gave birth to five kittens. While the mother was a pu re white thoroughbred Chinchila, the kittens were black and white tabbies of mixed breed. One of these came to our house about two weeks after its birth and was given the name Gonnosuke. At that time we already had one female Shiba dog and one female brown tabby cat in our hous

16/17

In our house we had a cat with the grandiose name of Gon nosuke. Usually with cats and dogs we know who the moth er is but not the father. A cat with a large belly wondered i nto the house of my younger sister and her husband and ga

24/25

In our house we had a cat with the gra ndiose name of Gonnosuke. Usually wit h cats and dogs we know who the moth

ABCDEFGHIJKLMN
OPQRSTUVWXYZ
abcdefghijklmnopq
rstuvwxyz
1234567890&$¢£¥
fiflœœÆŒÅßÇÌÎÍÏã
§†-–——/()''""":;.,!¡?¿

10/11

In our house we had a cat with the grandiose name of Gonnosuke. Usually with cats and dogs we know who the mother is but not the father. A cat with a large belly wondered into the house of my younger sister and her husband and gave birth to five kittens. While the mother was a p ure white thoroughbred Chinchila, the kittens were black and white tabbies of mixed breed. On e of these came to our house about two weeks after its birth and was given the name Gonnosuk e. At that time we already had one female Shiba dog and one female brown tabby cat in our ho

16/17

In our house we had a cat with the grandiose name of Gon nosuke. Usually with cats and dogs we know who the moth er is but not the father. A cat with a large belly wondered i nto the house of my younger sister and her husband and g

24/25

In our house we had a cat with the gra ndiose name of Gonnosuke. Usually wit h cats and dogs we know who the moth

ABCDEFGHIJKLM
NOPQRSTUVWXYZ
abcdefghijklmnopq
rstuvwxyz
1234567890&
$¢£¥fiflæœÆŒ
ÅßçÌÎÍÏã§†
-–—/()''""":;.,!¡?¿

10/11

In our house we had a cat with the grandiose name of Gonnosuke. Usually with cats and do
gs we know who the mother is but not the father. A cat with a large belly wondered into the
house of my younger sister and her husband and gave birth to five kittens. While the mothe
r was a pure white thoroughbred Chinchila, the kittens were black and white tabbies of mix
ed breed. One of these came to our house about two weeks after its birth and was given the
name Gonnosuke. At that time we already had one female Shiba dog and one female brown

16/17

In our house we had a cat with the grandiose name of Go
nnosuke. Usually with cats and dogs we know who the m
other is but not the father. A cat with a large belly wonde
red into the house of my younger sister and her husband

24/25

In our house we had a cat with the gr
andiose name of Gonnosuke. Usually
with cats and dogs we know who the

*ABCDEFGHIJKLM
NOPQRSTUVWXYZ
abcdefghijklmnop
qrstuvwxyz
1234567890&$¢£¥
fiflœœÆŒÅßÇÌÎÍÏã
§†-–—/()''""::,.,!¡?¿*

10/11

In our house we had a cat with the grandiose name of Gonnosuke. Usually with cats and d ogs we know who the mother is but not the father. A cat with a large belly wondered into t he house of my younger sister and her husband and gave birth to five kittens. While the m other was a pure white thoroughbred Chinchila, the kittens were black and white tabbies o f mixed breed. One of these came to our house about two weeks after its birth and was give n the name Gonnosuke. At that time we already had one female Shiba dog and one female

16/17

In our house we had a cat with the grandiose name of G onnosuke. Usually with cats and dogs we know who the mother is but not the father. A cat with a large belly won dered into the house of my younger sister and her husba

24/25

In our house we had a cat with the gr andiose name of Gonnosuke. Usually with cats and dogs we know who the

ABCDEFGHIJKL MNOPQRSTUVW XYZabcdefghijklm nopqrstuvwxyz 1234567890& $¢£¥fiflæœÆŒ ÅßçÌÎíÏã§† ---—/0''""";,.,!¡?¿

10/11

In our house we had a cat with the grandiose name of Gonnosuke. Usually with cats and dogs we know who the mother is but not the father. A cat with a large belly wondered in to the house of my younger sister and her husband and gave birth to five kittens. While t he mother was a pure white thoroughbred Chinchila, the kittens were black and white t abbies of mixed breed. One of these came to our house about two weeks after its birth a nd was given the name Gonnosuke. At that time we already had one female Shiba dog an

16/17

In our house we had a cat with the grandiose name of Gonnosuke. Usually with cats and dogs we know who th e mother is but not the father. A cat with a large belly wondered into the house of my younger sister and her

24/25

In our house we had a cat with the g randiose name of Gonnosuke. Usuall y with cats and dogs we know who th

ABCDEFGHIJKLM
NOPQRSTUVWXYZ
abcdefghijklmnop
qrstuvwxyz
1234567890&
$¢£¥fiflœœÆŒ
ÅßÇÌÎÍÏã§†
----—/()''""";.,!¡?¿

10/11

In our house we had a cat with the grandiose name of Gonnosuke. Usually with cats and dogs we know who the mother is but not the father. A cat with a large belly wondered in to the house of my younger sister and her husband and gave birth to five kittens. While t he mother was a pure white thoroughbred Chinchila, the kittens were black and white t abbies of mixed breed. One of these came to our house about two weeks after its birth an d was given the name Gonnosuke. At that time we already had one female Shiba dog an

16/17

In our house we had a cat with the grandiose name of Gonnosuke. Usually with cats and dogs we know who t he mother is but not the father. A cat with a large belly wondered into the house of my younger sister and her

24/25

In our house we had a cat with the g randiose name of Gonnosuke. Usuall y with cats and dogs we know who t

ABCDEFGHIJKL MNOPQRSTUVW XYZ abcdefghijklmnopqrs tuvwxyz 1234567890&$¢£¥ fiflæœÆŒÅßÇÌÎÍÏã §†-–—/()""""":;.,!¡?¿

10/11

In our house we had a cat with the grandiose name of Gonnosuke. Usually with cats and dogs we kno w who the mother is but not the father. A cat with a large belly wondered into the house of my young er sister and her husband and gave birth to five kittens. While the mother was a pure white thorough bred Chinchila, the kittens were black and white tabbies of mixed breed. One of these came to our hou se about two weeks after its birth and was given the name Gonnosuke. At that time we already had o ne female Shiba dog and one female brown tabby cat in our house comprising only 13 tsubo. The dog

16/17

In our house we had a cat with the grandiose name of Gonnosuk e. Usually with cats and dogs we know who the mother is but n ot the father. A cat with a large belly wondered into the house o f my younger sister and her husband and gave birth to five kitt

24/25

In our house we had a cat with the grandi ose name of Gonnosuke. Usually with cats and dogs we know who the mother is but

ABCDEFGHIJKL MNOPQRSTUVW XYZ

abcdefghijklmnopq
rstuvwxyz
1234567890&$¢£¥
fiflæœÆŒÅßÇÌÎÍÏã
§†-——/()''""'.;.,!¡?¿

10/11

In our house we had a cat with the grandiose name of Gonnosuke. Usually with cats and dogs we kno w who the mother is but not the father. A cat with a large belly wondered into the house of my younger sister and her husband and gave birth to five kittens. While the mother was a pure white thoroughbre d Chinchila, the kittens were black and white tabbies of mixed breed. One of these came to our house a bout two weeks after its birth and was given the name Gonnosuke. At that time we already had one fe male Shiba dog and one female brown tabby cat in our house comprising only 13 tsubo. The dog was

16/17

In our house we had a cat with the grandiose name of Gonnosu ke. Usually with cats and dogs we know who the mother is but not the father. A cat with a large belly wondered into the house of my younger sister and her husband and gave birth to five kit

24/25

In our house we had a cat with the grandi ose name of Gonnosuke. Usually with cat s and dogs we know who the mother is but

ABCDEFGHIJKL MNOPQRSTUVW XYZ

abcdefghijklmnopq rstuvwxyz 1234567890&$¢£¥ fiflæœÆŒÅßÇÌÎÍÏã §†-–—/()''""·;·,!¡?¿

10/11

In our house we had a cat with the grandiose name of Gonnosuke. Usually with cats and dogs we know who the mother is but not the father. A cat with a large belly wondered into the house of m y younger sister and her husband and gave birth to five kittens. While the mother was a pure wh ite thoroughbred Chinchila, the kittens were black and white tabbies of mixed breed. One of thes e came to our house about two weeks after its birth and was given the name Gonnosuke. At that t ime we already had one female Shiba dog and one female brown tabby cat in our house comprisin

16/17

In our house we had a cat with the grandiose name of Gonno suke. Usually with cats and dogs we know who the mother is but not the father. A cat with a large belly wondered into the house of my younger sister and her husband and gave birth t

24/25

In our house we had a cat with the gran diose name of Gonnosuke. Usually with cats and dogs we know who the mother i

ABCDEFGHIJKL
MNOPQRSTUVW
XYZ
abcdefghijklmnopq
rstuvwxyz
1234567890&$¢£¥
fiflæœÆŒÅßÇÌÎÍÏã§
†-——/()""""·;·,!¡?¿

10/11

In our house we had a cat with the grandiose name of Gonnosuke. Usually with cats and dogs we know who the mother is but not the father. A cat with a large belly wondered into the house of my younger sister and her husband and gave birth to five kittens. While the mother was a pure white t horoughbred Chinchila, the kittens were black and white tabbies of mixed breed. One of these cam e to our house about two weeks after its birth and was given the name Gonnosuke. At that time we already had one female Shiba dog and one female brown tabby cat in our house comprising only 1

16/17

In our house we had a cat with the grandiose name of Gonno suke. Usually with cats and dogs we know who the mother is but not the father. A cat with a large belly wondered into the house of my younger sister and her husband and gave birth t

24/25

In our house we had a cat with the gran diose name of Gonnosuke. Usually with cats and dogs we know who the mother i

ABCDEFGHIJKL
MNOPQRSTUVW
XYZabcdefghijkl
mnopqrstuvwxyz
1234567890&$¢£¥
fiflæœÆŒÅßÇÌÎÍÏ
ã§†-—––/()''""".;.,!¡?¿

10/11

In our house we had a cat with the grandiose name of Gonnosuke. Usually with cats an
d dogs we know who the mother is but not the father. A cat with a large belly wondere
d into the house of my younger sister and her husband and gave birth to five kittens. W
hile the mother was a pure white thoroughbred Chinchila, the kittens were black and
white tabbies of mixed breed. One of these came to our house about two weeks after its
birth and was given the name Gonnosuke. At that time we already had one female Shib

16/17

In our house we had a cat with the grandiose name of
Gonnosuke. Usually with cats and dogs we know who
the mother is but not the father. A cat with a large bell
y wondered into the house of my younger sister and h

24/25

In our house we had a cat with the
grandiose name of Gonnosuke. Usu
ally with cats and dogs we know wh

ABCDEFGHIJKL
MNOPQRSTUVW
XYZabcdefghijkl
mnopqrstuvwxyz
1234567890&$¢£¥
fiflæœÆŒÅßÇÌÎÍÏ
ã§†-----/()''"""".;.,!¡?¿

10/11

In our house we had a cat with the grandiose name of Gonnosuke. Usually with cats an d dogs we know who the mother is but not the father. A cat with a large belly wondered into the house of my younger sister and her husband and gave birth to five kittens. Whil e the mother was a pure white thoroughbred Chinchila, the kittens were black and whit e tabbies of mixed breed. One of these came to our house about two weeks after its birth and was given the name Gonnosuke. At that time we already had one female Shiba dog

16/17

In our house we had a cat with the grandiose name of Gonnosuke. Usually with cats and dogs we know who t he mother is but not the father. A cat with a large belly wondered into the house of my younger sister and her

24/25

In our house we had a cat with the g randiose name of Gonnosuke. Usual ly with cats and dogs we know who t

ABCDEFGHIJKLMN
OPQRSTUVWXYZ
abcdefghijklmnopq
rstuvwxyz
1234567890&$¢£¥
fiflæœÆŒÅßÇÌÎÍÏã
§†---——/()'''""":;.,!¡?¿

10/11

In our house we had a cat with the grandiose name of Gonnosuke. Usually with cats and dogs we kn
ow who the mother is but not the father. A cat with a large belly wondered into the house of my youn
ger sister and her husband and gave birth to five kittens. While the mother was a pure white thoroug
hbred Chinchila, the kittens were black and white tabbies of mixed breed. One of these came to our
house about two weeks after its birth and was given the name Gonnosuke. At that time we already h
ad one female Shiba dog and one female brown tabby cat in our house comprising only 13 tsubo. Th

16/17

In our house we had a cat with the grandiose name of Gonnos
uke. Usually with cats and dogs we know who the mother is bu
t not the father. A cat with a large belly wondered into the hous
e of my younger sister and her husband and gave birth to five

24/25

In our house we had a cat with the grandi
ose name of Gonnosuke. Usually with cat
s and dogs we know who the mother is bu

ABCDEFGHIJKLMN
OPQRSTUVWXYZ
abcdefghijklmnopq
rstuvwxyz
1234567890&$¢£¥
fiflæœÆŒÅßÇÌÎÍÏã
$†-–——/0""""·;·.,·!¡?¿

10/11

In our house we had a cat with the grandiose name of Gonnosuke. Usually with cats and dogs we kno
w who the mother is but not the father. A cat with a large belly wondered into the house of my younger
sister and her husband and gave birth to five kittens. While the mother was a pure white thoroughbre
d Chinchila, the kittens were black and white tabbies of mixed breed. One of these came to our house
about two weeks after its birth and was given the name Gonnosuke. At that time we already had one f
emale Shiba dog and one female brown tabby cat in our house comprising only 13 tsubo. The dog was

16/17

In our house we had a cat with the grandiose name of Gonnosu
ke. Usually with cats and dogs we know who the mother is but
not the father. A cat with a large belly wondered into the house
of my younger sister and her husband and gave birth to five kitt

24/25

In our house we had a cat with the grandi
ose name of Gonnosuke. Usually with cats
and dogs we know who the mother is but

ABCDEFGHIJKLMN
OPQRSTUVWXYZ
abcdefghijklmnopq
rstuvwxyz
1234567890&$¢£¥
fiflæœÆŒÅßÇÌÎÍÏĩ
§†-–—/()''""";.,!¡?¿

10/11

In our house we had a cat with the grandiose name of Gonnosuke. Usually with cats and dogs we k
now who the mother is but not the father. A cat with a large belly wondered into the house of my y
ounger sister and her husband and gave birth to five kittens. While the mother was a pure white th
oroughbred Chinchila, the kittens were black and white tabbies of mixed breed. One of these came
to our house about two weeks after its birth and was given the name Gonnosuke. At that time we a
lready had one female Shiba dog and one female brown tabby cat in our house comprising only 13

16/17

In our house we had a cat with the grandiose name of Gonno
suke. Usually with cats and dogs we know who the mother is
but not the father. A cat with a large belly wondered into the h
ouse of my younger sister and her husband and gave birth to

24/25

In our house we had a cat with the grand
iose name of Gonnosuke. Usually with c
ats and dogs we know who the mother is

ABCDEFGHIJKLMN
OPQRSTUVWXYZ
abcdefghijklmnopq
rstuvwxyz
1234567890&$¢£¥
fiflæœÆŒÅßÇÌÎÍÏã
$†-–—/()"'""'":;.,!¡?¿

10/11

In our house we had a cat with the grandiose name of Gonnosuke. Usually with cats and dogs we k now who the mother is but not the father. A cat with a large belly wondered into the house of my yo unger sister and her husband and gave birth to five kittens. While the mother was a pure white thor oughbred Chinchila, the kittens were black and white tabbies of mixed breed. One of these came to our house about two weeks after its birth and was given the name Gonnosuke. At that time we alrea dy had one female Shiba dog and one female brown tabby cat in our house comprising only 13 tsub

16/17

In our house we had a cat with the grandiose name of Gonnos uke. Usually with cats and dogs we know who the mother is b ut not the father. A cat with a large belly wondered into the ho use of my younger sister and her husband and gave birth to fi

24/25

In our house we had a cat with the grand iose name of Gonnosuke. Usually with ca ts and dogs we know who the mother is b

ABCDEFGHIJKLMN
OPQRSTUVWXYZ
abcdefghijklmnopq
rstuvwxyz
1234567890&$¢£¥
fiflæœÆŒÅßÇÌÎÍÏã
§†-‒––/()'"""‚;.,!¡?¿

10/11

In our house we had a cat with the grandiose name of Gonnosuke. Usually with cats and dogs we know who the mother is but not the father. A cat with a large belly wondered into the house of my younger sister and her husband and gave birth to five kittens. While the mother was a pure white thoroughbred Chinchila, the kittens were black and white tabbies of mixed breed. One of these ca me to our house about two weeks after its birth and was given the name Gonnosuke. At that time we already had one female Shiba dog and one female brown tabby cat in our house comprising on

16/17

In our house we had a cat with the grandiose name of Gonno suke. Usually with cats and dogs we know who the mother is but not the father. A cat with a large belly wondered into the house of my younger sister and her husband and gave birth t

24/25

In our house we had a cat with the grand iose name of Gonnosuke. Usually with c ats and dogs we know who the mother is

ABCDEFGHIJKLMN
OPQRSTUVWXYZ
abcdefghijklmnopq
rstuvwxyz
1234567890&$¢£¥
fiflæœÆŒÅßÇÌÎÍÏã
$†-–——/()''""'';.,.,!¡?¿

10/11

In our house we had a cat with the grandiose name of Gonnosuke. Usually with cats and dogs we k now who the mother is but not the father. A cat with a large belly wondered into the house of my yo unger sister and her husband and gave birth to five kittens. While the mother was a pure white tho roughbred Chinchila, the kittens were black and white tabbies of mixed breed. One of these came t o our house about two weeks after its birth and was given the name Gonnosuke. At that time we al ready had one female Shiba dog and one female brown tabby cat in our house comprising only 13

16/17

In our house we had a cat with the grandiose name of Gonno suke. Usually with cats and dogs we know who the mother is but not the father. A cat with a large belly wondered into the house of my younger sister and her husband and gave birth t

24/25

In our house we had a cat with the gran diose name of Gonnosuke. Usually with cats and dogs we know who the mother i

ABCDEFGHIJKL
MNOPQRSTUVW
XYZabcdefghijkl
mnopqrstuvwxyz
1234567890&$¢£¥
fiflæœÆŒÅßÇÌÎÍÏ
ã§†-‐–—/()'’"“”:;.,!¡?¿

10/11

In our house we had a cat with the grandiose name of Gonnosuke. Usually with cats and
dogs we know who the mother is but not the father. A cat with a large belly wondered int
o the house of my younger sister and her husband and gave birth to five kittens. While t
he mother was a pure white thoroughbred Chinchila, the kittens were black and white t
abbies of mixed breed. One of these came to our house about two weeks after its birth a
nd was given the name Gonnosuke. At that time we already had one female Shiba dog an

16/17

In our house we had a cat with the grandiose name of
Gonnosuke. Usually with cats and dogs we know who th
e mother is but not the father. A cat with a large belly w
ondered into the house of my younger sister and her h

24/25

In our house we had a cat with the gr
andiose name of Gonnosuke. Usuall
y with cats and dogs we know who th

ABCDEFGHIJKLM
NOPQRSTUVWXYZ
abcdefghijklmnopq
rstuvwxyz
1234567890&$¢£¥
fiflæœÆŒÅßÇÌÎÍÏã
§†-–——/()''""";.,!¡?¿

10/11

In our house we had a cat with the grandiose name of Gonnosuke. Usually with cats and dogs we know who the mother is but not the father. A cat with a large belly wondered into the hous e of my younger sister and her husband and gave birth to five kittens. While the mother was a pure white thoroughbred Chinchila, the kittens were black and white tabbies of mixed breed. One of these came to our house about two weeks after its birth and was given the name Gonno suke. At that time we already had one female Shiba dog and one female brown tabby cat in our

16/17

In our house we had a cat with the grandiose name of Gon nosuke. Usually with cats and dogs we know who the moth er is but not the father. A cat with a large belly wondered i nto the house of my younger sister and her husband and g

24/25

In our house we had a cat with the gra ndiose name of Gonnosuke. Usually wi th cats and dogs we know who the mot

ABCDEFGHIJKLM
NOPQRSTUVWXYZ
abcdefghijklmnopq
rstuvwxyz
1234567890&$¢£¥
fiflæœÆŒÅßÇÌÎÍÏã
§†–——/O'""":;.,!¡?¿

10/11

In our house we had a cat with the grandiose name of Gonnosuke. Usually with cats and dogs
we know who the mother is but not the father. A cat with a large belly wondered into the house o
f my younger sister and her husband and gave birth to five kittens. While the mother was a pure
white thoroughbred Chinchila, the kittens were black and white tabbies of mixed breed. One of t
hese came to our house about two weeks after its birth and was given the name Gonnosuke. At t
hat time we already had one female Shiba dog and one female brown tabby cat in our house co

16/17

In our house we had a cat with the grandiose name of Gonn
osuke. Usually with cats and dogs we know who the mother
is but not the father. A cat with a large belly wondered into t
he house of my younger sister and her husband and gave bi

24/25

In our house we had a cat with the gra
ndiose name of Gonnosuke. Usually wit
h cats and dogs we know who the moth

ABCDEFGHIJKL
MNOPQRSTUVW
XYZabcdefghijkl
mnopqrstuvwxyz
1234567890&$¢£¥
fiflæœÆŒÅßÇÌÎÍÏ
ã§†----——/()''"".;.,!¡?¿

10/11

In our house we had a cat with the grandiose name of Gonnosuke. Usually with cats and dogs we know who the mother is but not the father. A cat with a large belly wondered int o the house of my younger sister and her husband and gave birth to five kittens. While th e mother was a pure white thoroughbred Chinchila, the kittens were black and white tab bies of mixed breed. One of these came to our house about two weeks after its birth and was given the name Gonnosuke. At that time we already had one female Shiba dog and o

16/17

In our house we had a cat with the grandiose name of G onnosuke. Usually with cats and dogs we know who the mother is but not the father. A cat with a large belly wo ndered into the house of my younger sister and her hus

24/25

In our house we had a cat with the gr andiose name of Gonnosuke. Usually with cats and dogs we know who the

ABCDEFGHIJKL
MNOPQRSTUVW
XYZabcdefghijkl
mnopqrstuvwxyz
1234567890&$¢£¥
fiflæœÆŒÅßÇÌÎÍÏ
ã§†----/()''""·;·,!;?¿

10/11

In our house we had a cat with the grandiose name of Gonnosuke. Usually with cats and dogs we know who the mother is but not the father. A cat with a large belly wondered int o the house of my younger sister and her husband and gave birth to five kittens. While th e mother was a pure white thoroughbred Chinchila, the kittens were black and white ta bbies of mixed breed. One of these came to our house about two weeks after its birth and was given the name Gonnosuke. At that time we already had one female Shiba dog and o

16/17

In our house we had a cat with the grandiose name of Gonnosuke. Usually with cats and dogs we know who t he mother is but not the father. A cat with a large belly wondered into the house of my younger sister and her

24/25

In our house we had a cat with the g randiose name of Gonnosuke. Usual ly with cats and dogs we know who t

ABCDEFGHIJKLM
NOPQRSTUVWXY
Zabcdefghijklmn
opqrstuvwxyz123
4567890&$¢€¥fi
flæœÆŒÅßçÏÍÌÏã
—-—/()''""·:;.,!¡?¿

10/11

In our house we had a cat with the grandiose name of Gonnosuke. Usually with cats
and dogs we know who the mother is but not the father. A cat with a large belly won
dered into the house of my younger sister and her husband and gave birth to five kitt
ens. While the mother was a pure white thoroughbred Chinchila, the kittens were bl
ack and white tabbies of mixed breed. One of these came to our house about two we
eks after its birth and was given the name Gonnosuke. At that time we already had o

16/17

In our house we had a cat with the grandiose name
of Gonnosuke. Usually with cats and dogs we know
who the mother is but not the father. A cat with a lar
ge belly wondered into the house of my younger sist

24/25

In our house we had a cat with the
grandiose name of Gonnosuke. Usu
ally with cats and dogs we know w

ABCDEFGHIJKL
MNOPQRSTUVWX
YZabcdefghijklmn
opqrstuvwxyz
1234567890&
$¢£¥fiflæœÆŒ
ÅßÇÌÎÍÏ㧠†
---——/○''""".;.,!¡?¿

10/11

In our house we had a cat with the grandiose name of Gonnosuke. Usually with cats an
d dogs we know who the mother is but not the father. A cat with a large belly wondere
d into the house of my younger sister and her husband and gave birth to five kittens.
While the mother was a pure white thoroughbred Chinchila, the kittens were black and
white tabbies of mixed breed. One of these came to our house about two weeks after its
birth and was given the name Gonnosuke. At that time we already had one female Shib

16/17

In our house we had a cat with the grandiose name of
Gonnosuke. Usually with cats and dogs we know who t
he mother is but not the father. A cat with a large bell
y wondered into the house of my younger sister and h

24/25

In our house we had a cat with the
grandiose name of Gonnosuke. Usua
lly with cats and dogs we know who

ABCDEFGHIJKL
MNOPQRSTUVW
XYZabcdefghijkl
mnopqrstuvwxyz
1234567890&
$¢£¥fiflæœÆŒ
ÅßçÌÎÍÏã§†
-–—/()''""":;.,!¡?¿

10/11

In our house we had a cat with the grandiose name of Gonnosuke. Usually with cats and dogs we know who the mother is but not the father. A cat with a large belly wondered in to the house of my younger sister and her husband and gave birth to five kittens. While the mother was a pure white thoroughbred Chinchila, the kittens were black and white tabbies of mixed breed. One of these came to our house about two weeks after its birth a nd was given the name Gonnosuke. At that time we already had one female Shiba dog an

16/17

In our house we had a cat with the grandiose name of Gonnosuke. Usually with cats and dogs we know who t he mother is but not the father. A cat with a large belly wondered into the house of my younger sister and her

24/25

In our house we had a cat with the g randiose name of Gonnosuke. Usuall y with cats and dogs we know who t

ABCDEFGHIJKL MNOPQRSTUVW XYZ

abcdefghijklmnopq rstuvwxyz 1234567890&$¢£¥ fiflæœÆŒÅßÇÌÎÍÏã §‡-–—/()"'"":;.,!¡?¿

10/11

In our house we had a cat with the grandiose name of Gonnosuke. Usually with cats and dogs w e know who the mother is but not the father. A cat with a large belly wondered into the house of my younger sister and her husband and gave birth to five kittens. While the mother was a pure white thoroughbred Chinchila, the kittens were black and white tabbies of mixed breed. One of these came to our house about two weeks after its birth and was given the name Gonnosuke. At that time we already had one female Shiba dog and one female brown tabby cat in our house co

16/17

In our house we had a cat with the grandiose name of Gonn osuke. Usually with cats and dogs we know who the mother is but not the father. A cat with a large belly wondered into the house of my younger sister and her husband and gave b

24/25

In our house we had a cat with the gran diose name of Gonnosuke. Usually with cats and dogs we know who the mother

ABCDEFGHIJKL
MNOPQRSTUVW
XYZ
abcdefghijklmnopq
rstuvwxyz
1234567890&$¢£¥
fiflæœÆŒÅßÇÌÎÍÏã
§†-––—/()''""":;.,!¡?¿

10/11

In our house we had a cat with the grandiose name of Gonnosuke. Usually with cats and dogs w
e know who the mother is but not the father. A cat with a large belly wondered into the house of
my younger sister and her husband and gave birth to five kittens. While the mother was a pure
white thoroughbred Chinchila, the kittens were black and white tabbies of mixed breed. One of
these came to our house about two weeks after its birth and was given the name Gonnosuke. At
that time we already had one female Shiba dog and one female brown tabby cat in our house co

16/17

In our house we had a cat with the grandiose name of Gonn
osuke. Usually with cats and dogs we know who the mother
is but not the father. A cat with a large belly wondered into
the house of my younger sister and her husband and gave b

24/25

In our house we had a cat with the gran
diose name of Gonnosuke. Usually with
cats and dogs we know who the mother

ABCDEFGHIJKL MNOPQRSTUVW XYZ

abcdefghijklmnopq rstuvwxyz

1234567890&$¢£¥ fiflæœÆŒÅßÇÌÎÍÏã §‡-–——/()''""":;.,!¡?¿

10/11

In our house we had a cat with the grandiose name of Gonnosuke. Usually with cats and dogs we know who the mother is but not the father. A cat with a large belly wondered into the hous e of my younger sister and her husband and gave birth to five kittens. While the mother was a pure white thoroughbred Chinchila, the kittens were black and white tabbies of mixed breed. One of these came to our house about two weeks after its birth and was given the name Gonn osuke. At that time we already had one female Shiba dog and one female brown tabby cat in o

16/17

In our house we had a cat with the grandiose name of Gon nosuke. Usually with cats and dogs we know who the moth er is but not the father. A cat with a large belly wondered i nto the house of my younger sister and her husband and g

24/25

In our house we had a cat with the gra ndiose name of Gonnosuke. Usually wi th cats and dogs we know who the mot

ABCDEFGHIJKLMNO
PQRSTUVWXYZ
abcdefghijklmnopq
rstuvwxyz
1234567890&$¢£¥
fiflæœÆŒÅßÇÌÎÍÏã
§†-–—/O''""":;.,·¡?¿

10/11

In our house we had a cat with the grandiose name of Gonnosuke. Usually with cats and dogs we k now who the mother is but not the father. A cat with a large belly wondered into the house of my y ounger sister and her husband and gave birth to five kittens. While the mother was a pure white th oroughbred Chinchila, the kittens were black and white tabbies of mixed breed. One of these came to our house about two weeks after its birth and was given the name Gonnosuke. At that time we a lready had one female Shiba dog and one female brown tabby cat in our house comprising only 13

16/17

In our house we had a cat with the grandiose name of Gonnos uke. Usually with cats and dogs we know who the mother is b ut not the father. A cat with a large belly wondered into the h ouse of my younger sister and her husband and gave birth to

24/25

In our house we had a cat with the grand iose name of Gonnosuke. Usually with ca ts and dogs we know who the mother is

ABCDEFGHIJKLMNO PQRSTUVWXYZ abcdefghijklmnopq rstuvwxyz 1234567890&$¢£¥ fiflæœÆŒÅßÇÌÎÍÏã §†-——/()''""·,·,!¡?¿

10/11

In our house we had a cat with the grandiose name of Gonnosuke. Usually with cats and dogs we kno w who the mother is but not the father. A cat with a large belly wondered into the house of my younger sister and her husband and gave birth to five kittens. While the mother was a pure white thoroughbred Chinchila, the kittens were black and white tabbies of mixed breed. One of these came to our house a bout two weeks after its birth and was given the name Gonnosuke. At that time we already had one fe male Shiba dog and one female brown tabby cat in our house comprising only 13 tsubo. The dog was c

16/17

In our house we had a cat with the grandiose name of Gonnosu ke. Usually with cats and dogs we know who the mother is but n ot the father. A cat with a large belly wondered into the house o f my younger sister and her husband and gave birth to five kitte

24/25

In our house we had a cat with the grandi ose name of Gonnosuke. Usually with cats and dogs we know who the mother is but

743

ABCDEFGHIJKLMN
OPQRSTUVWXYZ
abcdefghijklmnopq
rstuvwxyz
1234567890&$¢£¥
fiflæœÆŒÅßÇÌÎÍÏĩ
§†·-—/O''""";.,!¡?¿

10/11

In our house we had a cat with the grandiose name of Gonnosuke. Usually with cats and dogs w
e know who the mother is but not the father. A cat with a large belly wondered into the house o
f my younger sister and her husband and gave birth to five kittens. While the mother was a pur
e white thoroughbred Chinchila, the kittens were black and white tabbies of mixed breed. One
of these came to our house about two weeks after its birth and was given the name Gonnosuke.
At that time we already had one female Shiba dog and one female brown tabby cat in our hous

16/17

In our house we had a cat with the grandiose name of Gonn
osuke. Usually with cats and dogs we know who the mother
is but not the father. A cat with a large belly wondered into
the house of my younger sister and her husband and gave b

24/25

In our house we had a cat with the gran
diose name of Gonnosuke. Usually with
cats and dogs we know who the mother

ABCDEFGHIJKLMN
OPQRSTUVWXYZ
abcdefghijklmnop
qrstuvwxyz
1234567890&$¢£¥
fiflœœÆŒÅßÇÌÎÍÏã
§†·---—/()''""";.,!¡?¿

10/11

In our house we had a cat with the grandiose name of Gonnosuke. Usually with cats and dogs we know who the mother is but not the father. A cat with a large belly wondered into the house of my younger sister and her husband and gave birth to five kittens. While the mother was a pure white thoroughbred Chinchila, the kittens were black and white tabbies of mixed breed. One of these came to our house about two weeks after its birth and was given the name Gonnosuke. At that time we already had one female Shiba dog and one female brown t

16/17

In our house we had a cat with the grandiose name of Gonnosuke. Usually with cats and dogs we know who the mother is but not the father. A cat with a large belly wondered into the house of my younger sister and her husband

24/25

In our house we had a cat with the grandiose name of Gonnosuke. Usually with cats and dogs we know who the

ABCDEFGHIJKL
MNOPQRSTUVW
XYZ
abcdefghijklmnop
qrstuvwxyz
1234567890&$¢£¥
fiflæœÆŒÅßÇÌÎÍÏã
§†-–—/()'"":;.,!¡?¿

10/11

In our house we had a cat with the grandiose name of Gonnosuke. Usually with cats and do
gs we know who the mother is but not the father. A cat with a large belly wondered into th
e house of my younger sister and her husband and gave birth to five kittens. While the mot
her was a pure white thoroughbred Chinchila, the kittens were black and white tabbies of
mixed breed. One of these came to our house about two weeks after its birth and was given
the name Gonnosuke. At that time we already had one female Shiba dog and one female bro

16/17

In our house we had a cat with the grandiose name of Go
nnosuke. Usually with cats and dogs we know who the
mother is but not the father. A cat with a large belly won
dered into the house of my younger sister and her husba

24/25

In our house we had a cat with the gr
andiose name of Gonnosuke. Usually
with cats and dogs we know who the

ABCDEFGHIJKL
MNOPQRSTUVW
XYZabcdefghijklm
nopqrstuvwxyz
1234567890&
$¢£¥fiflæœÆŒ
ÅßÇÌÎÍÏã§†
–——/()'""":;.,!¡?¿

10/11

In our house we had a cat with the grandiose name of Gonnosuke. Usually with cats and d
ogs we know who the mother is but not the father. A cat with a large belly wondered into t
he house of my younger sister and her husband and gave birth to five kittens. While the m
other was a pure white thoroughbred Chinchila, the kittens were black and white tabbies o
f mixed breed. One of these came to our house about two weeks after its birth and was give
n the name Gonnosuke. At that time we already had one female Shiba dog and one female b

16/17

In our house we had a cat with the grandiose name of Go
nnosuke. Usually with cats and dogs we know who the
mother is but not the father. A cat with a large belly won
dered into the house of my younger sister and her husba

24/25

In our house we had a cat with the gr
andiose name of Gonnosuke. Usually
with cats and dogs we know who the

ABCDEFGHIJKL MNOPQRSTUVW XYZabcdefghijkl mnopqrstuvwxyz 1234567890& $¢£¥fiflæœÆŒ ÅßÇÌÎÍÏã§† -–—/O''""",:;.,!¡?¿

10/11

In our house we had a cat with the grandiose name of Gonnosuke. Usually with cats an
d dogs we know who the mother is but not the father. A cat with a large belly wondere
d into the house of my younger sister and her husband and gave birth to five kittens.
While the mother was a pure white thoroughbred Chinchila, the kittens were black an
d white tabbies of mixed breed. One of these came to our house about two weeks after i
ts birth and was given the name Gonnosuke. At that time we already had one female S

16/17

In our house we had a cat with the grandiose name of
Gonnosuke. Usually with cats and dogs we know who
the mother is but not the father. A cat with a large bel
ly wondered into the house of my younger sister and h

24/25

In our house we had a cat with the
grandiose name of Gonnosuke. Usua
lly with cats and dogs we know who

ABCDEFGHIJKL
MNOPQRSTUVW
XYZabcdefghijkl
mnopqrstuvwxyz
1234567890&$¢£¥
fiflæœÆŒÅßÇÌÎÍÏ
ã§†–––—/0'""":;.,!¡?¿

10/11

In our house we had a cat with the grandiose name of Gonnosuke. Usually with cats and dogs we know who the mother is but not the father. A cat with a large belly wondered in to the house of my younger sister and her husband and gave birth to five kittens. While the mother was a pure white thoroughbred Chinchila, the kittens were black and white tabbies of mixed breed. One of these came to our house about two weeks after its birth and was given the name Gonnosuke. At that time we already had one female Shiba dog

16/17

In our house we had a cat with the grandiose name of Gonnosuke. Usually with cats and dogs we know who t he mother is but not the father. A cat with a large belly wondered into the house of my younger sister and her

24/25

In our house we had a cat with the g randiose name of Gonnosuke. Usual ly with cats and dogs we know who t

ABCDEFGHIJKL
MNOPQRSTUVW
XYZabcdefghijklm
nopqrstuvwxyz
1234567890&$¢£¥
fiflæœÆŒÅßÇÌÎÍÏã
§†-–—/()''""":;.,!¡?¿

10/11

In our house we had a cat with the grandiose name of Gonnosuke. Usually with cats and dog s we know who the mother is but not the father. A cat with a large belly wondered into the ho use of my younger sister and her husband and gave birth to five kittens. While the mother was a pure white thoroughbred Chinchila, the kittens were black and white tabbies of mixed bree d. One of these came to our house about two weeks after its birth and was given the name Go nnosuke. At that time we already had one female Shiba dog and one female brown tabby cat

16/17

In our house we had a cat with the grandiose name of Go nnosuke. Usually with cats and dogs we know who the mo ther is but not the father. A cat with a large belly wondere d into the house of my younger sister and her husband an

24/25

In our house we had a cat with the gra ndiose name of Gonnosuke. Usually w ith cats and dogs we know who the mo

ABCDEFGHIJKL
MNOPQRSTUVW
XYZabcdefghijkl
mnopqrstuvwxyz
1234567890&$¢£¥
fiflæœÆŒÅßÇÌÎÍÏ
ã§†-–——/()'""":;.,!¡?¿

10/11

In our house we had a cat with the grandiose name of Gonnosuke. Usually with cats and d
ogs we know who the mother is but not the father. A cat with a large belly wondered into t
he house of my younger sister and her husband and gave birth to five kittens. While the m
other was a pure white thoroughbred Chinchila, the kittens were black and white tabbies
of mixed breed. One of these came to our house about two weeks after its birth and was gi
ven the name Gonnosuke. At that time we already had one female Shiba dog and one fema

16/17

In our house we had a cat with the grandiose name of G
onnosuke. Usually with cats and dogs we know who the
mother is but not the father. A cat with a large belly wo
ndered into the house of my younger sister and her hus

24/25

In our house we had a cat with the gr
andiose name of Gonnosuke. Usually
with cats and dogs we know who the

ABCDEFGHIJKL MNOPQRSTUVW XYZ
abcdefghijklmnopq rstuvwxyz
1234567890&$¢£¥
fiflæœÆŒÅßÇÌÎÍÏã
§†-–—/()''""":;.,!¡?¿

10/11

In our house we had a cat with the grandiose name of Gonnosuke. Usually with cats and dogs we know who the mother is but not the father. A cat with a large belly wondered into the house of my younger sister and her husband and gave birth to five kittens. While the mother was a pu re white thoroughbred Chinchila, the kittens were black and white tabbies of mixed breed. One of these came to our house about two weeks after its birth and was given the name Gonnosuke. At that time we already had one female Shiba dog and one female brown tabby cat in our hous

16/17

In our house we had a cat with the grandiose name of Gonn osuke. Usually with cats and dogs we know who the mothe r is but not the father. A cat with a large belly wondered int o the house of my younger sister and her husband and gave

24/25

In our house we had a cat with the gran diose name of Gonnosuke. Usually with cats and dogs we know who the mother

ABCDEFGHIJKL
MNOPQRSTUVW
XYZ
abcdefghijklmnopq
rstuvwxyz
1234567890&$¢£¥
fiflœœÆŒÅßÇÌÎÍÏã
§†-——/()''""".;.,!¡?¿

10/11

In our house we had a cat with the grandiose name of Gonnosuke. Usually with cats and dogs
we know who the mother is but not the father. A cat with a large belly wondered into the house
of my younger sister and her husband and gave birth to five kittens. While the mother was a pu
re white thoroughbred Chinchila, the kittens were black and white tabbies of mixed breed. One
of these came to our house about two weeks after its birth and was given the name Gonnosuke.
At that time we already had one female Shiba dog and one female brown tabby cat in our house

16/17

In our house we had a cat with the grandiose name of Gonn
osuke. Usually with cats and dogs we know who the mothe
r is but not the father. A cat with a large belly wondered int
o the house of my younger sister and her husband and gave

24/25

In our house we had a cat with the gra
ndiose name of Gonnosuke. Usually wit
h cats and dogs we know who the moth

ABCDEFGHIJKL MNOPQRSTUVW XYZ
abcdefghijklmnopq rstuvwxyz
1234567890&$¢£¥ fiflæœÆŒÅßÇÌÎÍÏã §†·--—/()'""";.,!¡?¿

10/11

In our house we had a cat with the grandiose name of Gonnosuke. Usually with cats and dogs we know who the mother is but not the father. A cat with a large belly wondered into the house of my younger sister and her husband and gave birth to five kittens. While the mother was a pu re white thoroughbred Chinchila, the kittens were black and white tabbies of mixed breed. One of these came to our house about two weeks after its birth and was given the name Gonnosuke. At that time we already had one female Shiba dog and one female brown tabby cat in our hous

16/17

In our house we had a cat with the grandiose name of Gonn osuke. Usually with cats and dogs we know who the mothe r is but not the father. A cat with a large belly wondered int o the house of my younger sister and her husband and gave

24/25

In our house we had a cat with the gran diose name of Gonnosuke. Usually with cats and dogs we know who the mother

ABCDEFGHIJKLM
NOPQRSTUVWXYZ
abcdefghijklmnopq
rstuvwxyz
1234567890&$¢£¥
fiflæœÆŒÅßÇÌÎÍÏã§
†-–——/()''""":;.,!¡?¿

10/11

In our house we had a cat with the grandiose name of Gonnosuke. Usually with cats and dogs we know who the mother is but not the father. A cat with a large belly wondered into the hous e of my younger sister and her husband and gave birth to five kittens. While the mother was a pure white thoroughbred Chinchila, the kittens were black and white tabbies of mixed breed. One of these came to our house about two weeks after its birth and was given the name Gonno suke. At that time we already had one female Shiba dog and one female brown tabby cat in our

16/17

In our house we had a cat with the grandiose name of Gon nosuke. Usually with cats and dogs we know who the moth er is but not the father. A cat with a large belly wondered i nto the house of my younger sister and her husband and ga

24/25

In our house we had a cat with the gra ndiose name of Gonnosuke. Usually wit h cats and dogs we know who the mot

ABCDEFGHIJKL MNOPQRSTUVW XYZabcdefghijklmn opqrstuvwxyz 1234567890&$¢£¥ fiflæœÆŒÅßÇÌÎÍÏã §†-——/()''""":;.,!¡?¿

10/11

In our house we had a cat with the grandiose name of Gonnosuke. Usually with cats and dogs we know who the mother is but not the father. A cat with a large belly wondered into the hous e of my younger sister and her husband and gave birth to five kittens. While the mother was a pure white thoroughbred Chinchila, the kittens were black and white tabbies of mixed breed. One of these came to our house about two weeks after its birth and was given the name Gonn osuke. At that time we already had one female Shiba dog and one female brown tabby cat in o

16/17

In our house we had a cat with the grandiose name of Gon nosuke. Usually with cats and dogs we know who the mot her is but not the father. A cat with a large belly wondered into the house of my younger sister and her husband and g

24/25

In our house we had a cat with the gra ndiose name of Gonnosuke. Usually wit h cats and dogs we know who the mot

ABCDEFGHIJKL
MNOPQRSTUVW
XYZabcdefghijklm
nopqrstuvwxyz
1234567890&$¢£¥
fiflæœÆŒÅßÇÌÎÍÏ ã
§†-–—/()''""":;.,!¡?¿

10/11

In our house we had a cat with the grandiose name of Gonnosuke. Usually with cats and do
gs we know who the mother is but not the father. A cat with a large belly wondered into th
e house of my younger sister and her husband and gave birth to five kittens. While the moth
er was a pure white thoroughbred Chinchila, the kittens were black and white tabbies of mi
xed breed. One of these came to our house about two weeks after its birth and was given th
e name Gonnosuke. At that time we already had one female Shiba dog and one female brow

16/17

In our house we had a cat with the grandiose name of Go
nnosuke. Usually with cats and dogs we know who the
mother is but not the father. A cat with a large belly won
dered into the house of my younger sister and her husban

24/25

In our house we had a cat with the gr
andiose name of Gonnosuke. Usually
with cats and dogs we know who the

ABCDEFGHIJKL MNOPQRSTUVW XYZabcdefghijklm nopqrstuvwxyz 1234567890&$¢£¥ fiflæœÆŒÅßÇÌÎÍÏã §†-–—/()''""":;.,!¡?¿

10/11

In our house we had a cat with the grandiose name of Gonnosuke. Usually with cats and dogs we know who the mother is but not the father. A cat with a large belly wondered into the house of my younger sister and her husband and gave birth to five kittens. While the mother was a pure white thoroughbred Chinchila, the kittens were black and white tabbies of mixed breed. One of these came to our house about two weeks after its birth and was given the name Gonnosuke. At that time we already had one female Shiba dog and one female br

16/17

In our house we had a cat with the grandiose name of Go nnosuke. Usually with cats and dogs we know who the mother is but not the father. A cat with a large belly won dered into the house of my younger sister and her husba

24/25

In our house we had a cat with the gr andiose name of Gonnosuke. Usually with cats and dogs we know who the

ABCDEFGHIJKL
MNOPQRSTUVW
XYZabcdefghijkl
mnopqrstuvwxyz
1234567890&$¢£¥
fiflæœÆŒÅßÇÌÎÍÏ
ã§†-–——/()''""":;.,!¡?¿

10/11

In our house we had a cat with the grandiose name of Gonnosuke. Usually with cats and dogs we know who the mother is but not the father. A cat with a large belly wondered in to the house of my younger sister and her husband and gave birth to five kittens. While t he mother was a pure white thoroughbred Chinchila, the kittens were black and white t abbies of mixed breed. One of these came to our house about two weeks after its birth a nd was given the name Gonnosuke. At that time we already had one female Shiba dog a

16/17

In our house we had a cat with the grandiose name of Gonnosuke. Usually with cats and dogs we know who t he mother is but not the father. A cat with a large belly wondered into the house of my younger sister and her

24/25

In our house we had a cat with the g randiose name of Gonnosuke. Usual ly with cats and dogs we know who t

ABCDEFGHIJKL
MNOPQRSTUVW
XYZabcdefghijkl
mnopqrstuvwxyz
1234567890&$¢£¥
fiflæœÆŒÅßÇÌÎÍÏ
ã§†-—––/()''""":;.,!¡?¿

10/11

In our house we had a cat with the grandiose name of Gonnosuke. Usually with cats and dogs we know who the mother is but not the father. A cat with a large belly wondered int o the house of my younger sister and her husband and gave birth to five kittens. While th e mother was a pure white thoroughbred Chinchila, the kittens were black and white tab bies of mixed breed. One of these came to our house about two weeks after its birth and was given the name Gonnosuke. At that time we already had one female Shiba dog and

16/17

In our house we had a cat with the grandiose name of Gonnosuke. Usually with cats and dogs we know who t he mother is but not the father. A cat with a large belly wondered into the house of my younger sister and her h

24/25

In our house we had a cat with the g randiose name of Gonnosuke. Usual ly with cats and dogs we know who t

ABCDEFGHIJKL
MNOPQRSTUVW
XYZabcdefghijkl
mnopqrstuvwxyz
1234567890&$¢£¥
fiflæœÆŒÅßÇÌÎÍÏ
ã§†-–—/()''""‚;.,!¡?¿

10/11

In our house we had a cat with the grandiose name of Gonnosuke. Usually with cats and dogs we know who the mother is but not the father. A cat with a large belly wondered in to the house of my younger sister and her husband and gave birth to five kittens. While the mother was a pure white thoroughbred Chinchila, the kittens were black and white tabbies of mixed breed. One of these came to our house about two weeks after its birth and was given the name Gonnosuke. At that time we already had one female Shiba dog

16/17

In our house we had a cat with the grandiose name of Gonnosuke. Usually with cats and dogs we know who t he mother is but not the father. A cat with a large belly wondered into the house of my younger sister and her

24/25

In our house we had a cat with the g randiose name of Gonnosuke. Usua lly with cats and dogs we know who t

ABCDEFGHIJKLMNO
PQRSTUVWXYZ
abcdefghijklmnopq
rstuvwxyz
1234567890&$¢£¥
fiflæœÆŒÅßÇÌÎÍÏã§†
-–—/()'""":;.,!¡?¿

10/11

In our house we had a cat with the grandiose name of Gonnosuke. Usually with cats and dogs we know who the mother is but not the father. A cat with a large belly wondered into the house of my younger sist er and her husband and gave birth to five kittens. While the mother was a pure white thoroughbred Chinc hila, the kittens were black and white tabbies of mixed breed. One of these came to our house about two weeks after its birth and was given the name Gonnosuke. At that time we already had one female Shiba dog and one female brown tabby cat in our house comprising only 13 tsubo. The dog was called Momo

16/17

In our house we had a cat with the grandiose name of Gonnosuk e. Usually with cats and dogs we know who the mother is but no t the father. A cat with a large belly wondered into the house of m y younger sister and her husband and gave birth to five kittens. W

24/25

In our house we had a cat with the grandio se name of Gonnosuke. Usually with cats a nd dogs we know who the mother is but n

ABCDEFGHIJKLMNO
PQRSTUVWXYZ
abcdefghijklmnopq
rstuvwxyz
1234567890&$¢£¥
fiflæœÆŒÅßÇÌÎÍÏ㧆
––——/()''""":;.,!¡?¿

10/11

In our house we had a cat with the grandiose name of Gonnosuke. Usually with cats and dogs we know who the mother is but not the father. A cat with a large belly wondered into the house of my younger sist er and her husband and gave birth to five kittens. While the mother was a pure white thoroughbred Chin chila, the kittens were black and white tabbies of mixed breed. One of these came to our house about tw o weeks after its birth and was given the name Gonnosuke. At that time we already had one female Shib a dog and one female brown tabby cat in our house comprising only 13 tsubo. The dog was called Mom

16/17

In our house we had a cat with the grandiose name of Gonnosuk e. Usually with cats and dogs we know who the mother is but not the father. A cat with a large belly wondered into the house of my younger sister and her husband and gave birth to five kittens. Wh

24/25

In our house we had a cat with the grandio se name of Gonnosuke. Usually with cats a nd dogs we know who the mother is but no

ABCDEFGHIJKLMN
OPQRSTUVWXYZ
abcdefghijklmnopq
rstuvwxyz
1234567890&$¢£¥
fiflæœÆŒÅßÇÌÎÍÏã
§†-–——/()''"""':;.,!¡?¿

10/11

In our house we had a cat with the grandiose name of Gonnosuke. Usually with cats and dogs we kno
w who the mother is but not the father. A cat with a large belly wondered into the house of my younge
r sister and her husband and gave birth to five kittens. While the mother was a pure white thoroughbre
d Chinchila, the kittens were black and white tabbies of mixed breed. One of these came to our house
about two weeks after its birth and was given the name Gonnosuke. At that time we already had one fe
male Shiba dog and one female brown tabby cat in our house comprising only 13 tsubo. The dog was c

16/17

In our house we had a cat with the grandiose name of Gonnosu
ke. Usually with cats and dogs we know who the mother is but n
ot the father. A cat with a large belly wondered into the house o
f my younger sister and her husband and gave birth to five kitte

24/25

In our house we had a cat with the grandi
ose name of Gonnosuke. Usually with cats
and dogs we know who the mother is but

ABCDEFGHIJKLMN
OPQRSTUVWXYZ
abcdefghijklmnop
qrstuvwxyz
1234567890&$¢£¥
fiflæœÆŒÅßÇÌÎÍÏ
ã§†--—/()ˇ˝""˝:;.,¡?¿

10/11

In our house we had a cat with the grandiose name of Gonnosuke. Usually with cats and do
gs we know who the mother is but not the father. A cat with a large belly wondered into the
house of my younger sister and her husband and gave birth to five kittens. While the mothe
r was a pure white thoroughbred Chinchila, the kittens were black and white tabbies of mix
ed breed. One of these came to our house about two weeks after its birth and was given the
name Gonnosuke. At that time we already had one female Shiba dog and one female bro

16/17

In our house we had a cat with the grandiose name of G
onnosuke. Usually with cats and dogs we know who the
mother is but not the father. A cat with a large belly won
dered into the house of my younger sister and her husba

24/25

In our house we had a cat with the gr
andiose name of Gonnosuke. Usually
with cats and dogs we know who the

*ABCDEFGHIJKLM
NOPQRSTUVWXYZ
abcdefghijklmnop
qrstuvwxyz
1234567890&$¢£¥
fiflœœÆŒÅßÇÌÎÍÏ
ã§†-––—/()˘ˇ˝˜":;.,¡¿?¿*

10/11

*In our house we had a cat with the grandiose name of Gonnosuke. Usually with cats and d
ogs we know who the mother is but not the father. A cat with a large belly wondered into t
he house of my younger sister and her husband and gave birth to five kittens. While the mo
ther was a pure white thoroughbred Chinchila, the kittens were black and white tabbies of
mixed breed. One of these came to our house about two weeks after its birth and was given
the name Gonnosuke. At that time we already had one female Shiba dog and one female*

16/17

*In our house we had a cat with the grandiose name of G
onnosuke. Usually with cats and dogs we know who the
mother is but not the father. A cat with a large belly won
dered into the house of my younger sister and her husba*

24/25

*In our house we had a cat with the gr
andiose name of Gonnosuke. Usually
with cats and dogs we know who the*

ABCDEFGHIJKLM
NOPQRSTUVWXYZ
abcdefghijklmnop
qrstuvwxyz
1234567890&$¢£¥
fiflœœÆŒÅßÇÌÎÍÏ
ã§†——––/()''""":;.,¡¿?¿

10/11

In our house we had a cat with the grandiose name of Gonnosuke. Usually with cats and d
ogs we know who the mother is but not the father. A cat with a large belly wondered into t
he house of my younger sister and her husband and gave birth to five kittens. While the m
other was a pure white thoroughbred Chinchila, the kittens were black and white tabbies
of mixed breed. One of these came to our house about two weeks after its birth and was gi
ven the name Gonnosuke. At that time we already had one female Shiba dog and one fem

16/17

In our house we had a cat with the grandiose name of G
onnosuke. Usually with cats and dogs we know who the
mother is but not the father. A cat with a large belly won
dered into the house of my younger sister and her husba

24/25

In our house we had a cat with the gr
andiose name of Gonnosuke. Usually
with cats and dogs we know who the

ABCDEFGHIJKLM
NOPQRSTUVWXYZ
abcdefghijklmnop
qrstuvwxyz
1234567890&$¢£¥
fiflœœÆŒÅßÇÌÎÍÏ
ã§†-–—/()''""":;.,!¡?¿

10/11

In our house we had a cat with the grandiose name of Gonnosuke. Usually with cats and d
ogs we know who the mother is but not the father. A cat with a large belly wondered into t
he house of my younger sister and her husband and gave birth to five kittens. While the m
other was a pure white thoroughbred Chinchila, the kittens were black and white tabbies
of mixed breed. One of these came to our house about two weeks after its birth and was gi
ven the name Gonnosuke. At that time we already had one female Shiba dog and one fem

16/17

In our house we had a cat with the grandiose name of G
onnosuke. Usually with cats and dogs we know who the
mother is but not the father. A cat with a large belly wo
ndered into the house of my younger sister and her husb

24/25

In our house we had a cat with the gr
andiose name of Gonnosuke. Usually
with cats and dogs we know who the

ABCDEFGHIJKLMN
OPQRSTUVWXYZ
abcdefghijklmnopq
rstuvwxyz
1234567890&$¢£¥
fiflæœÆŒÅßÇÌÎÍÏã§
†-–—/()''""":;.,!¡?¿

10/11

In our house we had a cat with the grandiose name of Gonnosuke. Usually with cats and dogs we know who the mother is but not the father. A cat with a large belly wondered into the house of my younger sister and her husband and gave birth to five kittens. While the mother was a pure white t horoughbred Chinchila, the kittens were black and white tabbies of mixed breed. One of these ca me to our house about two weeks after its birth and was given the name Gonnosuke. At that time we already had one female Shiba dog and one female brown tabby cat in our house comprising on

16/17

In our house we had a cat with the grandiose name of Gonno suke. Usually with cats and dogs we know who the mother is but not the father. A cat with a large belly wondered into the house of my younger sister and her husband and gave birth t

24/25

In our house we had a cat with the grand iose name of Gonnosuke. Usually with c ats and dogs we know who the mother is

ABCDEFGHIJKLMN
OPQRSTUVWXYZ
abcdefghijklmnopq
rstuvwxyz
1234567890&$¢£¥
fiflæœÆŒÅßÇÌÎÍÏã
§†-–——/()''""":;.,!¡?¿

10/11

In our house we had a cat with the grandiose name of Gonnosuke. Usually with cats and dogs we know who the mother is but not the father. A cat with a large belly wondered into the house of my younger sister and her husband and gave birth to five kittens. While the mother was a pure white t horoughbred Chinchila, the kittens were black and white tabbies of mixed breed. One of these ca me to our house about two weeks after its birth and was given the name Gonnosuke. At that time we already had one female Shiba dog and one female brown tabby cat in our house comprising o

16/17

In our house we had a cat with the grandiose name of Gonno suke. Usually with cats and dogs we know who the mother is but not the father. A cat with a large belly wondered into the house of my younger sister and her husband and gave birth t

24/25

In our house we had a cat with the gran diose name of Gonnosuke. Usually with cats and dogs we know who the mother i

ABCDEFGHIJKL
MNOPQRSTUVW
XYZabcdefghijklmn
opqrstuvwxyz
1234567890&$¢£¥
fiflæœÆŒÅßÇÌÎÍÏã
§†-–——/()''""":;.,!¡?¿

10/11

In our house we had a cat with the grandiose name of Gonnosuke. Usually with cats and dogs w
e know who the mother is but not the father. A cat with a large belly wondered into the house of
my younger sister and her husband and gave birth to five kittens. While the mother was a pure
white thoroughbred Chinchila, the kittens were black and white tabbies of mixed breed. One of t
hese came to our house about two weeks after its birth and was given the name Gonnosuke. At t
hat time we already had one female Shiba dog and one female brown tabby cat in our house com

16/17

In our house we had a cat with the grandiose name of Gonn
osuke. Usually with cats and dogs we know who the mother
is but not the father. A cat with a large belly wondered into t
he house of my younger sister and her husband and gave bir

24/25

In our house we had a cat with the gran
diose name of Gonnosuke. Usually with
cats and dogs we know who the mother

ABCDEFGHIJKL
MNOPQRSTUVW
XYZabcdefghijklm
nopqrstuvwxyz
1234567890&$¢£¥
fiflæœÆŒÅßÇÌÎÍÏã
§†-–—/()''""",;.,!¡?¿

10/11

In our house we had a cat with the grandiose name of Gonnosuke. Usually with cats and dogs we know who the mother is but not the father. A cat with a large belly wondered into the hous e of my younger sister and her husband and gave birth to five kittens. While the mother was a pure white thoroughbred Chinchila, the kittens were black and white tabbies of mixed breed. One of these came to our house about two weeks after its birth and was given the name Gonno suke. At that time we already had one female Shiba dog and one female brown tabby cat in o

16/17

In our house we had a cat with the grandiose name of Gon nosuke. Usually with cats and dogs we know who the moth er is but not the father. A cat with a large belly wondered i nto the house of my younger sister and her husband and g

24/25

In our house we had a cat with the gra ndiose name of Gonnosuke. Usually wi th cats and dogs we know who the mot

ABCDEFGHIJKLMN
OPQRSTUVWXYZ
abcdefghijklmnopq
rstuvwxyz
1234567890&$¢£¥
fiflæœÆŒÅßÇÌÎÍÏã
§†-–—/()''""'":;.,!¡?¿

10/11

In our house we had a cat with the grandiose name of Gonnosuke. Usually with cats and dogs we know who the mother is but not the father. A cat with a large belly wondered into the house of my younger sister and her husband and gave birth to five kittens. While the mother was a pure white thoroughbred Chinchila, the kittens were black and white tabbies of mixed breed. One of these ca me to our house about two weeks after its birth and was given the name Gonnosuke. At that time we already had one female Shiba dog and one female brown tabby cat in our house comprising

16/17

In our house we had a cat with the grandiose name of Gonno suke. Usually with cats and dogs we know who the mother is but not the father. A cat with a large belly wondered into the house of my younger sister and her husband and gave birth

24/25

In our house we had a cat with the gran diose name of Gonnosuke. Usually with cats and dogs we know who the mother

ABCDEFGHIJKLMN
OPQRSTUVWXYZ
abcdefghijklmnopq
rstuvwxyz
1234567890&$¢£¥
fiflæœÆŒÅßÇÌÎÍÏã
§†-–——/()'''""":;.,!¡?¿

10/11

In our house we had a cat with the grandiose name of Gonnosuke. Usually with cats and dogs we know who the mother is but not the father. A cat with a large belly wondered into the house of my younger sister and her husband and gave birth to five kittens. While the mother was a pure white thoroughbred Chinchila, the kittens were black and white tabbies of mixed breed. One of these came to our house about two weeks after its birth and was given the name Gonnosuke. At that time we already had one female Shiba dog and one female brown tabby cat in our house comprising

16/17

In our house we had a cat with the grandiose name of Gonn osuke. Usually with cats and dogs we know who the mother i s but not the father. A cat with a large belly wondered into th e house of my younger sister and her husband and gave birt

24/25

In our house we had a cat with the gran diose name of Gonnosuke. Usually with cats and dogs we know who the mother

ABCDEFGHIJKLMN
OPQRSTUVWXYZ
abcdefghijklmnopq
rstuvwxyz
1234567890&$¢£¥
fiflæœÆŒÅßÇÌÎÍÏã
§†-–——/()""""':;.,!¡?¿

10/11

In our house we had a cat with the grandiose name of Gonnosuke. Usually with cats and dogs
we know who the mother is but not the father. A cat with a large belly wondered into the house
of my younger sister and her husband and gave birth to five kittens. While the mother was a pu
re white thoroughbred Chinchila, the kittens were black and white tabbies of mixed breed. One
of these came to our house about two weeks after its birth and was given the name Gonnosuke.
At that time we already had one female Shiba dog and one female brown tabby cat in our hous

16/17

In our house we had a cat with the grandiose name of Gonn
osuke. Usually with cats and dogs we know who the mother
is but not the father. A cat with a large belly wondered into
the house of my younger sister and her husband and gave

24/25

In our house we had a cat with the gran
diose name of Gonnosuke. Usually with
cats and dogs we know who the mother

ABCDEFGHIJKLMN
OPQRSTUVWXYZ
abcdefghijklmnopq
rstuvwxyz
1234567890&$¢£¥
fiflæœÆŒÅßÇÌÎÍÏã
§†-–——/()""''""''«».;.,!¡?¿

10/11

In our house we had a cat with the grandiose name of Gonnosuke. Usually with cats and dogs w e know who the mother is but not the father. A cat with a large belly wondered into the house of my younger sister and her husband and gave birth to five kittens. While the mother was a pure white thoroughbred Chinchila, the kittens were black and white tabbies of mixed breed. One of these came to our house about two weeks after its birth and was given the name Gonnosuke. At that time we already had one female Shiba dog and one female brown tabby cat in our house c

16/17

In our house we had a cat with the grandiose name of Gonn osuke. Usually with cats and dogs we know who the mother is but not the father. A cat with a large belly wondered into the house of my younger sister and her husband and gave b

24/25

In our house we had a cat with the gran diose name of Gonnosuke. Usually with cats and dogs we know who the mother

ABCDEFGHIJKLMN
OPQRSTUVWXYZ
abcdefghijklmnopq
rstuvwxyz
1234567890&$¢£¥
fiflæœÆŒÅßÇÌÎÍÏã
§†-–—/()''''"":;.,!¡?¿

10/11

In our house we had a cat with the grandiose name of Gonnosuke. Usually with cats and dogs
we know who the mother is but not the father. A cat with a large belly wondered into the house
of my younger sister and her husband and gave birth to five kittens. While the mother was a pu
re white thoroughbred Chinchila, the kittens were black and white tabbies of mixed breed. One
of these came to our house about two weeks after its birth and was given the name Gonnosuke.
At that time we already had one female Shiba dog and one female brown tabby cat in our hous

16/17

In our house we had a cat with the grandiose name of Gonn
osuke. Usually with cats and dogs we know who the mother
is but not the father. A cat with a large belly wondered into
the house of my younger sister and her husband and gave

24/25

In our house we had a cat with the gran
diose name of Gonnosuke. Usually with
cats and dogs we know who the mother

ABCDEFGHIJKLMN
OPQRSTUVWXYZ
abcdefghijklmnopq
rstuvwxyz
1234567890&$¢£¥
fiflæœÆŒÅßÇÌÎÍÏã
§†-–—/()''''"":;.,!¡?¿

10/11

In our house we had a cat with the grandiose name of Gonnosuke. Usually with cats and dogs w
e know who the mother is but not the father. A cat with a large belly wondered into the house of
my younger sister and her husband and gave birth to five kittens. While the mother was a pure
white thoroughbred Chinchila, the kittens were black and white tabbies of mixed breed. One of
these came to our house about two weeks after its birth and was given the name Gonnosuke. At
that time we already had one female Shiba dog and one female brown tabby cat in our house c

16/17

In our house we had a cat with the grandiose name of Gonn
osuke. Usually with cats and dogs we know who the mother
is but not the father. A cat with a large belly wondered into
the house of my younger sister and her husband and gave b

24/25

In our house we had a cat with the gran
diose name of Gonnosuke. Usually with
cats and dogs we know who the mother

ABCDEFGHIJK LMNOPQRSTUV WXYZabcdefghi jklmnopqrstuvw xyz1234567890 &$¢£¥fiflæœÆŒ ÅßçÌÎÍÏã§† ——/()""''""·;.,!¡?¿

10/11

In our house we had a cat with the grandiose name of Gonnosuke. Usually with cats and dogs we know who the mother is but not the father. A cat with a large belly wondered into the house of my younger sister and her husband and gave birth to five kittens. While the mother was a pure white thoroughbred Chinchill a, the kittens were black and white tabbies of mixed breed. One of these came t o our house about two weeks after its birth and was given the name Gonnosuke.

16/17

In our house we had a cat with the grandiose na me of Gonnosuke. Usually with cats and dogs we know who the mother is but not the father. A cat with a large belly wondered into the house of my

24/25

In our house we had a cat with t he grandiose name of Gonnosuk e. Usually with cats and dogs we

ABCDEFGHIJKLMNO
PQRSTUVWXYZ
abcdefghijklmno
pqrstuvwxyz
1234567890&
$¢£¥fiflæœÆŒ
ÅßÇÌÎÍÏã§†---—
/()''""':;.,!¡?¿

10/11

In our house we had a cat with the grandiose name of Gonnosuke. Usually wit
h cats and dogs we know who the mother is but not the father. A cat with a
large belly wondered into the house of my younger sister and her husband an
d gave birth to five kittens. While the mother was a pure white thoroughbre
d Chinchila, the kittens were black and white tabbies of mixed breed. One o
f these came to our house about two weeks after its birth and was given the

16/17

In our house we had a cat with the grandiose n
ame of Gonnosuke. Usually with cats and dogs w
e know who the mother is but not the father. A
cat with a large belly wondered into the house

24/25

In our house we had a cat with
the grandiose name of Gonnosuk
e. Usually with cats and dogs

ABCDEFGHIJKLMN
OPQRSTUVWXYZ
abcdefghijklmn
opqrstuvwxyz
1234567890&
$¢£¥fiflæœÆŒ
ÅßÇÌÎÍÏ㧠- - —
/ ( ) ' ' " " : ; . , ! ¡ ? ¿

10/11

In our house we had a cat with the grandiose name of Gonnosuke. Usually wit h cats and dogs we know who the mother is but not the father. A cat with a large belly wondered into the house of my younger sister and her husband an d gave birth to five kittens. While the mother was a pure white thoroughbre d Chinchila, the kittens were black and white tabbies of mixed breed. One o f these came to our house about two weeks after its birth and was given the

16/17

In our house we had a cat with the grandiose name of Gonnosuke. Usually with cats and dogs we know who the mother is but not the father. A cat with a large belly wondered into the ho

24/25

In our house we had a cat wit h the grandiose name of Gonno suke. Usually with cats and d

ABCDEFGHIJKLMNO
PQRSTUVWXYZ
abcdefghijklmno
pqrstuvwxyz
1234567890&
$¢£¥fiflæœÆŒ
ÅßÇÌÎÍÏã§†---—
/()''"" :;.,!¡?¿

10/11

In our house we had a cat with the grandiose name of Gonnosuke. Usually wit
h cats and dogs we know who the mother is but not the father. A cat with a
large belly wondered into the house of my younger sister and her husband an
d gave birth to five kittens. While the mother was a pure white thoroughbre
d Chinchila, the kittens were black and white tabbies of mixed breed. One o
f these came to our house about two weeks after its birth and was given the

16/17

In our house we had a cat with the grandiose n
ame of Gonnosuke. Usually with cats and dogs w
e know who the mother is but not the father. A
cat with a large belly wondered into the house

24/25

In our house we had a cat with
the grandiose name of Gonnosuk
e. Usually with cats and dogs

ABCDEFGHIJKLMN

OPQRSTUVWXYZ

abcdefghijklmn

opqrstuvwxyz

1234567890&

$¢£¥fiflæœÆŒ

ÅßÇÌÎÍÏãß†---—

/ () ' ' " " : ; . , ! ¡ ? ¿

10/11

In our house we had a cat with the grandiose name of Gonnosuke. Usually wit h cats and dogs we know who the mother is but not the father. A cat with a large belly wondered into the house of my younger sister and her husband an d gave birth to five kittens. While the mother was a pure white thoroughbre d Chinchila, the kittens were black and white tabbies of mixed breed. One o f these came to our house about two weeks after its birth and was given the

16/17

In our house we had a cat with the grandiose name of Gonnosuke. Usually with cats and dogs we know who the mother is but not the father. A cat with a large belly wondered into the ho

24/25

In our house we had a cat wit h the grandiose name of Gonnos uke. Usually with cats and do

ABCDEFGHIJKLMN
OPQRSTUVWXYZ
abcdefghijklmnopq
rstuvwxyz
1234567890&$¢£¥
fiflæœÆŒÅßÇÌÎÍÏã§†
——/()''""":;.,!¡?¿

10/11

In our house we had a cat with the grandiose name of Gonnosuke. Usually with cats and dogs we know who the mother is but not the father. A cat with a large belly wondered into the house of my younger sist er and her husband and gave birth to five kittens. While the mother was a pure white thoroughbred Chin chila, the kittens were black and white tabbies of mixed breed. One of these came to our house about tw o weeks after its birth and was given the name Gonnosuke. At that time we already had one female Shib a dog and one female brown tabby cat in our house comprising only 13 tsubo. The dog was called Momo

16/17

In our house we had a cat with the grandiose name of Gonnosuk e. Usually with cats and dogs we know who the mother is but not the father. A cat with a large belly wondered into the house of my younger sister and her husband and gave birth to five kittens. Wh

24/25

In our house we had a cat with the grandio se name of Gonnosuke. Usually with cats a nd dogs we know who the mother is but no

ABCDEFGHIJKLMN
OPQRSTUVWXYZ
abcdefghijklmnopq
rstuvwxyz
1234567890&$¢£¥
fiflæœÆŒÅßÇÌÎÍÏã§†
——––/()''""":;.,!¡?¿

10/11

In our house we had a cat with the grandiose name of Gonnosuke. Usually with cats and dogs we know who the mother is but not the father. A cat with a large belly wondered into the house of my younger sist er and her husband and gave birth to five kittens. While the mother was a pure white thoroughbred Chin chila, the kittens were black and white tabbies of mixed breed. One of these came to our house about tw o weeks after its birth and was given the name Gonnosuke. At that time we already had one female Shib a dog and one female brown tabby cat in our house comprising only 13 tsubo. The dog was called Momo

16/17

In our house we had a cat with the grandiose name of Gonnosuk e. Usually with cats and dogs we know who the mother is but not the father. A cat with a large belly wondered into the house of my younger sister and her husband and gave birth to five kittens. Wh

24/25

In our house we had a cat with the grandios e name of Gonnosuke. Usually with cats an d dogs we know who the mother is but not

ABCDEFGHIJKLM
NOPQRSTUVWXYZ
abcdefghijklmnopq
rstuvwxyz
1234567890&$¢£¥
fiflæœÆŒÅßÇÌÎÍÏĩ
§†-–—/()''"" ":;.,!¡?¿

10/11

In our house we had a cat with the grandiose name of Gonnosuke. Usually with cats and dogs we know who the mother is but not the father. A cat with a large belly wondered into the hous e of my younger sister and her husband and gave birth to five kittens. While the mother was a pure white thoroughbred Chinchila, the kittens were black and white tabbies of mixed breed. One of these came to our house about two weeks after its birth and was given the name Gonn osuke. At that time we already had one female Shiba dog and one female brown tabby cat in o

16/17

In our house we had a cat with the grandiose name of Gon nosuke. Usually with cats and dogs we know who the mot her is but not the father. A cat with a large belly wondered into the house of my younger sister and her husband and g

24/25

In our house we had a cat with the gra ndiose name of Gonnosuke. Usually wit h cats and dogs we know who the mot

ABCDEFGHIJKL
MNOPQRSTUVW
XYZabcdefghijklmn
opqrstuvwxyz
1234567890&$¢£¥
fiflæœÆŒÅßÇÌÎÍÏã
§†-–——/()''"":;.,!¡?¿

10/11

In our house we had a cat with the grandiose name of Gonnosuke. Usually with cats and dogs w
e know who the mother is but not the father. A cat with a large belly wondered into the house o
f my younger sister and her husband and gave birth to five kittens. While the mother was a pure
white thoroughbred Chinchila, the kittens were black and white tabbies of mixed breed. One of
these came to our house about two weeks after its birth and was given the name Gonnosuke. At
that time we already had one female Shiba dog and one female brown tabby cat in our house co

16/17

In our house we had a cat with the grandiose name of Gonn
osuke. Usually with cats and dogs we know who the mother
is but not the father. A cat with a large belly wondered into
the house of my younger sister and her husband and gave bi

24/25

In our house we had a cat with the gran
diose name of Gonnosuke. Usually with
cats and dogs we know who the mothe

ABCDEFGHIJKL MNOPQRSTUVW XYZabcdefghijklm nopqrstuvwxyz 1234567890&$¢£¥ fiflæœÆŒÅßÇÌÎÍÏã §†-–——/()'''""":;.,!¡?¿

10/11

In our house we had a cat with the grandiose name of Gonnosuke. Usually with cats and dog s we know who the mother is but not the father. A cat with a large belly wondered into the h ouse of my younger sister and her husband and gave birth to five kittens. While the mother was a pure white thoroughbred Chinchila, the kittens were black and white tabbies of mixe d breed. One of these came to our house about two weeks after its birth and was given the n ame Gonnosuke. At that time we already had one female Shiba dog and one female brown t

16/17

In our house we had a cat with the grandiose name of Go nnosuke. Usually with cats and dogs we know who the m other is but not the father. A cat with a large belly wonde red into the house of my younger sister and her husband

24/25

In our house we had a cat with the gra ndiose name of Gonnosuke. Usually w ith cats and dogs we know who the m

ABCDEFGHIJKL
MNOPQRSTUVW
XYZabcdefghijkl
mnopqrstuvwxyz
1234567890&$¢£¥
fiflæœÆŒÅßÇÌÎÍÏ
ã§†-–—/()''""":;.,!¡?¿

10/11

In our house we had a cat with the grandiose name of Gonnosuke. Usually with cats and dogs we know who the mother is but not the father. A cat with a large belly wondered i nto the house of my younger sister and her husband and gave birth to five kittens. Whil e the mother was a pure white thoroughbred Chinchila, the kittens were black and whit e tabbies of mixed breed. One of these came to our house about two weeks after its birth and was given the name Gonnosuke. At that time we already had one female Shiba dog

16/17

In our house we had a cat with the grandiose name of Gonnosuke. Usually with cats and dogs we know who t he mother is but not the father. A cat with a large belly wondered into the house of my younger sister and her

24/25

In our house we had a cat with the g randiose name of Gonnosuke. Usuall y with cats and dogs we know who t

❶ Serif Book ❷ Sans Serif, Decorative and Display Book

A

Akzidenz Grotesk Bold ❷ 50
Akzidenz Grotesk Black ❷ 51
Albertus Light ❷ 498
Albertus ❷ 499
Albertus Bold ❷ 500
Amazonia (Amazone) ❷ 614
Amelia ❷ 501
American Text ❷ 666
ITC American Typewriter Light ❶ 435
ITC American Typewriter Medium ❶ 436
ITC American Typewriter Bold ❶ 437
ITC American Typewriter Light Condensed ❶ 438
ITC American Typewriter Medium Condensed ❶ 439
ITC American Typewriter Bold Condensed ❶ 440
Americana Roman ❶ 218
Americana Italic ❶ 219
Americana Bold ❶ 220
Americana Extra Bold ❶ 221
Americana Extra Bold Condensed ❶ 222
Bitstream Amerigo ❷ 502
Bitstream Amerigo Italic ❷ 503
Bitstream Amerigo Medium ❷ 504
Bitstream Amerigo Medium Italic ❷ 505
Bitstream Amerigo Bold ❷ 506
Bitstream Amerigo Bold Italic ❷ 507
Antique No.3 ❶ 441
Antique Olive Light ❷ 52
Antique Olive ❷ 53
Antique Olive Italic ❷ 54
Antique Olive Bold ❷ 55
Antique Olive Black ❷ 56
Antique Olive Bold Condensed ❷ 57
Antique Olive Compact ❷ 58
Antique Olive Nord ❷ 59
Antique Olive Nord Italic ❷ 60
Aster Roman ❶ 74
Aster Italic ❶ 75
Aster Bold ❶ 76
Aster Bold Italic ❶ 77
Aurora Roman ❶ 442
Aurora Italic ❶ 443
Aurora Bold ❶ 444
Aurora (New Aurora Grotesque) ❷ 61
Aurora Bold (New Aurora Grotesque) ❷ 62
ITC Avant Garde Gothic Extra Light ❷ 63
ITC Avant Garde Gothic Extra Light Oblique ❷ 64
ITC Avant Garde Gothic Book ❷ 65
ITC Avant Garde Gothic Book Oblique ❷ 66
ITC Avant Garde Gothic Medium ❷ 67
ITC Avant Garde Gothic Medium Oblique ❷ 68
ITC Avant Garde Gothic Demi ❷ 69
ITC Avant Garde Gothic Demi Oblique ❷ 70
ITC Avant Garde Gothic Bold ❷ 71
ITC Avant Garde Gothic Bold Oblique ❷ 72
ITC Avant Garde Gothic Book Condensed ❷ 73
ITC Avant Garde Gothic Medium Condensed ❷ 74
ITC Avant Garde Gothic Demi Condensed ❷ 75
ITC Avant Garde Gothic Bold Condensed ❷ 76

B

Balloon Light ❷ 615
Balloon Bold ❷ 616
Balloon Extra Bold ❷ 617
Baskerville Roman ❶ 223
Baskerville Italic ❶ 224
Baskerville Bold ❶ 225
Baskerville Bold Italic ❶ 226

ITC New Baskerville ❶ 227
ITC New Baskerville Italic ❶ 228
ITC New Baskerville Semi Bold ❶ 229
ITC New Baskerville Semi Bold Italic ❶ 230
ITC New Baskerville Bold ❶ 231
ITC New Baskerville Bold Italic ❶ 232
ITC New Baskerville Black ❶ 233
ITC New Baskerville Black Italic ❶ 234
ITC Bauhaus Light ❷ 77
ITC Bauhaus Medium ❷ 78
ITC Bauhaus Demi ❷ 79
ITC Bauhaus Bold ❷ 80
ITC Bauhaus Heavy ❷ 81
Bell Gothic ❷ 82
Bell Gothic Bold ❷ 83
Bell Gothic Black ❷ 84
Belwe Light ❷ 508
Belwe Medium ❷ 509
Belwe Bold ❷ 510
Bembo Roman ❶ 78
Bembo Italic ❶ 79
Bembo Bold ❶ 80
Bembo Bold Italic ❶ 81
ITC Benguiat Book ❷ 511
ITC Benguiat Book Italic ❷ 512
ITC Benguiat Medium ❷ 513
ITC Benguiat Medium Italic ❷ 514
ITC Benguiat Bold ❷ 515
ITC Benguiat Bold Italic ❷ 516
ITC Benguiat Book Condensed ❷ 517
ITC Benguiat Book Condensed Italic ❷ 518
ITC Benguiat Medium Condensed ❷ 519
ITC Benguiat Medium Condensed Italic ❷ 520
ITC Benguiat Bold Condensed ❷ 521
ITC Benguiat Bold Condensed Italic ❷ 522
ITC Benguiat Gothic Book ❷ 85
ITC Benguiat Gothic Book Italic ❷ 86
ITC Benguiat Gothic Medium ❷ 87
ITC Benguiat Gothic Medium Italic ❷ 88
ITC Benguiat Gothic Bold ❷ 89
ITC Benguiat Gothic Bold Italic ❷ 90
ITC Benguiat Gothic Heavy ❷ 91
ITC Benguiat Gothic Heavy Italic ❷ 92
ITC Berkeley Old Style Book ❶ 82
ITC Berkeley Old Style Book Italic ❶ 83
ITC Berkeley Old Style Medium ❶ 84
ITC Berkeley Old Style Medium Italic ❶ 85
ITC Berkeley Old Style Bold ❶ 86
ITC Berkeley Old Style Bold Italic ❶ 87
ITC Berkeley Old Style Black ❶ 88
ITC Berkeley Old Style Black Italic ❶ 89
Berling ❶ 90
Berling Italic ❶ 91
Berling Bold ❶ 92
Berling Bold Italic ❶ 93
Bernhard Antique Bold Condensed ❷ 523
Bernhard Modern ❶ 235
Bernhard Modern Italic ❶ 236
Bernhard Modern Bold ❶ 237
Bernhard Modern Bold Italic ❶ 238
Bernhard Tango ❷ 618
Bingham Script ❷ 619
Bison ❷ 620
Blippo Black ❷ 93
Block Extra Condensed ❷ 94
Bauer Bodoni Roman ❶ 346
Bauer Bodoni Italic ❶ 347
Bauer Bodoni Bold ❶ 348

Bauer Bodoni Bold Italic ❶ 349
Bauer Bodoni Black ❶ 350
Bauer Bodoni Black Italic ❶ 351
Bauer Bodoni Bold Condensed ❶ 352
Bauer Bodoni Black Condensed ❶ 353
Bodoni Book Roman ❶ 354
Bodoni Book Italic ❶ 355
Bodoni Roman ❶ 356
Bodoni Italic ❶ 357
Bodoni Bold ❶ 358
Bodoni Bold Italic ❶ 359
Bodoni Bold Condensed ❶ 360
Poster Bodoni ❶ 361
Poster Bodoni Italic ❶ 362
Poster Bodoni Compressed ❶ 363
Bodoni Campanile ❶ 364
ITC Bolt Bold ❷ 95
Bookman Roman ❶ 239
Bookman Italic ❶ 240
Bookman Roman/Head ❶ 241
Bookman Italic/Head ❶ 242
ITC Bookman Light Roman ❶ 243
ITC Bookman Light Italic ❶ 244
ITC Bookman Medium ❶ 245
ITC Bookman Medium Italic ❶ 246
ITC Bookman Demi ❶ 247
ITC Bookman Demi Italic ❶ 248
ITC Bookman Bold ❶ 249
ITC Bookman Bold Italic ❶ 250
Broadway ❷ 524
Broadway Engraved ❷ 525
Bruce Old Style ❶ 251
Bruce Old Style Italic ❶ 252
Brush Script ❷ 621
Blumer ❶ 365
Blumer Italic ❶ 366
ITC Busorama Light ❷ 96
ITC Busorama Medium ❷ 97
ITC Busorama Bold ❷ 98

C

Caledonia Roman ❶ 367
Caledonia Italic ❶ 368
Caledonia Bold ❶ 369
Caledonia Bold Italic ❶ 370
Candida ❶ 445
Candida Italic ❶ 446
Candida Bold ❶ 447
Bitstream Carmina Light ❶ 94
Bitstream Carmina Light Italic ❶ 95
Bitstream Carmina Medium ❶ 96
Bitstream Carmina Medium Italic ❶ 97
Bitstream Carmina Bold ❶ 98
Bitstream Carmina Bold Italic ❶ 99
Bitstream Carmina Black ❶ 100
Bitstream Carmina Black Italic ❶ 101
Cascade ❷ 622
Caslon Old Face ❶ 253
Caslon Old Face Italic ❶ 254
Caslon Old Face Heavy ❶ 255
Caslon 540 Roman ❶ 256
Caslon 540 Italic ❶ 257
Caslon Bold Roman ❶ 258
Caslon Bold Italic ❶ 259
Caslon Openface ❶ 260
ITC Caslon 224 Book ❶ 261
ITC Caslon 224 Book Italic ❶ 262
ITC Caslon 224 Medium ❶ 263

ITC Caslon 224 Medium Italic ❶ 264
ITC Caslon 224 Bold ❶ 265
ITC Caslon 224 Bold Italic ❶ 266
ITC Caslon 224 Black ❶ 267
ITC Caslon 224 Black Italic ❶ 268
Caxton Light ❶ 102
Caxton Light Italic ❶ 103
Caxton Book ❶ 104
Caxton Book Italic ❶ 105
Caxton Bold ❶ 106
Caxton Bold Italic ❶ 107
Century Expanded Roman ❶ 371
Century Expanded Italic ❶ 372
Century Bold ❶ 373
Century Bold Italic ❶ 374
Century Oldstyle Roman ❶ 269
Century Oldstyle Italic ❶ 270
Century Oldstyle Bold ❶ 271
Century Schoolbook Roman ❶ 375
Century Schoolbook Italic ❶ 376
Century Schoolbook Bold ❶ 377
Century Schoolbook Bold Italic ❶ 378
Century Schoolbook Bold Condensed ❶ 379
Century Schoolbook Monospace ❶ 380
ITC Century Light Roman ❶ 381
ITC Century Light Italic ❶ 382
ITC Century Book ❶ 383
ITC Century Book Italic ❶ 384
ITC Century Bold ❶ 385
ITC Century Bold Italic ❶ 386
ITC Century Ultra ❶ 387
ITC Century Ultra Italic ❶ 388
ITC Century Light Condensed ❶ 389
ITC Century Light Condensed Italic ❶ 390
ITC Century Book Condensed ❶ 391
ITC Century Book Condensed Italic ❶ 392
ITC Century Bold Condensed ❶ 393
ITC Century Bold Condensed Italic ❶ 394
ITC Century Ultra Condensed ❶ 395
ITC Century Ultra Condensed Italic ❶ 396
Chapel Script ❷ 623
Bitstream Charter ❶ 272
Bitstream Charter Italic ❶ 273
Bitstream Charter Bold ❶ 274
Bitstream Charter Bold Italic ❶ 275
Bitstream Charter Black ❶ 276
Bitstream Charter Black Italic ❶ 277
Cheltenham ❶ 448
Cheltenham Italic ❶ 449
Cheltenham Bold/Head ❶ 450
Cheltenham Bold Italic/Head ❶ 451
Cheltenham Bold ❶ 452
Cheltenham Bold Italic ❶ 453
Cheltenham Bold Condensed ❶ 454
Cheltenham Bold Condensed Italic ❶ 455
Cheltenham Bold Extra Condensed ❶ 456
ITC Cheltenham Light Roman ❶ 457
ITC Cheltenham Light Italic ❶ 458
ITC Cheltenham Book ❶ 459
ITC Cheltenham Book Italic ❶ 460
ITC Cheltenham Bold ❶ 461
ITC Cheltenham Bold Italic ❶ 462
ITC Cheltenham Ultra ❶ 463
ITC Cheltenham Ultra Italic ❶ 464
City Light ❶ 465
City Medium ❶ 466
City Bold ❶ 467
Clarendon Light ❶ 468

Clarendon Roman ❶ 469
Clarendon Heavy ❶ 470
Clarendon Bold ❶ 471
Clarendon Black ❶ 472
Clarendon Condensed ❶ 473
Clarendon Bold Condensed ❶ 474
ITC Clearface Regular ❶ 278
ITC Clearface Regular Italic ❶ 279
ITC Clearface Bold ❶ 280
ITC Clearface Bold Italic ❶ 281
ITC Clearface Heavy ❶ 282
ITC Clearface Heavy Italic ❶ 283
ITC Clearface Black ❶ 284
ITC Clearface Black Italic ❶ 285
ITC Clearface Contour ❶ 286
Cloister Black ❷ 667
Cloister Open Face ❶ 108
Commercial Script ❷ 624
Compacta Light ❷ 99
Compacta ❷ 100
Compacta Italic ❷ 101
Compacta Bold ❷ 102
Compacta Bold Italic ❷ 103
Concorde ❶ 287
Concorde Italic ❶ 288
Concorde Bold ❶ 289
Bitstream Cooper Light ❷ 526
Bitstream Cooper Light Italic ❷ 527
Bitstream Cooper Medium ❷ 528
Bitstream Cooper Medium Italic ❷ 529
Bitstream Cooper Bold ❷ 530
Bitstream Cooper Bold Italic ❷ 531
Bitstream Cooper Black ❷ 532
Bitstream Cooper Black Italic ❷ 533
Bitstream Cooper Black/Head ❷ 534
Bitstream Cooper Black Italic/Head ❷ 535
Bitstream Cooper Black Outline ❷ 536
Corona Roman ❶ 475
Corona Italic ❶ 476
Corona Bold ❶ 477
Corona Bold Italic ❶ 478
Coronet ❷ 625
Coronet Bold ❷ 626
Courier 10 Pitch ❶ 479
Courier Italic 10 Pitch ❶ 480
Courier Bold 10 Pitch ❶ 481
Courier Bold Italic 10 Pitch ❶ 482
ITC Cushing Book ❶ 290
ITC Cushing Book Italic ❶ 291
ITC Cushing Medium ❶ 292
ITC Cushing Medium Italic ❶ 293
ITC Cushing Bold ❶ 294
ITC Cushing Bold Italic ❶ 295
ITC Cushing Heavy ❶ 296
ITC Cushing Heavy Italic ❶ 297

D

Davida Bold ❷ 537
De Vinne/Text ❶ 397
De Vinne Italic/Text ❶ 398
De Vinne/Text 8-pt. ❶ 399
De Vinne Italic/Text 8-pt. ❶ 400
Diotima ❶ 109
Diotima Italic ❶ 110
Dom Casual ❷ 627
Dom Bold ❷ 628
Dom Diagonal ❷ 629
Dom Diagonal Bold ❷ 630

E

Eckmann ❷ 538
Egyptian 505 Light ❶ 483
Egyptian 505 ❶ 484
Egyptian 505 Medium ❶ 485
Egyptian 505 Bold ❶ 486
Egyptienne 55 ❶ 487
Egyptienne Italic 56 ❶ 488
Egyptienne Bold 65 ❶ 489
Egyptienne Black 75 ❶ 490
Electra ❶ 298
Electra Cursive ❶ 299
Electra Bold ❶ 300
English Script ❷ 631
Engravers' Old English ❷ 668
Engravers' Old English Bold ❷ 669
ITC Eras Light ❷ 104
ITC Eras Book ❷ 105
ITC Eras Medium ❷ 106
ITC Eras Demi ❷ 107
ITC Eras Bold ❷ 108
ITC Eras Ultra ❷ 109
ITC Eras Outline ❷ 110
Eurostile ❷ 111
Eurostile Bold ❷ 112
Eurostile Condensed ❷ 113
Eurostile Bold Condensed ❷ 114
Eurostile Extended ❷ 115
Eurostile Bold Extended ❷ 116
Excelsior Roman ❶ 491
Excelsior Italic ❶ 492
Excelsior Bold ❶ 493
Excelsior Bold Italic ❶ 494

F

Fairfield ❶ 401
Fairfield Italic ❶ 402
ITC Fenice Light ❶ 403
ITC Fenice Light Italic ❶ 404
ITC Fenice Regular ❶ 405
ITC Fenice Regular Italic ❶ 406
ITC Fenice Bold ❶ 407
ITC Fenice Bold Italic ❶ 408
ITC Fenice Ultra/Head ❶ 409
ITC Fenice Ultra Italic/Head ❶ 410
Flemish Script ❷ 632
Florentine Script ❷ 633
Floridian ❷ 634
Folio Light ❷ 117
Folio Light Italic ❷ 118
Folio Book ❷ 119
Folio Medium ❷ 120
Folio Bold ❷ 121
Folio Extra Bold/Head ❷ 122
Folio Bold Condensed ❷ 123
Fraktur Light (Luther) ❷ 670
Franklin Gothic ❷ 124
Franklin Gothic Italic ❷ 125
Franklin Gothic Condensed ❷ 126
Franklin Gothic Extra Condensed ❷ 127
ITC Franklin Gothic Book ❷ 128
ITC Franklin Gothic Book Italic ❷ 129
ITC Franklin Gothic Medium ❷ 130
ITC Franklin Gothic Medium Italic ❷ 131
ITC Franklin Gothic Demi ❷ 132
ITC Franklin Gothic Demi Italic ❷ 133
ITC Franklin Gothic Heavy ❷ 134
ITC Franklin Gothic Heavy Italic ❷ 135

ITC Friz Quadrata ❷ 539
ITC Friz Quadrata Bold ❷ 540
Frutiger Light 45 ❷ 136
Frutiger Light Italic 46 ❷ 137
Frutiger 55 ❷ 138
Frutiger Italic 56 ❷ 139
Frutiger Bold 65 ❷ 140
Frutiger Bold Italic 66 ❷ 141
Frutiger Black 75 ❷ 142
Frutiger Black Italic 76 ❷ 143
Futura Light ❷ 144
Futura Light Italic ❷ 145
Futura Book ❷ 146
Futura Book Italic ❷ 147
Futura Medium ❷ 148
Futura Medium Italic ❷ 149
Futura Heavy ❷ 150
Futura Heavy Italic ❷ 151
Futura Bold ❷ 152
Futura Bold Italic ❷ 153
Futura Extra Black ❷ 154
Futura Extra Black Italic ❷ 155
Futura Light Condensed ❷ 156
Futura Medium Condensed ❷ 157
Futura Bold Condensed ❷ 158
Futura Bold Condensed Italic ❷ 159
Futura Extra Black Condensed ❷ 160
Furura Extra Black Condensed Italic ❷ 161
Futura Black ❷ 162

G
ITC Galliard Roman ❶ 111
ITC Galliard Italic ❶ 112
ITC Galliard Bold ❶ 113
ITC Galliard Bold Italic ❶ 114
ITC Galliard Black ❶ 115
ITC Galliard Black Italic ❶ 116
ITC Galliard Ultra ❶ 117
ITC Galliard Ultra Italic ❶ 118
Gando Ronde ❷ 635
Stempel Garamond ❶ 119
Stempel Garamond Italic ❶ 120
Stempel Garamond Bold ❶ 121
Stempel Garamond Bold Italic ❶ 122
Garamond No.3 Roman ❶ 123
Garamond No.3 Italic ❶ 124
Garamond No.3 Bold ❶ 125
Garamond No.3 Bold Italic ❶ 126
Simoncini Garamond ❶ 127
Simoncini Garamond Italic ❶ 128
Simoncini Garamond Bold ❶ 129
ITC Garamond Light Roman ❶ 130
ITC Garamond Light Italic ❶ 131
ITC Garamond Book ❶ 132
ITC Garamond Book Italic ❶ 133
ITC Garamond Bold ❶ 134
ITC Garamond Bold Italic ❶ 135
ITC Garamond Ultra ❶ 136
ITC Garamond Ultra Italic ❶ 137
ITC Garamond Light Condensed ❶ 138
ITC Garamond Light Condensed Italic ❶ 139
ITC Garamond Book Condensed ❶ 140
ITC Garamond Book Condensed Italic ❶ 141
ITC Garamond Bold Condensed ❶ 142
ITC Garamond Bold Condensed Italic ❶ 143
ITC Garamond Ultra Condensed ❶ 144
ITC Garamond Ultra Condensed Italic ❶ 145
Gill Sans Light ❷ 163

Gill Sans Light Italic ❷ 164
Gill Sans Roman ❷ 165
Gill Sans Italic ❷ 166
Gill Sans Bold ❷ 167
Gill Sans Bold Italic ❷ 168
Gill Sans Extra Bold ❷ 169
Gill Sans Ultra Bold ❷ 170
Gill Sans Condensed ❷ 171
Gill Sans Bold Condensed ❷ 172
Gill Sans Extra Bold Condensed ❷ 173
ITC Gorilla ❷ 541
Goudy Old Style ❶ 146
Goudy Old Style Italic ❶ 147
Goudy Bold ❶ 148
Goudy Bold Italic ❶ 149
Goudy Extra Bold ❶ 150
Goudy Catalogue ❶ 151
Goudy Handtooled ❶ 152
Goudy Heavyface ❶ 153
Goudy Heavyface Condensed ❶ 154
ITC Goudy Sans Light ❷ 174
ITC Goudy Sans Light Italic ❷ 175
ITC Goudy Sans Medium ❷ 176
ITC Goudy Sans Medium Italic ❷ 177
ITC Goudy Sans Bold ❷ 178
ITC Goudy Sans Bold Italic ❷ 179
ITC Goudy Sans Black ❷ 180
ITC Goudy Sans Black Italic ❷ 181
Granjon Roman ❶ 155
Granjon Italic ❶ 156
Granjon Bold ❶ 157
ITC Grizzly ❷ 182
Monotype Grotesque 126 ❷ 183
Monotype Grotesque 126 Italic ❷ 184
Monotype Grotesque 215 ❷ 185
Monotype Grotesque 215 Italic ❷ 186
Monotype Grotesque 216 ❷ 187
Monotype Grotesque 216 Italic ❷ 188
ITC Grouch ❶ 301

H
Handel Gothic ❷ 189
Hanseatic ❷ 190
Helvetica Thin ❷ 191
Helvetica Thin Italic ❷ 192
Helvetica Light ❷ 193
Helvetica Light Italic ❷ 194
Helvetica Roman ❷ 195
Helvetica Italic ❷ 196
Helvetica Medium ❷ 197
Helvetica Medium Italic ❷ 198
Helvetica Bold ❷ 199
Helvetica Bold Italic ❷ 200
Helvetica Heavy ❷ 201
Helvetica Heavy Italic ❷ 202
Helvetica Black ❷ 203
Helvetica Black Italic ❷ 204
Helvetica Black No.2 ❷ 205
Helvetica Bold Outline ❷ 206
Helvetica Black Outline ❷ 207
Helvetica Bold Condensed Outline ❷ 208
Helvetica Light Condensed ❷ 209
Helvetica Light Condensed Italic ❷ 210
Helvetica Condensed ❷ 211
Helvetica Condensed Italic ❷ 212
Helvetica Bold Condensed ❷ 213
Helvetica Bold Condensed Italic ❷ 214
Helvetica Black Condensed ❷ 215

Helvetica Black Condensed Italic ❷ 216
Helvetica Light Extended ❷ 217
Helvetica Extended ❷ 218
Helvetica Bold Extended ❷ 219
Helvetica Black Extended ❷ 220
Helvetica Bold Rounded ❷ 221
Helvetica Black Rounded ❷ 222
Helvetica Compressed ❷ 223
Helvetica Extra Compressed ❷ 224
Helvetica Ultra Compressed ❷ 225
Helvetica Inserat ❷ 226
Helvetica Monospace ❷ 227
Helvetica Italic Monospace ❷ 228
Helvetica Bold Monospace ❷ 229
Helvetica Bold Italic Monospace ❷ 230
Hobo ❷ 542

I
Imperial Roman ❶ 158
Imperial Italic ❶ 159
Imperial Bold ❶ 160
Impress ❷ 636
Imprint Roman ❶ 161
Imprint Italic ❶ 162
Imprint Bold ❶ 163
Impuls ❷ 637
Ionic No.5 ❶ 495
Ionic No.5 Italic ❶ 496
Ionic No.5 Bold ❶ 497
ITC Isbell Book ❷ 543
ITC Isbell Book Italic ❷ 544
ITC Isbell Medium ❷ 545
ITC Isbell Medium Italic ❷ 546
ITC Isbell Bold ❷ 547
ITC Isbell Bold Italic ❷ 548
ITC Isbell Heavy ❷ 549
ITC Isbell Heavy Italic ❷ 550
ITC Italia Book ❶ 498
ITC Italia Medium ❶ 499
ITC Italia Bold ❶ 500

J
Janson Roman ❶ 302
Janson Italic ❶ 303
Jefferson ❷ 638

K
ITC Kabel Book ❷ 231
ITC Kabel Medium ❷ 232
ITC Kabel Demi ❷ 233
ITC Kabel Bold ❷ 234
ITC Kabel Ultra ❷ 235
Kaufmann ❷ 639
Kaufmann Bold ❷ 640
ITC Korinna Regular ❷ 551
ITC Korinna Kursiv Regular ❷ 552
ITC Korinna Bold ❷ 553
ITC Korinna Kursiv Bold ❷ 554
ITC Korinna Extra Bold ❷ 555
ITC Korinna Kursiv Extra Bold ❷ 556
ITC Korinna Heavy ❷ 557
ITC Korinna Kursiv Heavy ❷ 558
ITC Korinna Bold Outline ❷ 559

L
Latin Extra Condensed/Head ❶ 411
ITC Leawood Book ❶ 164
ITC Leawood Book Italic ❶ 165

ITC Leawood Medium ❶ 166
ITC Leawood Medium Italic ❶ 167
ITC Leawood Bold ❶ 168
ITC Leawood Bold Italic ❶ 169
ITC Leawood Black ❶ 170
ITC Leawood Black Italic ❶ 171
Letter Gothic 12 Pitch ❷ 236
Letter Gothic Italic 12 Pitch ❷ 237
Letter Gothic Bold 12 Pitch ❷ 238
Letter Gothic Bold Italic 12 Pitch ❷ 239
Liberty ❷ 641
Libra ❷ 560
Life ❶ 304
Life Italic ❶ 305
Life Bold ❶ 306
Life Bold Italic ❶ 307
Linoscript ❷ 642
London Text ❷ 671
ITC Lubalin Graph Extra Light ❶ 501
ITC Lubalin Graph Extra Light Oblique ❶ 502
ITC Lubalin Graph Book ❶ 503
ITC Lubalin Graph Book Oblique ❶ 504
ITC Lubalin Graph Medium ❶ 505
ITC Lubalin Graph Medium Oblique ❶ 506
ITC Lubalin Graph Demi ❶ 507
ITC Lubalin Graph Demi Oblique ❶ 508
ITC Lubalin Graph Bold ❶ 509
ITC Lubalin Graph Bold Oblique ❶ 510
Lucia ❷ 643
Lydian ❷ 561
Lydian Italic ❷ 562
Lydian Bold ❷ 563
Lydian Bold Italic ❷ 564
Lydian Cursive ❷ 644

M
ITC Machine ❷ 240
Madison ❶ 412
Madison Italic ❶ 413
Madison Bold ❶ 414
Madison Black ❶ 415
Madison Condensed ❶ 416
Madison Bold Condensed ❶ 417
Matt Antique (Garth) ❶ 172
Matt Antique Italic ❶ 173
Matt Antique Bold ❶ 174
Maximus ❷ 565
Melior Roman ❶ 511
Melior Italic ❶ 512
Melior Bold ❶ 513
Melior Bold Italic ❶ 514
Memphis Light ❶ 515
Memphis Light Italic ❶ 516
Memphis Medium ❶ 517
Memphis Medium Italic ❶ 518
Memphis Bold ❶ 519
Memphis Bold Italic ❶ 520
Memphis Extra Bold ❶ 521
Memphis Extra Bold Italic ❶ 522
Memphis Medium Condensed ❶ 523
Memphis Bold Condensed ❶ 524
Memphis Extra Bold Condensed ❶ 525
Meridien Roman ❶ 308
Meridien Italic ❶ 309
Meridien Medium ❶ 310
Meridien Medium Italic ❶ 311
Meridien Bold ❶ 312
Meridien Bold Italic ❶ 313

Metro Lite ❷ 241
Metro Lite Italic ❷ 242
Metro Medium ❷ 243
Metro Medium Italic ❷ 244
Metro Black ❷ 245
Metro Black Italic ❷ 246
ITC Mixage Book ❷ 247
ITC Mixage Book Italic ❷ 248
ITC Mixage Medium ❷ 249
ITC Mixage Medium Italic ❷ 250
ITC Mixage Bold ❷ 251
ITC Mixage Bold Italic ❷ 252
ITC Mixage Black ❷ 253
ITC Mixage Black Italic ❷ 254
Mistral ❷ 645
Monoscript ❷ 646
Murray Hill ❷ 647
Murray Hill Bold ❷ 648

N
Neuzeit Roman ❷ 255
Neuzeit Black ❷ 256
Neuzeit Bold Condensed ❷ 257
Neuzeit Black Condensed ❷ 258
News Gothic Light ❷ 259
News Gothic Light Italic ❷ 260
News Gothic Roman ❷ 261
News Gothic Italic ❷ 262
News Gothic Demi ❷ 263
News Gothic Demi Italic ❷ 264
News Gothic Bold ❷ 265
News Gothic Bold Italic ❷ 266
News Gothic Condensed ❷ 267
News Gothic Condensed Italic ❷ 268
News Gothic Bold Condensed ❷ 269
News Gothic Bold Condensed Italic ❷ 270
News Gothic Extra Condensed ❷ 271
News Gothic Extra Bold Condensed ❷ 272
ITC Newtext Light ❷ 566
ITC Newtext Light Italic ❷ 567
ITC Newtext Book ❷ 568
ITC Newtext Book Italic ❷ 569
ITC Newtext Regular ❷ 570
ITC Newtext Regular Italic ❷ 571
ITC Newtext Demi ❷ 572
ITC Newtext Demi Italic ❷ 573
Normande ❶ 418
Normande Italic ❶ 419
ITC Novarese Book ❶ 175
ITC Novarese Book Italic ❶ 176
ITC Novarese Medium ❶ 177
ITC Novarese Medium Italic ❶ 178
ITC Novarese Bold ❶ 179
ITC Novarese Bold Italic ❶ 180
ITC Novarese Ultra ❶ 181

O
Ondine ❷ 649
Optima Roman ❷ 273
Optima Italic ❷ 274
Optima Demi ❷ 275
Optima Demi Italic ❷ 276
Optima Bold ❷ 277
Optima Bold Italic ❷ 278
Optima Ultra ❷ 279
Optima Ultra Italic ❷ 280
Orator (90% with lower case) ❷ 281
Orbit-B ❷ 574

P
Palatino Roman ❶ 182
Palatino Italic ❶ 183
Palatino Bold ❶ 184
Palatino Bold Italic ❶ 185
Palette ❷ 650
Parisian ❷ 575
Park Avenue ❷ 651
Peignot Light ❷ 576
Peignot Demi-Bold ❷ 577
Peignot Bold ❷ 578
Perpetua Roman ❶ 314
Perpetua Italic ❶ 315
Perpetua Bold ❶ 316
Perpetua Bold Italic ❶ 317
Perpetua Black ❶ 318
Pica 10 Pitch ❶ 526
ITC Pioneer ❷ 579
Piranesi Italic ❷ 652
Plantin Light ❶ 186
Plantin Light Italic ❶ 187
Plantin Roman ❶ 188
Plantin Italic ❶ 189
Plantin Bold ❶ 190
Plantin Bold Italic ❶ 191
Plantin Bold Condensed ❶ 192
Playbill ❶ 527
Prestige 12 Pitch ❶ 528
Prestige Italic 12 Pitch ❶ 529
Prestige Bold 12 Pitch ❶ 530
Prestige Bold Italic 12 Pitch ❶ 531
Primer ❶ 420
Primer Italic ❶ 421
Profil ❷ 580
P.T. Barnum ❶ 532

Q
ITC Quorum Light ❷ 581
ITC Quorum Book ❷ 582
ITC Quorum Medium ❷ 583
ITC Quorum Bold ❷ 584
ITC Quorum Black ❷ 585

R
Revue ❷ 586
Rockwell Light Roman ❶ 533
Rockwell Light Italic ❶ 534
Rockwell Medium ❶ 535
Rockwell Medium Italic ❶ 536
Rockwell Bold ❶ 537
Rockwell Extra Bold ❶ 538
Romana Normal ❶ 319
Romana Bold ❶ 320
ITC Ronda Light ❷ 282
ITC Ronda ❷ 283
ITC Ronda Bold ❷ 284

S
Sabon Roman ❶ 193
Sabon Italic ❶ 194
Sabon Bold ❶ 195
Sabon Bold Italic ❶ 196
Schneidler Light ❶ 197
Schneidler Light Italic ❶ 198
Schneidler ❶ 199
Schneidler Italic ❶ 200
Schneidler Medium ❶ 201
Schneidler Medium Italic ❶ 202

Schneidler Bold ❶ 203
Schneidler Bold Italic ❶ 204
Schneidler Black ❶ 205
Schneidler Black Italic ❶ 206
Seagull Light ❷ 587
Seagull Medium ❷ 588
Seagull Bold ❷ 589
Seagull Heavy ❷ 590
ITC Serif Gothic Light ❷ 591
ITC Serif Gothic Regular ❷ 592
ITC Serif Gothic Bold ❷ 593
ITC Serif Gothic Extra Bold ❷ 594
ITC Serif Gothic Heavy ❷ 595
ITC Serif Gothic Black ❷ 596
ITC Serif Gothic Bold Outline ❷ 597
Serifa Thin 35 ❶ 539
Serifa Thin Italic 36 ❶ 540
Serifa Light 45 ❶ 541
Serifa Light Italic 46 ❶ 542
Serifa 55 ❶ 543
Serifa Italic 56 ❶ 544
Serifa Bold 65 ❶ 545
Serifa Black 75 ❶ 546
Serifa Bold Condensed 67 ❶ 547
Shelley Andante ❷ 653
Shelley Allegro ❷ 654
Shelley Volante ❷ 655
Shotgun ❷ 598
Shotgun Blanks ❷ 599
Snell Roundhand ❷ 656
Snell Roundhand Bold ❷ 657
Snell Roundhand Black ❷ 658
ITC Souvenir Light ❷ 600
ITC Souvenir Light Italic ❷ 601
ITC Souvenir Medium ❷ 602
ITC Souvenir Medium Italic ❷ 603
ITC Souvenir Demi ❷ 604
ITC Souvenir Demi Italic ❷ 605
ITC Souvenir Bold ❷ 606
ITC Souvenir Bold Italic ❷ 607
ITC Souvenir Bold Outline ❷ 608
Spartan Classified Book ❷ 285
Spartan Classified Heavy ❷ 286
Spartan Book Condensed ❷ 287
Spartan Heavy Condensed ❷ 288
Stencil ❷ 609
Stuyvesent Script ❷ 659
Stymie Light Roman ❶ 548
Stymie Light Italic ❶ 549
Stynue Medium ❶ 550
Stymie Medium Italic ❶ 551
Stymie Bold ❶ 552
Stymie Bold Italic ❶ 553
Stymie Extra Bold ❶ 554
Stymie Extra Bold Condensed ❶ 555
ITC Symbol Book ❷ 289
ITC Symbol Book Italic ❷ 290
ITC Symbol Medium ❷ 291
ITC Symbol Medium Italic ❷ 292
ITC Symbol Bold ❷ 293
ITC Symbol Bold Italic ❷ 294
ITC Symbol Black ❷ 295
ITC Symbol Black Italic ❷ 296
Syntax ❷ 297
Syntax Bold ❷ 298
Syntax Black ❷ 299
Syntax Ultra Black ❷ 300

T
Telegraph (Linotype Modern) ❶ 422
Telegraph Italic (Linotype Modern) ❶ 423
Telegraph Bold (Linotype Modern) ❶ 424
Textype Roman ❶ 556
Textype Italic ❶ 557
Textype Bold ❶ 558
Textype Bold Italic ❶ 559
Thunderbird ❷ 610
ITC Tiffany Light ❶ 321
ITC Tiffany Light Italic ❶ 322
ITC Tiffany Medium ❶ 323
ITC Tiffany Medium Italic ❶ 324
ITC Tiffany Demi ❶ 325
ITC Tiffany Demi Italic ❶ 326
ITC Tiffany Heavy ❶ 327
ITC Tiffany Heavy Italic ❶ 328
Times Roman (18pt) ❶ 329
Times Italic (18pt) ❶ 330
Times Roman ❶ 331
Times Italic ❶ 332
Times Semi-Bold ❶ 333
Times Semi-Bold Italic ❶ 334
Times Bold ❶ 335
Times Bold Italic ❶ 336
Times Extra Bold ❶ 337
ITC Tom's Roman ❶ 207
Torino ❶ 425
Torino Italic ❶ 426
Trump Mediaeval ❶ 208
Trump Mediaeval Italic ❶ 209
Trump Mediaeval Bold ❶ 210
Trump Mediaeval Bold Italic ❶ 211
Trump Mediaeval Black ❶ 212

U
Univers Light 45 ❷ 301
Univers Light Italic 46 ❷ 302
Univers 55 ❷ 303
Univers Italic 56 ❷ 304
Univers Bold 65 ❷ 305
Univers Bold Italic 66 ❷ 306
Univers Black 75 ❷ 307
Univers Black Italic 76 ❷ 308
Univers Extra Black 85 ❷ 309
Univers Light Condensed 47 ❷ 310
Univers Light Condensed Italic 48 ❷ 311
Univers Condensed 57 ❷ 312
Univers Condensed Italic 58 ❷ 313
Univers Bold Condensed 67 ❷ 314
Univers Bold Condensed Italic 68 ❷ 315
Univers Light Extra Condensed ❷ 316
Univers Extra Condensed ❷ 317
Univers Bold Extra Condensed ❷ 318
Univers Extended 53 ❷ 319
Univers Bold Extended 63 ❷ 320
Univers Black Extended 73 ❷ 321
Univers Ultra Black Extended 83 ❷ 322
University Roman ❷ 611
University Bold ❷ 612

V
VAG Rounded ❷ 323
Vineta ❷ 613

W
Wedding Text ❷ 672
Windsor Light ❶ 213

Windsor Roman ❶ 214
Windsor Light Condensed ❶ 215
Windsor Elongated ❶ 216
Windsor Outline ❶ 217

Z
ITC Zapf Book Light ❶ 427
ITC Zapf Book Light Italic ❶ 428
ITC Zapf Book Medium ❶ 429
ITC Zapf Book Medium Italic ❶ 430
ITC Zapf Book Demi ❶ 431
ITC Zapf Book Demi Italic ❶ 432
ITC Zapf Book Heavy ❶ 433
ITC Zapf Book Heavy Italic ❶ 434
ITC Zapf Chancery Light ❷ 660
ITC Zapf Chancery Light Italic ❷ 661
ITC Zapf Chancery Medium ❷ 662
ITC Zapf Chancery Medium Italic ❷ 663
ITC Zapf Chancery Demi ❷ 664
ITC Zapf Chancery Bold ❷ 665
ITC Zapf International Light ❶ 338
ITC Zapf International Light Italic ❶ 339
ITC Zapf International Medium ❶ 340
ITC Zapf International Medium Italic ❶ 341
ITC Zapf International Demi ❶ 342
ITC Zapf International Demi Italic ❶ 343
ITC Zapf International Heavy ❶ 344
ITC Zapf International Heavy Italic ❶ 345

❶ Serif Book ❷ Sans Serif, Decorative and Display Book

A

Aachen Bold ❶ 736
Akzidenz-Grotesk Light ❷ 324
Akzidenz-Grotesk Roman ❷ 325
Akzidenz-Grotesk Bold ❷ 326
Akzidenz-Grotesk Black ❷ 327
ITC American Typewriter Medium ❶ 737
ITC American Typewriter Bold ❶ 738
Americana Roman ❶ 629
Americana Italic ❶ 630
Americana Bold ❶ 631
Americana Extra Bold ❶ 632
Antique Olive Light ❷ 328
Antique Olive Roman ❷ 329
Antique Olive Italic ❷ 330
Antique Olive Bold ❷ 331
Antique Olive Black ❷ 332
Antique Olive Compact ❷ 333
Antique Olive Bold Condensed ❷ 334
Antique Olive Nord ❷ 335
Antique Olive Nord Italic ❷ 336
Arnold Böcklin ❷ 673
New Aster Roman ❶ 560
New Aster Italic ❶ 561
New Aster Semi Bold ❶ 562
New Aster Semi Bold Italic ❶ 563
New Aster Bold ❶ 564
New Aster Bold Italic ❶ 565
New Aster Black ❶ 566
New Aster Black Italic ❶ 567
ITC Avant Garde Gothic Book ❷ 337
ITC Avant Garde Gothic Oblique ❷ 338
ITC Avant Garde Gothic Demi ❷ 339
ITC Avant Garde Gothic Demi Oblique ❷ 340
Avenir 35 Light ❷ 341
Avenir 35 Light Oblique ❷ 342
Avenir 45 Book ❷ 343
Avenir 45 Book Oblique ❷ 344
Avenir 55 Roman ❷ 345
Avenir 55 Oblique ❷ 346
Avenir 65 Medium ❷ 347
Avenir 65 Medium Oblique ❷ 348
Avenir 85 Heavy ❷ 349
Avenir 85 Heavy Oblique ❷ 350
Avenir 95 Black ❷ 351
Avenir 95 Black Oblique ❷ 352

B

ITC New Baskerville Roman ❶ 633
ITC New Baskerville Italic ❶ 634
ITC New Baskerville Bold ❶ 635
ITC New Baskerville Bold Italic ❶ 636
ITC Bauhaus Light ❷ 353
ITC Bauhaus Medium ❷ 354
ITC Bauhaus Demi ❷ 355
ITC Bauhaus Bold ❷ 356
ITC Bauhaus Heavy ❷ 357
Belwe Light ❷ 674
Belwe Medium ❷ 675
Belwe Bold ❶ 676
Belwe Condensed ❷ 677
ITC Benguiat Book ❷ 678
ITC Benguiat Bold ❷ 679
ITC Berkeley Oldstyle Book ❶ 568
ITC Berkeley Oldstyle Book Italic ❶ 569
ITC Berkeley Oldstyle Medium ❶ 570
ITC Berkeley Oldstyle Medium Italic ❶ 571
ITC Berkeley Oldstyle Bold ❶ 572

ITC Berkeley Oldstyle Bold Italic ❶ 573
ITC Berkeley Oldstyle Black ❶ 574
ITC Berkeley Oldstyle Black Italic ❶ 575
Bauer Bodoni Roman ❶ 694
Bauer Bodoni Italic ❶ 695
Bauer Bodoni Bold ❶ 696
Bauer Bodoni Bold Italic ❶ 697
Bodoni Roman ❶ 698
Bodoni Italic ❶ 699
Bodoni Bold ❶ 700
Bodoni Bold Italic ❶ 701
Poster Bodoni Black ❶ 702
ITC Bookman Light ❶ 637
ITC Bookman Light Italic ❶ 638
ITC Bookman Demi ❶ 639
ITC Bookman Demi Italic ❶ 640
Brush Script ❷ 719

C

New Caledonia Roman ❶ 703
New Caledonia Italic ❶ 704
New Caledonia Semi Bold ❶ 705
New Caledonia Semi Bold Italic ❶ 706
New Caledonia Bold ❶ 707
New Caledonia Bold Italic ❶ 708
New Caledonia Black ❶ 709
New Caledonia Black Italic ❶ 710
Candida Roman ❶ 739
Candida Italic ❶ 740
Candida Bold ❶ 741
Cascade Script ❷ 720
Caslon 3 Roman ❶ 641
Caslon 3 Italic ❶ 642
Caslon 540 Roman ❶ 643
Caslon 540 Italic ❶ 644
Caslon Open Face ❷ 645
Linotype Centennial 45 Light ❶ 711
Linotype Centennial 46 Light Italic ❶ 712
Linotype Centennial 55 Roman ❶ 713
Linotype Centennial 56 Italic ❶ 714
Linotype Centennial 75 Bold ❶ 715
Linotype Centennial 76 Bold Italic ❶ 716
Linotype Centennial 95 Black ❶ 717
Linotype Centennial 96 Black Italic ❶ 718
Century Expanded Roman ❶ 719
Century Expanden Italic ❶ 720
Century Old Style Roman ❶ 646
Century Old Style Italic ❶ 647
Century Old Style Bold ❶ 648
New Century Schoolbook Roman ❶ 721
New Century Schoolbook Italic ❶ 722
New Century Schoolbook Bold ❶ 723
New Century Schoolbook Bold Italic ❶ 724
ITC Cheltenham Book ❶ 742
ITC Cheltenham Book Italic 743
ITC Cheltenham Bold ❶ 744
ITC Cheltenham Bold Italic ❶ 745
Clarendon Light ❶ 746
Clarendon Roman ❶ 747
Clarendon Bold ❶ 748
ITC Clearface Regular ❷ 649
ITC Clearface Regular Italic ❶ 650
ITC Clearface Bold ❶ 651
ITC Clearface Bold Italic ❶ 652
ITC Clearface Heavy ❶ 653
ITC Clearface Heavy Italic ❶ 654
ITC Clearface Black ❶ 655
ITC Clearface Black Italic ❶ 656

Cochin Roman ❶ 657
Cochin Italic ❶ 658
Cochin Bold ❶ 659
Cochin Bold Italic ❶ 660
Concorde Roman ❶ 661
Concorde Italic ❶ 662
Concorde Bold ❶ 663
Concorde Bold Italic ❶ 664
Cooper Black ❷ 680
Cooper Black Italic ❷ 681
Corona Roman ❶ 749
Corona Italic ❶ 750
Corona Bold Face 2 ❶ 751

D

Dom Casual ❷ 721
Dom Casual Bold ❷ 722

E

ITC Eras Light ❷ 358
ITC Eras Book ❷ 359
ITC Eras Medium ❷ 360
ITC Eras Demi ❷ 361
ITC Eras Bold ❷ 362
ITC Eras Ultra ❷ 363
Eurostile Roman ❷ 364
Eurostile Oblique ❷ 365
Eurostile Demi ❷ 366
Eurostile Demi Oblique ❷ 367
Eurostile Bold ❷ 368
Eurostile Bold Oblique ❷ 369
Excelsior Roman ❶ 752
Excelsior Italic ❶ 753
Excelsior Bold ❶ 754

F

Fette Fraktur ❷ 734
Folio Light ❷ 370
Folio Medium ❷ 371
Folio Bold ❷ 372
Folio Extra Bold ❷ 373
Folio Bold Condensed ❷ 374
Franklin Gothic 2 Roman ❷ 375
Franklin Gothic Condensed ❷ 376
Franklin Gothic Extra Condensed ❷ 377
ITC Franklin Gothic Book ❷ 378
ITC Franklin Gothic Book Oblique ❷ 379
ITC Franklin Gothic Demi ❷ 380
ITC Franklin Gothic Demi Oblique ❷ 381
ITC Franklin Gothic Heavy ❷ 382
ITC Franklin Gothic Heavy Oblique ❷ 383
ITC Friz Quadrata Roman ❷ 682
ITC Friz Quadrata Bold ❷ 683
Frutiger 45 Light ❷ 384
Frutiger 46 Light Italic ❷ 385
Frutiger 55 Roman ❷ 386
Frutiger 56 Italic ❷ 387
Frutiger 65 Bold ❷ 388
Frutiger 66 Bold Italic ❷ 389
Frutiger 75 Black ❷ 390
Frutiger 76 Black Italic ❷ 391
Frutiger 95 Ultra Black ❷ 392
Futura Light ❷ 393
Futura Light Oblique ❷ 394
Futura Book ❷ 395
Futura Book Oblique ❷ 396
Futura Medium ❷ 397

Futura Medium Oblique ❷ 398
Futura Heavy ❷ 399
Futura Heavy Oblique ❷ 400
Futura Bold ❷ 401
Futura Bold Oblique ❷ 402
Futura Extra Bold ❷ 403
Futura Extra Bold Oblique ❷ 404
Futura Condensed Light ❷ 405
Futura Condensed Light Oblique ❷ 406
Futura Condensed Medium ❷ 407
Futura Condensed Meidum Oblique ❷ 408
Futura Condensed Bold ❷ 409
Futura Condensed Bold Oblique ❷ 410
Futura Condensed Extra Bold ❷ 411
Futura Condensed Extra Bold Oblique ❷ 412

G
ITC Galliard Roman ❶ 576
ITC Galliard Italic ❶ 577
ITC Galliard Bold ❶ 578
ITC Galliard Bold Italic ❶ 579
Adobe Garamond Regular ❶ 580
Adobe Garamond Italic ❶ 581
Adobe Garamond Semi Bold ❶ 582
Adobe Garamond Semi Bold Italic ❶ 583
Adobe Garamond Bold ❶ 584
Adobe Garamond Bold Italic ❶ 585
Stempel Garamond Roman ❶ 586
Stempel Garamond Italic ❶ 587
Stempel Garamond Bold ❶ 588
Stempel Garamond Bold Italic ❶ 589
Garamond 3 Roman ❶ 590
Garamond 3 Italic ❶ 591
Garamond 3 Bold ❶ 592
Garamond 3 Bold Italic ❶ 593
ITC Garamond Light ❶ 594
ITC Garamond Light Italic ❶ 595
ITC Garamond Bold ❶ 596
ITC Garamond Bold Italic ❶ 597
Glypha Roman ❶ 755
Glypha Oblique ❶ 756
Glypha Bold ❶ 757
Glypha Bold Oblique ❶ 758
Gothic 13 ❷ 413
Goudy Old Style Roman ❶ 598
Goudy Old Style Italic ❶ 599
Goudy Bold ❶ 600
Goudy Bold Italic ❶ 601
Goudy Extra Bold ❶ 602
Goudy Heavyface ❶ 603
Goudy Heavyface Italic ❶ 604

H
Neue Helvetica 25 Ultra Light ❷ 414
Neue Helvetica 26 Ultra Light Italic ❷ 415
Neue Helvetica 35 Thin ❷ 416
Neue Helvetica 36 Thin Italic ❷ 417
Neue Helvetica 45 Light ❷ 418
Neue Helvetica 46 Light Italic ❷ 419
Neue Helvetica 55 Roman ❷ 420
Neue Helvetica 56 Italic ❷ 421
Neue Helvetica 65 Medium ❷ 422
Neue Helvetica 66 Medium Italic ❷ 423
Neue Helvetica 75 Bold ❷ 424
Neue Helvetica 76 Bold Italic ❷ 425
Neue Helvetica 85 Heavy ❷ 426
Neue Helvetica 86 Heavy Italic ❷ 427
Neue Helvetica 95 Black ❷ 428

Neue Helvetica 96 Black Italic ❷ 429
Helvetica Light ❷ 430
Helvetica Light Oblique ❷ 431
Helvetica Black ❷ 432
Helvetica Black Oblique ❷ 433
Helvetica Light Condensed ❷ 434
Helvetica Light Condensed Oblique ❷ 435
Helvetica Condensed ❷ 436
Helvetica Condensed Oblique ❷ 437
Helvetica Bold Condensed ❷ 438
Helvetica Bold Condensed Oblique ❷ 439
Helvetica Black Condensed ❷ 440
Helvetica Black Condensed Oblique ❷ 441
Helvetica Compressed ❷ 442
Helvetica Extra Compressed ❷ 443
Helvetica Ultra Compressed ❷ 444
Helvetica Inserat ❷ 445
Hiroshige Book ❶ 605
Hiroshige Book Italic ❶ 606
Hiroshige Medium ❶ 607
Hiroshige Medium Italic ❶ 608
Hiroshige Bold ❶ 609
Hiroshige Bold Italic ❶ 610
Hiroshige Black ❶ 611
Hiroshige Black Italic ❶ 612
Hobo ❷ 684

I
Impressum Roman ❶ 759
Impressum Italic ❶ 760
Impressum Bold ❶ 761
ITC Italia Book ❶ 762
ITC Italia Medium ❶ 763
ITC Italia Bold ❶ 764

J
Janson Text Roman ❶ 665
Janson Text Italic ❶ 666
Janson Text Bold ❶ 667
Janson Text Bold Italic ❶ 668

K
ITC Kabel Book ❷ 446
ITC Kabel Medium ❷ 447
ITC Kabel Demi ❷ 448
ITC Kabel Bold ❷ 449
ITC Kabel Ultra ❷ 450
Kaufmann ❷ 724
Kaufmann Bold ❷ 725
ITC Korinna Regular ❷ 685
ITC Korinna Kursiv Regular ❷ 686
ITC Korinna Bold ❷ 687
ITC Korinna Kursiv Bold ❷ 688

L
Letter Gothic Roman ❷ 451
Letter Gothic Slanted ❷ 452
Letter Gothic Bold ❷ 453
Letter Gothic Bold Slanted ❷ 454
Life Roman ❶ 669
Life Italic ❶ 670
Life Bold ❶ 671
Linoscript ❷ 726
Linotext ❷ 735
ITC Lubalin Graph Book ❶ 765
ITC Lubalin Graph Book Oblique ❶ 766
ITC Lubalin Graph Demi ❶ 767
ITC Lubalin Graph Demi Oblique ❶ 768

Lucida Roman ❷ 689
Lucida Italic ❷ 690
Lucida Bold ❷ 691
Lucida Bold Italic ❷ 692
Lucida Sans Roman ❷ 455
Lucida Sans Italic ❷ 456
Lucida Sans Bold ❷ 457
Lucida Sans Bold Italic ❷ 458

M
ITC Machine Medium ❷ 459
Medici Script ❷ 727
Melior Roman ❶ 769
Melior Italic ❶ 770
Melior Bold ❶ 771
Melior Bold Italic ❶ 772
Memphis Light ❶ 773
Memphis Light Italc ❶ 774
Memphis Medium ❶ 775
Memphis Medium Italic ❶ 776
Memphis Bold ❶ 777
Memphis Bold Italic ❶ 778
Memphis Extra Bold ❶ 779
Meridien Roman ❶ 672
Meridien Italic ❶ 673
Meridien Medium ❶ 674
Meridien Medium Italic ❶ 675
Meridien Bold ❶ 676
Meridien Bold Italic ❶ 677
Mistral ❷ 728

N
News Gothic Roman ❷ 460
News Gothic Oblique ❷ 461
News Gothic Bold ❷ 462
News Gothic Bold Oblique ❷ 463
Nuptial Script ❷ 729

O
Optima Roman ❷ 464
Optima Oblique ❷ 465
Optima Bold ❷ 466
Optima Bold Oblique ❷ 467
Orator Roman ❷ 468
Orator Slanted ❷ 469

P
Palatino Roman ❶ 613
Palatino Italic ❶ 614
Palatino Bold ❶ 615
Palatino Bold Italic ❶ 616
Parisian ❷ 693
Park Avenue ❷ 730
Peignot Light ❷ 694
Peignot Demi ❷ 695
Peignot Bold ❷ 696
Post-Antiqua Roman ❷ 697
Post-Antiqua Bold ❷ 698
Present ❷ 731
Prestige Elite Roman ❶ 780
Prestige Elite Slanted ❶ 781
Prestige Elite Bold ❶ 782
Prestige Elite Bold Slanted ❶ 783

R
Reporter 2 ❷ 732
Revue ❷ 699

S

Sabon Roman ❶ 617
Sabon Italic ❶ 618
Sabon Bold ❶ 619
Sabon Bold Italic ❶ 620
ITC Serif Gothic Light ❷ 700
ITC Serif Gothic Roman ❷ 701
ITC Serif Gothic Bold ❷ 702
ITC Serif Gothic Extra Bold ❷ 703
ITC Serif Gothic Heavy ❷ 704
ITC Serif Gothic Black ❷ 705
Serifa 45 Light ❶ 784
Serifa 46 Light Italic ❶ 785
Serifa 55 Roman ❶ 786
Serifa 56 Italic ❶ 787
Serifa 65 Bold ❶ 788
Serifa 75 Black ❶ 789
ITC Souvenir Light ❷ 706
ITC Souvenir Light Italic ❷ 707
ITC Souvenir Demi ❷ 708
ITC Souvenir Demi Italic ❷ 709
Stencil ❷ 710
Stone Informal Medium ❷ 711
Stone Informal Medium Italic ❷ 712
Stone Informal Semi Bold ❷ 713
Stone Informal Semi Bold Italic ❷ 714
Stone Informal Bold ❷ 715
Stone Informal Bold Italic ❷ 716
Stone Sans Medium ❷ 470
Stone Sans Medium Italic ❷ 471
Stone Sans Semi Bold ❷ 472
Stone Sans Semi Bold Italic ❷ 473
Stone Sans Bold ❷ 474
Stone Sans Bold Italic ❷ 475
Stone Serif Medium ❶ 678
Stone Serif Medium Italic ❶ 679
Stone Serif Semi Bold ❶ 680
Stone Serif Semi Bold Italic ❶ 681
Stone Serif Bold ❶ 682
Stone Serif Bold Italic ❶ 683

T

Tempo Heavy Condensed ❷ 476
Tempo Heavy Condensed Italic ❷ 477
ITC Tiffany Medium ❶ 684
ITC Tiffany Medium Italic ❶ 685
ITC Tiffany Demi ❶ 686
ITC Tiffany Demi Italic ❶ 687
ITC Tiffany Heavy ❶ 688
ITC Tiffany Heavy Italic ❶ 689
Times Roman (10pt.) ❶ 690
Times Italic (10pt.) ❶ 691
Times Bold (10pt.) ❶ 692
Times Bold Italic (10pt.) ❶ 693
Trump Mediaeval Roman ❶ 621
Trump Mediaeval Italic ❶ 622
Trump Mediaeval Bold ❶ 623
Trump Mediaeval Bold Italic ❶ 624

U

Umbra ❷ 717
Univers 45 Light ❷ 478
Univers 45 Light Oblique ❷ 479
Univers 55 Roman ❷ 480
Univers 55 Oblique ❷ 481
Univers 65 Bold ❷ 482
Univers 65 Bold Oblique ❷ 483
Univers 75 Black ❷ 484

Univers 75 Black Oblique ❷ 485
Univers 47 Condensed Light ❷ 486
Univers 47 Condensed Light Oblique ❷ 487
Univers 57 Condensed ❷ 488
Univers 57 Condensed Oblique ❷ 489
Univers 67 Condensed Bold ❷ 490
Univers 67 Condensed Bold Obliuqe ❷ 491
University Roman ❷ 718
Utopia Regular ❶ 725
Utopia Italic ❶ 726
Utopia Semi Bold ❶ 727
Utopia Semi Bold Italic ❶ 728
Utopia Bold ❶ 729
Utopia Bold Italic ❶ 730
Utopia Black ❶ 731

V

VAG Rounded Thin ❷ 492
VAG Rounded Light ❷ 493
VAG Rounded Bold ❷ 494
VAG Rounded Black ❷ 495

W

Walbaum Roman ❶ 732
Walbaum Italic ❶ 733
Walbaum Bold ❶ 734
Walbaum Bold Italic ❶ 735
Weiss Roman ❶ 625
Weiss Italic ❶ 626
Weiss Bold ❶ 627
Weiss Extra Bold ❶ 628

Z

ITC Zapf Chancery Medium Italic ❷ 733

Emigre Alphabetical Index

❶ Serif Book   ❷ Sans Serif, Decorative and Display Book

E
Elektrix Light ❷ 736
Elektrix Bold ❷ 737
Emigre 8 ❷ 738
Emigre 10 ❷ 739
Emigre 14 ❷ 740
Emigre 15 ❷ 741
Emperor 8 ❷ 742
Emperor 10 ❷ 743
Emperor 15 ❷ 744
Emperor 19 ❷ 745

L
Lunatix Light ❷ 746
Lunatix Bold ❷ 747

M
Matrix Book ❷ 748
Matrix Regular ❷ 749
Matrix Bold ❷ 750
Matrix Extra Bold ❷ 751
Matrix Narrow ❷ 752
Matrix Wide ❷ 753
Modula Regular ❷ 754
Modula Bold ❷ 755
Modula Black ❷ 756
Modula Serif Regular ❶ 757
Modula Serif Bold ❶ 758
Modula Serif Black ❶ 759

O
Oakland 6 ❷ 760
Oakland 8 ❷ 761
Oakland 10 ❷ 762
Oakland 15 ❷ 763
Oblong Regular ❷ 764
Oblong Bold ❷ 765

S
Senator Thin ❷ 766
Senator Demi ❷ 767
Senator Ultra ❷ 768

T
Triplex Light ❷ 769
Triplex Bold ❷ 770
Triplex Extra Bold ❷ 771
Triplex Serif Light ❶ 772
Triplex Serif Bold ❶ 773
Triplex Serif Extra Bold ❶ 774

U
Universal 8 ❷ 775
Universal 19 ❷ 776

V
Variex Light ❷ 777
Variex Regular ❷ 778
Variex Bold ❷ 779